Celebrate Togetherness
Make the most of holidays and the everyday with hundreds of ideas

PAGE 58

PAGE 272

PAGE 243

Nothing brings families together like a scrumptious homemade meal. For generations, *Taste of Home* has served as the go-to hub for passionate cooks looking to exchange the cherished dishes that never fail to satisfy loved ones.

Within the pages of *Taste of Home Annual Recipes*, you'll uncover tantalizing recipes shared by today's best home cooks. Beat the clock with an entire section of fast-to-fix favorites, round out meals with an abundance of sides, salads and breads, and whip up desserts, cookies, cakes and pies sure to steal the spotlight.

In fact, as you flip through this book, you'll find 432 step-by-step recipes, dozens of which are accompanied by helpful variations and how-to photos. Highlights also include:

- **Appetizers & Beverages**
  Prepare to dazzle with crowd-pleasing dishes that are both delicious and easy to share. Whether you crave a creamy dip, refreshing new beverage or an irresistibly addictive party snack, our curated collection has you covered.

- **Main Dishes**
  This chapter brims with meal options for weekdays and special occasions alike. Dig in to dozens of memorable entrees from Bombay shrimp and fried lasagna to Reuben casseroles and homey slow-cooker pork chops.

- **Holiday & Seasonal Celebrations**
  Discover festive snack boards for grazing, holiday menus, gift-worthy Christmas treats and New Year's drinks that truly sparkle.

Icons throughout help make the most of your time and resources:

🕐 = Ready in 30 minutes or less

🍎 = Lower in calories, fat and sodium

🍲 = Pressure-cooked recipe

🍲 = Made in a slow cooker

🍳 = Made in an air fryer

5i = Uses 5 or fewer ingredients
(may call for water, salt, pepper and canola/olive oil)

❄ = Includes freezing/reheating instructions

EVERYTHING IS BEAUTIFUL

Even weeknight dinners, casual sippers and store-bought candies get a gorgeous upgrade with inspiration from *Taste of Home Annual Recipes*. In just 25 minutes, sit down to family-pleasing Cheeseburger Tacos (top). They're a mash-up of two favorite meals that families flip for. Serve zero-proof cocktails with ease when you prepare Cherry-Lime Shrub (center). The old-fashioned shrub is having a moment—taste why! Finally, "every bunny" loves the pretty pastel sweets tucked inside Easter Candy Board (bottom). Unleash your creativity and make your own spring masterpiece! Step-by-step directions show you how.

© 2024 RDA Enthusiast Brands, LLC.
1610 N. 2nd St., Suite 102, Milwaukee WI 53212-3906
All rights reserved. Taste of Home is a registered trademark of
RDA Enthusiast Brands, LLC.

Visit us at **tasteofhome.com** for other Taste of Home books and products.

International Standard Book Number:
D 978-1-62145-957-6
U 978-1-62145-958-3

Component Number:
D 117400112H
U 117400114H

Content Director: Mark Hagen
Creative Director: Raeann Thompson
Senior Editor: Christine Rukavena
Editor: Hazel Wheaton
Senior Art Director: Courtney Lovetere
Deputy Editor, Copy Desk: Dulcie Shoener
Senior Copy Editor: Ann Walter
Contributing Copy Editor: Pam Grandy
Contributing Designer: Jennifer Ruetz

Cover Photography:
Photographer: Mark Derse
Set Stylist: Melissa Franco
Food Stylist: Josh Rink

Pictured on front cover:
Twice-Cooked Fried Chicken, p. 96;
Freezer Mashed Potatoes, p. 125;
Sunny Grapefruit Avocado Salad, p. 227
Fresh Strawberry Pie, p. 227

Pictured on back cover:
Tortellini Bean Soup Mix, p. 110;
Chicken Tikka Meatballs with Ginger Rice, p. 75;
Easy Cheesy Biscuits, p. 260

Printed in China
1 3 5 7 9 10 8 6 4 2

PAGE 197

MORE WAYS TO CONNECT WITH US:

Contents

FIRE-ROASTED
VEGETABLE SALSA
PAGE 6

Appetizers & Beverages

Whether you're looking for a melty dip, festive new drink or addictive party snack, this selection has you covered. It's packed full of tasty dishes you'll be proud to share.

MOST-REQUESTED RECIPES

AIR-FRYER QUESADILLAS

I like to make these for party appetizers. Just cut them into thinner triangles. You can also switch up the cheese and the salsa to suit your taste.
—*Terri Keeney, Greeley, CO*

TAKES: 10 min. • **MAKES:** 6 servings

- 1½ cups shredded Mexican cheese blend
- ½ cup salsa
- 4 flour tortillas (8 in.), warmed
  Cooking spray

1. Preheat air fryer to 375°. Combine the cheese and salsa; spread over half of each tortilla. Fold tortilla over. In batches, place tortillas in a single layer on a greased tray in air-fryer basket; spritz with cooking spray. Cook until golden brown and cheese has melted, 5-7 minutes. Cut into wedges.

NOTE: In our testing, we find cook times vary dramatically between brands of air fryers. As a result, we give wider than normal ranges on suggested cook times. Begin checking at the first time listed and adjust as needed.

1 SERVING: 223 cal., 11g fat (5g sat. fat), 25mg chol., 406mg sod., 21g carb. (1g sugars, 1g fiber), 9g pro.

TEST KITCHEN TIP

The fun part about these quesadillas is that they're so customizable. The cheese and salsa pair nicely with most other fillings, such as shredded chicken or pork, taco meat, or fajita veggies. Cilantro, pickled jalapenos and onion are flavorful additions too!

AIR-FRYER QUESADILLAS

FIRE-ROASTED VEGETABLE SALSA

(SHOWN ON PAGE 4)

We love having company over to grill by the pool. This salsa gets the party started as soon as guests arrive. Make this recipe ahead of time, then serve it warm or cold with pita chips.
—*Lisa J. Bradley, Apopka, FL*

PREP: 25 min. • **GRILL:** 15 min.
MAKES: 6 cups salsa (6 dozen chips)

- 2 medium ears sweet corn, husked
- 1 medium red onion, cut into ½-in. slices
- 2 jalapeno peppers, halved and seeded
- 5 large plum tomatoes
- 1 small eggplant, cut into ¼-in. slices
- 1 can (15 oz.) black beans, rinsed and drained
- 2 garlic cloves, minced
- ½ tsp. salt
- ½ tsp. hot pepper sauce, optional
- ¼ tsp. pepper

CHIPS
- 9 whole wheat pita breads (6 in.)
  Olive oil-flavored cooking spray
- 1 tsp. garlic salt

1. Grill the corn and onion on an oiled rack, covered, over medium heat until tender, 10-12 minutes, turning occasionally. During the last 5-7 minutes of cooking, add peppers. Add tomatoes and eggplant during the last 3-5 minutes of cooking.
2. Cool vegetables slightly. Remove corn from cobs; transfer to a large bowl. Chop the remaining vegetables and add to corn. Stir in the beans, garlic, salt, pepper sauce if desired, and pepper.
3. Spritz pitas with cooking spray; sprinkle with the garlic salt. Grill, covered, over medium-low heat for 1-2 minutes on each side or until golden brown. Cut each into 8 wedges. Serve with salsa.

NOTE: Wear disposable gloves when cutting hot peppers; the oils can burn skin. Avoid touching your face.

¼ CUP WITH 3 PITA CHIPS: 97 cal., 1g fat (0 sat. fat), 0 chol., 288mg sod., 19g carb. (2g sugars, 4g fiber), 4g pro. **DIABETIC EXCHANGES:** 1 starch, 1 vegetable.

BLACKBERRY BALSAMIC MANHATTAN

I sampled this tantalizing twist on my favorite cocktail while visiting the Elk Store Winery & Distillery in Texas. I was so smitten, I brought the bartender's southern recipe all the way upstate with me so I could enjoy it at home.
—*Susan Stetzel, Gainesville, NY*

TAKES: 10 min. • **MAKES:** 1 serving

- 5 fresh blackberries
  Ice cubes
- 2½ oz. bourbon
- 1 oz. sweet vermouth
- 1 tsp. simple syrup
- ½ tsp. aged balsamic vinegar
- 2 dashes bitters

In a shaker, muddle blackberries. Fill shaker three-fourths full with ice. Add the remaining ingredients; stir until beverage is well-chilled, 20-30 seconds. Strain into a coupe or cocktail glass, or an ice-filled rocks glass. Garnish as desired.

1 SERVING: 232 cal., 0 fat (0 sat. fat), 0 chol., 3mg sod., 10g carb. (6g sugars, 0 fiber), 0 pro.

SHRIMP COCKTAIL

During the '60s, shrimp cocktail was one of the most popular party foods around. And it's still a crowd favorite. It's the one appetizer that I serve for every special occasion as well as for munchie meals.
—*Peggy Allen, Pasadena, CA*

PREP: 30 min. + chilling
MAKES: about 6 dozen (1¼ cups sauce)

- 3 qt. water
- 1 small onion, sliced
- ½ medium lemon, sliced
- 2 sprigs fresh parsley
- 1 Tbsp. salt
- 5 whole peppercorns
- 1 bay leaf
- ¼ tsp. dried thyme
- 3 lbs. uncooked shrimp (26-30 per lb.), peeled and deveined (tails on)

SHRIMP COCKTAIL

SAUCE
- 1 cup chili sauce
- 2 Tbsp. lemon juice
- 2 Tbsp. prepared horseradish
- 4 tsp. Worcestershire sauce
- ½ tsp. salt
  Dash cayenne pepper
  Lemon wedges, optional

1. In a Dutch oven, combine the first 8 ingredients; bring to a boil. Add shrimp. Reduce heat; simmer, uncovered, until shrimp turn pink, 4-5 minutes.
2. Drain the shrimp and immediately rinse in cold water. Refrigerate 2-3 hours or until cold. In a small bowl, combine the next 6 ingredients. Refrigerate until serving.
3. Arrange shrimp on a serving platter; serve with sauce. If desired, serve with lemon wedges.

1 OZ. COOKED SHRIMP WITH ABOUT 2 TSP. SAUCE: 59 cal., 1g fat (0 sat. fat), 66mg chol., 555mg sod., 4g carb. (2g sugars, 0 fiber), 9g pro.

HOW-TO

Keep Shrimp Cold on a Buffet

You can serve shrimp attractively and keep it at a safe temperature with a lettuce-lined bowl. Fill a large shallow bowl (plastic is great here because it's a natural insulator) two-thirds full with crushed ice placed in a zippered plastic bag. Disguise the ice with lettuce leaves, then place the shrimp on top. If serving a shrimp sauce, nestle the bowl down into the center.

DARK CHERRY
SYRUP

SPINACH &
FETA BOUREKAS

DARK CHERRY SYRUP

Quick, easy and packed with flavor, this is a perfect condiment for cocktails, desserts, savory recipes or mixing into sparkling water.
—Francine Lizotte, Langley, BC

TAKES: 25 min. • MAKES: ¾ cup

1½ cups fresh or frozen dark sweet cherries, pitted
1½ cups water
¾ cup sugar
   Sparkling water, optional

In a saucepan, stir together first 3 ingredients over medium-high heat. Bring to a boil; reduce heat. Simmer until liquid turns a dark purple and cherries are tender, 10-15 minutes, crushing cherries with a spoon or masher. Remove from heat; let stand 10 minutes. Strain mixture through a fine sieve; discard solids. Refrigerate, covered, until serving. If desired, combine 8 oz. sparkling water with 1 Tbsp. of syrup to serve.
1 TBSP: 59 cal., 0 fat (0 sat. fat), 0 chol., 1mg sod., 15g carb. (15g sugars, 0 fiber), 0 pro.

❄ SPINACH & FETA BOUREKAS

Light and soft with a bit of crunch, these bourekas are one of my favorite holiday appetizers. They can be filled with almost anything, but spinach and feta is one of my favorite fillings. Topped with everything seasoning, these little triangles are out of this world.
—Alex Stepanov, Matawan, NJ

PREP: 25 min. • BAKE: 25 min. • MAKES: 8 servings

1 Tbsp. olive oil or avocado oil
1 lb. fresh spinach, trimmed
½ cup chopped shallots
1 Tbsp. minced garlic
½ tsp. salt
¼ tsp. pepper
1 pkg. (17.3 oz.) frozen puff pastry, thawed
½ cup crumbled feta cheese
½ cup whole-milk ricotta cheese
1 large egg, beaten
1 Tbsp. everything seasoning blend

1. Preheat oven to 400°. In a large skillet, heat oil over medium-high heat. Add spinach, shallots and garlic; cook and stir until spinach is wilted, 2-3 minutes. Remove from the heat; strain off any excess water. Stir in salt and pepper; set aside to cool to room temperature.
2. On a lightly floured surface, unfold puff pastry. Cut each sheet into 4 squares. In a small bowl, combine feta and ricotta; stir in spinach mixture. Spoon cheese mixture diagonally over half of each square to within ½ in. of edges. Brush pastry edges with egg. Fold 1 corner over filling to the opposite corner, forming a triangle; press edges with a fork to seal. Place on parchment-lined baking sheets. Brush remaining egg over pastries; sprinkle with the seasoning blend. Bake until golden brown, 25-30 minutes.
FREEZE OPTION: Freeze unbaked pastries on a parchment-lined baking sheet until firm. Transfer to an airtight container; return to freezer. To use, cook frozen pastries as directed until golden brown and heated through, increasing time to 30-32 minutes; cover with foil if pastries begin to brown too quickly.
1 PASTRY: 383 cal., 21g fat (6g sat. fat), 22mg chol., 635mg sod., 39g carb. (2g sugars, 6g fiber), 9g pro.

TEST KITCHEN TIP

Other fillings, such as potato and dill or ricotta and caramelized onion, are delicious too!

SWEET CURRY
ROASTED PISTACHIOS

ASPARAGUS PASTRY PUFFS

When the first asparagus of the season appears, we serve it rolled inside puff pastry with a yummy cheese filling. Our guests always compliment these lovely treats.
—*Cindy Jamieson, Tonawanda, NY*

- -

PREP: 30 min. • **BAKE:** 25 min. • **MAKES:** 16 servings

- 1   lb. fresh asparagus, trimmed
- 4   oz. cream cheese, softened
- ¼   cup grated Parmesan cheese
- 1   Tbsp. stone-ground mustard
- 2   tsp. lemon juice
- ¼   tsp. salt
- ¼   tsp. pepper
- 1   pkg. (17.3 oz.) frozen puff pastry, thawed
- 1   large egg
- 2   Tbsp. water

1. Preheat oven to 400°. In a large skillet, bring 1½ in. water to a boil. Add asparagus; cook, uncovered, until crisp-tender, 1-3 minutes. Remove asparagus and immediately drop into ice water. Drain and pat dry.
2. In a small bowl, mix cream cheese, Parmesan cheese, mustard, lemon juice, salt and pepper until blended. Unfold puff pastry sheets; cut each sheet in half to make a total of 4 rectangles. Spread each rectangle with a fourth of the cream cheese mixture to within ¼ in. of edges. Arrange asparagus over top, allowing tips to show at each end; roll up jelly-roll style. Using a serrated knife, cut each roll crosswise into 4 sections.
3. Place on a parchment-lined baking sheet, seam side down. In a small bowl, whisk egg and water until blended; brush lightly over tops.
4. Bake until golden brown, 25-30 minutes. Remove from pan to a wire rack; serve warm.
1 PASTRY: 188 cal., 11g fat (4g sat. fat), 21mg chol., 211mg sod., 18g carb. (1g sugars, 3g fiber), 4g pro.

SWEET CURRY ROASTED PISTACHIOS

I was looking for a way to spice up plain pistachios and came up with this winning flavor combination. They're great for anytime snacking. When I have a batch on hand, I like to share them with the guys at work since they enjoy them so much.
—*Redawna Kalynchuk, Rochester, AB*

- -

PREP: 15 min. • **BAKE:** 15 min. + cooling • **MAKES:** 3 cups

- 2   Tbsp. curry powder
- 2   Tbsp. coconut oil or canola oil
- 1   Tbsp. maple syrup
- ½   tsp. salt
- ⅛   tsp. cayenne pepper
- 3   cups shelled roasted and salted pistachios
- 3   Tbsp. brown sugar

1. Preheat oven to 300°. In a small saucepan, combine the first 5 ingredients. Cook and stir over low heat until fragrant and oil is melted. Remove from heat; stir in pistachios. Spread into a parchment-lined 15x10x1-in. baking pan.
2. Bake 15-18 minutes or until pistachios are lightly toasted and appear dry, stirring occasionally. Sprinkle with brown sugar; toss to coat. Cool completely. Store in an airtight container.
⅓ CUP: 288 cal., 22g fat (5g sat. fat), 0 chol., 309mg sod., 18g carb. (9g sugars, 5g fiber), 9g pro.

ASPARAGUS
PASTRY PUFFS

BLT BITES

BLT BITES

These quick hors d'oeuvres may be mini, but their bacon and tomato flavor is full size. I serve them at parties, brunches and picnics, and they're always a hit—even my kids love them.
—*Kellie Remmen, Detroit Lakes, MN*

PREP: 25 min. + chilling
MAKES: 20 appetizers

- 20 cherry tomatoes
- 1 lb. sliced bacon, cooked and crumbled
- ½ cup mayonnaise
- ⅓ cup chopped green onions
- 3 Tbsp. grated Parmesan cheese
- 2 Tbsp. snipped fresh parsley

1. Cut a thin slice off each tomato top. Scoop out and discard pulp. Invert the tomatoes on a paper towel to drain.
2. In a small bowl, combine the remaining ingredients. Spoon into tomatoes. Refrigerate for several hours.
1 STUFFED TOMATO: 113 cal., 10g fat (3g sat. fat), 11mg chol., 206mg sod., 1g carb. (1g sugars, 0 fiber), 3g pro.

TURKEY TEA SANDWICHES WITH BASIL MAYONNAISE

Basil mayonnaise is the secret to these tasty little sandwiches. Keep any extra mayo in the fridge to spread on other sandwiches, stir into egg salad or layer on pizza crust before topping it with other ingredients.
—*Lara Pennell, Mauldin, SC*

TAKES: 15 min. • **MAKES:** 20 tea sandwiches

- ½ cup mayonnaise
- ⅓ cup loosely packed basil leaves
- 10 slices white bread, crusts removed
- 10 oz. thinly sliced deli turkey
- 5 slices provolone cheese

Place mayonnaise and basil in a food processor; process until basil is finely chopped, scraping down side as needed. Spread mayonnaise mixture over each bread slice. Layer 5 bread slices with turkey and cheese; top with remaining bread slices. Cut each into 4 long pieces.
1 TEA SANDWICH: 90 cal., 6g fat (2g sat. fat), 9mg chol., 230mg sod., 4g carb. (0 sugars, 0 fiber), 5g pro.

LEMON BASIL TEA

Our pros sure know how to brew a great pot of tea! Infused with basil and lemon, this oh-so-drinkable recipe tastes as good as it smells.
—Taste of Home *Test Kitchen*

TAKES: 10 min. • **MAKES:** 12 servings

- 3 qt. water
- 1 cup thinly sliced fresh basil leaves
- ¼ cup grated lemon zest
- ¼ cup English breakfast or other black tea leaves

In a large saucepan, bring water to a boil. Remove from the heat. Add basil, lemon zest and tea leaves; cover and steep for 4 minutes. Strain, discarding basil, zest and tea leaves. Serve immediately.
1 CUP: 2 cal., 0 fat (0 sat. fat), 0 chol., 7mg sod., 1g carb. (0 sugars, 0 fiber), 0 pro. **DIABETIC EXCHANGES:** 1 free food.

LEMON BASIL TEA

BUTTERBEER

BUTTERBEER

Witches and wizards, get your Butterbeer here! Bring this fictional drink from the Harry Potter series to life by serving it either foamy and hot in a mug or cold, as shown here.
—*Lauren Habermehl, Pewaukee, WI*

- -

PREP: 20 min. + chilling • **MAKES:** 2 servings

BUTTERBEER FOAM
- ¼ cup hot water
- ½ cup marshmallow creme
- ½ envelope whipped topping mix (Dream Whip)
- 1 Tbsp. confectioners' sugar
- 1 pinch salt
- ½ tsp. butterscotch flavoring syrup
- ¼ tsp. butter extract
- ¼ tsp. caramel extract
- ⅛ tsp. vanilla extract

BUTTERBEER
- 2 cans (12 oz. each) cream soda, chilled
- 2 tsp. butterscotch flavoring syrup

1. In a large bowl, stir together hot water and marshmallow creme until smooth. Freeze until cool, 20-25 minutes. Stir in whipped topping mix, confectioners' sugar and salt; blend with a hand mixer until foamy, 30-60 seconds. Stir in butterscotch syrup and extracts.

2. Pour soda into two 16-oz. mugs; stir in butterscotch syrup. Top with Butterbeer Foam. Serve immediately.

1 SERVING: 351 cal., 2g fat (2g sat. fat), 0 chol., 138mg sod., 86g carb. (80g sugars, 0 fiber), 0 pro.

BRIE APPETIZERS WITH BACON-PLUM JAM

Among friends I'm known as the pork master, in part because of these tasty bites topped with a sweet-sour bacon jam.
—*Rick Pascocello, New York, NY*

- -

PREP: 25 min. • **COOK:** 1¼ hours • **MAKES:** 2½ dozen

- 1 lb. bacon strips, chopped
- 1 cup thinly sliced sweet onion
- 1 shallot, finely chopped
- 5 garlic cloves, minced
- 1 cup brewed coffee
- ½ cup water
- ¼ cup cider vinegar
- ¼ cup pitted dried plums (prunes), coarsely chopped
- 3 Tbsp. brown sugar
- 1 Tbsp. maple syrup
- 1 Tbsp. Sriracha chili sauce
- ½ tsp. pepper
- 30 slices Brie cheese (¼ in. thick)
- 30 slices French bread baguette (¼ in. thick), toasted

1. In a large skillet, cook bacon over medium heat until partially cooked but not crisp. Remove to paper towels with a slotted spoon; drain skillet, reserving 1 Tbsp. drippings.

2. Add onion and shallot to drippings; cook and stir 5 minutes. Add garlic; cook 2 minutes longer. Stir in coffee, water, vinegar, dried plums, brown sugar, maple syrup, chili sauce and pepper. Bring to a boil. Stir in bacon. Reduce heat; simmer, uncovered, until liquid is syrupy, 1¼-1½ hours, stirring occasionally. Remove from heat. Cool to room temperature.

3. Transfer mixture to a food processor; pulse until jam reaches desired consistency. Place cheese slices on toasted baguette slices. Top each with 2 tsp. jam.

1 APPETIZER: 91 cal., 5g fat (3g sat. fat), 17mg chol., 205mg sod., 6g carb. (3g sugars, 0 fiber), 4g pro.

BRIE APPETIZERS WITH BACON-PLUM JAM

CHEESEBURGER EGG ROLLS

CHEESEBURGER EGG ROLLS

Filled with juicy ground beef, a touch of crumbled bacon, diced pickles and plenty of melty cheddar cheese, these crunchy wonton-wrapped wonders are a Cheesecake Factory bestseller for a reason.
—Taste of Home *Test Kitchen*

PREP: 30 min. • **COOK:** 5 min./batch
MAKES: 1 dozen (1½ cups sauce)

- 1   lb. ground beef
- 1   small onion, chopped
- 2   garlic cloves, minced
- 1   cup shredded cheddar cheese
- ½   cup chopped dill pickles
- 4   bacon strips,
      cooked and crumbled
- 1   Tbsp. Worcestershire sauce
- 1   Tbsp. yellow mustard
- 1   Tbsp. ketchup
- ¼   tsp. salt
- ¼   tsp. pepper
- 12 egg roll wrappers
- 1   large egg, lightly beaten
      Oil for deep-fat frying

DIPPING SAUCE
- 1   cup mayonnaise
- ½   cup ketchup
- ½   tsp. garlic powder
- ½   tsp. paprika

1. In a large skillet, cook the beef, onion and garlic over medium heat until beef is no longer pink and onion is tender, 4-5 minutes, breaking up beef into crumbles; drain. Return to pan. Stir in

cheese, pickles, bacon, Worcestershire sauce, mustard, ketchup, salt and pepper.
2. With 1 corner of an egg roll wrapper facing you, place about ⅓ cup filling just below center of wrapper. (Cover the remaining wrappers with a damp paper towel until ready to use.) Fold bottom corner over filling; moisten remaining wrapper edges with beaten egg. Fold side corners toward center over filling. Roll egg roll up tightly, pressing at tip to seal. Repeat.

3. In an electric skillet or deep-fat fryer, heat oil to 375°. Fry egg rolls, a few at a time, until golden brown, 3-4 minutes, turning occasionally. Drain on paper towels. Combine sauce ingredients; serve with egg rolls.
1 EGG ROLL WITH 2 TBSP. SAUCE:
451 cal., 32g fat (7g sat. fat), 61mg chol., 712mg sod., 26g carb. (4g sugars, 1g fiber), 14g pro.

FRICO (CHEESE CRISPS)

FRICO

In batches, sprinkle ¼ cup shredded **Parmesan, aged cheddar** or **Manchego cheese** into a large nonstick skillet over medium heat. Cook 3-4 minutes or until melted and edges start to brown. Flip; cook for 30 seconds longer. Transfer to a paper towel-lined cutting board to cool. *Makes 4 crisps.*

SUN-DRIED TOMATO FRICO

Stir 2 Tbsp. finely chopped **sun-dried tomatoes** and ½ tsp. **dried thyme** into shredded **Parmesan** cheese before adding it to skillet. Prepare the frico as directed.

APPLE-PEPPER FRICO

Stir 2 Tbsp. finely chopped **dried apples** and ½ tsp. freshly cracked **black pepper** into shredded **aged cheddar cheese** before adding it to skillet. Prepare frico as directed.

WARM OLIVE BRUSCHETTA

Cream cheese and olives add heartiness to the bruschetta typically made with tomatoes. The flavors blend beautifully.
—*Lori Harmon, Billings, MT*

PREP: 25 min. • **BAKE:** 10 min.
MAKES: 2 dozen

- 24 slices French bread baguette (¼ in. thick)
- 3 Tbsp. olive oil
- 1 celery rib, chopped
- ½ cup chopped pimiento-stuffed olives
- 1 can (2¼ oz.) sliced ripe olives, drained and chopped
- 1 Tbsp. prepared Italian salad dressing
- 2 garlic cloves, minced
- ¾ cup spreadable chive and onion cream cheese
- ¾ cup chopped cherry tomatoes

1. Place bread on ungreased baking sheets; brush lightly with oil. Bake at 400° for 3-4 minutes or until lightly browned.
2. Meanwhile, in a small bowl, combine celery, olives, salad dressing and garlic. Spread cream cheese over toast; top each slice with 2 tsp. olive mixture. Bake for 6-8 minutes or until heated through. Top with tomatoes.
1 PIECE: 80 cal., 6g fat (2g sat. fat), 8mg chol., 165mg sod., 6g carb. (1g sugars, 1g fiber), 1g pro.

CHILEAN BEEF EMPANADAS

Lorain is known as the International City because people came here from all over the world to work. During the summer, the city hosts a festival to celebrate the diverse community. One year I got to help my Chilean friend's mom prepare these for the festival. They bring back happy memories!
—*Kristyne Mcdougle Walter, Lorain, OH*

PREP: 40 min. + chilling • **BAKE:** 20 min.
MAKES: 20 servings

- 1 lb. ground beef
- ½ large onion, finely chopped
- 3 hard-boiled large eggs, chopped
- ⅓ cup chopped pitted green olives
- 1 Tbsp. ground cumin
- 1 Tbsp. chili powder
- 1 tsp. smoked paprika

CHILEAN BEEF EMPANADAS

- 1 tsp. salt
- ½ tsp. pepper
- 1 large egg, beaten
- 2 pkg. (14 oz. each) frozen empanada dough disks, thawed
  Salsa verde, optional

1. Preheat oven to 400°. In a large skillet, cook beef and onion over medium heat until beef is no longer pink and onion is tender, 6-8 minutes, breaking up beef into crumbles; do not drain. Stir in hard-boiled eggs, olives and seasonings; heat through. Remove from the heat.
2. Brush beaten egg over edges of dough circles. Place 3 Tbsp. filling on 1 side of each. Fold dough over filling. Crimp edges and press to seal. Place on parchment-lined baking sheets. Brush tops with remaining beaten egg. Refrigerate for 15 minutes.
3. Bake until golden brown, 20-25 minutes; serve warm, with salsa verde if desired.
1 EMPANADA: 184 cal., 8g fat (3g sat. fat), 51mg chol., 338mg sod., 21g carb. (0 sugars, 1g fiber), 9g pro.

TEST KITCHEN TIPS

If you want to feed a larger crowd, stretch this recipe by reducing the filling to 2 Tbsp. per empanada for 30 empanadas total. If making these on a warm day, remove 10 shells from the refrigerator at a time, so they remain easy to work with.

FROSTY PEPPERMINT POPCORN

Whether you need a quick gift idea or yummy munchies for movie night, we've got you covered with this peppermint twist on regular popped popcorn.
—Taste of Home *Test Kitchen*

PREP: 10 min. + standing
MAKES: 3½ qt.

8 oz. white candy coating, melted
3½ qt. popped popcorn
⅓ cup crushed peppermint candies
Assorted sprinkles, optional

1. Drizzle candy coating over popcorn; sprinkle with candies and, if desired, sprinkles and toss. Immediately spread onto waxed paper; let stand until set.
2. Break into pieces. Store in airtight containers.

1 CUP: 159 cal., 9g fat (5g sat. fat), 0 chol., 76mg sod., 19g carb. (13g sugars, 1g fiber), 1g pro.

PARMESAN RANCH POPCORN

Make ho-hum popcorn worthy of a carnival with a savory seasoning blend.
—Taste of Home *Test Kitchen*

TAKES: 10 min. • **MAKES:** 3½ qt.

¼ cup grated Parmesan cheese
2 Tbsp. ranch salad dressing mix
1 tsp. dried parsley flakes
¼ tsp. onion powder
⅓ cup butter, melted
3½ qt. popped popcorn

Mix first 4 ingredients. Drizzle butter over popcorn; toss with cheese mixture. Store in airtight containers.
1 CUP: 112 cal., 10g fat (4g sat. fat), 13mg chol., 243mg sod., 6g carb. (0 sugars, 1g fiber), 1g pro.

ITALIAN CHEESE POPCORN

Perfect for movie night, here's a tasty Italian twist on regular popped popcorn.
—Taste of Home *Test Kitchen*

TAKES: 10 min. • **MAKES:** 3½ qt.

⅓ cup grated Romano cheese
2¼ tsp. Italian seasoning
¾ tsp. garlic salt
⅓ cup butter, melted
3½ qt. popped popcorn

Mix cheese and seasonings. Drizzle butter over popcorn; toss with cheese mixture. Store in airtight containers.
1 CUP: 114 cal., 10g fat (4g sat. fat), 12mg chol., 257mg sod., 5g carb. (0 sugars, 1g fiber), 2g pro.

FROSTY PEPPER-MINT POPCORN

PARMESAN RANCH POPCORN

ITALIAN CHEESE POPCORN

CHICKEN SAMOSAS

CHICKEN SAMOSAS

This chicken samosa recipe is best served with yogurt dipping sauce or chutney (like coriander and mint, tamarind or sweet mango). The dough and filling can be made ahead for quick assembly before guests arrive.
—Taste of Home *Test Kitchen*

PREP: 15 min. + resting • **COOK:** 25 min. • **MAKES:** 16 servings

- 4 cups all-purpose flour
- 1 tsp. salt
- ⅔ cup canola oil
- ¾ cup water

FILLING

- 1 Tbsp. canola oil
- 1 small onion
- ½ cup chopped peeled potato
- 2 Tbsp. curry powder
- 2 garlic cloves, minced
- 2 tsp. minced fresh gingerroot
- ½ tsp. ground cumin
- ½ tsp. ground coriander
- ¼ tsp. cayenne pepper
- ¾ lb. ground chicken
- ½ cup frozen peas
- ½ tsp. salt
  Oil for deep-fat frying
  Chutney, optional

1. In a small bowl, combine flour, salt and oil until mixture resembles bread crumbs. Gradually stir in water until smooth. Turn onto a lightly floured surface; knead until smooth and elastic, 6-8 minutes. Cover and let rest for 30 minutes.
2. Meanwhile, in a large skillet, heat oil over medium heat. Add onion and potato; cook and stir until potato is almost tender, 5-7 minutes. Add curry, garlic, ginger, cumin, coriander and cayenne; cook 2 minutes longer. Add chicken; cook and stir until chicken is no longer pink and potato is tender, 5-6 minutes, breaking chicken into crumbles. Stir in peas and salt. Remove from heat.

3. Divide dough into 8 pieces. Roll 1 piece of dough into a 9x6-in. oval. Cut dough in half. Moisten straight edge with water. Bring 1 corner of half moon up to meet the other corner of the half moon, forming a cone. Pinch seam to seal. Fill with about 2 Tbsp. chicken mixture. Moisten curved edge of dough with water; fold over top of filling and press seam to seal. Repeat with remaining dough and filling.
4. In an electric skillet or deep fryer, heat oil to 375°. Add samosas, a few at a time, into hot oil. Fry until golden brown, 2-3 minutes on each side. Drain on paper towels. Serve warm, with chutney if desired.
1 SAMOSA: 325 cal., 21g fat (2g sat. fat), 14mg chol., 240mg sod., 26g carb. (1g sugars, 2g fiber), 7g pro

CRANBERRY DARK CHOCOLATE TRAIL MIX

A close friend once gave me a jar of trail mix that was absolutely delicious. My re-creation comes pretty close to the original and is truly one of my favorite snacks!
—*Nancy Johnson, Laverne, OK*

TAKES: 5 min. • **MAKES:** 6 cups

- 1 pkg. (10 oz.) dark chocolate chips
- 1½ cups dried cranberries (about 8 oz.)
- 1½ cups sliced almonds
- 1 cup raisins
- 1 cup coarsely chopped walnuts
- ½ cup pistachios

Toss together all ingredients. Store in airtight containers.
¼ CUP: 176 cal., 11g fat (3g sat. fat), 0 chol., 16mg sod., 21g carb. (15g sugars, 3g fiber), 3g pro.

CRANBERRY DARK CHOCOLATE TRAIL MIX

SPICY SWEET POTATO CHIPS & CILANTRO DIP

KNISH

Knish is a classic Jewish comfort food. Sometimes I make this recipe as tiny appetizers, which are more like rolls.
—*Marlena Spieler, Waterlooville, England*

PREP: 15 min. + chilling • **BAKE:** 15 min.
MAKES: 4 dozen

- 6½ cups all-purpose flour
- 3 tsp. baking powder
- 1½ tsp. salt
- 1½ cups cold butter
- 9 oz. sour cream
- 3 to 4 Tbsp. water

FILLING

- 1 lb. medium potatoes, peeled and cubed (about 2 cups)
- ¼ cup butter, cubed
- 3 medium onions, finely chopped
- 1 tsp. salt
- ¼ tsp. pepper
- 2 large eggs, divided use
  Sour cream, optional

1. For pastry, in a large bowl, combine flour, baking powder and salt. Cut in butter until crumbly. Stir in sour cream and enough water to form a dough. Shape into a disk; mixture will be crumbly. Wrap and refrigerate at least 2 hours or overnight.
2. Place potatoes in a large saucepan; add water to cover. Bring to a boil. Reduce heat; cook, uncovered, until tender, 8-10 minutes.
3. Meanwhile, in a large skillet, melt butter over medium-high heat. Add onions; cook and stir until tender, 8-10 minutes.
4. Drain potatoes; return to pan and stir over low heat 1 minute to dry. Mash potatoes; stir in onion mixture, salt and pepper. Set aside to cool. Lightly beat 1 egg; stir into potato mixture.
5. Preheat oven to 400°. On a lightly floured surface, roll the dough into three 10x12-in. rectangles. Cut each into 16 squares. Spoon 1 Tbsp. potato filling in the middle of each square. Brush the edges with water. Fold each corner toward the center, meeting in the middle. Arrange, seam side down, on ungreased baking sheets. Lightly beat remaining egg; brush over knish. Bake until lightly browned, 15-20 minutes. If desired, serve with sour cream.
1 KNISH: 143 cal., 8g fat (5g sat. fat), 29mg chol., 212mg sod., 15g carb. (1g sugars, 1g fiber), 2g pro.

SPICY SWEET POTATO CHIPS & CILANTRO DIP

This irresistible combo could become your new signature snack food. Park the spicy baked chips next to a bowl of the cool, creamy dip and let the gang have at it. What a fantastic twist on traditional chips and dip!
—*Elizabeth Godecke, Chicago, IL*

PREP: 20 min. • **BAKE:** 25 min./batch
MAKES: 12 servings (1½ cups dip)

- 2 to 3 large sweet potatoes (1¾ lbs.), peeled and cut into ⅛-in. slices
- 2 Tbsp. canola oil
- 1 tsp. chili powder
- ½ tsp. garlic powder
- ½ tsp. taco seasoning
- ¼ tsp. salt
- ¼ tsp. ground cumin
- ¼ tsp. pepper
- ⅛ tsp. cayenne pepper

DIP

- ¾ cup mayonnaise
- ½ cup sour cream
- 2 oz. cream cheese, softened
- 4½ tsp. minced fresh cilantro
- 1½ tsp. lemon juice
- ½ tsp. celery salt
- ⅛ tsp. pepper

1. Preheat oven to 400°. Place sweet potatoes in a large bowl. In a small bowl, mix oil and seasonings; drizzle over potatoes and toss to coat.
2. Arrange half the sweet potatoes in a single layer in 2 ungreased 15x10x1-in. baking pans. Bake 25-30 minutes or until golden brown, turning once. Repeat with remaining sweet potatoes.
3. In a small bowl, beat dip ingredients until blended. Serve with chips.
½ CUP CHIPS WITH ABOUT 1 TBSP. DIP: 285 cal., 16g fat (4g sat. fat), 8mg chol., 217mg sod., 33g carb. (14g sugars, 4g fiber), 3g pro.

KNISH

SMOKY BLACK-EYED PEA CAKES

Black-eyed peas conjure up memories of New Year's Day feasts prepared by my nana. This is my spin on the classic.
—JennÈ Claiborne, Atlanta, GA

PREP: 40 min. • COOK: 5 min./batch
MAKES: 8 servings

- 1 cup chopped roasted sweet red peppers, drained
- ½ cup vegan mayonnaise
- ¼ cup chopped fresh dill
- 1 Tbsp. red wine vinegar
- 1 tsp. freshly ground pepper
- 1 tsp. sugar, optional

SMOKY BLACK-EYED PEA CAKES
- 2 Tbsp. water
- 1 Tbsp. ground flaxseed
- 1 can (15½ oz.) black-eyed peas, rinsed and drained
- ½ cup finely chopped onion
- 6 Tbsp. panko bread crumbs, divided
- ¼ cup cornmeal
- 1 jalapeno pepper, seeded and minced
- 2 garlic cloves, minced
- 1 tsp. fine sea salt
- 1 tsp. ground cumin
- 1 tsp. smoked paprika
- ½ to 1 tsp. dried thyme
- 1 tsp. cider vinegar
- 2 Tbsp. dry bread crumbs
  Oil for frying

1. Place roasted peppers, mayonnaise, dill, vinegar, pepper and sugar, if desired, in a blender. Cover and process until smooth. Transfer to a small bowl. Refrigerate, covered, until serving.
2. In a small bowl, stir together water and flaxseed. Let stand until thickened, at least 3 minutes. Place peas, onion, 4 Tbsp. panko, cornmeal, jalapeno, garlic, seasonings, vinegar and flaxseed mixture in a food processor. Pulse until just combined. In a shallow bowl, combine bread crumbs and remaining 2 Tbsp. panko.
3. In a deep cast-iron or electric skillet, heat ¼ in. oil to 350°. Form pea mixture into eight 2-in.-wide patties. Dip in crumb mixture, patting to help coating adhere. Fry patties, a few at a time, until golden brown, 2-3 minutes on each side. Drain on paper towels. Serve warm.
NOTE: Wear disposable gloves when cutting hot peppers; the oils can burn skin. Avoid touching your face.
1 CAKE WITH 3 TBSP. AIOLI: 235 cal., 16g fat (2g sat. fat), 0 chol., 516mg sod., 17g carb. (2g sugars, 2g fiber), 4g pro.

🍎 PECAN MUHAMMARA

This sauce is a little smoky, spicy and sweet—it adds so much vibrancy to the black-eyed pea cakes!
—Jenné Claiborne, Atlanta, GA

PREP: 25 min. + standing • MAKES: 1¼ cups

- 1 large sweet red pepper
- 1 cup chopped pecans, lightly toasted
- 1 Tbsp. Aleppo pepper flakes or smoked paprika
- 1 Tbsp. lemon juice
- 1 Tbsp. pomegranate molasses
- 1 garlic clove, chopped
- 1 tsp. ground cumin
- ¼ cup dry bread crumbs
- 1 to 2 Tbsp. olive oil

1. Place pepper on a foil-lined baking sheet. Broil 4 in. from heat until skin blisters, about 5 minutes. With tongs, rotate pepper a quarter turn. Broil and rotate until all sides are blistered and blackened. Immediately place pepper in a small bowl; let stand, covered, 20 minutes.
2. Peel off and discard charred skin. Quarter pepper. Remove stems and seeds.
3. Place the roasted red pepper pieces, pecans, Aleppo pepper flakes, lemon juice, pomegranate molasses, garlic and cumin in food processor or mortar with pestle. Pulse or grind until slightly pureed (not as creamy as hummus). Add bread crumbs and 1 Tbsp. olive oil. Pulse or grind until blended. If desired, add remaining 1 Tbsp. oil to achieve desired consistency.
¼ CUP: 223 cal., 19g fat (2g sat. fat), 0 chol., 43mg sod., 13g carb. (5g sugars, 4g fiber), 3g pro.

PECAN MUHAMMARA

SMOKY BLACK-EYED PEA CAKES

COGNAC
CHAMPAGNE
COCKTAIL

COGNAC CHAMPAGNE COCKTAIL

Celebrate the new year or any special occasion with this festive champagne cocktail. Not only is it fruity and refreshing, but it also packs a punch!
—*Francine Lizotte, Langley, BC*

TAKES: 10 min. • **MAKES:** 8 servings

- 1 cup pulp-free orange juice, chilled
- 1 can (7½ oz.) lemon-lime soda, chilled
- 1 can (6 oz.) unsweetened pineapple juice, chilled
- ⅓ cup Cognac or brandy
- ¼ cup simple syrup, chilled
- 1 bottle (750 ml) champagne or other sparkling wine, chilled

In a large pitcher or punch bowl, combine the first 5 ingredients. Stir in champagne. Serve immediately.
¾ CUP: 309 cal., 0 fat (0 sat. fat), 0 chol., 7mg sod., 38g carb. (32g sugars, 0 fiber), 1g pro.

PORK & CHIVE POT STICKERS

Here's my top make-ahead appetizer. My three kids are old enough to cook these themselves, right from the freezer. They're a lot more nutritious than the ones you get at a restaurant.
—*Marisa Raponi, Vaughan, ON*

PREP: 1 hour • **COOK:** 5 min./batch • **MAKES:** 5 dozen

- 2 medium carrots, finely chopped
- 1 small onion, finely chopped
- ½ cup finely chopped water chestnuts
- ⅓ cup minced fresh chives
- 1 large egg white, lightly beaten
- 3 Tbsp. reduced-sodium soy sauce
- ½ tsp. pepper

- 1 lb. ground pork
- 60 pot sticker or gyoza wrappers
- 3 Tbsp. canola oil, divided
- 1 cup chicken broth, divided
  Optional: Additional reduced-sodium soy sauce and minced fresh chives

1. In a large bowl, combine the first 7 ingredients. Add pork; mix lightly but thoroughly. Working with a few at a time, place 1 scant Tbsp. filling in center of each wrapper. (Cover remaining wrappers with a damp paper towel until ready to use.)
2. Moisten wrapper edges with water. Fold wrapper over filling; seal edges, pleating the front side several times to form a pleated pouch. Stand pot stickers on a work surface to flatten bottoms; curve slightly to form crescent shapes if desired.
3. In a large nonstick skillet, heat 1 Tbsp. oil over medium-high heat. Arrange a third of the pot stickers in concentric circles in pan, flat side down; cook until bottoms are golden brown, 1-2 minutes.
4. Carefully add ⅓ cup broth (broth may splatter); reduce heat to medium-low. Cook, covered, until broth is almost absorbed and filling is cooked through, 2-3 minutes. Uncover; cook until bottoms are crisp and broth is completely evaporated, about 1 minute. Repeat with remaining oil, pot stickers and broth. If desired, serve with additional soy sauce and chives.
FREEZE OPTION: Place uncooked pot stickers on waxed paper-lined baking sheets; freeze until firm. Transfer to airtight freezer containers; return to freezer. To use, cook frozen pot stickers as directed, increasing broth to ½ cup and simmering time to 4-6 minutes for each batch.
1 POT STICKER: 39 cal., 2g fat (0 sat. fat), 6mg chol., 66mg sod., 4g carb. (0 sugars, 0 fiber), 2g pro.

PORK & CHIVE
POT STICKERS

CRISPY SRIRACHA SPRING ROLLS

2. In a large bowl, mix cream cheese and chili sauce; stir in chicken and coleslaw mixture. With a corner of a spring roll wrapper facing you, place about 2 Tbsp. filling just below center of wrapper. (Cover remaining wrappers with a damp paper towel until ready to use.) Fold bottom corner over filling; moisten remaining edges with water. Fold side corners toward center over filling; roll up tightly, pressing tip to seal. Repeat.

3. In a cast-iron Dutch oven or electric skillet, heat oil to 375°. Fry spring rolls, a few at a time, until golden brown, 6-8 minutes, turning occasionally. Drain on paper towels. If desired, serve with sweet chili sauce.

FREEZE OPTION: Freeze uncooked spring rolls in freezer containers, spacing them so they don't touch, and separating layers with waxed paper. To use, fry frozen spring rolls as directed, increasing time as necessary.

1 SPRING ROLL: 186 cal., 14g fat (4g sat. fat), 30mg chol., 215mg sod., 10g carb. (1g sugars, 0 fiber), 6g pro.

HEALTHY PARTY SNACK MIX

Party mix has always been a tradition in our home. I lightened my mom's classic recipe, replacing margarine with heart-healthy olive oil. No one even noticed!
—*Melissa Hansen, Ellison Bay, WI*

- -

PREP: 15 min. • **BAKE:** 1 hour + cooling • **MAKES:** 3½ qt.

 3 cups Corn Chex
 3 cups Rice Chex
 3 cups Wheat Chex
 3 cups Multi Grain Cheerios
 1 cup salted peanuts
 1½ cups pretzel sticks
 ⅓ cup olive oil
 4 tsp. Worcestershire sauce
 1 tsp. seasoned salt
 ⅛ tsp. garlic powder

1. In a large bowl, combine the cereals, peanuts and pretzels. In a small bowl, combine the remaining ingredients; pour over cereal mixture and toss to coat.

2. Transfer to two 15x10x1-in. baking pans coated with cooking spray. Bake at 250° for 1 hour, stirring every 15 minutes. Cool completely in pans on wire racks. Store in an airtight container.

¾ CUP: 150 cal., 8g fat (1g sat. fat), 0 chol., 310mg sod., 19g carb. (3g sugars, 2g fiber), 4g pro. **DIABETIC EXCHANGES:** 1½ starch, 1½ fat.

CRISPY SRIRACHA SPRING ROLLS

While in the Bahamas, friends suggested a restaurant that served amazing chicken spring rolls. When I got home, I created my own version. The Sriracha chili sauce adds a wonderful zing. It's the perfect appetizer to have waiting in the freezer!
—*Carla Mendres, Winnipeg, MB*

- -

PREP: 50 min. • **COOK:** 10 min./batch **MAKES:** about 2 dozen

 3 cups coleslaw mix (about 7 oz.)
 3 green onions, chopped
 1 Tbsp. soy sauce
 1 tsp. sesame oil
 1 lb. boneless skinless chicken breasts
 1 tsp. seasoned salt
 2 pkg. (8 oz. each) cream cheese, softened
 2 Tbsp. Sriracha chili sauce
 1 pkg. (24 to 28 each) spring roll wrappers, thawed
   Oil for deep-fat frying
   Sweet chili sauce, optional

1. Toss coleslaw mix, onions, soy sauce and sesame oil; let stand while cooking chicken. In a saucepan, bring 4 cups water to a boil. Reduce heat to maintain a simmer. Add chicken; cook, covered, 15-20 minutes or until a thermometer inserted in chicken reads 165°. Remove chicken; cool slightly. Finely chop chicken; toss with seasoned salt.

ROSEMARY-GRAPEFRUIT
CASHEWS

MOJITO
HAZELNUTS

OLD BAY
MIXED NUTS

SRIRACHA-
MOLASSES PECANS

CHOCOLATE-RASPBERRY
MACADAMIA NUTS

AW, NUTS!

These seasoned snacks are the perfect nosh during prep time,
while watching the game or as a pre-feast fuel.

RECIPES BY DANA SWEARENGIN

SRIRACHA-
MOLASSES PECANS

Stir together 3 Tbsp. **maple syrup** and 3 Tbsp. **Sriracha chili sauce**. Add 2 cups **pecans**; stir to combine. Spread on a parchment-lined baking sheet. Bake at 350° until fragrant and nuts start to brown, 8-10 minutes. Cool on a wire rack.

THAI-CURRY PEANUTS

Stir together 2 Tbsp. **mayonnaise** and 2 tsp. **red or green curry paste**. Add 2 cups **salted peanuts**; stir to combine. Spread on a parchment-lined baking sheet. Bake at 350°until fragrant and nuts start to brown, 8-10 minutes. Cool on a wire rack.

OLD BAY MIXED NUTS

Stir together 2 Tbsp. **butter**, 2 tsp. **seafood seasoning** and **lemon zest**, and ½ tsp. **pepper sauce**. Add 2 cups **mixed nuts**; stir to combine. Spread on a parchment-lined

baking sheet. Bake at 350° until fragrant and nuts start to brown, 12-15 minutes. Cool on a wire rack.

HONEY-ROSE PISTACHIOS

Combine 3 Tbsp. **honey**, 2 tsp. **lemon juice** and ¼ tsp. **rose water**. Add 2 cups shelled **pistachios**; toss to coat. Spread on a parchment-lined baking sheet. Bake at 350° until fragrant and nuts start to brown, 8-10 minutes. Toss with 2 tsp. **dried rose petals** if desired. Cool on a wire rack.

ROSEMARY-GRAPEFRUIT
CASHEWS

Stir together 2 Tbsp. ruby red **grapefruit juice**, 1 Tbsp. grated **grapefruit zest** and 1 Tbsp. minced fresh **rosemary**. Add 2 cups **cashews**; stir to combine. Spread on a parchment-lined baking sheet. Bake at 350° until fragrant and nuts start to brown, 8-10 minutes. Cool on a wire rack.

CHOCOLATE-RASPBERRY
MACADAMIA NUTS

In a food processor, process 1 oz. freeze-dried **raspberries** to a fine powder; add 3 Tbsp. **confectioners' sugar** and pulse to combine. Stir together 2 cups **toasted almonds** and 3 oz. melted **dark chocolate**. Add raspberry mixture; toss to coat. Spread nuts on a parchment-lined sheet pan; let stand until set.

MOJITO HAZELNUTS

Combine 3 Tbsp. **honey**, 4 tsp. **lime zest** and 1 tsp. **dried mint**. Add 2 cups **hazelnuts**; stir to combine. Spread on a parchment-lined baking sheet. Bake at 350° until fragrant and nuts start to brown, 8-10 minutes. Cool on a wire rack.

MAPLE-LEMON WALNUTS

Stir together 4 Tbsp. **maple syrup** and 2 Tbsp. **lemon zest**. Add 2 cups **walnuts**; stir to combine.

Spread on a parchment-lined baking sheet. Bake at 350° until fragrant and nuts start to brown, 8-10 minutes. Cool on a wire rack.

PUMPKIN SPICE
PECANS

Stir together 3 Tbsp. **maple syrup** and 1½ tsp. **pumpkin pie spice**. Add 2 cups **pecans**; stir to combine. Spread on a parchment-lined baking sheet. Bake at 350° until fragrant and nuts start to brown, 8-10 minutes. Cool on a wire rack.

HONEY, PAPRIKA
& ORANGE ALMONDS

Stir together 3 Tbsp. **honey**, 2 Tbsp. **orange zest** and 2 tsp. **smoked paprika**. Add 2 cups unblanched **almonds**; stir to combine. Spread on a parchment-lined baking sheet. Bake until fragrant and nuts start to brown, 8-10 minutes. Cool on a wire rack.

CHICKEN & CASHEW STEAMED BUNS

CHICKEN & CASHEW STEAMED BUNS

Served with hoisin or soy sauce, steamed buns are a tasty starter with a surprise inside. Cook them in batches so the steamer doesn't get overcrowded.
—*Greg Fontenot, The Woodlands, TX*

- -

PREP: 30 min. + resting
COOK: 20 min./batch • **MAKES:** 1 dozen

- ½ lb. ground chicken
- 3 green onions, finely chopped
- 2 Tbsp. finely chopped cashews
- 1 Tbsp. large egg white
- 1½ tsp. brown sugar
- 1½ tsp. soy sauce
- 1 tsp. minced fresh gingerroot
- ¼ tsp. sesame oil
- 1 lb. fresh or frozen pizza dough, thawed
- 1 cup thinly sliced cabbage
  Hoisin sauce, optional

1. In a small bowl, combine the first 8 ingredients until mixture forms a paste. On a lightly floured surface, roll dough into a 12x9-in. rectangle. Cut into twelve 3-in. squares. Divide chicken mixture among squares. Bring 4 corners of dough together; twist and pinch to seal. Let rest 15 minutes.
2. In a Dutch oven, place a steamer basket over 1 in. water. Line basket with cabbage. In batches, place 4 buns in basket. Bring water to a boil. Reduce heat to maintain a simmer; steam buns, covered, until a thermometer reads 165°, 18-20 minutes. Carefully remove lid to avoid dripping condensation onto buns. Serve with hoisin sauce if desired.
1 STEAMED BUN: 132 cal., 4g fat (1g sat. fat), 13mg chol., 155mg sod., 18g carb. (1g sugars, 1g fiber), 7g pro.

CHICKEN SALAD IN BASKETS

When I first made these cute little cups, they were a big hit. They make a yummy appetizer for an Easter gathering.
—*Gwendolyn Fae Trapp, Strongsville, OH*

- -

PREP: 15 min. • **BAKE:** 15 min. + chilling• **MAKES:** 20 appetizers

- 1 cup diced cooked chicken
- 3 bacon strips, cooked and crumbled
- ⅓ cup chopped mushrooms
- 2 Tbsp. chopped pecans
- 2 Tbsp. diced peeled apple
- ¼ cup mayonnaise
- ⅛ tsp. salt
  Dash pepper
- 20 slices bread
- 6 Tbsp. butter, melted
- 2 Tbsp. minced fresh parsley

1. In a small bowl, combine the first 5 ingredients. Combine mayonnaise, salt and pepper; add to chicken mixture and stir to coat. Cover and refrigerate until serving.
2. Preheat oven to 350°. Cut each slice of bread with a 3-in. round cookie cutter; brush both sides with butter. Press into ungreased mini muffin cups. Bake until golden brown and crisp, 11-13 minutes.
3. Cool 3 minutes before removing from pans to wire racks to cool completely. Spoon 1 Tbsp. chicken salad into each bread basket. Cover and refrigerate up to 2 hours. Just before serving, sprinkle with parsley.
1 PIECE: 140 cal., 8g fat (3g sat. fat), 17mg chol., 223mg sod., 12g carb. (2g sugars, 1g fiber), 5g pro.

CHICKEN SALAD IN BASKETS

MINI
BURGERS WITH
THE WORKS

EASY BUFFALO CHICKEN DIP

Everyone will simply devour this savory and delicious dip with shredded chicken throughout. The spicy kick makes it perfect football-watching food, and the recipe always brings raves.
—*Janice Foltz, Hershey, PA*

TAKES: 30 min. • MAKES: 4 cups

1 pkg. (8 oz.) reduced-fat cream cheese
1 cup reduced-fat sour cream
½ cup Louisiana-style hot sauce
3 cups shredded cooked chicken breast
Assorted crackers

1. Preheat oven to 350°. In a large bowl, beat cream cheese, sour cream and hot sauce until smooth; stir in chicken.
2. Transfer to an 8-in. square baking dish coated with cooking spray. Cover and bake until heated through, 18-22 minutes. Serve warm, with crackers.
3 TBSP: 77 cal., 4g fat (2g sat. fat), 28mg chol., 71mg sod., 1g carb. (1g sugars, 0 fiber), 8g pro.

READER REVIEW

"I served this with fresh-cut veggies and Triscuits. My company loved it!"
—LAURIEPAR, TASTEOFHOME.COM

MINI BURGERS WITH THE WORKS

I started preparing these mini burgers several years ago as a creative way to use up bread crusts accumulating in my freezer. Their tiny size makes them simply irresistible.
—*Linda Lane, Bennington, VT*

TAKES: 30 min. • MAKES: 1 dozen

¼ lb. ground beef
3 slices American cheese
4 slices white bread (heels of loaves recommended)
2 Tbsp. prepared Thousand Island salad dressing
2 pearl onions, thinly sliced
4 baby dill pickles, thinly sliced
3 cherry tomatoes, thinly sliced

1. Shape beef into twelve 1-in. patties. Place on a microwave-safe plate lined with paper towels. Cover with another paper towel; microwave on high for 1 minute or until the meat is no longer pink. Cut each slice of cheese into fourths; set aside.
2. Using a 1-in. round cookie cutter, cut out 6 circles from each slice of bread. Spread half the bread circles with dressing. Layer with burgers, cheese, onions, pickles and tomatoes. Top with remaining bread circles; secure with toothpicks.
1 BURGER: 68 cal., 3g fat (1g sat. fat), 11mg chol., 153mg sod., 5g carb. (1g sugars, 0 fiber), 4g pro.

EASY BUFFALO CHICKEN DIP

STICKY SESAME CAULIFLOWER

Sesame chicken is one of my favorite takeout dishes, but I'm doing what I can to cut unnecessary calories and fat. This recipe gives me an alternative that uses fresh vegetables and never compromises on flavor.

—Anthony Ashmore, Bohemia, NY

PREP: 40 min. • **BAKE:** 25 min.
MAKES: 12 servings

- 1 cup dry bread crumbs
- ½ cup cornmeal
- 2 Tbsp. all-purpose flour
- ½ tsp. salt
- ½ tsp. garlic powder
- ½ tsp. pepper

BATTER

- 1 cup all-purpose flour
- 1 Tbsp. adobo seasoning
- 1 tsp. garlic powder
- ½ tsp. salt
- ½ tsp. pepper
- 1 bottle (12 oz.) beer
- 1 large head cauliflower, broken into florets (about 8 cups)
- 1 Tbsp. peanut oil

SAUCE

- ¼ cup orange juice
- ¼ cup sweet chili sauce
- ¼ cup island teriyaki sauce
- 2 Tbsp. sesame oil
- 1 tsp. soy sauce
- ½ tsp. rice vinegar
- ½ tsp. Sriracha chili sauce
  Optional: Thinly sliced green onions, grated orange zest and sesame seeds

1. Preheat oven to 400°. In a shallow bowl, combine the first 6 ingredients. For batter, in a large bowl, mix flour, adobo seasoning, garlic powder, salt and pepper; whisk in beer until smooth. Dip cauliflower in batter, then in bread crumb mixture. Place on a greased baking sheet. Drizzle with peanut oil; gently toss to coat. Bake until golden brown and cauliflower is just tender, 25-30 minutes.
2. Meanwhile, for sauce, in a small saucepan, combine orange juice, chili sauce, teriyaki sauce, sesame oil, soy sauce, vinegar and Sriracha chili sauce. Cook and stir over low heat just until warmed, about 5 minutes.
3. Transfer cauliflower to a large bowl. Drizzle with sauce; gently toss to coat. Serve with toppings of your choice.
⅔ CUP: 140 cal., 4g fat (1g sat. fat), 0 chol., 714mg sod., 23g carb. (8g sugars, 2g fiber), 4g pro.

ONION PAKODAS

Onion *pakodas* are iconic and beloved in India. This classic dish is part of the fabric of the culture—as rich in flavor as in tradition. These golden-crisp onion fritters are jam-packed with flavors from green chiles, red Kashmiri chili powder, garlic, carom seeds, turmeric, and of course onions! Serve this epic dish as a snack with green chutney or ketchup or serve it alongside your favorite Indian meal.

—Archana Mundhe, Ridgewood, NJ

PREP: 25 min. • **COOK:** 15 min./batch
MAKES: 9 servings

- 1 large red onion
- ½ cup fresh cilantro leaves
- 1 tsp. kosher salt
- ¼ cup gram flour
- 1 Tbsp. white rice flour
- 1 tsp. minced garlic
- 1 tsp. Kashmiri red chili powder
- 1 tsp. carom seeds (Ajwain)
- ½ tsp. minced seeded green chile pepper , such as serrano
- ¼ tsp. ground turmeric
- 1½ tsp. canola oil
  Cooking spray

1. Cut onion in half; thinly slice each half. In a bowl, combine onion, cilantro and salt. Gently massage the mixture to release moisture (do not drain). In a small bowl, stir together gram flour, rice flour, garlic, chili powder, carom seeds, chile pepper and turmeric; add to onion mixture. Mix well, forming a thick mixture. In a small skillet, heat canola oil; stir into the onion mixture.
2. Preheat air fryer to 400°. In batches, drop mixture by tablespoonfuls into a greased air fryer; spread into ½-in.-thick patties. Reduce heat to 350°; cook for 10 minutes. Spray patties with cooking spray; cook until golden brown and the edges are crispy, 2-3 minutes. Serve immediately.
NOTE: Wear disposable gloves when cutting hot peppers; the oils can burn skin. Avoid touching your face.
1 PAKODA: 36 cal., 1g fat (0 sat. fat), 0 chol., 223mg sod., 5g carb. (1g sugars, 1g fiber), 1g pro.

STICKY SESAME CAULIFLOWER

HERBED GOAT CHEESE BAGUETTE SLICES

This fun appetizer is guaranteed to wow guests! It takes just moments to whip up the herb-infused goat cheese spread.
—Taste of Home *Test Kitchen*

- -

PREP: 15 min. + chilling
MAKES: 4 servings

- 2 oz. fresh goat cheese
- 1 tsp. minced fresh parsley
- ¾ tsp. minced fresh rosemary
- ¼ tsp. minced garlic
  Dash salt
  Dash coarsely ground pepper
- 8 slices French bread baguette (¼ in. thick)
- 1 plum tomato, cut into 8 thin slices
  Additional coarsely ground pepper, optional

1. In a small bowl, combine the cheese, parsley, rosemary, garlic, salt and pepper; roll into a 3-in. log. Cover and refrigerate for at least 1 hour.

2. Spread over bread; top with tomato slices. Sprinkle with additional pepper if desired.

2 APPETIZERS: 45 cal., 2g fat (1g sat. fat), 9mg chol., 142mg sod., 5g carb. (0 sugars, 0 fiber), 2g pro.

AIR-FRYER PIZZA PUFFS

I love pizza in any form so it seemed only logical to turn my pizza love into an appetizer. These little bundles can be made ahead of time and chilled until you're ready to pop them into the air fryer.
—*Vivi Taylor, Middleburg, FL*

- -

PREP: 20 min. • **COOK:** 10 min./batch
MAKES: 20 servings

- 1 loaf (1 lb.) frozen pizza dough, thawed
- 20 slices pepperoni
- 8 oz. part-skim mozzarella cheese, cut into 20 cubes
- ¼ cup butter
- 2 small garlic cloves, minced
  Dash salt
  Marinara sauce, warmed
  Optional: Crushed red pepper flakes and grated Parmesan cheese

AIR-FRYER PIZZA PUFFS

1. Preheat air fryer to 350°. Shape the dough into 1½-in. balls; flatten into ⅛-in.-thick circles. Place 1 pepperoni slice and 1 cheese cube in center of each circle; wrap dough around pepperoni and cheese. Pinch edges to seal; shape into a ball. Repeat with remaining dough, cheese and pepperoni.

2. In batches, place seam side up in a single layer on greased tray in air-fryer basket; cook until light golden brown, 6-8 minutes. Cool slightly.

3. Meanwhile, in a small saucepan, melt butter over low heat. Add garlic and salt, taking care not to brown butter or garlic; brush over puffs. Serve with marinara sauce; if desired, sprinkle with red pepper flakes and Parmesan.

FREEZE OPTION: Cover and freeze unbaked pizza puffs on waxed paper-lined baking sheets until firm. Transfer to a freezer container; seal and return to freezer. To use, preheat air fryer to 350°; cook pizza puffs on greased tray in air-fryer basket as directed, increasing time as necessary until golden brown.

NOTE: In our testing, we find cook times vary dramatically between brands of air fryers. As a result, we give wider than normal ranges on suggested cook times. Begin checking at the first time listed and adjust as needed.

1 PIZZA PUFF: 120 cal., 6g fat (3g sat. fat), 15mg chol., 189mg sod., 11g carb. (1g sugars, 0 fiber), 5g pro.

EASY EGG ROLLS

PISTACHIO & DATE RICOTTA CROSTINI

My husband and I regularly have date nights at home where we make a four-course meal. For appetizers, I like to keep things simple but dressed up. I've found that making a special appetizer helps transform the atmosphere into a fancy meal. We've grown to really cherish these long and luxurious evenings together in our living room. Fresh figs can be used in lieu of dates if that's what you have on hand!
—Kristin Bowers, Gilbert, AZ

PREP: 20 min. • BAKE: 15 min. • MAKES: 3 dozen

- 36 slices French bread baguette (¼ in. thick)
- 2 Tbsp. olive oil
- ⅛ tsp. plus ¼ tsp. salt, divided
- 1 cup whole-milk ricotta cheese
- 4 oz. cream cheese, softened
- 3 Tbsp. honey, divided
- 4 tsp. grated lemon zest, divided
- 10 pitted medjool dates, chopped (about 1½ cups)
- ½ cup shelled pistachios, finely chopped

1. Preheat oven to 400°. Place bread slices on a large ungreased baking sheet. Brush tops with olive oil and sprinkle with ⅛ tsp. salt. Bake until golden brown, 12-15 minutes. Cool on baking sheet.
2. Meanwhile, place ricotta, cream cheese, 2 Tbsp. honey, 2 tsp. zest and remaining ¼ tsp. salt in a food processor; process until almost smooth. Spread mixture over bread slices. Top with dates and pistachios. Drizzle with remaining 1 Tbsp. honey and 2 tsp. zest. Serve immediately.
1 APPETIZER: 57 cal., 3g fat (1g sat. fat), 6mg chol., 74mg sod., 6g carb. (3g sugars, 0 fiber), 1g pro.

EASY EGG ROLLS

I've always loved egg rolls, but every recipe I saw seemed too complicated. So I decided to start with a packaged coleslaw mix. Now I can make these yummy treats at a moment's notice.
—Samantha Dunn, Leesville, LA

PREP: 30 min. • COOK: 5 min./batch • MAKES: 28 egg rolls

- 1 lb. ground beef
- 1 pkg. (14 oz.) coleslaw mix
- 2 Tbsp. soy sauce
- ½ tsp. garlic powder
- ¼ tsp. ground ginger
- ⅛ tsp. onion powder
- 1 Tbsp. all-purpose flour
- 28 egg roll wrappers
  Canola oil for frying

1. In a large skillet, cook beef over medium heat until no longer pink, 5-7 minutes, breaking into crumbles; drain and cool slightly. In a bowl, combine beef, coleslaw mix, soy sauce, garlic powder, ginger and onion powder. In a small bowl, combine flour and enough water to make a paste.
2. With 1 corner of an egg roll wrapper facing you, place ¼ cup filling just below center of wrapper. (Cover remaining wrappers with a damp paper towel until ready to use.) Fold bottom corner over filling; moisten remaining wrapper edges with flour paste. Fold side corners toward center over filling. Roll egg roll up tightly, pressing at tip to seal. Repeat.
3. In an electric skillet or deep-fat fryer, heat oil to 375°. Fry egg rolls, a few at a time, until golden brown, 3-4 minutes, turning occasionally. Drain on paper towels.
1 EGG ROLL: 185 cal., 9g fat (1g sat. fat), 13mg chol., 261mg sod., 20g carb. (1g sugars, 1g fiber), 6g pro.

PISTACHIO & DATE RICOTTA CROSTINI

CHILI NACHOS

GRUYERE & CARAMELIZED ONION TARTS

Garlic and onion is a match made in heaven in my opinion, so I love creating new recipes to showcase the pair. Gruyere cheese adds impeccable flavor to the eye-catching starter.
—*Lisa Speer, Palm Beach, FL*

- -

PREP: 45 min. • **BAKE:** 15 min. • **MAKES:** 2 dozen

- 1 large sweet onion, thinly sliced
- 2 Tbsp. olive oil
- 1 Tbsp. butter
- 3 garlic cloves, minced
- ¼ tsp. salt
- ¼ tsp. pepper
- 1 pkg. (17.3 oz.) frozen puff pastry, thawed
- 1 cup shredded Gruyere or Swiss cheese
- ¼ cup grated Parmesan cheesew
- 2 Tbsp. minced fresh thyme

1. In a large skillet, saute onion in oil and butter until softened. Reduce heat to medium-low; cook, uncovered, for 40 minutes or until deep golden brown, stirring occasionally. Add garlic; cook 1 minute longer. Stir in salt and pepper.
2. Unfold each puff pastry sheet onto an ungreased baking sheet. Using a knife, score decorative lines around the edges of each sheet. Spread onion mixture to within ½ in. of edges. Sprinkle with cheeses and thyme.
3. Bake at 400° for 12-15 minutes or until golden brown. Cut each tart into 12 pieces. If desired, top with additional fresh thyme and Parmesan cheese. Serve warm.
1 PIECE: 142 cal., 9g fat (3g sat. fat), 7mg chol., 125mg sod., 13g carb. (1g sugars, 2g fiber), 3g pro.

CHILI NACHOS

This creamy, chili-like dish is so warm and filling that we often prepare it when we take skiing trips to Colorado. We keep it warm in a slow cooker to serve as a hearty dip at parties. It can also be served over corn chips and eaten with a fork.
—*Laurie Withers, Wildomar, CA*

- -

TAKES: 20 min. • **MAKES:** 16 servings

- 2½ lbs. ground beef
- 3 cans (15 oz. each) tomato sauce
- 2 cans (15 oz. each) pinto beans, rinsed and drained
- 1 can (10 oz.) diced tomatoes and green chiles, undrained
- 2 envelopes chili mix
- 2 lbs. Velveeta, cubed
- 1 cup heavy whipping cream
- 2 pkg. (16 oz. each) corn chips
  Optional: Sour cream, sliced jalapeno and lime wedges

In a Dutch oven, cook the beef until no longer pink; drain. Add tomato sauce, beans, tomatoes and chili mix; heat through. Add cheese and cream; cook until the cheese is melted. Serve over chips. If desired, top with sour cream, sliced jalapeno and lime wedges.
1 SERVING: 550 cal., 36g fat (16g sat. fat), 91mg chol., 1379mg sod., 28g carb. (6g sugars, 3g fiber), 28g pro.

GRUYERE & CARAMELIZED ONION TARTS

COLORFUL
CORNBREAD SALAD
PAGE 34

Salads & Dressings

Crisp, refreshing salads are a thoughtful way to round out the meal. Turn here for green salads, picnic favorites, a retro gelatin salad, cool veggies and main-dish salads sure to satisfy.

DISHES WE LOVE

Gingered Spaghetti Salad p. 31

Kentucky Coleslaw p. 34

Pesto Corn Salad with Shrimp p. 36

COPYCAT SOUTHWEST CHICKEN SALAD

GRILLED SHRIMP COBB SALAD

I often use a grill pan for this healthy salad, but you can simply saute the shrimp too. Use any salad greens you like.
—*Nicholas Monfre, Hudson, FL*

- -

TAKES: 30 min. • **MAKES:** 2 servings

- ½ lb. uncooked shrimp (31-40 per lb.), peeled and deveined
- 2 Tbsp. olive oil
- 1 tsp. lemon juice
- ½ tsp. salt
- ¼ tsp. white pepper

DRESSING
- ¼ cup mayonnaise
- 2 Tbsp. crumbled Gorgonzola cheese
- 1 Tbsp. water
- ½ tsp. dried parsley flakes
- ¼ tsp. white wine vinegar

SALAD
- 4 cups spring mix salad greens
- 1 medium ripe avocado, peeled and cut into wedges
- 4 pieces bacon strips, cooked and chopped
- 2 hard-boiled large eggs, sliced
- 1 medium tomato, sliced
- ¼ cup slices red onion

1. Toss the shrimp with oil, lemon juice, salt and pepper; refrigerate, covered, 15 minutes. Mix dressing ingredients, mashing cheese with a fork.
2. Place greens on a platter; top with remaining ingredients. Grill shrimp, covered, over medium heat until pink, 2-3 minutes per side. Place over salad. Serve with dressing.

1 SERVING: 726 cal., 59g fat (12g sat. fat), 349mg chol., 1392mg sod., 16g carb. (3g sugars, 8g fiber), 36g pro.

GRILLED SHRIMP COBB SALAD

COPYCAT SOUTHWEST CHICKEN SALAD

My husband and I loved this salad the first time we ate it at Applebee's. After the third time ordering it, we asked our waitress what what was in the dressing. She told us the ingredients, so I went home and worked on a version we feel tastes just as delicious.
—*Pamela Shank, Parkersburg, WV*

- -

TAKES: 30 min. • **MAKES:** 2 servings

- ⅓ cup chopped red onion
- ¼ cup pickled jalapeno slices, chopped
- ¼ cup coleslaw salad dressing
- 1 Tbsp. juice from pickled jalapeno slices
- 1 Tbsp. lime juice
- 2 boneless skinless chicken breast halves (6 oz. each)
- ¼ cup frozen corn
- 3 cups chopped romaine
- ¼ cup chopped sweet red pepper
- ¼ cup chopped seeded tomatoes
- ¼ cup canned black beans, rinsed and drained
- ½ cup shredded cheddar cheese
- ½ cup tricolor tortilla strips

1. Place the first 5 ingredients in a jar with a tight-fitting lid; shake well. Refrigerate until serving.
2. Place the chicken on oiled grill rack. Grill, covered, over medium heat or broil 3 in. from heat until a thermometer reads 165°, 5-7 minutes on each side. Let stand 5 minutes before slicing. Meanwhile, prepare corn according to the package directions.
3. Divide romaine between 2 salad bowls. Arrange chicken over romaine; top with corn, red pepper, tomatoes and beans. Sprinkle with cheese and tortilla strips. Shake dressing again; drizzle over salads. Serve immediately.

1 SERVING: 557 cal., 26g fat (8g sat. fat), 132mg chol., 826mg sod., 33g carb. (9g sugars, 4g fiber), 45g pro.

FRUITY LIME SALAD MOLD

A dear friend shared this recipe with me over 30 years ago, and it has appeared on our table frequently since then. It's rich tasting, plus the touch of red maraschino cherries gives it a pretty accent for the holidays or any special occasion.
—*Jean Kirkland, Newport, OR*

PREP: 10 min. + chilling
MAKES: 8 servings

- 1 pkg. (3 oz.) lime gelatin
- 1 cup boiling water
- 3 oz. cream cheese, softened
- 1 can (8 oz.) crushed pineapple, undrained
- 1 cup heavy whipping cream, whipped
- ¼ cup chopped pecans
- ¼ cup chopped maraschino cherries

1. In a large bowl, dissolve gelatin in boiling water; chill until syrupy. In a small bowl, combine cream cheese and pineapple; stir into cooled gelatin.
2. Fold in the whipped cream, pecans and cherries. Pour into a 4-cup mold coated with cooking spray. Refrigerate for 3 hours or overnight.
1 SERVING: 229 cal., 17g fat (9g sat. fat), 45mg chol., 70mg sod., 18g carb. (16g sugars, 1g fiber), 3g pro.

GINGERED SPAGHETTI SALAD

We love to make this chilled chicken salad brimming with veggies. Make it meatless by omitting the chicken and tossing in more edamame.
—*Cindy Heinbaugh, Aurora, CO*

TAKES: 30 min. • **MAKES:** 8 servings

- 1 pkg. (16 oz.) whole wheat spaghetti
- 1 cup frozen shelled edamame
- 1 tsp. minced fresh gingerroot
- 1 cup reduced-fat sesame ginger salad dressing
- 3 cups cubed cooked chicken breast
- 1 English cucumber, chopped
- 1 medium sweet red pepper, chopped
- 1 small sweet yellow pepper, chopped
- 1 small red onion, finely chopped
- 3 green onions, sliced

1. Cook spaghetti according to package directions, adding edamame during the last 5 minutes of cooking. Rinse mixture in cold water and drain well. Meanwhile, stir ginger into salad dressing.
2. In a large bowl, combine spaghetti, chicken, cucumber, peppers and red onion. Add the dressing; toss to coat. Sprinkle with green onions.
1¾ CUPS: 355 cal., 6g fat (1g sat. fat), 40mg chol., 431mg sod., 52g carb. (8g sugars, 7g fiber), 26g pro.

GINGERED SPAGHETTI SALAD

MEDITERRANEAN
SHRIMP ORZO SALAD

SWEET POTATO PANZANELLA

This is my favorite cool-weather salad. It is filled with flavor and texture but isn't too high in calories.
—*Mary M. Leverette, Columbia, SC*

TAKES: 30 min. • **MAKES:** 8 servings

- 2 cups cubed peeled sweet potatoes
- 4 cups cubed French bread
- 4 Tbsp. olive oil, divided
- ⅛ tsp. salt
- ⅛ tsp. pepper
- 4 cups fresh baby spinach
- ½ small red onion, thinly sliced
- ¼ cup minced fresh basil
- ¼ cup minced fresh cilantro
- ⅓ cup red wine vinegar

1. Preheat oven to 450°. Place the sweet potatoes in a large saucepan; add water to cover. Bring to a boil. Reduce heat; cook, covered, until just tender, 8-12 minutes. Drain; cool slightly.
2. Meanwhile, toss the bread cubes with 2 Tbsp. oil, salt and pepper. Spread evenly in an ungreased 15x10x1-in. pan. Bake until golden brown, about 5 minutes. Transfer to a large bowl; cool slightly.
3. Add spinach, red onion, herbs and sweet potatoes to toasted bread. In a small bowl, whisk together vinegar and remaining oil. Drizzle over salad; toss gently to combine.
¾ CUP: 142 cal., 7g fat (1g sat. fat), 0 chol., 150mg sod., 17g carb. (3g sugars, 2g fiber), 2g pro. **DIABETIC EXCHANGES:** 1½ fat, 1 starch.

MEDITERRANEAN SHRIMP ORZO SALAD

Loaded with veggies and shrimp, this crowd pleaser is a tasty change from standard pasta salads.
—*Ginger Johnson, Pottstown, PA*

TAKES: 30 min. • **MAKES:** 8 servings

- 1 pkg. (16 oz.) orzo pasta
- ¾ lb. peeled and deveined cooked shrimp (31-40 per lb.)
- 1 can (14 oz.) water-packed quartered artichoke hearts, rinsed and drained
- 1 cup finely chopped green pepper
- 1 cup finely chopped sweet red pepper
- ¾ cup finely chopped red onion
- ½ cup pitted Greek olives
- ½ cup minced fresh parsley
- ⅓ cup chopped fresh dill
- ¾ cup Greek vinaigrette

1. Cook orzo according to package directions. Drain; rinse with cold water and drain well.
2. In a large bowl, combine orzo, shrimp, vegetables, olives and herbs. Add vinaigrette; toss to coat. Refrigerate, covered, until serving.
1½ CUPS: 397 cal., 12g fat (2g sat. fat), 65mg chol., 574mg sod., 52g carb. (4g sugars, 3g fiber), 18g pro.

SWEET POTATO
PANZANELLA

VEGETABLE COUSCOUS SALAD

1. For the dressing, in a small bowl, whisk the first 10 ingredients. Refrigerate until serving.
2. Cook couscous according to package directions. Meanwhile, brush the zucchini, yellow peppers and eggplant with oil; sprinkle with salt and pepper. Grill, covered, over medium heat until crisp-tender, 10-12 minutes, turning once.
3. Chop grilled vegetables; place in a large bowl. Add the tomatoes, olives, parsley, basil and couscous. Pour dressing over salad and toss to coat. Serve warm or chilled.

¾ CUP: 272 cal., 16g fat (2g sat. fat), 0 chol., 244mg sod., 29g carb. (5g sugars, 3g fiber), 5g pro. **DIABETIC EXCHANGES:** 2 fat, 1½ starch, 1 vegetable.

WATERMELON TOMATO SALAD

Watermelon and tomatoes may seem an unlikely pair, but they team up to make a winning combination in this eye-catching salad.
—*Matthew Denton, Seattle, WA*

- -

TAKES: 25 min. • **MAKES:** 18 servings

- 10 cups cubed seedless watermelon
- 2 pints yellow grape or pear tomatoes, halved
- 1 medium red onion, chopped
- ½ cup minced fresh parsley
- ½ cup minced fresh basil
- ¼ cup lime juice

In a large bowl, combine the watermelon, tomatoes and onion. In a small bowl, combine the parsley, basil and lime juice. Pour over watermelon mixture and toss to coat. Refrigerate until serving.
¾ CUP: 33 cal., 0 fat (0 sat. fat), 0 chol., 7mg sod., 10g carb. (8g sugars, 1g fiber), 1g pro. **DIABETIC EXCHANGES:** ½ fruit.

VEGETABLE COUSCOUS SALAD

This healthy salad features our homegrown eggplant and bell peppers and the fresh herbs we keep in hanging pots in our small condo. It's a welcome partner for any grilled meat or fish. Feel free to add a little crumbled goat cheese or tangy feta.
—*Patricia Levenson, Santa Ana, CA*

- -

PREP: 35 min. • **GRILL:** 10 min. • **MAKES:** 10 servings

- ½ cup olive oil
- ⅓ cup balsamic vinegar
- 4 tsp. capers, drained
- 4 tsp. lemon juice
- 2 garlic cloves, minced
- ¾ tsp. Dijon mustard
- 1¼ tsp. minced fresh rosemary or ½ tsp. dried rosemary, crushed
- 1¼ tsp. minced fresh thyme or ½ tsp. dried thyme
- ⅛ tsp. salt
- ⅛ tsp. pepper

SALAD

- 1 pkg. (10 oz.) uncooked couscous
- 2 medium zucchini or yellow summer squash, halved lengthwise
- 2 medium sweet yellow or red peppers, quartered
- 1 Japanese eggplant, halved lengthwise
- 2 Tbsp. olive oil
- ¼ tsp. salt
- ¼ tsp. pepper
- 1 cup grape tomatoes, halved
- ½ cup Greek olives, pitted and sliced
- 1 Tbsp. minced fresh parsley or 1 tsp. dried parsley flakes
- 1 Tbsp. minced fresh basil or 1 tsp. dried basil

WATERMELON TOMATO SALAD

KENTUCKY
COLESLAW

COLORFUL CORNBREAD SALAD

(SHOWN ON PAGE 28)

When my garden comes in, I harvest the vegetables for potluck dishes. I live in the South, and we think bacon and cornbread make everything better, even salad!
—*Rebecca Clark, Warrior, AL*

- -

PREP: 30 min. + chilling
BAKE: 15 min. + cooling
MAKES: 14 servings

- 1 pkg. (8½ oz.) cornbread/muffin mix
- 1 cup mayonnaise
- ½ cup sour cream
- 1 envelope ranch salad dressing mix
- 1 to 2 Tbsp. adobo sauce from canned chipotle peppers
- 4 to 6 cups torn romaine
- 4 medium tomatoes, chopped
- 1 medium green pepper, chopped
- 1 medium onion, chopped
- 1 lb. bacon strips, cooked and crumbled
- 4 cups shredded cheddar cheese

1. Preheat oven to 400°. Prepare cornbread batter according to package directions. Pour into a greased 8-in. square baking pan. Bake until a toothpick inserted in the center comes out clean, 15-20 minutes. Cool completely in pan on a wire rack.

2. Coarsely crumble cornbread into a large bowl. In a small bowl, mix mayonnaise, sour cream, salad dressing mix and adobo sauce.

3. In a 3-qt. trifle bowl or glass bowl, layer a third of the cornbread and half of each of the following: romaine, tomatoes, pepper, onion, bacon, cheese and mayonnaise mixture. Repeat layers. Top with remaining cornbread and, if desired, additional chopped tomato and bacon. Refrigerate, covered, 2-4 hours before serving.

¾ CUP: 407 cal., 31g fat (11g sat. fat), 61mg chol., 821mg sod., 18g carb. (6g sugars, 2g fiber), 14g pro.

KENTUCKY COLESLAW

My crew enjoys a number of coleslaw recipes, but sometimes we just can't help but crave Kentucky Fried Chicken's version of the creamy side. We used to buy several pints at a time, but now that I've come up with this perfect copycat, we don't have to!
—*Donna Gribbins, Shelbyville, KY*

- -

PREP: 20 min. + chilling
MAKES: 8 servings

- ½ cup buttermilk
- ½ cup mayonnaise
- ⅓ cup sugar
- 2 Tbsp. lemon juice
- 4½ tsp. white vinegar
- 1 tsp. salt
- ½ tsp. pepper
- 1 lb. finely chopped cabbage (about 8 cups)
- 2 medium carrots, finely chopped (about 2 cups)
- 3 Tbsp. grated onion

In a large bowl, whisk the first 7 ingredients until combined. Add remaining ingredients; toss to coat. Refrigerate, covered, at least 2 hours and up to 3 days before serving.

¾ CUP: 160 cal., 10g fat (2g sat. fat), 6mg chol., 421mg sod., 16g carb. (13g sugars, 3g fiber), 2g pro.

TEST KITCHEN TIP

if you're looking for convenience, you can use a prepackaged coleslaw mix from the grocery store (the mixes usually contain carrots too!).

AMISH MACARONI SALAD

This Amish macaroni salad is a crowd favorite. It's supposed to be sweet, but you can lessen the sugar to suit your taste. Garnish with sliced hard-boiled eggs and paprika, if desired.
—*Mishelle Johnson, Wyoming, MI*

PREP: 20 min. • **COOK:** 15 min. • **MAKES:** 10 servings

- 2   cups uncooked elbow macaroni
- 2   cups Miracle Whip or mayonnaise
- ¾   cup sugar
- 3   Tbsp. sweet pickle relish
- 3   Tbsp. yellow mustard
- 2¼ tsp. cider vinegar
- ¾   tsp. celery seed
- ¼   tsp. salt
- 3   celery ribs, chopped
- 1   medium onion, finely chopped
- 1   medium sweet red pepper, chopped
- 3   hard-boiled large eggs, chopped

1. Cook macaroni according to package directions; drain and rinse with cold water. Cool completely.

2. For dressing, in a small bowl, combine Miracle Whip, sugar, relish, mustard, vinegar, celery seed and salt. In a large bowl, combine macaroni, celery, onion, red pepper and eggs. Add dressing; gently toss to coat. Cover and refrigerate until serving.

½ CUP: 283 cal., 13g fat (2g sat. fat), 72mg chol., 496mg sod., 37g carb. (21g sugars, 1g fiber), 4g pro.

AMISH MACARONI SALAD

AVOCADO-LIME RANCH DRESSING

This avocado lime ranch dressing is a Chick-fil-A copycat recipe. This version has no sugar added, is half the calories of the original, and is made with buttermilk, avocado, fresh cilantro, spices and lime for a tangy, zesty twist on a classic. Dairy-based salad dressings will last in the refrigerator for up to one week. Using freshly opened sour cream and buttermilk will help it last as long as possible.
—*Kelsey Reddick Smith, Knoxville, TN*

PREP: 15 min. + chilling • **MAKES:** 2 cups

- ½   cup buttermilk
- ½   cup sour cream
- ¼   cup mayonnaise
- 1   medium ripe avocado, peeled and cubed
- 2   Tbsp. chopped fresh cilantro
- 2   Tbsp. lime juice
- 1½ tsp. dill weed
- ½   tsp. salt
- ½   tsp. garlic powder
- ½   tsp. ground cumin
- ¼   tsp. pepper

Place all ingredients in a blender; cover and process until combined. Transfer to a jar. Refrigerate, covered, at least 1 hour before serving.

2 TBSP: 56 cal., 5g fat (1g sat. fat), 7mg chol., 109mg sod., 2g carb. (1g sugars, 1g fiber), 1g pro. **DIABETIC EXCHANGES:** 1 fat.

PESTO CORN SALAD WITH SHRIMP

GRAPE & FETA QUINOA

This is my favorite grain salad with all the crunchy nuts, salty feta, herbs and juicy grapes. The light, tangy dressing is just enough to season the salad, and you can serve the quinoa with almost anything. Try it with pork chops, roast chicken or burgers. It's good in the summer, at a picnic, or with Thanksgiving dinner. Use any color grapes you like.
—Tara Bench, TasteofHome.com

PREP: 20 min. • **COOK:** 15 min.
MAKES: 6 servings

- 1 cup quinoa, rinsed
- 2 cups water
   Dash salt
- 1 cup (6 oz.) California grapes, halved
- ⅔ cup (3 oz.) crumbled feta cheese
- ⅓ cup coarsely chopped walnuts, toasted
- ⅓ cup chopped fresh flat-leaf parsley

DRESSING

- 1½ tsp. grated lemon zest
- 3 Tbsp. fresh lemon juice
- 2 Tbsp. olive oil
- 1 small garlic clove, minced
- ¼ tsp. kosher salt

1. In a medium saucepan, combine water, quinoa and salt. Bring to a boil. Reduce heat; simmer, covered, until quinoa is tender and liquid is absorbed, about 15 minutes. Remove from the heat and cool.

2. Meanwhile, in a small bowl, whisk dressing ingredients together. In a large bowl, combine quinoa, grapes, feta, walnuts and parsley. Add dressing and toss to coat. Cover and refrigerate for up to 1 day.

¾ CUP: 239 cal., 13g fat (3g sat. fat), 7mg chol., 229mg sod., 25g carb. (5g sugars, 3g fiber), 8g pro. **DIABETIC EXCHANGES:** 2 fat, 1½ starch.

DID YOU KNOW?

Quinoa (pronounced KEEN-wah) is an ancient South American grain. It's often referred to as the "the perfect grain" because, unlike other grains, it offers a complete protein. This makes quinoa an excellent choice for vegetarian and vegan meals, which can otherwise tend to be low in protein.

PESTO CORN SALAD WITH SHRIMP

This recipe showcases the beautiful bounty of summer with its fresh corn, tomatoes and delicious basil. Prevent browning by spritzing the salad with lemon juice.
—Deena Bowen, Chico, CA

TAKES: 30 min. • **MAKES:** 4 servings

- 4 medium ears sweet corn, husked
- ½ cup packed fresh basil leaves
- ¼ cup olive oil
- ½ tsp. salt, divided
- 1½ cups cherry tomatoes, halved
- ⅛ tsp. pepper
- 1 medium ripe avocado, peeled and chopped
- 1 lb. uncooked shrimp (31-40 per lb.), peeled and deveined

1. In a pot of boiling water, cook corn until tender, about 5 minutes. Drain; cool slightly. Meanwhile, in a food processor, pulse basil, oil and ¼ tsp. salt until blended.

2. Cut corn from cob and place in a bowl. Stir in tomatoes, pepper and remaining ¼ tsp. salt. Add avocado and 2 Tbsp. basil mixture; toss gently to combine.

3. Thread shrimp onto metal or soaked wooden skewers; brush with remaining basil mixture. Grill, covered, over medium heat until shrimp turn pink, 2-4 minutes per side. Remove shrimp from skewers; serve with corn mixture.

1 SERVING: 371 cal., 22g fat (3g sat. fat), 138mg chol., 450mg sod., 25g carb. (8g sugars, 5g fiber), 23g pro.

EASY TOMATO AVOCADO SALAD

I came up with this recipe one day when avocados were on sale at the market. It's a nice change from a lettuce salad, plus it's quick to make.
—*Pamela Raybon, Edna, TX*

- -

PREP: 20 min. + chilling
MAKES: 2 servings

- 1½ tsp. lemon juice
- ¾ tsp. lime juice
- ⅛ to ¼ tsp. garlic powder
- ⅛ tsp. salt
- ⅛ tsp. pepper
- 1 medium ripe avocado, peeled and cubed
- ½ cup cubed tomato
- ¼ cup chopped red onion

In a bowl, combine the lemon juice, lime juice, garlic powder, salt and pepper. Add remaining ingredients; toss gently to coat. Refrigerate for 30 minutes before serving.
1 CUP: 173 cal., 15g fat (2g sat. fat), 0 chol., 163mg sod., 11g carb. (3g sugars, 5g fiber), 3g pro. **DIABETIC EXCHANGES:** 3 fat, 1 vegetable.

DIN TAI FUNG CHILLED CUCUMBER SALAD

My family and I are obsessed with Din Tai Fung, a famous Taiwanese restaurant in California, and its chilled cucumber salad. This is a copycat version I created at home.
—*Andrea Potischman, Menlo Park, CA*

- -

PREP: 35 min. + marinating
MAKES: 4 servings

- 5 Persian or small cucumbers, cut into ½-in. rounds
- 4½ tsp. kosher salt

MARINADE
- 3 Tbsp. rice vinegar
- 2 Tbsp. mirin (sweet rice wine)
- 2 Tbsp. honey
- 2 tsp. canola oil
- 2 tsp. sesame oil
- ½ tsp. chili garlic sauce
- ½ tsp. kosher salt

1. Place cucumbers in a colander over a plate; sprinkle with salt and toss. Let stand 20 minutes. Rinse and blot dry with paper towels.
2. In a large bowl or shallow dish, combine marinade ingredients. Add cucumbers; turn to coat. Refrigerate, covered, at least 4 hours or overnight.
3. Drain cucumbers, reserving ¼ cup marinade. Arrange cucumbers on a serving plate; drizzle with reserved marinade. Serve cold.
¾ CUP: 66 cal., 3g fat (0 sat. fat), 0 chol., 439mg sod., 9g carb. (7g sugars, 1g fiber), 1g pro. **DIABETIC EXCHANGES:** 1 vegetable, ½ fat.

DIN TAI FUNG CHILLED CUCUMBER SALAD

LEMON BASIL
CHICKEN SALAD

BLUE CHEESE KALE SALAD

Instead of the standard spinach, romaine or iceberg, try kale in your salad! I didn't even like the leafy green until I made this recipe, and now I'm a total convert!
—*Kathryn Egly, CO Springs, CO*

TAKES: 20 min. • **MAKES:** 12 servings

- ½ cup olive oil
- 3 Tbsp. lime juice
- 2 Tbsp. honey
- ¼ tsp. salt
- ⅛ tsp. pepper
- 12 oz. kale, trimmed and chopped (about 14 cups)
- ½ cup sliced almonds, toasted
- ½ cup dried cranberries
- ½ cup shredded Parmesan cheese
- ½ cup crumbled blue cheese

In a small bowl, whisk the first 5 ingredients. Place kale in a large bowl. Drizzle with dressing; toss to coat. Top with the remaining ingredients.
1¼ CUPS: 181 cal., 14g fat (3g sat. fat), 7mg chol., 183mg sod., 13g carb. (8g sugars, 1g fiber), 4g pro. **DIABETIC EXCHANGES:** 3 fat, 1 vegetable, ½ starch.

LEMON BASIL CHICKEN SALAD

This copycat from the Chicken Salad Chick restaurant chain has become one of my favorite meals. It is ideal for a light lunch, brunch or supper any time of year. Serve it alone, with crackers or on a sandwich. It's also a good centerpiece for a crudite platter.
—*Laura Wilhelm, West Hollywood, CA*

TAKES: 15 min. • **MAKES:** 6 servings

- 4 cups cubed cooked chicken
- 1 cup fat-free plain Greek yogurt
- 1 cup chopped pecans
- 1 bunch fresh basil leaves, chopped
- ½ cup grated Parmesan cheese
- 4 Tbsp. lemon juice
- 1¼ tsp. salt
- 1 tsp. lemon-pepper seasoning
  Dash sugar
  Chopped fresh parsley

In a small bowl, combine the first 9 ingredients. Refrigerate, covered, until serving. Sprinkle with parsley.
⅔ CUP: 362 cal., 22g fat (4g sat. fat), 89mg chol., 766mg sod., 6g carb. (3g sugars, 2g fiber), 36g pro.

BLUE CHEESE
KALE SALAD

**GREEN BEAN SALAD
WITH CREAMY DRESSING**

SWEET PEA & RADISH SALAD

In the spring and summer I like to eat light and fresh foods. I created this salad recipe with ingredients I normally have on hand. Serve as a side dish or salad.
—*Colleen Delawder, Herndon, VA*

- -

PREP: 10 min. + chilling • **COOK:** 5 min. • **MAKES:** 10 servings

  3 cups frozen peas (about 12 oz.)
  ¼ cup mayonnaise
  3 Tbsp. heavy whipping cream
  2 tsp. dill weed
  ½ tsp. kosher salt
  ½ tsp. pepper
  1 lb. radishes, thinly sliced
  4 oz. dill Havarti cheese, cubed

1. In a large saucepan, bring 8 cups water to a boil. Add peas; cook, uncovered, just until peas turn bright green, 3-4 minutes. Drain and immediately drop into ice water. Drain and pat dry.
2. In a large bowl, whisk mayonnaise, cream, dill, salt and pepper. Stir in radishes, cheese and peas. Refrigerate at least 1 hour before serving.
¾ CUP: 132 cal., 9g fat (4g sat. fat), 16mg chol., 250mg sod., 8g carb. (3g sugars, 3g fiber), 5g pro.

🍎 GREEN BEAN SALAD
WITH CREAMY DRESSING

My grandmother passed this refreshing side dish recipe on to me. It's always devoured at my house.
—*Jodi Galanis, Murray, UT*

- -

PREP: 15 min. + chilling • **MAKES:** 2 servings

  1 cup cut fresh green beans (2 in.)
  ½ medium cucumber, halved lengthwise and sliced
  ⅓ cup julienned sweet red pepper
  ¼ cup thinly sliced onion
DRESSING
  2 Tbsp. cream cheese, softened
  1 Tbsp. 2% milk
  1 Tbsp. tarragon vinegar
  2 tsp. sugar
  ¼ tsp. salt
  ¼ tsp. pepper

1. In a saucepan of boiling water, cook green beans, uncovered, until crisp-tender, 3-5 minutes. Remove beans with a slotted spoon; drop immediately into ice water. Drain and pat dry.
2. Place cucumber, red pepper, onion and beans in a large bowl. Whisk together dressing ingredients; toss with vegetables. Refrigerate, covered, until cold.
1 CUP: 107 cal., 5g fat (3g sat. fat), 15mg chol., 349mg sod., 13g carb. (9g sugars, 3g fiber), 3g pro. **DIABETIC EXCHANGES:** 1 vegetable, 1 fat.

**SWEET PEA
& RADISH SALAD**

THAI MEATBALL
SOUP, PAGE 50

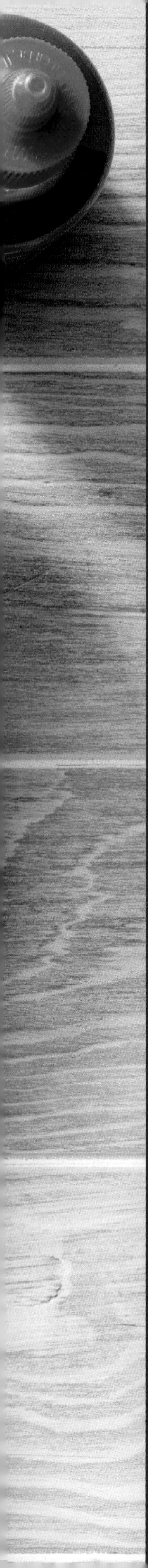

Soups & Sandwiches

Craft your own pairing of lunchtime classics with our collection of cozy soups and hearty sandwiches. Plus, you can master classic cioppino, find new riffs on ramen and explore exciting new sliders.

BEST OF THE BEST DISHES

AIR-FRYER SHRIMP PO'BOYS

1. For the remoulade, in a small bowl, combine first 6 ingredients. Refrigerate, covered, until serving.
2. Preheat air fryer to 375°. In a shallow bowl, mix flour, herbes de Provence, sea salt, garlic powder, pepper and cayenne. In a separate shallow bowl, whisk egg, milk and hot pepper sauce. Place coconut in a third shallow bowl. Dip shrimp in flour to coat both sides; shake off excess. Dip in egg mixture, then in coconut, patting to help adhere.
3. In batches, arrange shrimp in a single layer on greased tray in air-fryer basket; spritz with cooking spray. Cook until the coconut is lightly browned and shrimp turn pink, 3-4 minutes on each side.
4. Spread cut side of buns with remoulade. Top with shrimp, lettuce and tomato.

1 SANDWICH: 716 cal., 40g fat (16g sat. fat), 173mg chol., 944mg sod., 60g carb. (23g sugars, 4g fiber), 31g pro.

❄️
ONE-POT COCONUT CURRY LENTIL SOUP

This curry soup might be vegan, but it's still as creamy as ever. If you prefer a meatier bowl, toss some chicken and chicken broth into the recipe.
—*Kijan Zendi, San Diego, CA*

PREP: 10 min. • **COOK:** 25.
MAKES: 8 servings (2 qt.)

- 1 pkg. (16 oz.) dried lentils, rinsed
- 1 carton (32 oz.) vegetable broth
- 2 Tbsp. curry powder
- 1 garlic clove, minced
- 2 cans (13.66 oz. each) coconut milk
- ½ tsp. kosher salt
  Chopped green onions

Place lentils, broth, curry powder and garlic in a Dutch oven. Bring to a boil; reduce heat. Add coconut milk; simmer, uncovered, 25-30 minutes or until lentils are tender. Stir in salt. Serve with chopped green onions.

FREEZE OPTION: Before adding green onions, freeze soup in freezer containers. To use, partially thaw in refrigerator overnight. Heat through in a saucepan, stirring occasionally; add broth or water if necessary. Sprinkle with green onions.

1 CUP: 365 cal., 16g fat (16g sat. fat), 0 chol., 493mg sod., 40g carb. (4g sugars, 7g fiber), 16g pro.

✈️
AIR-FRYER SHRIMP PO'BOYS

My husband loves crispy coconut shrimp and po'boys, so I combined them with a spicy remoulade and voila! This air-fryer shrimp is frequently requested. For catfish po'boys, substitute cornmeal for the coconut and add a few minutes to the cooking time.
—*Marla Clark, Albuquerque, NM*

PREP: 35 min. • **COOK:** 10 min./batch
MAKES: 4 servings

- ½ cup mayonnaise
- 1 Tbsp. Creole mustard
- 1 Tbsp. chopped cornichons or dill pickles
- 1 Tbsp. minced shallot
- 1½ tsp. lemon juice
- ⅛ tsp. cayenne pepper

COCONUT SHRIMP
- 1 cup all-purpose flour
- 1 tsp. herbes de Provence
- ½ tsp. sea salt
- ½ tsp. garlic powder
- ½ tsp. pepper
- ¼ tsp. cayenne pepper
- 1 large egg
- ½ cup 2% milk
- 1 tsp. hot pepper sauce
- 2 cups sweetened shredded coconut
- 1 lb. uncooked shrimp (26-30 per lb.), peeled and deveined
  Cooking spray
- 4 hoagie buns, split
- 2 cups shredded lettuce
- 1 medium tomato, thinly sliced

BARBECUE
SLIDERS

BARBECUE SLIDERS

When company dropped in by surprise, all I had was sausage and ground beef defrosted. We combined the two for juicy burgers on the grill.
—B.J. Larsen, Erie, CO

- -

TAKES: 25 min. • **MAKES:** 8 servings

- 1 lb. ground beef
- 1 lb. bulk pork sausage
- 1 cup barbecue sauce, divided
- 16 Hawaiian sweet rolls, split
   Optional: Lettuce leaves, sliced plum tomatoes
   and red onion

1. In a large bowl, mix beef and sausage lightly but thoroughly. Shape into sixteen ½-in.-thick patties.
2. Grill patties, covered, over medium heat or broil 4-5 in. from heat until a thermometer reads 160°, 3-4 minutes on each side. Brush with ¼ cup sauce during the last 2 minutes of cooking. Serve on rolls with remaining barbecue sauce; top as desired.
FREEZE OPTION: Place patties on a waxed paper-lined baking sheet; cover and freeze until firm. Remove from pan and transfer to an airtight container; return to freezer. To use, grill frozen patties as directed, increasing time as necessary.
2 SLIDERS: 499 cal., 24g fat (9g sat. fat), 96mg chol., 885mg sod., 47g carb. (23g sugars, 2g fiber), 24g pro.

TEST KITCHEN TIP

Make these with 90% lean ground beef and turkey breakfast sausage and you'll save nearly 100 calories per serving and cut the fat by more than half.

AUTUMN BISQUE

I like cozy comfort soups that taste creamy—without the cream. This one's full of good stuff like rutabagas, leeks, fresh herbs and almond milk.
—Merry Graham, Newhall, CA

- -

PREP: 25 min. • **COOK:** 50 min. • **MAKES:** 12 servings (3 qt.)

- ¼ cup dairy-free spreadable margarine
- 2 tsp. minced fresh chives
- 2 tsp. minced fresh parsley
- ½ tsp. grated lemon zest

BISQUE
- 2 Tbsp. olive oil
- 2 large rutabagas, peeled and cubed (about 9 cups)
- 1 large celery root, peeled and cubed (about 3 cups)
- 3 medium leeks (white portion only), chopped (about 2 cups)
- 1 large carrot, cubed (about ⅔ cup)
- 3 garlic cloves, minced
- 7 cups vegetable stock
- 2 tsp. minced fresh thyme
- 1½ tsp. minced fresh rosemary
- 1 tsp. salt
- ½ tsp. coarsely ground pepper
- 2 cups almond milk
- 2 Tbsp. minced fresh chives

1. Mix first 4 ingredients. Using a melon baller or 1-tsp. measuring spoon, shape mixture into 12 balls. Freeze on a waxed paper-lined baking sheet until firm. Transfer to a freezer container; freeze up to 2 months.
2. In a 6-qt. stock pot, heat oil over medium heat; saute rutabagas, celery root, leeks and carrot for 8 minutes. Add garlic; cook and stir for 2 minutes. Stir in stock, herbs, salt and pepper; bring to a boil. Reduce heat; simmer, covered, until vegetables are tender, 30-35 minutes.
3. Puree soup using an immersion blender. Or cool slightly and puree in batches in a blender; return to pan. Stir in milk; heat through. Remove herbed margarine from freezer 15 minutes before serving. Top servings with chives and margarine.
1 CUP: 146 cal., 7g fat (2g sat. fat), 0 chol., 672mg sod., 20g carb. (9g sugars, 5g fiber), 3g pro. **DIABETIC EXCHANGES:** 1 starch, 1 fat.

AUTUMN
BISQUE

CHEESEBURGER SOUP

A local restaurant serves a similar soup but wouldn't share its recipe with me. I developed my own, modifying a recipe I already had for potato soup. I was really pleased with the way this all-American dish turned out.

—Joanie Shawhan, Madison, WI

PREP: 30 min. • **COOK:** 25 min.
MAKES: 8 servings (2 qt.)

- ½ lb. ground beef
- 4 Tbsp. butter, divided
- ¾ cup chopped onion
- ¾ cup shredded carrots
- ¾ cup diced celery
- 1 tsp. dried basil
- 1 tsp. dried parsley flakes
- 1¾ lbs. (about 4 cups) cubed peeled potatoes
- 3 cups chicken broth
- ¼ cup all-purpose flour
- 8 to 16 oz. Velveeta, cubed
- 1½ cups whole milk
- ¾ tsp. salt
- ¼ to ½ tsp. pepper
- ¼ cup sour cream
  Optional: Onion rings and thinly sliced green onions

1. In a large saucepan over medium heat, cook and crumble beef until no longer pink, 6-8 minutes; drain and set aside. In same saucepan, melt 1 Tbsp. butter over medium heat. Saute onion, carrots, celery, basil and parsley until vegetables are tender, about 10 minutes. Add potatoes, ground beef and broth; bring to a boil. Reduce heat; simmer, covered, until potatoes are tender, 10-12 minutes.

2. Meanwhile, in a small skillet, melt remaining butter. Add flour; cook and stir until bubbly, 3-5 minutes. Add to soup; bring to a boil. Cook and stir 2 minutes. Reduce heat to low. Stir in cheese, milk, salt and pepper; cook until cheese melts. Remove from heat; blend in sour cream. If desired, serve with onion rings and green onions.

1 CUP: 450 cal., 27g fat (15g sat. fat), 100mg chol., 1421mg sod., 33g carb. (8g sugars, 3g fiber), 19g pro.

CHEESEBURGER SOUP

VIETNAMESE CHICKEN BANH MI SANDWICHES

VIETNAMESE CHICKEN BANH MI SANDWICHES

My version of the classic Vietnamese sandwich combines the satisfying flavor of chicken sausage with tangy vegetables pickled in rice vinegar. Stuff the ingredients in a hoagie bun and lunch is ready to go!

—Angela Spengler, Niceville, FL

TAKES: 25 min. • **MAKES:** 4 servings

- 1 pkg. (12 oz.) fully cooked spicy chicken sausage links
- 2 tsp. olive oil, divided
- ⅓ cup hoisin sauce
- 1 Tbsp. honey
- 2 tsp. reduced-sodium soy sauce
- 1 garlic clove, minced
- ¼ tsp. Chinese five-spice powder
- 1 medium onion, thinly sliced
- ½ cup shredded cabbage
- ½ cup shredded carrots
- 2 tsp. rice vinegar
- 4 hoagie buns, split
- 4 lettuce leaves

1. Cut each sausage in half lengthwise. In a large skillet, brown sausage in 1 tsp. oil. Remove and keep warm.

2. Add the hoisin, honey, soy sauce, garlic and five-spice powder to the skillet. Bring to a boil. Cook and stir until garlic is tender and sauce is thickened. Return sausages to pan; toss to coat.

3. In a small skillet, saute onion, cabbage and carrots in remaining oil until crisp-tender. Stir in vinegar. Serve sausage in buns with lettuce and onion mixture.

1 SANDWICH: 452 cal., 15 g fat (3 g sat. fat), 66 mg chol., 1,331 mg sod., 57 g carb., 3 g fiber, 25 g pro.

TUNA CHEESE-WAFFLE SANDWICHES

I love cheddar chaffles and tuna salad sandwiches. Combining the two makes an incredible sandwich with a crunchy, cheesy element for the bread. The dill pickles in the chaffle and the tuna salad add extra crunch and flavor to make this sandwich a real treat.
—Arlene Erlbach, Morton Grove, IL

TAKES: 30 min. • **MAKES:** 4 sandwiches

- 5 Tbsp. mayonnaise
- 2 Tbsp. cream cheese, softened
- 2 cans light tuna in water (5 oz. each), well drained
- 1 celery rib, finely chopped
- ¼ cup finely chopped red onion
- 2 Tbsp. minced fresh parsley
- 1 Tbsp. lemon juice
- ½ cup diced dill pickle, divided
- 4 large eggs, beaten
- 2 cups shredded extra sharp cheddar cheese
- 8 slices tomato
  Lettuce leaves, optional

1. Preheat waffle maker. In a large bowl, whisk mayonnaise and cream cheese until smooth. Add tuna, celery, onion, parsley, lemon juice and 2 Tbsp. diced pickles. Set aside.
2. In a separate bowl, whisk eggs. In the preheated waffle maker, sprinkle ½ cup cheese and half the remaining pickles. Pour half the whisked egg over the cheese. Top with ½ cup cheese. Close lid and bake according to manufacturer's directions until golden brown, 4-5 minutes. Repeat with remaining cheese, pickles and eggs.
3. Spread the tuna mixture evenly over half the waffle pieces; top with tomatoes, lettuce leaves if desired and remaining waffle pieces to make sandwiches.
1 SANDWICH: 515 cal., 39g fat (16g sat. fat), 281mg chol., 881mg sod., 6g carb. (3g sugars, 1g fiber), 34g pro.

JALAPENO SLOPPY JOES

JALAPENO SLOPPY JOES

My husband loves jalapenos—and I just love any and all heat. This savory meal with some spice is a perfect make-ahead solution for busy weeknights. Serve with your favorite chips.
—Julie Herrera-Lemler, Rochester, MN

PREP: 20 min. • **COOK:** 15 min. • **MAKES:** 8 servings

- 1 Tbsp. butter
- 1½ lbs. ground turkey
- 1 small onion, chopped
- 1 jalapeno pepper, seeded and finely chopped
- 4 garlic cloves, minced
- 1 cup ketchup
- ½ cup juice from pickled jalapeno slices
- 2 tsp. minced pickled jalapeno slices
- 2 Tbsp. brown sugar
- 2 Tbsp. Worcestershire sauce
- 1½ tsp. chili powder
- ½ tsp. crushed red pepper flakes
- ¼ tsp. salt
- 8 sesame seed hamburger buns, split

1. Heat butter in a large skillet over medium heat. Add turkey, onion, fresh jalapeno and garlic; cook until turkey is no longer pink and vegetables are tender, 8-10 minutes, breaking up turkey into crumbles.
2. Stir in ketchup, jalapeno juice, pickled jalapenos, brown sugar, Worcestershire sauce and seasonings. Bring to a boil. Reduce heat; simmer, uncovered, 15-20 minutes to allow flavors to blend, stirring occasionally. Serve on buns.
FREEZE OPTION: Freeze cooled meat mixture in freezer containers. To use, partially thaw in refrigerator overnight. Heat through in a saucepan, stirring occasionally; add broth or water if necessary.
NOTE: Wear disposable gloves when cutting hot peppers; the oils can burn skin. Avoid touching your face.
1 SANDWICH: 322 cal., 11g fat (4g sat. fat), 60mg chol., 888mg sod., 37g carb. (15g sugars, 1g fiber), 22g pro.

TUNA CHEESE-WAFFLE SANDWICHES

CAPRESE
EGGPLANT HERO

STONE SOUP

We enjoyed concocting this version of the folktale classic. It's packed with veggies and chicken. Re-enact the legend by asking guests to bring an ingredient to add to the hearty soup.
—Taste of Home *Test Kitchen*

PREP: 15 min. • COOK: 35 min.
MAKES: 12 servings (3 qt.)

- 4 cans (14½ oz. each) chicken broth
- 4 medium red potatoes, cut into eighths
- 1 yellow summer squash, chopped
- 2 medium carrots, chopped
- 1 medium onion, chopped
- 2 celery ribs, chopped
- 1 tsp. dried thyme
- ½ tsp. pepper
- 4 cups cubed cooked chicken
- 1 cup frozen cut green beans
- ½ cup quick-cooking barley
- 1 can (14½ oz.) diced tomatoes, undrained
- 4 cups salad croutons
- 1 cup shredded Parmesan cheese

1. In a Dutch oven, combine the first 8 ingredients. Bring to a boil. Reduce heat; cover and simmer until vegetables are crisp-tender, 10-15 minutes.
2. Stir in the chicken, beans and barley. Bring to a boil. Reduce heat; cover and simmer until vegetables and barley are tender, 10-12 minutes. Add tomatoes; heat through. Serve with croutons and cheese.
1 CUP: 260 cal., 8g fat (3g sat. fat), 47mg chol., 868mg sod., 26g carb. (4g sugars, 4g fiber), 21g pro.

TEST KITCHEN TIP

Stone soup is a versatile recipe, and different ingredients can be used depending on what you have on hand. You can easily omit a veggie or two and add more of another to make up the difference. Or, try swapping in different vegetables like zucchini, frozen peas or lima beans.

CAPRESE EGGPLANT HERO

Eggplant Caprese is a wonderful way to showcase fresh produce including tomatoes, eggplant and basil. During the summer when tomatoes are at their peak, I love to create new recipes to eat as many tomatoes as possible! This recipe is so tasty that my family enjoys eating it in every season. If you prefer, you can keep the peel on the eggplant. The peel adds some texture and nutrients, and it helps holds the form a little better. It's a taste preference.
—*Stacy Corday, Waxhaw, NC*

PREP: 20 min. + standing
GRILL: 10 min. • MAKES: 6 servings

- 1 large eggplant
- 1 tsp. kosher salt, divided
- ¼ cup olive oil, divided
- 3 Tbsp. honey
- 1 tsp. coarsely ground pepper
- ¼ cup balsamic glaze, divided
- 1 loaf (1 lb.) unsliced Italian bread
- 2 large tomatoes, cut into ¼-in. slices
- 1 lb. fresh mozzarella cheese, thinly sliced
- 2 cups fresh arugula
- ½ cup fresh basil leaves, julienned

1. Peel and slice eggplant lengthwise into ¼-in.-thick slices. Place in a colander over a plate; sprinkle with salt and toss. Let stand 30 minutes.
2. Brush eggplant slices with 2 Tbsp. oil. Drizzle with honey; sprinkle with ½ tsp. salt and pepper. Grill eggplant, covered, over medium heat 3-4 minutes per side or until tender, Drizzle with 2 Tbsp. glaze.
3. Cut bread in half horizontally. Drizzle cut sides with remaining 2 Tbsp. olive oil and 2 Tbsp. glaze. Layer eggplant, tomato and mozzarella slices on bread bottom; top with arugula and basil. Replace top. Cut crosswise into 6 slices.
1 PIECE: 600 cal., 28g fat (12g sat. fat), 59mg chol., 856mg sod., 64g carb. (22g sugars, 6g fiber), 22g pro.

PRESSURE-COOKER ITALIAN WEDDING SOUP

I like to buy large bags of frozen meatballs to have on hand for quick-fix meals. Meatballs can be used in so many different ways when I'm in a pinch for time, and they work so nicely in this soup.
—*Rebecca Yankovich, Springfield, VA*

PREP: 25 min. • **COOK:** 10 min. + releasing
MAKES: 10 servings (3¾ qt.)

- 1 Tbsp. butter
- 1 Tbsp. olive oil
- 4 medium carrots, chopped
- 1 celery rib, chopped
- 1 medium onion, chopped
- 2 cartons (32 oz. each) chicken stock
- 1 pkg. (26 oz.) frozen fully cooked Italian meatballs
- 1 can (10½ oz.) condensed cream of mushroom soup, undiluted
- ½ cup uncooked ditalini or other small pasta
- ½ tsp. dried oregano
- ¼ tsp. pepper
- 1 pkg. (10 oz.) fresh spinach (about 13 cups), chopped

1. Select saute setting on a 6-qt. electric pressure cooker. Adjust for medium heat; add butter and oil. When hot, add carrots, celery and onion; cook and stir until crisp-tender, 4-6 minutes. Press cancel. Stir in stock, meatballs, condensed soup, ditalini, oregano and pepper.
2. Lock lid; close pressure-release valve. Adjust to pressure-cook on high for 10 minutes. Allow pressure to naturally release. Stir in spinach until wilted.
1½ CUPS: 321 cal., 21g fat (9g sat. fat), 40mg chol., 1242mg sod., 17g carb. (3g sugars, 3g fiber), 18g pro.

POTATO, SAUSAGE & KALE SOUP

POTATO, SAUSAGE & KALE SOUP

I let my young son pick out seed packets and he chose kale, which grew like crazy. This hearty soup helped make good use of it and rivals the Olive Garden's Zuppa Toscana.
—*Michelle Babbie, Malone, NY*

TAKES: 30 min. • **MAKES:** 4 servings

- ½ lb. bulk pork sausage
- 1 medium onion, finely chopped
- 2 tsp. chicken bouillon granules
- ½ tsp. garlic powder
- ½ tsp. pepper
- 2 medium red potatoes, cut into ½-in. cubes
- 2 cups sliced fresh kale
- 3 cups 2% milk
- 1 cup heavy whipping cream
- 1 Tbsp. cornstarch
- ¼ cup cold water
  Crumbled cooked bacon, optional

1. In a large saucepan, cook sausage and onion over medium heat 4-6 minutes or until sausage is no longer pink and onion is tender, breaking up sausage into crumbles; drain.
2. Stir in bouillon and seasonings. Add potatoes, kale, milk and cream; bring to a boil. Reduce heat; simmer, covered, until potatoes are tender, 10-15 minutes.
3. In a small bowl, mix cornstarch and water until smooth; stir into soup. Return to a boil, stirring constantly; cook and stir until thickened, 1-2 minutes. If desired, top with bacon.
1½ CUPS: 504 cal., 38g fat (20g sat. fat), 128mg chol., 881mg sod., 26g carb. (12g sugars, 2g fiber), 15g pro.

PRESSURE-COOKER ITALIAN WEDDING SOUP

**MUSHROOM
CORN CHOWDER**

GUACAMOLE CHICKEN SALAD SANDWICHES

This chicken salad recipe is inspired by a truly inventive guacamole I tried at a local restaurant, which was studded with pomegranate seeds. This is an extremely simple recipe to make since rotisserie chicken is used. I serve this salad on homemade tomato bread that is a great contrast in flavor and color. It can also be served on lettuce leaves instead of bread.
—Debra Keil, Owasso, OK

TAKES: 20 min. • **MAKES:** 10 servings

- 1 rotisserie chicken, skin removed, cubed
- 2 medium ripe avocados, peeled and mashed
- ¾ cup pomegranate seeds
- 6 green onions, chopped
- 8 cherry tomatoes, halved
- 1 jalapeno pepper, seeded and minced
- ¼ cup fresh cilantro leaves, chopped
- 3 Tbsp. mayonnaise
- 2 Tbsp. lime juice
- 1 garlic clove, minced
- ½ tsp. salt
- ½ tsp. ground cumin
- ¼ tsp. pepper
- 20 slices multigrain bread, toasted

In a large bowl, combine all ingredients but the bread. Spread chicken salad over 10 bread slices; top each prepared slice with remaining bread.

NOTE: Wear disposable gloves when cutting hot peppers; the oils can burn skin. Avoid touching your face.

1 SANDWICH: 295 cal., 12g fat (2g sat. fat), 35mg chol., 370mg sod., 28g carb. (6g sugars, 6g fiber), 19g pro. **DIABETIC EXCHANGES:** 2 starch, 2 lean meat, 2 fat.

READER REVIEW

"Absolutely love this recipe! I could not get any pomegranate and it was still delish! For even more flavor, I topped mine off with crispy bacon. Thanks for the amazing recipe!"
—POOKIE72710, TASTEOFHOME.COM

MUSHROOM CORN CHOWDER

Chock-full of veggies, ham and cheese in every spoonful, this thick, creamy chowder will take the chill off even the nippiest of fall evenings. Serve it with crusty French bread.
—Elaine Krupsky, Las Vegas, NV

TAKES: 30 min. • **MAKES:** 8 servings

- 1¼ cups sliced fresh carrots
- 1 cup chopped celery with leaves
- ¾ cup sliced fresh mushrooms
- 3 green onions, sliced
- ¼ cup butter, cubed
- 1 can (10½ oz.) condensed cream of mushroom soup, undiluted
- 1⅓ cups 2% milk
- 1½ cups frozen corn, thawed
- ½ cup cubed fully cooked ham
- ½ tsp. seasoned salt
- ½ cup cubed Velveeta
  Additional chopped celery leaves, optional

In a large saucepan, saute the carrots, celery, mushrooms and onions in butter until tender. Stir in the soup, milk, corn, ham and seasoned salt. Bring to a boil. Reduce heat; stir in cheese. Cook and stir 3-5 minutes longer or until cheese is melted. If desired, serve with additional celery leaves.

FREEZE OPTION: Cool and transfer to freezer containers. Freeze soup for up to 3 months. To use, thaw in the refrigerator overnight. Transfer to a saucepan. Cover and cook over medium-low heat until heated through, stirring occasionally (do not boil).

¾ CUP: 184 cal., 12g fat (6g sat. fat), 31mg chol., 652mg sod., 15g carb. (5g sugars, 2g fiber), 6g pro.

GUACAMOLE
CHICKEN SALAD
SANDWICHES

GRILLED SHRIMP & WATERMELON SLIDERS

3. Drain shrimp, discarding marinade. Arrange shrimp on a grilling grid; place grid on grill rack. Grill, covered, over medium heat 2-3 minutes on each side or until shrimp turn pink.
4. Chop shrimp; transfer to a small bowl. Stir in watermelon, jalapeno and cilantro. Spread guacamole over bun tops and bottoms. Top bun bottoms with lettuce and shrimp mixture; replace tops.
NOTE: Wear disposable gloves when cutting hot peppers; the oils can burn skin. Avoid touching your face.
1 SLIDER: 208 cal., 9g fat (1g sat. fat), 59mg chol., 391mg sod., 24g carb. (4g sugars, 4g fiber), 10g pro.

THAI MEATBALL SOUP
(SHOWN ON PAGE 40)

This son-approved, Thai-inspired soup—with meatballs, kale, carrots and creamy coconut milk—is warm deliciousness on a chilly day.
—*Arlene Erlbach, Morton Grove, IL*

PREP: 20 min. • **COOK:** 30 min. • **MAKES:** about 7 servings

- ½ cup fresh cilantro, finely chopped
- ⅓ cup unsweetened shredded coconut
- 3 Tbsp. teriyaki sauce, divided
- ½ tsp. salt
- ½ tsp. ground ginger
- 1½ lbs. ground chicken
- ¼ cup sesame oil
- 3 cups chicken broth
- 1 can (13.66 oz.) coconut milk
- 1½ cups julienned carrots
- 2 cups torn fresh kale
- 4½ tsp. lime juice
- 1 Tbsp. brown sugar
  Lime wedges, optional

1. In a large bowl, combine cilantro, coconut, 4½ tsp. teriyaki sauce, salt and ginger. Add chicken; mix lightly but thoroughly. Shape into 1½-in. balls. In a Dutch oven, brown meatballs in batches in sesame oil over medium-high heat; remove and keep warm. Drain any excess oil from pan. Add broth to pan; cook 1 minute, stirring to loosen browned bits from pan.
2. Return all meatballs to pan. Add coconut milk, carrots and remaining 4½ tsp. teriyaki sauce; bring to a boil. Reduce heat; simmer, covered, until meatballs are cooked through, 5-7 minutes. Stir in kale, lime juice and brown sugar. Cook until kale just begins to wilt, about 5 minutes longer. Serve with additional chopped cilantro and lime wedges if desired.
ABOUT 1 CUP: 400 cal., 32g fat (17g sat. fat), 75mg chol., 1040mg sod., 10g carb. (7g sugars, 2g fiber), 21g pro.

GRILLED SHRIMP & WATERMELON SLIDERS

These fun little sliders combine my favorite Mexican flavors and seafood into a handheld treat. They make such a fresh summer meal!
—*Jeanette Decker, Corpus Christi, TX*

PREP: 40 min. + marinating • **GRILL:** 5 min. • **MAKES:** 10 servings

- ¾ cup minced fresh cilantro
- 1 small onion, chopped
- ¼ cup olive oil
- 2 Tbsp. lemon juice
- 1 envelope Goya sazon with coriander and annatto
- 2 tsp. reduced-sodium soy sauce
- 1 garlic clove, minced
- ½ tsp. pepper
- ¾ lb. uncooked shrimp (26-30 per lb.), peeled and deveined

GUACAMOLE
- 2 medium ripe avocados, peeled and cubed
- 1 medium tomato, chopped
- 1 small onion, chopped
- 3 Tbsp. lemon juice
- 1 Tbsp. minced fresh cilantro
- ½ tsp. salt
- ½ tsp. pepper

SLIDERS
- 1 cup seeded watermelon, finely chopped
- 2 Tbsp. finely chopped seeded jalapeno pepper
- 2 Tbsp. minced fresh cilantro
- 10 slider buns or dinner rolls, split
- ½ cup chopped lettuce

1. Place the first 8 ingredients in a blender; process until blended. Transfer to a bowl or shallow dish. Add shrimp and turn to coat. Cover and refrigerate 1 hour.
2. In a small bowl, mash avocados with a fork. Stir in tomato, onion, lemon juice, cilantro, salt and pepper. Refrigerate until serving.

SOPA
AJOBLANCO

SOPA AJOBLANCO

This white gazpacho was a staple when I was young; I remember slurping it directly from the bowl. It's made from stale bread and on-hand seasonings and then topped with grapes for a traditional touch.
—*Francine Lizotte, Langley, BC*

PREP: 20 min. + chilling • **COOK:** 5 min. • **MAKES:** 4 servings

- 1 cup blanched almonds
- 1½ cups cubed white bread, crusts removed
- ⅓ cup heavy whipping cream or unsweetened almond milk
- 2½ cups reduced-sodium chicken broth
- 3 Tbsp. sherry vinegar
- 2 garlic cloves, minced
- ½ tsp. fine sea salt
- ¼ tsp. white pepper
- ½ cup plus 1 Tbsp. olive oil, divided
- ⅛ tsp. hot Hungarian paprika
- ¼ cup halved green grapes
- ¼ cup chopped blanched almonds

1. Rinse almonds in cold water; drain. Place in a large bowl; add enough water to cover by 3 in. Cover and let stand overnight. Spread bread cubes onto a baking sheet; let stand overnight.
2. Place 1 cup bread cubes in a small bowl. Pour cream over bread; let stand 15 minutes. Drain almonds, discarding soaking liquid. Transfer almonds to a blender. Add bread mixture, broth, vinegar, garlic, salt and white pepper; process until blended. While processing, gradually add ½ cup oil in a steady stream. Transfer to a large bowl. Refrigerate, covered, at least 6 hours.
3. In a large skillet, heat remaining 1 Tbsp. oil over medium heat; stir in paprika. Add remaining ½ cup bread cubes; cook and stir until golden brown, 3-4 minutes.
4. Remove soup from refrigerator, stir to redistribute settled out oil. Divide soup among 4 bowls; top with toasted croutons, grapes, chopped almonds and additional oil.
1 CUP WITH 2 TBSP. TOPPING: 660 cal., 62g fat (11g sat. fat), 23mg chol., 677mg sod., 19g carb. (6g sugars, 5g fiber), 14g pro.

SLOW-COOKER LASAGNA SOUP

Try this soup if you're looking for a healthier, unique take on lasagna.
—*Sharon Gerst, North Liberty, IA*

PREP: 35 min. • **COOK:** 5 hours + standing
MAKES: 8 servings (about 2½ qt.)

- 1½ lbs. bulk Italian sausage
- 1 large onion, chopped
- 2 medium carrots, chopped
- 2 cups sliced fresh mushrooms
- 3 garlic cloves, minced
- 1 carton (32 oz.) chicken broth
- 2 cans (14½ oz. each) Italian stewed tomatoes
- 1 can (15 oz.) tomato sauce
- 6 lasagna noodles, broken into 1-in. pieces
- 2 cups coarsely chopped fresh spinach
- 1 cup cubed or shredded part-skim mozzarella cheese
- ½ cup shredded Parmesan cheese
  Thinly sliced fresh basil, optional

1. In a large skillet, cook sausage over medium-high heat until no longer pink, breaking into crumbles, 8-10 minutes; drain. Transfer to a 5- or 6-qt. slow cooker.
2. Add onion and carrots to same skillet; cook and stir until softened, 2-4 minutes. Stir in mushrooms and garlic; cook and stir until mushrooms are softened, 2-4 minutes. Transfer to slow cooker. Stir in broth, tomatoes and tomato sauce. Cook, covered, on low until vegetables are tender. 4-6 hours.
3. Skim fat from soup. Add noodles; cook 1 hour longer or until tender. Stir in spinach. Remove insert; let stand 10 minutes. Divide mozzarella cheese among serving bowls; ladle soup over cheese. Sprinkle with Parmesan cheese and, if desired, basil.
1⅓ CUPS: 420 cal., 24g fat (9g sat. fat), 63mg chol., 1731mg sod., 30g carb. (8g sugars, 4g fiber), 21g pro.

SLOW-COOKER
LASAGNA SOUP

FRENCH ONION
TORTELLINI SOUP

AVOCADO EGG SALAD TOAST

After purchasing far too many unripe avocados for an event, I had a surplus of ripe ones each day in my kitchen for a week after! I was making some egg salad sandwiches for lunch on one of these avocado surplus days, and I had the great idea to use avocado to bind it together instead of traditional mayo. Not only was this version unbelievably delicious, the healthy fats in the avocado make this a much better option than the traditional mayo-laden version.
—Shannon Dobos, Calgary, AB

TAKES: 20 min. • MAKES: 4 servings

1   medium ripe avocado, peeled and cubed
6   hard-boiled large eggs, chopped
1   green onion, finely chopped
1   tsp. lemon juice
¼   tsp. salt
⅛   tsp. pepper
4   large slices sourdough bread, halved and toasted

In a large bowl, mash avocado to desired consistency. Gently stir in eggs, green onion, lemon juice, salt and pepper. Spread over toast. Serve immediately.
2 PIECES: 367 cal., 15g fat (4g sat. fat), 280mg chol., 671mg sod., 41g carb. (4g sugars, 4g fiber), 18g pro.

AVOCADO
EGG SALAD
TOAST

FRENCH ONION TORTELLINI SOUP

This soup is delicious, pretty and unbelievably fast to make. For a creamy variation, I sometimes substitute cream of mushroom soup for the French onion soup. If there are any leftovers, they taste even better the next day.
—Marsha Farley, Bangor, ME

TAKES: 30 min. • MAKES: 8 servings

1   lb. ground beef
3½   cups water
1   can (28 oz.) diced tomatoes, undrained
1   can (10½ oz.) condensed French onion soup, undiluted
1   pkg. (9 oz.) frozen cut green beans
1   pkg. (9 oz.) refrigerated cheese tortellini
1   medium zucchini, chopped
1   tsp. dried basil

In a large saucepan, cook beef over medium heat until no longer pink; drain. Add the remaining ingredients; bring to a boil. Cook, uncovered, for 7-9 minutes or until tortellini is tender.
1 SERVING: 241 cal., 9g fat (4g sat. fat), 43mg chol., 608mg sod., 25g carb. (7g sugars, 4g fiber), 16g pro.

CHORIZO BURGERS WITH GREEN CHILE AIOLI

2. Meanwhile, combine mayonnaise, chiles, cilantro and lime juice. Top burgers with sauce, tomato, avocado and, if desired, pickled onions and hot pepper sauce. Wrap in lettuce leaves.
1 BURGER: 677 cal., 56g fat (19g sat. fat), 145mg chol., 1225mg sod., 5g carb. (1g sugars, 2g fiber), 36g pro.

EASY SHRIMP & SCALLOPS RAMEN SOUP

This recipe is delicious and so easy to make at home on a weeknight. You can add any vegetables, seafood or meat that you have on hand.
—*Aleni Salcedo, East Elmhurst, NY*

- -

TAKES: 30 min. • **MAKES:** 6 servings (2¼ qt.)

- ½ **lb. sea scallops**
- ½ **lb. uncooked shrimp (16-20 per lb.), peeled and deveined**
- 2 **pkg. (3 oz. each) shrimp ramen noodles**
- 2 **tsp. sesame oil**
- 2 **garlic cloves, minced**
- 2 **cartons (32 oz. each) chicken broth**
- 2 **Tbsp. lime juice**
- 3 **cups fresh bean sprouts**
  Optional: Fresh cilantro leaves, black and white sesame seeds and lime wedges

1. Sprinkle scallops and shrimp with contents of 1 seasoning packet from the noodles (discard second packet or save for another use). In a Dutch oven, heat sesame oil over medium heat. In batches, cook scallops and shrimp until scallops are firm and opaque and shrimp turn pink. Remove and keep warm. To the same pan, add garlic; cook 1 minute longer.
2. Add broth and lime juice. Bring to a boil; reduce heat. Add noodles. Cook for 3 minutes. Add bean sprouts. Return scallops and shrimp to pan; heat through. Serve with desired toppings.
1½ CUPS: 231 cal., 8g fat (3g sat. fat), 59mg chol., 1603mg sod., 24g carb. (4g sugars, 1g fiber), 17g pro.

CHORIZO BURGERS WITH GREEN CHILE AIOLI

Low-carb doesn't have to mean boring in taste and complicated to prepare. For these burgers, the chorizo does all the work to season the meat, and the aioli comes together in just a few minutes. Wrap in lettuce for a low-carb/keto version, and those carb lovers in your house can still have their burgers on buns. Lots of topping options make them completely customizable.
—*Becky Woollands, North Ridgeville, OH*

- -

TAKES: 30 min. • **MAKES:** 6 servings

- 1 **lb. ground beef**
- 1 **lb. fresh chorizo or bulk spicy pork sausage**
- 6 **slices pepper jack cheese**
- ½ **cup mayonnaise**
- 3 **Tbsp. canned chopped green chiles**
- 2 **Tbsp. minced fresh cilantro**
- 1 **Tbsp. lime juice**
- 6 **slices tomato**
- 1 **medium ripe avocado, peeled and sliced**
  Optional: Pickled red onions and hot pepper sauce, such as Cholula
- 6 **Bibb lettuce leaves**

1. In a large bowl, combine beef and chorizo, mixing lightly but thoroughly. Shape into six 6-in. patties. Grill burgers, covered, over medium heat (or broil 3-4 in. from heat) until a thermometer reads 160°, 6-8 minutes on each side. Top with cheese; grill, covered, until cheese is melted, 1-2 minutes longer.

EASY SHRIMP & SCALLOPS RAMEN SOUP

SAN FRANCISCO
CIOPPINO

Cook Classic Cioppino
The impressive soup is actually easy to prepare.

Prep. Before you begin, clean all the seafood well, which includes deveining the shrimp. A sharp paring knife makes this easy.

Saute. Aromatics like fennel and shallot are the foundation for the broth. Saute them until golden for the best flavor.

Simmer. Layer on the flavor for the broth with tomatoes, clam juice, red wine and plenty of herbs.

Final touches. Finish by adding a bounty of seafood. A few minutes is all it takes to cook it through.

SAN FRANCISCO CIOPPINO

Traditionally, cioppino is made with whatever seafood was caught that day or whatever seafood is on hand. It began as a soup for the working class, but with how delicious it tastes, it's no wonder this dish made its way into high-end restaurants and hotels. Feel free to use whatever fish, shellfish and seafood you can find.
—*Barbara Pletzke, Herndon, VA*

- -

PREP: 35 min. • **COOK:** 50 min.
MAKES: 8 servings (4 qt.)

- 2 Tbsp. olive oil
- 1 medium fennel bulb, thinly sliced
- 1 shallot, minced
- 3 garlic cloves, minced
- 6 fresh thyme sprigs
- 2 fresh rosemary sprigs
- 2 Tbsp. minced fresh parsley
- ½ tsp. crushed red pepper flakes
- 2 cans (15 oz. each) crushed tomatoes, undrained
- 2 bottles (8 oz. each) clam juice
- 1 cup dry red wine
- ½ tsp. salt
- ½ tsp. freshly ground pepper
- 16 fresh topneck clams
- 16 fresh mussels, scrubbed and beards removed
- 16 uncooked shrimp (26-30 per lb.), peeled and deveined
- 1 lb. halibut fillets, cut into 1-in. cubes
- 16 snow crab claws
- 16 bay scallops
- 2 cleaned fresh or frozen calamari (squid) tubes, thawed and sliced into ⅛-in. rings (about 2 oz.)
- 4 Tbsp. anise liqueur, such as sambuca

1. In a Dutch oven, heat oil over medium-high heat. Add fennel; cook until crisp-tender, 2-3 minutes. Add shallot and garlic; cook 1 minute longer. Add thyme, rosemary, parsley and red pepper flakes; cook 1 minute longer. Stir in tomatoes, clam juice, wine, salt and pepper. Bring to a boil. Reduce heat; simmer, uncovered, for 20 minutes. Discard herb stems.
2. Add clams, mussels and shrimp. Bring to a boil. Reduce heat; simmer, uncovered, for 4 minutes, stirring occasionally. Stir in halibut; cook 3 minutes. Add crab claws, scallops and calamari; cook until clams and mussels open, shrimp turn pink and scallops are opaque, 5-7 minutes longer. Discard any unopened clams or mussels.
3. Serve in bowls; top with liqueur and additional minced parsley.
2 CUPS: 298 cal., 8g fat (1g sat. fat), 140mg chol., 830mg sod., 15g carb. (6g sugars, 3g fiber), 35g pro.

PORK & BOK CHOY UDON SOUP

While traveling in Thailand, my husband sampled a local version of this tasty soup from street vendors. We have tried many variations, and this comes the closest to his recollection. We double the recipe so we have lots of leftovers.

—Donna Noecker, Tulalip, WA

- -

TAKES: 25 min.
MAKES: 6 servings (2¼ qt.)

- 6 oz. dried Japanese udon noodles or fettuccine
- 1 small bunch bok choy, coarsely chopped
- 1 pork tenderloin (1 lb.), cut into ¼-in. slices
- 6 cups reduced-sodium chicken broth
- 3 Tbsp. reduced-sodium soy sauce
- 4 tsp. minced fresh gingerroot
- 3 garlic cloves, minced
  Optional: Thinly sliced green onions and Sriracha chili sauce

1. Cook noodles according to package directions; drain and rinse with water. Meanwhile, in a Dutch oven, combine bok choy, pork, broth, soy sauce, ginger and garlic; bring just to a boil. Reduce heat; gently simmer, uncovered, 5-7 minutes or just until bok choy and pork are tender.
2. Add noodles to soup. Serve immediately. If desired, sprinkle with green onions and serve with chili sauce.
1½ CUPS: 225 cal., 4g fat (1g sat. fat), 42mg chol., 1309mg sod., 24g carb. (5g sugars, 3g fiber), 25g pro.

PRESSURE-COOKER JALAPENO POPPER CHICKEN CHILI

This quick and comforting chili tastes like liquid jalapeno poppers! You can't have just one bowl.

—Natasha Galbreath, Spanaway, WA

- -

PREP: 30 min. • **COOK:** 10 min.
MAKES: 7 servings (1¾ qt.)

- 2 Tbsp. butter
- 1 lb. ground chicken
- 1 large onion, chopped
- 2 to 4 jalapeno peppers, seeded and finely chopped
- 4 garlic cloves, minced
- 1 can (15¼ oz.) whole kernel corn, undrained
- 1 can (15 oz.) black beans, rinsed and drained
- 1 can (10 oz.) diced tomatoes and green chiles, undrained
- 1 pkg. (8 oz.) cream cheese, cubed
- ¼ cup water or chicken broth
- 2 Tbsp. ranch salad dressing mix
- 1 Tbsp. chili powder
- 1 tsp. onion powder
- 1 tsp. ground cumin
- ¼ tsp. crushed red pepper flakes
  Shredded cheddar cheese, sour cream and crumbled cooked bacon

1. Select saute setting on a 6-qt. electric pressure cooker and adjust for medium heat; add butter. When butter is hot, add the chicken, onion, jalapenos and garlic; cook and stir 6-8 minutes or until chicken is no longer pink and vegetables are tender, breaking up chicken into crumbles. Stir in corn, beans, diced tomatoes and chiles, cream cheese, water, dressing mix and seasonings. Press cancel.
2. Lock lid; close pressure-release valve. Adjust to pressure-cook on high for 8 minutes. Quick-release pressure. Stir before serving. Garnish with shredded cheddar cheese, sour cream, bacon and additional jalapenos.
FREEZE OPTION: Before adding toppings, cool chili. Freeze chili in freezer containers. To use, partially thaw in refrigerator overnight. Heat through in a saucepan, stirring occasionally; add water or broth if necessary. Sprinkle with toppings.
NOTE: Wear disposable gloves when cutting hot peppers; the oils can burn skin. Avoid touching your face.
1 CUP: 344 cal., 20g fat (10g sat. fat), 84mg chol., 1141mg sod., 25g carb. (6g sugars, 5g fiber), 17g pro.

PRESSURE-COOKER JALAPENO POPPER CHICKEN CHILI

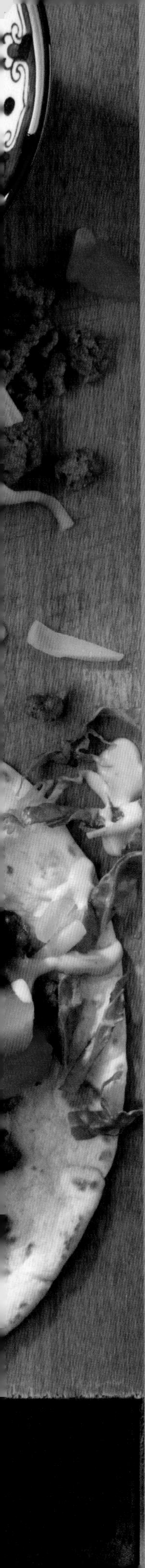

Quick Fixes

Sit down to a hot homemade meal no matter how busy you are. Here's a full month's worth of weeknight dinners that can all be on the table in 30 minutes or less.

ALL-TIME FAVORITES

CREAMY BEEF & ONION PASTA

I created this delicious pasta sauce after noticing a box of onion soup packets in my cupboard. I could not believe how much flavor the soup mix added as a seasoning blend! To my delight, my whole family gave this dish rave reviews, including my infamously picky children. Now it is my go-to dinner when I want to serve an easy, comforting dish after an especially difficult week or when the weather is cold and dreary.
—Kristin Bowers, Gilbert, AZ

TAKES: 30 min. • MAKES: 6 servings

- 3 cups uncooked spiral pasta
- 1 lb. ground beef
- ½ small onion, diced
- 1 cup heavy whipping cream
- 1 cup 2% milk
- 1 envelope onion soup mix
- ¼ cup shredded Gruyere cheese
- ¼ cup shredded Swiss cheese
  Optional: Chopped fresh thyme and green onions

1. Cook the pasta according to package directions; drain. In a large skillet, cook ground beef and onion over medium-high heat until beef is no longer pink and onions are tender, 5-7 minutes, breaking up beef into crumbles; drain and return to the pan. Stir in cream, milk and onion soup mix; bring to a boil. Reduce heat; simmer, uncovered until mixture thickens, 8-10 minutes.
2. Remove from heat and stir in the cheeses and cooked pasta. Serve with thyme and green onions if desired.
1 CUP: 505 cal., 28g fat (15g sat. fat), 105mg chol., 521mg sod., 38g carb. (5g sugars, 2g fiber), 24g pro.

CHEESEBURGER TACOS

Here's a mashup of two our favorite dinners. Load the shells with all your favorite burger fixin's.
—Taste of Home *Test Kitchen*

TAKES: 25 min. • MAKES: 8 servings

- 1 lb. ground beef
- 1 tsp. onion powder
- ½ tsp. kosher salt
- ¼ tsp. freshly ground pepper
- 1 cup shredded cheddar cheese
- ½ cup mayonnaise
- ¼ cup ketchup
- 2 tsp. dill or sweet pickle juice
- ¼ tsp. hot pepper sauce
- 8 flour tortillas (6 in.)
- 1¼ cups shredded lettuce
- 1 medium tomato, chopped
- ¼ cup chopped dill or sweet pickles

1. In a large skillet, cook beef over medium heat, until no longer pink, 6-8 minutes, crumbling beef; drain. Stir in onion powder, salt and pepper. Sprinkle with cheese; cover and let stand until cheese is melted.
2. Meanwhile, in a small bowl, combine mayonnaise, ketchup, pickle juice and hot pepper sauce. Divide beef mixture between tortillas. Top with lettuce, tomato, pickles and sauce.
1 TACO WITH 2 TBSP. SAUCE: 369 cal., 26g fat (9g sat. fat), 61mg chol., 752mg sod., 16g carb. (4g sugars, 1g fiber), 18g pro.

CHEESEBURGER TACOS

EASY
STUFFED
POBLANOS

EASY STUFFED POBLANOS

My partner adores these saucy stuffed peppers—and I love how quickly they come together. Top with low-fat sour cream and your favorite salsa.
—*Jean Erhardt, Portland, OR*

TAKES: 25 min. • MAKES: 4 servings

- ½ lb. Italian turkey sausage links, casings removed
- ½ lb. lean ground beef (90% lean)
- 1 pkg. (8.8 oz.) ready-to-serve Spanish rice
- 4 large poblano peppers
- 1 cup enchilada sauce
- ½ cup shredded Mexican cheese blend
  Minced fresh cilantro, optional

1. Preheat broiler. In a large skillet, cook turkey and beef over medium heat until no longer pink, 5-7 minutes, breaking into crumbles; drain.
2. Prepare rice according to package directions. Add rice to meat mixture.
3. Cut peppers lengthwise in half; remove seeds. Place on a foil-lined 15x10x1-in. baking pan, cut side down. Broil 4 in. from heat until skins blister, about 5 minutes. With tongs, turn peppers.
4. Fill with turkey mixture; top with enchilada sauce and sprinkle with cheese. Broil until cheese is melted, 1-2 minutes longer. If desired, top with cilantro.
NOTE: Wear disposable gloves when cutting hot peppers; the oils can burn skin. Avoid touching your face.
2 STUFFED PEPPER HALVES: 312 cal., 13g fat (4g sat. fat), 63mg chol., 1039mg sod., 27g carb. (5g sugars, 2g fiber), 22g pro.

TASTY ONION CHICKEN

French-fried onions are the secret to a yummy, crunchy coating that keeps the chicken juicy and tender. This is perfect with green beans and buttermilk biscuits.
—*Jennifer Hoeft, Thorndale, TX*

TAKES: 30 min. • MAKES: 4 servings

- ½ cup butter, melted
- 1 Tbsp. Worcestershire sauce
- 1 tsp. ground mustard
- 1 can (2.8 oz.) French-fried onions, crushed
- 4 boneless skinless chicken breast halves (4 oz. each)

1. In a shallow bowl, combine butter, Worcestershire sauce and mustard. Place onions in another shallow bowl. Dip chicken in butter mixture, then coat with onions.
2. Place in a greased 11x7-in. baking dish; drizzle with remaining butter mixture. Bake, uncovered, at 400° for 20-25 minutes or until a thermometer reads 165°.
1 CHICKEN BREAST HALF: 460 cal., 36g fat (18g sat. fat), 124mg chol., 449mg sod., 10g carb. (0 sugars, 0 fiber), 23g pro.

TASTY ONION
CHICKEN

FARMERS MARKET STREET TACOS

BEEF & MUSHROOMS WITH SMASHED POTATOES

I was inspired to make this recipe after I couldn't stop thinking of a similar dish served in my elementary school cafeteria more than 50 years ago! I like that it's quick to make, and my husband and grandkids love it.

—*Ronna Farley, Rockville, MD*

- -

TAKES: 30 min. • **MAKES:** 4 servings

- 1½ lbs. red potatoes (about 6 medium), cut into 1½-in. pieces
- 1 lb. ground beef
- ½ lb. sliced fresh mushrooms
- 1 medium onion, halved and sliced
- 3 Tbsp. all-purpose flour
- ¾ tsp. pepper, divided
- ½ tsp. salt, divided
- 1 can (14½ oz.) beef broth
- 2 Tbsp. butter, softened
- ½ cup half-and-half cream
- ½ cup french-fried onions

1. Place potatoes in a large saucepan; add water to cover. Bring to a boil. Reduce heat to medium; cook, uncovered, until tender, 10-15 minutes.

2. Meanwhile, in a large skillet, cook and crumble the beef with mushrooms and onion over medium-high heat until no longer pink, 6-8 minutes; drain. Stir in flour, ½ tsp. pepper and ¼ tsp. salt until blended. Gradually stir in broth; bring to a boil. Reduce heat; simmer, uncovered, until thickened, about 5 minutes, stirring occasionally.

3. Drain potatoes; return to pan. Mash potatoes to desired consistency, adding butter, cream and the remaining salt and pepper. Spoon into bowls; top with beef mixture. Sprinkle with fried onions.

1 SERVING: 517 cal., 26g fat (12g sat. fat), 100mg chol., 896mg sod., 40g carb. (5g sugars, 4g fiber), 28g pro.

READER REVIEW

"Made this last night; it's true comfort food! The recipe is very easy and quick."

—DIANE468, TASTEOFHOME.COM

FARMERS MARKET STREET TACOS

No matter what I bring home from the local farmers market, I always end up stuffing it into a taco for a fresh, veggie-filled treat. You really can't go wrong.

—*Ralph Jones, San Diego, CA*

- -

TAKES: 30 min. • **MAKES:** 4 servings

- 1 bunch green onions
- 2 bunches bok choy, halved
- 1 medium zucchini, cut into 3-in. sticks
- ½ lb. fresh asparagus spears
- 2 medium ripe avocados, peeled and quartered
- 2 jalapeno peppers, halved and seeded
- 2 Tbsp. olive oil
- ½ tsp. kosher salt
- ½ tsp. pepper
- 8 mini corn tortillas
  Fresh cilantro leaves
  Optional: Pickled red onions, lime wedges, sliced radishes and salsa verde

1. Prepare grill for medium-high heat. Cut partially through the green onions, leaving tops intact. Brush green onions, bok choy, zucchini, asparagus, avocados and jalapenos with olive oil; sprinkle with salt and pepper. Transfer to a greased grill rack. Grill, covered, or broil 4 in. from heat until the vegetables are crisp-tender and slightly charred, 4-5 minutes, turning occasionally.

2. Grill the mini tortillas until warmed and slightly charred, 30-45 seconds per side. Cut the vegetables to desired sizes; serve in tortillas with cilantro and toppings of your choice.

NOTE: Wear disposable gloves when cutting hot peppers; the oils can burn skin. Avoid touching your face.

2 TACOS: 319 cal., 19g fat (3g sat. fat), 0 chol., 536mg sod., 33g carb. (9g sugars, 13g fiber), 11g pro.

SAUSAGE & BEAN SKILLET WITH CRISPY PLANTAINS

Caribbean flavors flourish in this one-pot entree topped with crushed plantain chips. The whole family loves it—plus, it's so fast. Swap in spicy chicken sausage for the smoked links if you'd like.
—Elisabeth Larsen, Pleasant Grove, UT

TAKES: 30 min. • **MAKES:** 6 servings

- 2   Tbsp. canola oil
- 2   celery ribs, thinly sliced
- 1   medium sweet red pepper, chopped
- 1   small onion, chopped
- 1   pkg. (14 oz.) smoked sausage, cut diagonally into ½-in. slices
- 2   garlic cloves, minced
- ½   tsp. dried thyme
- 1   can (15 oz.) black beans, rinsed and drained
- 1   can (14½ oz.) diced tomatoes, undrained
- ¼   tsp. pepper
- 1   cup plantain chips, crushed
- ¼   cup fresh cilantro leaves, chopped
      Hot cooked rice, optional

1. In a large skillet, heat oil over medium-high heat. Add celery, red pepper and onion; cook and stir 4-5 minutes or until crisp-tender, Add sausage; cook and stir 4 minutes longer or until browned. Add garlic and thyme; cook 1 minute longer. Stir in beans, tomatoes and pepper. Reduce heat; cook, uncovered, until sauce is slightly thickened, 4-6 minutes longer.
2. Top with plantain chips and cilantro. If desired, serve with rice.
1 CUP: 379 cal., 25g fat (8g sat. fat), 44mg chol., 1017mg sod., 24g carb. (6g sugars, 5g fiber), 14g pro.

SAUSAGE & BEAN SKILLET WITH CRISPY PLANTAINS

GRILLED SESAME ORANGE TUNA STEAKS

GRILLED SESAME ORANGE TUNA STEAKS

This recipe was a collaboration between my son and me. He wanted to enter a contest because he aspires to be a chef someday. Although they look fancy, these tuna steaks are easy to make.
—Lorna McFadden, Port Orchard, WA

TAKES: 25 min. • **MAKES:** 4 servings

- 1½ cups instant brown rice
- 2   cups fresh sugar snap peas
- 2   Tbsp. honey
- 1   Tbsp. butter
- 1   snack-size cup (4 oz.) mandarin oranges, drained
- ¼   cup unsalted cashews, coarsely chopped
- 4   tuna steaks (6 oz. each)
- 5   Tbsp. sesame ginger marinade, divided

1. Cook rice according to package directions. In a large skillet, saute peas in butter and honey until crisp-tender. Add oranges and cashews; cook and stir 1 minute longer.
2. Brush tuna with 2 Tbsp. marinade. Moisten a paper towel with cooking oil; using long-handled tongs, rub on grill rack to coat lightly. Grill tuna, covered, over high heat or broil 3-4 in. from the heat for 3-4 minutes on each side for medium-rare or until slightly pink in the center.
3. Brush tuna with remaining marinade; serve with rice and snap pea mixture.
1 STEAK WITH ¾ CUP RICE AND ½ CUP SNAP PEA MIXTURE: 506 cal., 10g fat (3g sat. fat), 84mg chol., 822mg sod., 56g carb. (24g sugars, 4g fiber), 47g pro.

BLACKENED TILAPIA WITH ZUCCHINI NOODLES

I love quick and bright meals like this one-skillet wonder. Homemade pico de gallo is easy to make the night before.
—*Tammy Brownlow, Dallas, TX*

TAKES: 30 min. • **MAKES:** 4 servings

- 2 large zucchini (about 1½ lbs.)
- 1½ tsp. ground cumin
- ¾ tsp. salt, divided
- ½ tsp. smoked paprika
- ½ tsp. pepper
- ¼ tsp. garlic powder
- 4 tilapia fillets (6 oz. each)
- 2 tsp. olive oil
- 2 garlic cloves, minced
- 1 cup pico de gallo

1. Trim ends of zucchini. Using a spiralizer, cut zucchini into thin strands.

2. Mix cumin, ½ tsp. salt, smoked paprika, pepper and garlic powder; sprinkle mixture generously onto both sides of tilapia. In a large nonstick skillet, heat oil over medium-high heat. In batches, cook tilapia until fish just begins to flake easily with a fork, 2-3 minutes per side. Remove from pan; keep warm.

3. In same pan, cook zucchini with garlic over medium-high heat until zucchini is slightly softened, 1-2 minutes, tossing constantly with tongs (do not overcook). Sprinkle with remaining ¼ tsp. salt. Serve with tilapia and pico de gallo.

NOTE: If a spiralizer is not available, the zucchini may also be cut into ribbons using a vegetable peeler. Saute as directed, increasing time as necessary.

1 SERVING: 203 cal., 4g fat (1g sat. fat), 83mg chol., 522mg sod., 8g carb. (5g sugars, 2g fiber), 34g pro. **DIABETIC EXCHANGES:** 5 lean meat, 1 vegetable, ½ fat.

PASTA WITH WHITE CLAM SAUCE

Garlic and oregano enhance the flavor of this delicious main dish. My mom's Italian friend passed on the recipe to her, and I began making it when I was 14 years old.
—*Kelli Soike, Tallahassee, FL*

TAKES: 30 min. • **MAKES:** 5 servings

- 12 oz. uncooked linguine
- 2 garlic cloves, minced
- 1 can (2 oz.) anchovies, undrained
- 1 Tbsp. olive oil
- 1 bottle (8 oz.) clam juice
- 1 can (6½ oz.) minced clams, undrained
- ⅓ cup water
- 2 Tbsp. dried oregano
- 1 Tbsp. minced fresh parsley
- ¼ tsp. salt
- ½ tsp. pepper
- 5 Tbsp. shredded Parmesan cheese
  Optional: Chopped fresh parsley and fresh oregano leaves

1. Cook pasta according to package directions. In a saucepan, saute garlic and anchovies in oil for 3 minutes, breaking up anchovies. Stir in the clam juice, clams, water, oregano, parsley, salt and pepper. Bring to a boil. Reduce heat; simmer, uncovered, for 15 minutes or until sauce is reduced by half.

2. Drain pasta; toss with clam sauce. Sprinkle with Parmesan; if desired, top with parsley and oregano.

1 CUP: 379 cal., 13g fat (2g sat. fat), 19mg chol., 874mg sod., 50g carb. (0 sugars, 4g fiber), 16g pro. **DIABETIC EXCHANGES:** 3 starch, 2 fat, 1 lean meat.

BLACKENED TILAPIA WITH ZUCCHINI NOODLES

SWEET PEPPER BURRITOS

SKILLET PORK CHOPS IN PINEAPPLE-SOY SAUCE

We try to eat a variety of foods and although we like pork, it really has very little flavor. One night I was fixing some beautiful boneless pork loin chops and decided to add a fruity sauce. They were moist and juicy and the sauce was delicious. They were perfect served over rice. This dinner takes 30 minutes to prepare, so it is great for weeknight meals but nice enough for company too.
—*Donna Gribbins, Shelbyville, KY*

- -

TAKES: 30 min. • **MAKES:** 6 servings

- 6 boneless pork loin chops (5 oz. each)
- ½ tsp. salt
- ½ tsp. pepper
- 3 Tbsp. olive oil
- 2 shallots, minced
- 1 cup pineapple preserves
- ¼ cup soy sauce
- 1 Tbsp. Dijon mustard
- 1 bunch green onions, thinly sliced

1. Season pork chops with salt and pepper. In a large nonstick skillet, heat oil over medium heat. Cook the pork chops until a thermometer reads 145°, 6-8 minutes on each side; remove from pan, reserving drippings.
2. In same pan, saute shallots in drippings until lightly browned. Whisk together pineapple preserves, soy sauce and Dijon; add to pan. Bring to a boil. Reduce heat; simmer, until thickened slightly, about 5 minutes.
3. Add chops back to pan, turning to coat. Sprinkle with sliced green onions.
1 PORK CHOP WITH 2 TBSP. SAUCE: 407 cal., 15g fat (4g sat. fat), 68mg chol., 914mg sod., 38g carb. (33g sugars, 1g fiber), 29g pro.

SWEET PEPPER BURRITOS

This meatless mainstay is bursting with cheese, rice, onion and peppers. The burritos are a fun change of pace from tacos or sandwiches.
—*Marian Platt, Sequim, WA*

- -

TAKES: 30 min. • **MAKES:** 6 servings

- 1 medium onion, chopped
- 1 Tbsp. canola oil
- 2 medium sweet red peppers, diced
- 1 medium sweet yellow pepper, diced
- 1 medium green pepper, diced
- 2 tsp. ground cumin
- 2 cups cooked brown rice
- 1½ cups shredded reduced-fat cheddar cheese
- 3 oz. fat-free cream cheese, cubed
- ½ tsp. salt
- ½ tsp. pepper
- 6 flour tortillas (10 in.), warmed
   Salsa, optional

1. In a large nonstick skillet, saute onion in oil for 2 minutes. Add peppers; saute for 5 minutes or until crisp-tender. Sprinkle with cumin; saute 1 minute longer. Stir in the rice, cheeses, salt and pepper.
2. Spoon about ⅔ cup of filling off center on each tortilla; fold sides and ends over filling and roll up. Place seam side down in a 13x9-in. baking dish coated with cooking spray.
3. Cover and bake at 425° for 10-15 minutes or until heated through. Let stand for 5 minutes. Serve with salsa if desired.
1 SERVING: 429 cal., 13g fat (5g sat. fat), 21mg chol., 671mg sod., 54g carb. (0 sugars, 9g fiber), 18g pro. **DIABETIC EXCHANGES:** 3 starch, 2 vegetable, 2 fat, 1 lean meat.

SKILLET PORK CHOPS IN PINEAPPLE-SOY SAUCE

LOW-CARB SHRIMP
SUSHI BOWL

BEST SALISBURY STEAK

A good recipe for Salisbury steak is hard to find. I remember enjoying it often when I was growing up, but when I decided to add it to my recipe collection, I wasn't able to find it in my modern cookbooks. I came up with these ingredients on my own and experimented until it tasted like the dish I remembered.
—*Faye Hintz, Springfield, MO*

TAKES: 30 min. • **MAKES:** 2 servings

- 1   large egg
- 3   Tbsp. crushed butter-flavored crackers
- 1   Tbsp. finely chopped onion
- ½   tsp. salt
- ¼   tsp. pepper
- ¼   tsp. rubbed sage
- ¾   lb. ground beef
- 1   can (4 oz.) mushroom stems and pieces, drained
- 2   Tbsp. butter
- 3   Tbsp. all-purpose flour
- 1¾ cups water
- 2   beef bouillon cubes
- ¼   tsp. browning sauce, optional
       Hot mashed potatoes
       Minced fresh parsley, optional

1. In a medium bowl, combine the egg, cracker crumbs, onion, salt, pepper and sage. Add beef and mix well. Shape into 2 patties.
2. In a medium skillet, cook patties until browned, 4-5 minutes per side; drain. Remove to a platter and keep warm.
3. In the same skillet, saute mushrooms in butter for 2 minutes. Stir in flour; blend well. Add water and bouillon; cook and stir until smooth and thickened. Stir in browning sauce if desired. Return the patties to gravy and cook, uncovered, over low heat until heated through, about 10 minutes, turning occasionally. Serve with mashed potatoes. If desired, sprinkle with parsley.
1 STEAK: 581 cal., 37g fat (17g sat. fat), 250mg chol., 1960mg sod., 18g carb. (2g sugars, 2g fiber), 41g pro.

LOW-CARB SHRIMP SUSHI BOWL

Sushi is one of our family's favorite treats. This is an easy-to-prepare version that can be ready 30 minutes or less. It's low carb and packed with vegetables. With all the flavor, no one misses the carbs. If you don't like shrimp, you can substitute cooked shredded chicken or firm tofu. If you like your food extra spicy, change the ratio of red curry paste to mayonnaise.
—*Kristyne Mcdougle Walter, Lorain, OH*

TAKES: 30 min. • **MAKES:** 4 servings

- 5   Tbsp. mayonnaise
- 2   tsp. red curry paste
- 2   pkg. frozen riced cauliflower (10 oz. each)
- 3   Tbsp. sesame oil
- 1½ lbs. uncooked shrimp (31-40 per lb.), peeled and deveined
- 2   garlic cloves, minced
- 1   tsp. seasoned salt
- 1   medium ripe avocado, peeled and sliced
- ½   medium cucumber, sliced
- ½   cup julienned carrots
- 2   green onions, thinly sliced
- 1   medium lime, quartered

1. In a small bowl, mix mayonnaise and red curry paste.
2. Prepare riced cauliflower according to package directions.
3. Meanwhile, in a large skillet, heat oil over medium heat. Add shrimp; cook until shrimp turn pink, 5-7 minutes. Add garlic and salt; cook 1 minute longer. Remove from heat.
4. Divide cauliflower among 4 bowls. Top each bowl with shrimp, avocado, cucumber, carrot and green onions. Drizzle with curry mayonnaise and garnish each bowl with a lime quarter.
1 BOWL: 460 cal., 31g fat (5g sat. fat), 213mg chol., 783mg sod., 16g carb. (5g sugars, 7g fiber), 32g pro.

SALSA VERDE CHICKEN CASSEROLE

This is a rich and surprisingly tasty rendition of a number of Tex-Mex dishes molded into one packed, beautiful casserole. Best of all, it's ready in hardly any time!
—*Janet McCormick, Proctorville, OH*

TAKES: 30 min. • **MAKES:** 6 servings

- 2 cups shredded rotisserie chicken
- 1 cup sour cream
- 1½ cups salsa verde, divided
- 8 corn tortillas (6 in.)
- 2 cups chopped tomatoes
- ¼ cup minced fresh cilantro
- 2 cups shredded Monterey Jack cheese
  Optional toppings: Avocado slices, thinly sliced green onions and fresh cilantro leaves

1. In a small bowl, combine the chicken, sour cream and ¾ cup salsa. Spread ¼ cup salsa on the bottom of a greased 8-in. square baking dish.

2. Layer with half the tortillas and chicken mixture; sprinkle with half the tomatoes, the minced cilantro and half the cheese. Repeat layers with remaining tortillas, chicken mixture, tomatoes and cheese.

3. Bake, uncovered, at 400° until bubbly, 20-25 minutes. Serve with remaining salsa and toppings of your choice.

1 SERVING: 400 cal., 23g fat (13g sat. fat), 102mg chol., 637mg sod., 22g carb. (5g sugars, 3g fiber), 26g pro.

SALSA VERDE
CHICKEN CASSEROLE

PASTA & VEGGIES
IN GARLIC SAUCE

PASTA & VEGGIES IN GARLIC SAUCE

Big garlic flavor and a little heat from red pepper flakes help perk up this fresh-tasting pasta dish. It's wonderful with chicken and beef entrees.
—*Doris Heath, Franklin, NC*

TAKES: 20 min. • **MAKES:** 6 servings

- 12 oz. uncooked penne pasta
- 6 garlic cloves, minced
- ¼ tsp. crushed red pepper flakes
- 2 Tbsp. olive oil
- 1 can (15 oz.) garbanzo beans or chickpeas, rinsed and drained
- 2 medium tomatoes, seeded and cut into ½-in. pieces
- 1 pkg. (9 oz.) fresh baby spinach
- ¼ tsp. salt
- ¼ cup grated Parmesan cheese

1. Cook pasta according to package directions. Meanwhile, in a large skillet, saute garlic and pepper flakes in oil for 1 minute. Add garbanzo beans and tomatoes; cook and stir for 2 minutes. Add spinach and salt; cook and stir until spinach is wilted.

2. Drain pasta; add to vegetable mixture. Sprinkle with Parmesan cheese; toss to coat. If desired, serve with additional Parmesan and red pepper flakes.

1½ CUPS: 370 cal., 8g fat (2g sat. fat), 3mg chol., 432mg sod., 62g carb. (0 sugars, 6g fiber), 15g pro. **DIABETIC EXCHANGES:** 3½ starch, 1 vegetable, 1 lean meat, 1 fat.

PRESSURE-COOKER PENNE WITH MEAT SAUCE

I like to serve this super easy pasta with a chopped salad and Italian dressing.
—Virginia Butterfield,
Cranberry Township, PA

TAKES: 30 min. • **MAKES:** 6 servings

- 1 Tbsp. olive oil
- 1½ lbs. lean ground beef (90% lean)
- ¾ cup finely chopped onion
- 1 medium green pepper, chopped
- 12 oz. uncooked penne pasta
- 2¼ cups water
- 2 tsp. Italian seasoning
- ¾ tsp. salt
- ½ tsp. pepper
- 1 jar pasta sauce (24 oz.)
  Optional: Shredded Parmesan cheese and torn fresh basil leaves

1. Select saute setting on a 6-qt. electric pressure cooker. Adjust for medium heat; add oil. When oil is hot, cook beef, onion and pepper until the beef is no longer pink and vegetables are tender, 8-10 minutes, breaking up beef into crumbles; drain. Press cancel; add penne pasta, water and seasonings; cover with pasta sauce. Lock lid; close pressure-release valve. Adjust to pressure-cook on high for 6 minutes.
2. Quick-release pressure. Remove lid; stir to combine. If desired, sprinkle with Parmesan cheese and basil.
1½ CUPS: 472 cal., 14g fat (4g sat. fat), 71mg chol., 775mg sod., 55g carb. (12g sugars, 5g fiber), 31g pro.

HOW-TO

Safely Vent Your Pressure Cooker

For safe, easy venting of your electric pressure cooker, use a pair of tongs to carefully turn the release valve— and keep your hands and face clear of the steam vent.

PRESSURE-COOKER PENNE WITH MEAT SAUCE

SPEEDY SALMON PATTIES

When I was a girl growing up on the farm, my mom often fixed these nicely seasoned patties when we were out working late in the field.
—Bonnie Evans, Cameron, NC

TAKES: 25 min. • **MAKES:** 3 servings

- ⅓ cup finely chopped onion
- 1 large egg, beaten
- 5 saltines, crushed
- ½ tsp. Worcestershire sauce
- ¼ tsp. salt
- ⅛ tsp. pepper
- 1 can (14¾ oz.) salmon, drained, bones and skin removed
- 2 tsp. butter

1. In a large bowl, combine the onion, egg, saltines, Worcestershire, salt and pepper. Crumble salmon over mixture and mix well. Shape into 6 patties.
2. In a large skillet over medium heat, fry patties in butter for 3-4 minutes on each side or until set and golden brown.
2 SALMON PATTIES: 288 cal., 15g fat (4g sat. fat), 139mg chol., 1063mg sod., 5g carb. (1g sugars, 0 fiber), 31g pro.

PARMESAN-CRUSTED TILAPIA

I usually serve this crispy fish with tartar sauce and seasoned steamed veggies. It's like a Friday night fish fry without all the calories!
—Christi McElroy, Neenah, WI

TAKES: 25 min. • **MAKES:** 4 servings

- ½ cup all-purpose flour
- 1 large egg, beaten
- ½ cup crushed Ritz crackers (about 10 crackers)
- ¼ cup grated Parmesan cheese
- ½ tsp. salt
- 4 tilapia fillets (5 oz. each)
- 2 Tbsp. olive oil
  Lemon wedges

1. Place flour and egg in separate shallow bowls. In another shallow bowl, combine the crackers, cheese and salt. Dip fillets in the flour, then egg, then cracker mixture; turn until coated.

2. In a large cast-iron or other heavy skillet, cook fillets in oil over medium heat until fish just begins to flake easily with a fork. Serve with lemon wedges.
1 FILLET: 287 cal., 13g fat (3g sat. fat), 125mg chol., 440mg sod., 12g carb. (1g sugars, 0 fiber), 31g pro.

CHICKEN RAMEN NOODLE BOWL

This healthier take on ramen uses ingredients I usually have on hand. It is an easy, quick and satisfying lunch. You can also make this with leftover chicken or pork. Fresh lime or bean sprouts would be a nice garnish.
—Alicia Rooker, Milwaukee, WI

TAKES: 20 min. • **MAKES:** 2 servings

- 1 pkg. (3 oz.) chicken ramen noodles
- 1 cup frozen stir-fry vegetable blend
- 1 can (5 oz.) chunk white chicken, drained
- 2 medium fresh mushrooms, thinly sliced
- 1 garlic clove, minced
- ½ tsp. Sriracha chili sauce
- 2 soft-boiled large eggs
- 1 green onion, thinly sliced

Cook noodles and stir-fry blend according to package directions. Stir chicken, mushrooms, garlic, chili sauce and cooked stir-fry blend into noodles; heat through. Divide between 2 bowls. Serve with soft-boiled eggs and green onion; if desired, serve with additional chili sauce.
1½ CUPS: 368 cal., 14g fat (5g sat. fat), 230mg chol., 1199mg sod., 36g carb. (4g sugars, 3g fiber), 24g pro.

CHICKEN RAMEN NOODLE BOWL

ASPARAGUS & SHRIMP WITH ANGEL HAIR

We've all heard that the way to a man's heart is through his stomach, so when I plan a romantic dinner, this is one dish I like to serve. It is easy on the budget and turns out perfectly for two.
—*Shari Neff, Takoma Park, MD*

TAKES: 30 min. • **MAKES:** 2 servings

- 3 oz. uncooked angel hair pasta
- ½ lb. uncooked shrimp (16-20 per lb.), peeled and deveined
- ¼ tsp. salt
- ⅛ tsp. crushed red pepper flakes
- 2 Tbsp. olive oil, divided
- 8 fresh asparagus spears, trimmed and cut into 2-in. pieces
- ½ cup sliced fresh mushrooms
- ¼ cup chopped seeded tomato, peeled
- 4 garlic cloves, minced
- 2 tsp. chopped green onion
- ½ cup white wine or chicken broth
- 1½ tsp. minced fresh basil
- 1½ tsp. minced fresh oregano
- 1½ tsp. minced fresh parsley
- 1½ tsp. minced fresh thyme
- ¼ cup grated Parmesan cheese
  Lemon wedges

1. Cook pasta according to package directions. Meanwhile, sprinkle the shrimp with salt and pepper flakes. In a large skillet or wok, heat 1 Tbsp. oil over medium-high heat. Add the shrimp; stir-fry until pink, 2-3 minutes. Remove and keep warm.
2. In same skillet, stir-fry the next 5 ingredients in remaining oil until vegetables are crisp-tender, about 5 minutes. Add wine and seasonings. Return shrimp to pan.
3. Drain pasta; add to shrimp mixture and toss gently. Cook and stir until heated through, 1-2 minutes. Sprinkle with Parmesan cheese. Serve with lemon wedges.
1¾ CUPS: 488 cal., 19g fat (4g sat. fat), 132mg chol., 584mg sod., 41g carb. (4g sugars, 3g fiber), 29g pro.

AIR-FRYER CHICKEN PARMESAN

AIR-FRYER CHICKEN PARMESAN

Quick, simple and oh-so-tasty, this air-fryer chicken Parmesan recipe is the perfect weeknight dish to have on hand. It's just as crispy as the classic, if not crispier!
—Taste of Home *Test Kitchen*

TAKES: 20 min. • **MAKES:** 4 servings

- 2 large eggs
- ½ cup seasoned bread crumbs
- ⅓ cup grated Parmesan cheese
- ¼ tsp. pepper
- 4 boneless skinless chicken breast halves (6 oz. each)
- 1 cup pasta sauce
- 1 cup shredded mozzarella cheese
  Optional: Chopped fresh basil and hot cooked pasta

1. Preheat air fryer to 375°. In a shallow bowl, lightly beat eggs. In another shallow bowl, combine bread crumbs, Parmesan cheese and pepper. Dip chicken in egg, then coat with crumb mixture.
2. Place chicken in a single layer on greased tray in air-fryer basket. Cook until a thermometer reads 165°, 10-12 minutes, turning halfway through. Top chicken with sauce and mozzarella. Cook until cheese is melted, 3-4 minutes longer. If desired, sprinkle with chopped basil and additional Parmesan cheese and serve with pasta.
NOTE: In our testing, we find cook times vary dramatically among brands of air fryers. As a result, we give wider than normal ranges on suggested cook times. Begin checking at the first time listed and adjust as needed.
1 CHICKEN BREAST HALF: 416 cal., 16g fat (7g sat. fat), 215mg chol., 863mg sod., 18g carb. (6g sugars, 2g fiber), 49g pro.

**ASPARAGUS
& SHRIMP WITH
ANGEL HAIR**

SWEET
& HOT
CHICKEN
WITH DILL
PICKLE
SAUCE,
PAGE 85

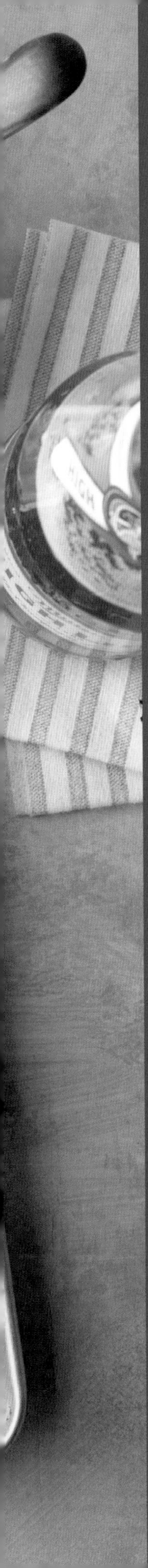

Main Dishes

Find dozens of memorable entrees ready to star at your dinner table on these pages. The chapter is brimming with mealtime choices for weekdays, holidays and every day in between.

CHECK OUT THESE SPECIALTIES

**PRESSURE-COOKER
LEMON CHICKEN PASTA**

PRESSURE-COOKER
LEMON CHICKEN PASTA

In the past two weeks I was getting ready for a very demanding race in the mountains of Lake Tahoe area. Normally, before the race you want to eat a lot of carbs and some proteins to get enough energy for the following day to perform at your best. It inspired me to make this very special creamy pasta dish with chicken, mushrooms, artichokes, capers and lemons.
—*Ilya Khayn, San Jose, CA*

PREP: 20 min. • **COOK:** 25 min. • **MAKES:** 10 servings

- 2 Tbsp. avocado oil
- 2½ lbs. boneless skinless chicken breasts, cubed
- 1 large onion, diced
- 5 garlic cloves, minced
- 4 cups chicken broth, divided
- 7 oz. fresh shiitake mushrooms, sliced
- 1 can (14 oz.) water-packed artichoke hearts, drained
- ¼ cup white wine
- 2 medium lemons, juiced and zested
- 1 tsp. dried oregano
- 1 tsp. paprika
- ¾ tsp. pepper
- ¼ tsp. salt
- 1 lb. uncooked rigatoni pasta
- 1½ cups grated Parmesan cheese
- ¼ cup capers, drained
- ¼ cup sliced ripe olives, drained
    Optional: Minced parsley, red pepper flakes, additional Parmesan and lemon wedges

1. Select saute setting on a 6-qt. electric pressure cooker. Adjust for medium heat; add the oil. When oil is hot, brown chicken in batches on all sides. Remove with slotted spoon. Add onion; cook and stir until tender, 4-5 minutes. Add garlic, cook 1 additional minute. Press cancel. Add 1 cup broth, stirring to loosen browned bits from pan. Add browned chicken, mushrooms, artichokes, wine, lemon juice and zest, oregano, paprika, pepper and salt. Add pasta and remaining 3 cups broth. Lock lid; close pressure-release valve.

2. Adjust to pressure-cook on high for 6 minutes. Quick-release pressure. Remove lid, add Parmesan, capers and olives. If desired, garnish with minced parsley, red pepper flakes, additional Parmesan and lemon wedges.
1½ CUPS: 577 cal., 15g fat (4g sat. fat), 104mg chol., 1260mg sod., 60g carb. (5g sugars, 4g fiber), 49g pro.

EASY SAUSAGE & VEGETABLE SKILLET

This is an old recipe that has been passed down in our family through my sister-in-law. When I was a child, she did most of the cooking in our house, and this was my favorite meal. The variety of vegetables makes this an attractive dish, and the cooking time is minimal.
—*Ruby Williams, Bogalusa, LA*

TAKES: 25 min. • **MAKES:** 2 servings

- ½ lb. Italian sausage links
- 1 Tbsp. canola oil
- 1 cup cubed yellow summer squash (¾-in. pieces)
- ½ cup chopped green onions
- 2 garlic cloves, minced
- 1½ cups chopped fresh tomatoes
- 2 tsp. Worcestershire sauce
- ⅛ tsp. cayenne pepper

1. In a large skillet, cook sausage over medium heat in oil until a thermometer reads 160°; drain.
2. Cut into ½-in. slices. Add the sausage, squash and onions to the skillet; cook for 3-4 minutes or until vegetables are tender. Add garlic; cook 1 minute longer. Stir in the tomatoes, Worcestershire sauce and cayenne pepper; heat through.
1 SERVING: 304 cal., 22g fat (6g sat. fat), 45mg chol., 607mg sod., 14g carb. (7g sugars, 3g fiber), 14g pro.

EASY SAUSAGE & VEGETABLE SKILLET

SLOW-COOKER
GARLIC CLOVE CHICKEN

SLOW-COOKER GARLIC CLOVE CHICKEN

Dinner guests and cooks alike will rave about this chicken recipe.
Your company will be delighted with the tasty poultry, and you'll
appreciate the stress-free preparation in the slow cooker.
—Ruth Rigoni, Hurley, WI

PREP: 45 min. • **COOK:** 3½ hours • **MAKES:** 6 servings

- 40 garlic cloves, peeled
- 4 celery ribs, sliced
- 1 broiler/fryer chicken (3 to 4 lbs.), cut up and skin removed
- ½ tsp. salt
- ¼ tsp. pepper
- 1 Tbsp. olive oil
- ¼ cup white wine or reduced-sodium chicken broth
- 3 Tbsp. lemon juice
- 2 Tbsp. dry vermouth
- 2 Tbsp. grated lemon zest
- 2 Tbsp. minced fresh parsley
- 2 tsp. dried basil
- 1 tsp. dried oregano
  Dash crushed red pepper flakes

1. Place garlic and celery in a 5-qt. slow cooker. Sprinkle chicken
with salt and pepper. In a large nonstick skillet, brown chicken in
oil in batches; transfer to slow cooker.
2. In a small bowl, combine the remaining ingredients. Pour over
chicken. Cover and cook on low for 3½-4 hours or until chicken
juices run clear.
4 OZ. COOKED CHICKEN: 230 cal., 8g fat (2g sat. fat), 73mg chol.,
287mg sod., 10g carb. (1g sugars, 1g fiber), 26g pro.

HOT CHICKEN SALAD PIES

These pies come together in a snap! They're perfect for when you
have leftover chicken on hand and need to use it up.
—Shirley Gudenschwager, Orchard, NE

PREP: 20 min. + chilling • **BAKE:** 35 min.
MAKES: 2 pies (6 servings each)

- 1 pkg. (15 oz.) refrigerated pie pastry
- 3 cups diced cooked chicken
- 2 cups cooked long grain rice
- 4 hard-boiled large eggs, chopped
- 1 can (10¾ oz.) condensed cream of mushroom soup, undiluted
- 1 cup mayonnaise
- 1 medium onion, chopped
- ½ cup chopped celery
- ¼ cup lemon juice
- 1 tsp. salt
- 1½ cups crushed cornflakes
- ¼ cup butter, melted

1. Unroll crusts into 9-in. pie plates; flute edges. Refrigerate
30 minutes. Preheat oven to 400°. Line unpricked crusts with
a double thickness of foil. Fill with pie weights, dried beans or
uncooked rice. Bake on a lower oven rack until edges are light
golden brown, 10-15 minutes. Remove foil and weights; bake until
crusts are golden brown, 3-6 minutes longer. Cool on a wire rack;
reduce heat to 350°.
2. In a large bowl, combine the chicken, rice, eggs, soup,
mayonnaise, onion, celery, lemon juice and salt. Spoon chicken
mixture into crusts. Combine cornflakes and butter; sprinkle
over tops. Bake on lowest oven rack until lightly browned,
20-25 minutes.
1 PIECE: 505 cal., 32g fat (10g sat. fat), 112mg chol., 771mg sod.,
38g carb. (3g sugars, 1g fiber), 15g pro.

HOT CHICKEN
SALAD PIES

BASIL CHICKEN WITH
SMOKED TOMATO JAM

BASIL CHICKEN WITH SMOKED TOMATO JAM

I grow my own herbs and veggies in the summer, and when they are at peak, I incorporate them into my recipes. This is one I developed using fresh basil, parsley and tomatoes when they were at their best and ripest.
—*Sheryl Little, Cabot, AR*

PREP: 45 min. • **BAKE:** 15 min. • **MAKES:** 4 servings

- 1 lb. tomatoes, peeled, seeded and quartered
- 2 Tbsp. honey
- 1 Tbsp. chopped green onions
- 1 Tbsp. minced fresh parsley
- 1½ tsp. lemon juice
- 1 garlic clove, minced
- ¼ tsp. grated lemon zest
- 1 tsp. liquid smoke, optional
- ½ tsp. salt, divided
- ¼ tsp. pepper, divided
- 4 boneless skinless chicken breast halves (6 oz. each)
- 1 log (4 oz.) fresh goat cheese
- 2 Tbsp. chopped fresh basil
- 2 Tbsp. butter
- 2 Tbsp. olive oil
  Fresh basil leaves, julienned

1. Preheat oven to 350°. Place the first 7 ingredients in a small heavy saucepan. Add liquid smoke if desired. Bring to a boil; reduce heat. Simmer, uncovered, until thickened to consistency of jam, about 25 minutes. Stir in ¼ tsp. salt and ⅛ tsp. pepper. Remove from heat; keep warm.
2. Meanwhile, pound chicken breasts with a meat mallet to ¼-in. thickness. Sprinkle goat cheese and chopped basil over chicken. Roll up chicken from a short side; secure with toothpicks. Sprinkle with remaining ¼ tsp. salt and ⅛ tsp. pepper.
3. In a large ovenproof skillet, heat butter and olive oil over medium heat. Add chicken; brown on all sides. Bake, uncovered, until chicken is no longer pink, 12-15 minutes. Discard toothpicks. Serve with tomato jam and julienned basil.
1 STUFFED CHICKEN BREAST WITH 2 TBSP. JAM: 396 cal., 20g fat (8g sat. fat), 128mg chol., 543mg sod., 15g carb. (12g sugars, 2g fiber), 38g pro.

SHRIMP SPAGHETTI WITH CHERRY TOMATOES

This is a very tasty pasta dish, full of umami flavors and, if done properly, an insanely silky sauce. Shut your eyes and you will swear you're in Sicily.
—*Hassan Nurullah, Hapeville, GA*

PREP: 15 min. • **COOK:** 25 min. • **MAKES:** 6 servings

- 1 lb. uncooked spaghetti
- 3 Tbsp. olive oil
- 2 garlic cloves, smashed
- 1 tsp. crushed red pepper flakes
- 4 cups heirloom cherry tomatoes
- 2 shallots, thinly sliced
- 1 can anchovy fillets (2 oz.)
- ¾ cup muffuletta mix or olive bruschetta topping
- 4 Tbsp. unsalted butter
- 1 lb. uncooked shrimp (26-30 per lb.), peeled and deveined
- 1½ cups grated Romano cheese
- 2 Tbsp. minced fresh parsley

1. In a Dutch oven, cook pasta according to package directions; drain, reserving 1 cup cooking liquid. Set aside.
2. In the same Dutch oven, heat oil over medium-high heat. Add garlic and red pepper flakes until fragrant. Discard garlic cloves; add tomatoes, shallots, anchovy filets, olive salad and butter. Cook until tomatoes begin to burst, 4-5 minutes. Add shrimp; cook until shrimp turn pink, 4-5 minutes. Add reserved pasta, pasta water and Romano to pan; stir until creamy. Garnish with parsley and additional Romano.
1¾ CUPS: 726 cal., 35g fat (13g sat. fat), 150mg chol., 1163mg sod., 66g carb. (5g sugars, 4g fiber), 38g pro.

SHRIMP SPAGHETTI
WITH CHERRY TOMATOES

CIDER-GLAZED HAM

Here is a heartwarming and classic way to serve ham. Apple cider and mustard perfectly accent the ham's rich, smoky flavor.
—Jennifer Foos-Furer, Marysville, OH

PREP: 15 min. • **COOK:** 4 hours
MAKES: 8 servings

- 1   boneless fully cooked ham (3 lbs.)
- 1¾ cups apple cider or juice
- ¼   cup packed brown sugar
- ¼   cup Dijon mustard
- ¼   cup honey
- 2   Tbsp. cornstarch
- 2   Tbsp. cold water

1. Place ham in a 5-qt. slow cooker. In a small bowl, combine the cider, brown sugar, mustard and honey; pour over ham. Cover and cook on low for 4-5 hours or until heated through. Remove ham and keep warm.
2. Pour the cooking juices into a small saucepan. Combine cornstarch and water until smooth; stir into cooking juices. Bring to a boil; cook and stir for 2 minutes or until thickened. Serve with ham.

4 OZ. COOKED HAM WITH ABOUT ¼ CUP GLAZE: 280 cal., 6g fat (2g sat. fat), 86mg chol., 1954mg sod., 26g carb. (21g sugars, 0 fiber), 31g pro.

BAKED CIDER-GLAZED HAM: Place ham on a rack in a shallow roasting pan. Score the surface of the ham, making diamond shapes ½ in. deep. Pour cider over ham. Combine the brown sugar, mustard and honey; spread over ham. Cover and bake at 325° for 45 minutes. Uncover; bake 15-30 minutes longer or until a meat thermometer reads 140°, basting occasionally. Serve as directed.

DID YOU KNOW?

Dijon, a town in Eastern France's famous Burgundy wine-growing region, is the home of Dijon mustard. Mustard is commonly grown as a cover crop among grape vines. The plants attract beneficial insects and give nutrients back to the soil. And, the scores of tiny mustard seeds mean the crop replants itself year after year. Dijon mustard contains white wine instead of vinegar.

CHICKEN TIKKA MEATBALLS WITH GINGER RICE

CHICKEN TIKKA MEATBALLS WITH GINGER RICE

Tikka is an Indian dish made of small pieces of meat or veggies marinated in spices. Our version features chicken meatballs served over flavored rice.
—Taste of Home Test Kitchen

PREP: 1 hour • **COOK:** 25 min.
MAKES: 8 servings

- 5   in. fresh gingerroot, peeled
- 6   garlic cloves, halved
- 4   tsp. canola oil, divided
- 1½ cups uncooked long grain rice
- 3   cups water
- 6   green onions, sliced and divided
- 4½ tsp. garam masala, divided
- 1   can (28 oz.) crushed tomatoes
- ½   cup heavy whipping cream
- 1½ tsp. salt, divided
- ⅔   cup chopped fresh cilantro leaves, divided
- ¼   tsp. pepper
- 2   lbs. ground chicken

TOPPING
- ½   cup sour cream
- 1   Tbsp. lime juice
- ¼   tsp. ground cumin
     Dash salt

1. Process ginger in a food processor until it forms a paste. Remove and set aside. Repeat with garlic; remove and set aside.

2. In a small saucepan, heat 1 tsp. oil over medium heat. Add rice and 1 tsp. ginger paste; cook and stir until rice is lightly browned, 3-4 minutes. Stir in water; bring to a boil. Reduce heat; simmer, covered, until rice is tender, 15-20 minutes.
3. Meanwhile, for sauce, in a Dutch oven, heat remaining 1 Tbsp. oil over medium heat. Add half the garlic paste and half the remaining ginger paste. Cook and stir until fragrant, about 1 minute. Add half the green onions and 1 Tbsp. garam masala; cook and stir 1 minute longer. Stir in tomatoes, cream and ½ tsp. salt; heat through (do not allow to boil).
4. For meatballs, preheat oven to 375°. In a large bowl, combine half the cilantro, the pepper and the remaining green onions, ginger and garlic pastes, 1½ tsp. garam masala and 1 tsp. salt. Add chicken; mix lightly but thoroughly. Shape mixture into 1½-in. balls. Place meatballs on a greased rack in a 15x10x1-in. baking pan. Bake until browned, 15-20 minutes. Transfer meatballs to sauce; cook until heated through. Stir in remaining cilantro.
5. For topping, combine sour cream, lime juice, cumin and salt. Fluff rice with a fork; serve with meatballs and sauce. Drizzle with topping; top with additional cilantro and green onions if desired.
1 SERVING: 441 cal., 21g fat (8g sat. fat), 95mg chol., 731mg sod., 42g carb. (6g sugars, 3g fiber), 24g pro.

BOURBON BARBECUE
CHICKEN TACOS

SHEET-PAN SALMON WITH SIMPLE BREAD SALAD

The abundant fatty acids in salmon make it extremely healthful and ideal for baking. The vibrant salad, made on the same sheet pan, complements the rich fish perfectly.
—*Laura Wilhelm, West Hollywood, CA*

PREP: 20 min. • **BAKE:** 30 min.
MAKES: 6 servings

- 3 cups cubed sourdough bread
- 1 pint cherry tomatoes
- 1 medium red onion, cut into wedges
- ½ cup pitted Greek olives
- 3 Tbsp. olive oil, divided
- 1½ tsp. sea salt, such as Maldon, divided
- ⅛ tsp. pepper
- 6 salmon fillets (6 oz. each)
- 1 tsp. paprika

DRESSING
- 2 Tbsp. red wine vinegar
- 1 Tbsp. olive oil
- ⅓ cup fresh Italian parsley leaves, coarsely chopped
- 1 Tbsp. capers, drained

1. Preheat oven to 375°. Place cubed bread, tomatoes, red onion and olives on a 15x10x1-in. pan. Drizzle with 2 Tbsp. oil and sprinkle with ½ tsp. salt and the pepper; toss to coat. Bake until bread cubes just begin to brown, 15-20 minutes.
2. Arrange salmon fillets over crouton mixture in pan. Drizzle with remaining 1 Tbsp. oil; sprinkle with paprika and remaining 1 tsp. salt. Bake until salmon just begins to flake easily with a fork, 12-15 minutes.
3. For dressing, in a small bowl, whisk vinegar and oil. Add parsley and capers. Drizzle over salmon; sprinkle with additional parsley if desired.
1 SALMON FILLET WITH 1 CUP BREAD SALAD: 442 cal., 28g fat (5g sat. fat), 85mg chol., 875mg sod., 14g carb. (3g sugars, 2g fiber), 31g pro.

BOURBON BARBECUE CHICKEN TACOS

I wanted to try a different take on taco night and decided on a barbecue theme. Even my father enjoyed this meal, and he doesn't usually care for tacos.
—*LaDale Hymer, Branson, MO*

PREP: 30 min. • **COOK:** 3 hours
MAKES: 8 servings

- 1 cup ketchup
- 1 small red onion, finely chopped
- ¼ cup packed brown sugar
- 2 Tbsp. Worcestershire sauce
- 2 Tbsp. maple syrup
- 2 Tbsp. cider vinegar
- 1 Tbsp. chopped fresh parsley
- 2 garlic cloves, minced
- ¼ tsp. pepper
- 3 Tbsp. bourbon, divided
- 1½ lbs. boneless skinless chicken breasts

SALSA
- 2 cups fresh or thawed frozen corn
- 1 cup chopped sweet red pepper
- ½ cup finely chopped red onion
- 2 medium limes, zest and juice
- ⅛ tsp. hot pepper sauce
- ½ tsp. salt
- ¼ tsp. pepper
- 8 flour tortillas (8 in.)
  Minced cilantro, optional

1. In a 3-qt. slow cooker, combine the first 9 ingredients and 2 Tbsp. bourbon. Add chicken; turn to coat. Cook, covered, on low until a thermometer reads 165°, 3-4 hours. Remove chicken; shred with 2 forks. Return to slow cooker; stir in remaining 1 Tbsp. bourbon. Heat through.
2. Meanwhile, for salsa, combine corn, red pepper, onion, lime zest and juice, hot sauce, salt and pepper in a bowl. Serve chicken in tortillas with salsa. If desired, top with cilantro.
1 TACO: 387 cal., 6g fat (2g sat. fat), 47mg chol., 855mg sod., 58g carb. (22g sugars, 4g fiber), 23g pro.

TEST KITCHEN TIP

The zesty salsa is a great complement to the sweet chicken. Adding 1 Tbsp. of bourbon after the chicken cooks really balances the flavor of the sauce.

SHEET-PAN SALMON WITH
SIMPLE BREAD SALAD

ARROZ
VERDE CON
POLLO

ARROZ VERDE CON POLLO

This Peruvian-style recipe is hands-off and surprisingly family-friendly—even my 16-month-old son loves it. Want it spicier? Use jalapenos instead of poblanos.
—*Libby Kast, Madison, WI*

PREP: 45 min. • **BAKE:** 40 min.
MAKES: 4 servings

1¾	cups chopped onion, divided
1¾	cups chopped green pepper, divided
¼	cup fresh cilantro (leaves and stems)
3	garlic cloves, halved
2	Tbsp. lime juice
1	tsp. ground cumin
½	tsp. salt
½	tsp. dried marjoram
2	cups chicken stock
1	Tbsp. olive oil
1½	lbs. bone-in chicken thighs
¾	cup chopped seeded fresh poblano pepper
1	cup uncooked jasmine rice, rinsed

1. Preheat oven to 325°. Place 1 cup onion, 1 cup green pepper, cilantro, garlic, lime juice, cumin, salt and marjoram in a food processor; process until blended. Stir in stock; set aside.
2. In a large cast-iron or other ovenproof skillet, heat oil over medium heat. Pat chicken dry with paper towels. Brown chicken in batches. Remove chicken and keep warm.
3. Add poblano pepper, remaining ¾ cup onion and ¾ cup green pepper to the drippings; cook and stir until crisp-tender, 3-4 minutes. Add rice; cook and stir until lightly browned, 2-3 minutes. Stir in broth mixture until blended. Return chicken to the pan.
4. Bake, covered, until rice is tender and a thermometer inserted in chicken reads 170°-175°, 35-40 minutes. Remove lid. Preheat broiler. Broil 3-4 in. from heat until skin is crispy, 5-7 minutes.
5. To serve, remove chicken from pan. Fluff rice with a fork. If desired, serve with additional cilantro and lime juice.
NOTE: Wear disposable gloves when cutting hot peppers; the oils can burn skin. Avoid touching your face.
1 CHICKEN THIGH WITH 1 CUP RICE: 507 cal., 18g fat (5g sat. fat), 80mg chol., 628mg sod., 55g carb. (7g sugars, 4g fiber), 30g pro.

PORK TENDERLOIN WITH
SUN-DRIED TOMATO CREAM SAUCE

PORK TENDERLOIN WITH
SUN-DRIED TOMATO CREAM SAUCE

This is my go-to dish for both special occasions and weekday dinners because it's so easy and delicious. We love it because the pork tenderloin is, without fail, moist and tender but also the sauce is really unique. In fact, this past Thanksgiving, my husband suggested it would be good to have available along with turkey gravy and he was right. It was a huge hit!
—Kim Wells, Worthington, OH

- -

PREP: 35 min. • **BAKE:** 25 min. + standing • **MAKES:** 4 servings

- 1 pork tenderloin (1 lb.)
- 2 Tbsp. honey garlic seasoning
- 1 Tbsp. olive oil
- ¼ cup butter, cubed
- ¼ cup white wine or chicken broth
- ⅔ cup heavy whipping cream
- 1 shallot, thinly sliced
- 2 Tbsp. golden Carolina-style barbecue sauce
- 2 tsp. all-purpose flour
- ¼ cup chicken broth
- 2 cups fresh baby spinach
- ½ cup oil-packed sun-dried tomatoes, chopped

1. Preheat oven to 300°. Pat pork dry with paper towels; rub honey garlic rub over pork. In a large nonstick skillet, heat oil over medium heat. Brown roast on all sides. Place in center of an 18x12-in. piece of heavy-duty foil; dot with butter. Fold foil around pork and crimp edges to seal; place on a baking sheet. Bake until a thermometer reads 145°, 25-30 minutes. Remove roast from oven; let stand 10 minutes before slicing. Reserve pan drippings in foil.
2. While pork is resting, in the same skillet, add wine, stirring to loosen browned bits from pan. Stir in cream, shallot and barbecue sauce. In a small bowl, whisk flour and broth until smooth; stir into pan. Add reserved pan drippings. Bring to a boil, stirring constantly; cook and stir 1-2 minutes or until thickened. Add the spinach and sun-dried tomatoes; heat through. Remove from heat. Serve with sliced pork.
4 OZ. COOKED PORK WITH ABOUT ½ CUP SAUCE: 487 cal., 35g fat (19g sat. fat), 139mg chol., 678mg sod., 16g carb. (8g sugars, 1g fiber), 26g pro.

SHREDDED GREEN CHILE BEEF

This Tex-Mex pulled beef roast is tender, slightly spicy, juicy and so delicious served over mashed potatoes or rice. The beef also makes the best soft tacos you've ever had. Save any leftover pulled beef in the liquid to prevent it from drying out.
—Colleen Delawder, Herndon, VA

- -

PREP: 25 min. • **COOK:** 7 hours • **MAKES:** 12 servings

- 2 large sweet onions, halved and thinly sliced
- 4 Tbsp. packed brown sugar
- 1 Tbsp. paprika
- 1½ tsp. salt
- 1 tsp. cayenne pepper
- 1 tsp. chili powder
- 1 tsp. garlic powder
- ½ tsp. pepper
- 1 boneless beef chuck roast (about 3 lbs.)
- 2 Tbsp. canola oil
- 1 can (28 oz.) green enchilada sauce
   Mashed potatoes, optional

1. Place onions and 3 Tbsp. brown sugar in a 5- or 6-qt. slow cooker. Combine remaining 1 Tbsp. brown sugar and the next 6 ingredients; coat beef with mixture.
2. In a large skillet, heat oil over medium-high heat; brown beef, 1-2 minutes on each side. Transfer to slow cooker; pour enchilada sauce over beef. Cook, covered, on low until beef is tender, 7-9 hours. Remove beef; shred meat with 2 forks. Return to slow cooker; heat through. If desired, serve over potatoes.
1 CUP BEEF MIXTURE: 278 cal., 15g fat (4g sat. fat), 74mg chol., 658mg sod., 14g carb. (8g sugars, 1g fiber), 23g pro. **DIABETIC EXCHANGES:** 3 lean meat, 1 starch, ½ fat.

SHREDDED
GREEN CHILE
BEEF

PIZZA ON THE GRILL

I make pizza at least once a week, and recruiting the grill for help is a wonderful way to switch things up. The barbecue flavor mingles with the cheese to create a delicious end result.
—*Lisa Boettcher, Columbus, WI*

- -

PREP: 30 min. + resting • **GRILL:** 10 min.
MAKES: 4 servings

- 1 pkg. (¼ oz.) active dry yeast
- 1 cup warm water (110° to 115°)
- 2 Tbsp. canola oil
- 2 tsp. sugar
- 1 tsp. baking soda
- 1 tsp. salt
- 2¾ to 3 cups all-purpose flour

TOPPINGS

- ½ to ¾ cup barbecue sauce
- 2 cups shredded Monterey Jack cheese
- 2 cups shredded or cubed cooked chicken
- ½ cup julienned green pepper

1. In a large bowl, dissolve yeast in water. Add the oil, sugar, baking soda, salt and 2 cups flour. Stir in enough remaining flour to form a soft dough.
2. Turn onto a floured surface; knead until smooth and elastic, 6-8 minutes. Cover and let rest for 10 minutes. On a floured surface, roll dough into a 13-in. circle. Transfer to a greased 12-in. pizza pan. Build up edge slightly.
3. Grill, covered, over medium heat for 5 minutes. Remove from grill. Spread barbecue sauce over the crust. Sprinkle with cheese, chicken and green pepper. Grill, covered, 5-10 minutes longer or until crust is golden and cheese is melted.
1 PIECE: 757 cal., 31g fat (13g sat. fat), 113mg chol., 1525mg sod., 73g carb. (8g sugars, 3g fiber), 44g pro.

CRISPY CHEESE TACO BOWLS

These low-carb taco bowls are high in protein and keto-friendly.
—*Eric Jones, Houston, TX*

- -

PREP: 30 min. + cooling
COOK: 10 min. • **MAKES:** 8 servings

- 8 oz. sharp white cheddar cheese, shredded
- 1 lb. lean ground beef (90% lean)
- 1 tsp. garlic powder
- 1 tsp. smoked paprika
- ½ tsp. sea salt
- ½ tsp. dried cilantro flakes
- ½ tsp. pepper
- ¼ tsp. onion powder
- 1 cup pico de gallo
- 1 Tbsp. Sriracha chili sauce

AVOCADO CREMA

- 1 large ripe avocado, peeled and cubed
- ⅓ cup sour cream
- 1 tsp. dried cilantro flakes
- ¼ tsp. sea salt
- ¼ tsp. pepper
- 1 cup shredded Monterey Jack cheese
  Shredded lettuce and jalapeno pepper slices

1. Preheat oven to 375°. Mound ¼ cups of cheddar cheese 3 in. apart on parchment-lined baking sheets. Bake until the edges are golden brown, 5-7 minutes. Invert a muffin tin; spray with cooking spray. Remove cheese from oven; let stand 30 seconds. Gently peel off parchment; place over 8 prepared muffin tins and press to form bowl shapes. Let cool 10 minutes.
2. Meanwhile, in a large skillet, cook the beef and seasonings over medium heat until beef is no longer pink, 6-8 minutes, breaking meat into crumbles; drain. Stir in pico de gallo and Sriracha; heat through. Remove from heat. For avocado crema, mash avocado, sour cream, cilantro, salt and pepper until smooth.
3. Spoon beef mixture into cheese cups. Top with Monterey Jack cheese, lettuce, jalapenos and avocado crema.
NOTE: Wear disposable gloves when cutting hot peppers; the oils can burn skin. Avoid touching your face.
1 BOWL: 315 cal., 23g fat (11g sat. fat), 83mg chol., 547mg sod., 5g carb. (2g sugars, 2g fiber), 22g pro.

PIZZA ON THE GRILL

BOMBAY RICE
WITH SHRIMP

CRANBERRY-ORANGE CHICKEN RISOTTO

This pressure-cooker risotto is impressive enough to be on a restaurant menu. The ingredients are comforting and make for a wonderful dinner at home.
—*Christiane Smith-Lafarier, Leominster, MA*

- -

PREP: 30 min. + marinating • **COOK:** 15 min. • **MAKES:** 8 servings

- 4 large navel oranges
- 4 garlic cloves, minced
- 1 Tbsp. dried tarragon
- 2 tsp. rubbed sage
- 1 tsp. kosher salt
- 2 lbs. boneless skinless chicken thighs, cut into 1-in. cubes
- 4 Tbsp. unsalted butter, divided
- 1½ cups uncooked arborio rice
- 3 cups reduced-sodium chicken broth
- ¾ cup grated Romano or Parmesan cheese
- ¾ cup slivered almonds, toasted
- ¾ cup dried cranberries

1. Finely grate enough zest from the oranges to measure 1 Tbsp. Cut oranges crosswise in half; squeeze juice from oranges. Place zest and juice in a large bowl. Whisk in garlic, tarragon, sage and salt until blended. Pour ¾ cup marinade into a shallow dish. Add chicken; turn to coat. Cover and refrigerate 2-3 hours. Cover and refrigerate remaining marinade.

2. Drain chicken, discarding marinade in dish. Select saute setting on a 6-qt. electric pressure cooker. Adjust for medium heat; add 2 Tbsp. butter. When butter is melted, cook and stir chicken until no longer pink, 6-8 minutes. Add rice; cook 1 minute longer. Add reserved marinade to pressure cooker. Stir in broth. Press cancel.

3. Lock lid; close the pressure-release valve. Adjust to pressure-cook on high for 12 minutes. Let pressure release naturally for 4 minutes; quick-release any remaining pressure. Stir in cheese, almonds, cranberries and remaining 2 Tbsp. butter. Serve immediately.

1 CUP: 518 cal., 23g fat (9g sat. fat), 102mg chol., 474mg sod., 48g carb. (14g sugars, 3g fiber), 32g pro.

BOMBAY RICE WITH SHRIMP

This recipe was given to me by a co-worker whose family is from India. I have served it many times at family get-togethers and brunches. I even made it for an engagement shower for a friend and enclosed this recipe with her gift.
—*Sherry Flaquel, Cutler Bay, FL*

- -

PREP: 25 min. • **BAKE:** 20 min. • **MAKES:** 6 servings

- 1½ cups uncooked instant rice
- 1 can (10½ oz.) condensed cream of celery soup, undiluted
- ½ cup water
- 2 tsp. curry powder
- 1 tsp. salt
- 1 lb. cooked shrimp (31-40 per lb.), peeled and deveined
- 1 medium onion, chopped
- ½ cup chopped walnuts
- ½ cup sweetened shredded coconut
- ½ cup golden raisins
- 1 small tart apple, such as Pink Lady, Braeburn or Granny Smith, chopped
  Optional: Minced fresh cilantro and lime wedges

1. Preheat oven to 350°. Cook rice according to package directions.

2. Meanwhile, in a large bowl, combine soup, water, curry and salt. Stir in shrimp, onion, walnuts, coconut, raisins, apple and rice. Transfer to a greased 11x7-in. baking dish.

3. Bake, uncovered, until heated through, 20-25 minutes. If desired, serve with cilantro and lime wedges.

1⅓ CUPS: 367 cal., 13g fat (4g sat. fat), 117mg chol., 802mg sod., 43g carb. (14g sugars, 4g fiber), 20g pro.

CRANBERRY-ORANGE
CHICKEN RISOTTO

SLOW-COOKER
MEMPHIS-STYLE RIBS

82   **TASTE OF HOME ANNUAL RECIPES**

SLOW-COOKER MEMPHIS-STYLE RIBS

After my dad and I had dinner at the legendary Rendezvous Restaurant in Memphis, I was inspired to create a slow-cooked version of tasty dry-rub Memphis ribs. Smoked paprika in the rub mimics the flavor that the ribs would get from being grilled over hot coals.
—Matthew Hass, Ellison Bay, WI

PREP: 15 min. • COOK: 5 hours
MAKES: 6 servings

- ½ cup white vinegar
- ½ cup water
- 2 racks pork baby back ribs (about 5 lbs.)
- 3 Tbsp. smoked paprika
- 2 Tbsp. brown sugar
- 2 tsp. salt
- 2 tsp. coarsely ground pepper
- 1 tsp. garlic powder
- 1 tsp. onion powder
- 1 tsp. ground cumin
- 1 tsp. ground mustard
- 1 tsp. dried thyme
- 1 tsp. dried oregano
- 1 tsp. celery salt
- ¾ tsp. cayenne pepper

1. Combine vinegar and water; brush over ribs. Pour remaining vinegar mixture into a 6-qt. slow cooker. Mix together remaining ingredients. Sprinkle ribs with half the seasoning blend; reserve the other half. Cut the ribs into serving-sized pieces; transfer to slow cooker.
2. Cook, covered, on low until tender, 5-6 hours. Remove the ribs; skim fat from cooking juices. Using a clean brush, brush ribs generously with skimmed cooking juices; sprinkle with reserved seasoning mixture. Serve ribs with remaining juices.
1 SERVING: 509 cal., 35g fat (13g sat. fat), 136mg chol., 1137mg sod., 8g carb. (5g sugars, 2g fiber), 38g pro.

BACON CHEESEBURGER CASSEROLE

BACON CHEESEBURGER CASSEROLE

This casserole has it all: ground beef, bacon, onions and cheese, all baked up in your trusty 13x9 pan.
—Taste of Home Test Kitchen

PREP: 20 min. • BAKE: 35 min. + standing
MAKES: 12 servings

- 2 lbs. ground beef
- 1 large onion, chopped
- 2 garlic cloves, minced
- 12 bacon strips, cooked and crumbled
- 3 cups shredded cheddar cheese, divided
- 8 large eggs
- 1 can (6 oz.) tomato paste
- 1 cup heavy whipping cream
- 1 Tbsp. Worcestershire sauce
- ½ tsp. salt
- ¼ tsp. pepper
  Optional toppings: Dill pickle slices, thinly sliced green onions, slices red onion and cherry tomatoes, halved

1. Preheat oven to 350°. In a large skillet, cook beef, onion and garlic over medium until beef is no longer pink and onion is tender, 10-12 minutes, breaking up beef into crumbles; drain.
2. Transfer to a greased 13x9-in. baking dish. Sprinkle with bacon and 1 cup cheddar cheese. In a large bowl, whisk together eggs, tomato paste, heavy cream, tomato paste, Worcestershire sauce, salt, and pepper until well combined. Pour over beef mixture. Sprinkle with remaining 2 cups cheddar cheese.
3. Bake, uncovered, until set and golden brown, 30-35 minutes. Let stand for 10 minutes before serving. Garnish with toppings as desired.
1 PIECE: 418 cal., 32g fat (15g sat. fat), 230mg chol., 602mg sod., 4g carb. (2g sugars, 0 fiber), 28g pro.

CAFE RIO COPYCAT PORK BOWLS

My friends are big fans of Cafe Rio's sweet pork tacos, so I came up with this fake-out to eat in the comfort of our own homes. Serve the pork in flour tortillas or taco shells, or enjoy it on its own.
—Donna Gribbins, Shelbyville, KY

PREP: 20 min. + marinating • COOK: 10 hours • MAKES: 8 servings

- 2   cans (12 oz. each) cola, divided
- 1   cup packed brown sugar, divided
- 1   bone-in pork shoulder roast (5 to 7 lbs.)
- 1   Tbsp. kosher salt
- 1   Tbsp. garlic powder
- 1   Tbsp. onion powder
- 1   tsp. pepper
- 1½ cups enchilada sauce
- 1   can (7 oz.) chopped green chiles
     Hot cooked rice, optional
     Optional toppings: Black beans, chopped red onion, crumbled Cotija cheese and salsa

1. In a large bowl or shallow dish, combine 1 can cola and ½ cup brown sugar. Add pork; turn to coat. Cover and refrigerate for 8 hours or overnight.
2. Drain pork, discarding marinade. Place pork in a 5- or 6-qt. slow cooker. Add salt, garlic powder, onion powder, pepper and remaining can of cola. Cook, covered, on low until meat is tender, 8-10 hours.
3. Set meat aside until cool enough to handle. Remove meat from bones; discard bones. Shred meat with 2 forks. Discard cooking juices and return meat to slow cooker. Stir in enchilada sauce, green chiles and remaining ½ cup brown sugar. Cook, covered, on low until heated through, about 2 hours.
4. Serve pork in bowls over rice with toppings as desired.
FREEZE OPTION: Freeze cooled meat mixture in freezer containers. To use, partially thaw in refrigerator overnight. Heat through in a saucepan, stirring occasionally.
1 CUP COOKED PORK: 419 cal., 22g fat (8g sat. fat), 125mg chol., 560mg sod., 18g carb. (15g sugars, 0 fiber), 37g pro.

FRITO PIE

FRITO PIE

CAFE RIO COPYCAT PORK BOWLS

Frito pie is legendary in the Southwest for being spicy, salty and cheesy fabulous. Here's my easy take on this crunchy classic.
—Jan Moon, Alamogordo, NM

TAKES: 30 min. • MAKES: 6 servings

- 1   lb. ground beef
- 1   medium onion, chopped
- 2   cans (15 oz. each) Ranch Style beans (pinto beans in seasoned tomato sauce)
- 1   pkg. (9¼ oz.) Frito corn chips
- 2   cans (10 oz. each) enchilada sauce
- 2   cups shredded cheddar cheese
     Thinly sliced green onions, optional

1. Preheat oven to 350°. In a large skillet, cook beef and onion over medium heat 6-8 minutes or until beef is no longer pink and onion is tender, crumbling meat; drain. Stir in the beans; heat through.
2. Reserve 1 cup corn chips for topping. Place remaining corn chips in a greased 13x9-in. baking dish. Layer with meat mixture, enchilada sauce and cheese; top with reserved chips.
3. Bake, uncovered, 15-20 minutes or until cheese is melted. If desired, sprinkle with green onions.
1 SERVING: 731 cal., 41g fat (14g sat. fat), 84mg chol., 1733mg sod., 54g carb. (6g sugars, 8g fiber), 34g pro.

TEST KITCHEN TIP

This is a flexible casserole that you can customize with other stir-ins such as minced green chilies, sliced black olives, diced tomatoes, chopped onion or frozen corn kernels.

EASY TAMALE PIE WITH PEPPERS

My family loves anything with southwestern flavor, so this recipe is a big hit. It's super quick and easy to prepare, and cleanup afterwards is fast because everything cooks in one dish.
—*Joan Hallford, North Richland Hills, TX*

PREP: 20 min. + standing • **BAKE:** 30 min. • **MAKES:** 6 servings

- 2 poblano peppers
- 6 chicken or beef tamales
- 1 can (15 oz.) chili with beans
- 2 cups shredded sharp cheddar cheese
- 1 small onion, chopped
  Chopped fresh cilantro and thinly sliced green onions

1. Cut peppers lengthwise in half; remove stems and seeds. Place peppers on a foil-lined baking sheet, skin side up. Broil 4 in. from heat until skins blister, about 5 minutes. Immediately place the peppers in a large bowl; let stand, covered, 20 minutes. Reduce oven setting to 350°.

2. Peel off and discard charred skins. Place peppers in a greased 11x7-in. baking dish. Remove husks from tamales. Cut tamales into quarters; place over peppers. Top with chili, cheese and chopped onion. Bake until hot and bubbly, 30-35 minutes. Serve with cilantro and green onions.

NOTE: Wear disposable gloves when cutting hot peppers; the oils can burn skin. Avoid touching your face.

1 SERVING: 439 cal., 25g fat (9g sat. fat), 59mg chol., 1152mg sod., 34g carb. (3g sugars, 5g fiber), 23g pro.

EASY TAMALE PIE
WITH PEPPERS

SWEET & HOT CHICKEN WITH DILL PICKLE SAUCE

(SHOWN ON PAGE 70)

This is my low-carb version of Nashville hot chicken. We try to cut carbs as much as possible, so the breaded and fried version and the sandwich version of this dish are out. Instead, I make a baked version with the same delicious flavors. This is also great made with chicken tenders and served as wraps.
—*Fay Moreland, Wichita Falls, TX*

PREP: 25 min. + marinating • **BAKE:** 40 min. • **MAKES:** 8 servings

- 1 cup sweet pickle juice
- 2 Tbsp. hot pepper sauce
- 1 tsp. granulated garlic
- ½ tsp. pepper
- 8 bone-in chicken thighs (about 3 lbs.)

PICKLE SAUCE

- ½ cup sour cream
- ½ cup chopped sliced sweet pickles
- ¼ cup sweet pickle juice
- 2 tsp. dill weed
- ½ tsp. salt
- ½ tsp. onion powder
- ¼ tsp. granulated garlic
- ¼ tsp. pepper

SPICE RUB

- 1 Tbsp. sweet smoked paprika
- ½ tsp. granulated garlic
- ¼ tsp. salt
- ¼ tsp. pepper

HOT SAUCE DIP

- 1 cup hot sauce
- ½ cup unsalted butter
- ½ cup brown sugar substitute blend equivalent to 1 cup brown sugar

1. In a bowl or shallow dish, combine the sweet pickle juice, hot sauce, granulated garlic and pepper. Add chicken and turn to coat. Refrigerate, covered, 2-3 hours.

2. Preheat oven to 375°. In a small bowl, combine pickle sauce ingredients until well blended. Refrigerate until serving.

3. In another small bowl, combine the spice rub ingredients. Remove chicken from marinade, discarding marinade. Place chicken on a greased, foil-lined baking sheet. Sprinkle with spice rub. Bake 30 minutes.

4. Meanwhile, in a small saucepan, heat hot sauce and butter until butter is melted. Whisk in brown sugar blend, simmer until sauce thickens slightly, 1-2 minutes. Remove chicken from oven. Using tongs, dunk cooked pieces into sauce; return to baking sheet. Increase oven temperature to 400°; bake until a thermometer reads 170°-175°, about 10 minutes. Serve chicken with dipping sauces and, if desired, additional pickle slices.

1 CHICKEN THIGH WITH 2 TBSP. PICKLE SAUCE: 350 cal., 23g fat (9g sat. fat), 106mg chol., 484mg sod., 12g carb. (10g sugars, 1g fiber), 23g pro.

FIVE-SPICE CHICKEN LETTUCE WRAPS

HEARTY PENNE BEEF

This is comfort food at its finest! The best of everything is found here—it's tasty, easy and a smart way to sneak in some spinach for extra nutrition.
—Taste of Home *Test Kitchen*

TAKES: 30 min. • **MAKES:** 4 servings

- 1¾ cups uncooked penne pasta
- 1 lb. ground beef
- 1 tsp. minced garlic
- 1 can (15 oz.) tomato puree
- 1 can (14½ oz.) beef broth
- 1½ tsp. Italian seasoning
- 1 tsp. Worcestershire sauce
- ¼ tsp. salt
- ¼ tsp. pepper
- 2 cups chopped fresh spinach
- 2 cups shredded part-skim mozzarella cheese

1. Cook pasta according to package directions. Meanwhile, in a Dutch oven, cook beef over medium heat until no longer pink, breaking it into crumbles. Add garlic; cook 1 minute longer. Drain. Stir in tomato puree, broth, Italian seasoning, Worcestershire sauce, salt and pepper.
2. Bring to a boil. Reduce the heat; simmer, uncovered, until slightly thickened, 10-15 minutes. Add spinach; cook until wilted, 1-2 minutes.
3. Drain pasta; stir into beef mixture. Sprinkle with cheese; cover and cook until cheese is melted, 3-4 minutes.
FREEZE OPTION: Freeze cooled pasta mixture in freezer containers. To use, partially thaw in refrigerator overnight. Heat through in a saucepan, stirring occasionally; add broth or water if necessary.
1½ CUPS: 482 cal., 20g fat (10g sat. fat), 88mg chol., 1001mg sod., 33g carb. (5g sugars, 2g fiber), 41g pro.

HEARTY
PENNE
BEEF

FIVE-SPICE CHICKEN LETTUCE WRAPS

With this lettuce wrap, I get all the satisfaction without all the carbs. The pickled carrots really make it feel special. Use them on other sandwiches and wraps for an extra pop of flavor, crunch and color.
—*Stacy Schneidmiller, Beaumont, AB*

PREP: 25 min. + marinating • **GRILL:** 20 min. • **MAKES:** 6 servings

- 3 Tbsp. soy sauce
- 4 garlic cloves, crushed
- 1 Tbsp. packed brown sugar
- 2 tsp. Chinese five-spice powder
- 1 tsp. salt, divided
- 2 lbs. boneless skinless chicken thighs
- ½ cup white vinegar
- ¼ cup water
- 1 Tbsp. sugar
- 2 medium carrots, shredded
- 12 Bibb lettuce leaves
- ¼ cup thinly sliced green onions
- 2 Tbsp. fresh cilantro leaves
  Sweetened shredded coconut, optional

1. In a bowl or shallow dish, combine the first 4 ingredients and ½ tsp. salt. Add chicken and turn to coat. Cover and refrigerate 8 hours or overnight.
2. In a small saucepan, combine vinegar, water, sugar and remaining ½ tsp. salt. Bring to a boil; whisk until sugar is dissolved. Remove from heat. Place carrots in a small bowl; pour vinegar mixture over top. Refrigerate 8 hours or overnight.
3. Drain chicken, discarding marinade. On a lightly oiled rack, grill chicken, covered, over medium heat or broil 4 in. from heat until a thermometer reads 170°, 6-8 minutes on each side. Cool slightly; slice into strips.
4. Divide chicken among lettuce leaves; top with pickled carrots, green onions and cilantro. Sprinkle with coconut if desired.
2 WRAPS: 236 cal., 11g fat (3g sat. fat), 101mg chol., 625mg sod., 4g carb. (2g sugars, 1g fiber), 29g pro. **DIABETIC EXCHANGES:** 4 lean meat.

GRILLED
FLANK STEAK

MINI REUBEN CASSEROLES

These cute and creamy individual corned beef casseroles have the classic flavors of a Reuben sandwich.
—Taste of Home *Test Kitchen*

PREP: 20 min. • **BAKE:** 20 min. • **MAKES:** 4 servings

- 2 tsp. olive oil
- 1 medium onion, chopped
- 1 medium green pepper, chopped
- 2 cups cooked corned beef or roast beef
- 1 can (14 oz.) sauerkraut, rinsed and well drained
- 1 can (10½ oz.) condensed cream of chicken soup, undiluted
- 1¼ cups shredded Swiss cheese, divided
- ⅓ cup 2% milk
- ½ cup Thousand Island salad dressing
- 2 slices rye bread, cubed
- 1 Tbsp. butter, melted
- ½ tsp. onion powder

1. Preheat oven to 350°. In a large skillet, heat oil over medium heat; add onion and pepper. Cook and stir 3-5 minutes or until tender. Stir in beef, sauerkraut, soup, 1 cup cheese, milk and salad dressing; heat through. Transfer to 4 greased 10-oz. ramekins or custard cups. Place ramekins on a baking sheet.
2. In a small bowl, toss bread cubes with butter and onion powder. Arrange over tops. Bake, uncovered, 15 minutes. Sprinkle with remaining ¼ cup cheese. Bake until cheese is melted, 5-10 minutes longer.

1 SERVING: 650 cal., 41g fat (15g sat. fat), 130mg chol., 1782mg sod., 31g carb. (12g sugars, 5g fiber), 37g pro.

GRILLED FLANK STEAK

This recipe is from my sister and it's a favorite of mine for serving company. The meat and vegetables can be prepared ahead of time. When the company arrives, I just fire up the grill and serve a meaty main dish in minutes!
—Jenny Reece, Farwell, MN

PREP: 20 min. + marinating • **GRILL:** 15 min. • **MAKES:** 5 servings

- ¼ cup soy sauce
- 2 Tbsp. white vinegar
- 1 green onion, sliced
- 1½ tsp. garlic powder
- 1½ tsp. ground ginger
- 3 Tbsp. honey
- ¾ cup vegetable oil
- 1 beef flank steak (about 1½ lbs.)
- 1 lb. fresh mushrooms, sliced
- 1 green pepper, cut into thin strips
- 1 yellow or sweet red pepper, cut into thin strips
- 3 carrots, cut into julienned strips

1. In a bowl, combine the first 7 ingredients. Pour ¾ cup marinade into a shallow dish; add beef. Turn to coat; refrigerate, covered, for up to 24 hours, turning once. Cover and refrigerate the remaining marinade.
2. Drain and discard marinade. Grill flank steak, uncovered, over medium heat for 6-8 minutes on each side or until meat reaches desired doneness (for medium-rare, a thermometer should read 135°; medium, 140°; medium-well, 145°).
3. Meanwhile, in a skillet, cook vegetables in reserved marinade until crisp-tender. Thinly slice steak across the grain. Serve with the vegetables.

3 OZ. COOKED BEEF WITH ⅔ CUP VEGETABLES: 265 cal., 12g fat, 65mg chol., 173mg sod., 11g carb., 28g pro. **DIABETIC EXCHANGES:** 3 lean meat, 2 vegetable, 1 fat.

MINI REUBEN
CASSEROLES

POLYNESIAN
ROAST BEEF

3. Add pineapple and green pepper. Cook 1 hour longer or until meat is tender.

4 OZ. COOKED BEEF: 253 cal., 5g fat (2g sat. fat), 82mg chol., 560mg sod., 16g carb. (10g sugars, 1g fiber), 34g pro.

PIZZA POTATO TOPPERS

Not only is this recipe quick and easy to make, but it's an economical dinner as well. I don't know of a more satisfying way to stretch a half pound of meat!
—*Sheila Friedrich, Antelope, MT*

TAKES: 25 min. • **MAKES:** 4 servings

- 4 medium baking potatoes
- ½ lb. ground beef
- ½ cup chopped green pepper
- 1 small onion, chopped
- 1 tomato, chopped
- ½ to ¾ cup pizza sauce
- 1 cup shredded part-skim mozzarella cheese
  Optional: Fresh oregano, basil or parsley

1. Prick potatoes with a fork; cook in a microwave until tender. Meanwhile, in a large skillet, cook beef and green pepper with onion until meat is no longer pink; crumble meat; drain. Stir in tomato and pizza sauce; heat through.

2. Split potatoes lengthwise; flake potato centers with a fork. Spoon meat mixture into each; top with mozzarella cheese. Sprinkle with herbs if desired.

1 SERVING: 486 cal., 11g fat (5g sat. fat), 44mg chol., 325mg sod., 74g carb. (10g sugars, 7g fiber), 26g pro.

TEST KITCHEN TIPS

Italian sausage also tastes great in this recipe. If you have leftover potatoes from last night's dinner, this is a good way to repurpose them. Baked sweet potatoes will work, too!

POLYNESIAN ROAST BEEF

This marvelous recipe from my sister has been a family favorite for years. Pineapple and peppers add a perfect contrast to the rich and savory beef.
—*Annette Mosbarger, Peyton, CO*

PREP: 15 min. • **COOK:** 7 hours
MAKES: 10 servings

- 1 beef top round roast (3¼ lbs.)
- 2 Tbsp. browning sauce, optional
- ¼ cup all-purpose flour
- 1 tsp. salt
- ¼ tsp. pepper
- 1 medium onion, sliced
- 1 can (8 oz.) unsweetened sliced pineapple
- ¼ cup packed brown sugar
- 2 Tbsp. cornstarch
- ¼ tsp. ground ginger
- ½ cup beef broth
- ¼ cup reduced-sodium soy sauce
- ½ tsp. minced garlic
- 1 medium green pepper, sliced

1. Cut roast in half; brush with browning sauce if desired. Combine the flour, salt and pepper; rub over meat. Place onion in a 3-qt. slow cooker; top with roast.

2. Drain the pineapple, reserving juice; refrigerate the pineapple slices. In a small bowl, combine brown sugar, cornstarch and ginger; whisk in the broth, soy sauce, garlic and reserved pineapple juice until smooth. Pour over meat. Cook, covered, on low for 6-8 hours.

GLAZED
SPATCHCOCKED
CHICKEN

HOW-TO

How to Spatchcock a Chicken

For the crispiest, juiciest grilled chicken, try this method, which calls for removing the backbone of the bird and laying it flat to cook. It may seem intimidating, but three easy steps is all it takes!

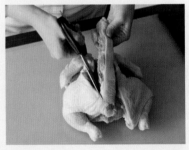

Place the chicken breast-side down. Then, starting at the tail, use a sharp pair of kitchen shears to cut alongside spine.

Flip the bird breast-side up. With two hands, press down firmly on the center until you hear a crack.

Once the wishbone is cracked, twist the splayed-out wings and tuck them under the body of the bird.

5i

GLAZED SPATCHCOCKED CHICKEN

A few pantry items, such as mustard and apricot preserves, inspired this recipe. And since then it has been the successful centerpiece for both small weeknight meals and big parties.
—*James Schend, Pleasant Prairie, WI*

PREP: 15 min.
GRILL: 40 minutes + standing
MAKES: 6 servings

- 1 cup white wine or chicken broth
- 1 cup apricot preserves or quince jelly
- 1 Tbsp. stone-ground mustard
- 1 broiler/fryer chicken (3 to 4 lbs.)
- ¾ tsp. salt
- ½ tsp. pepper

1. In a small saucepan, bring wine to a boil; cook 3-4 minutes or until wine is reduced by half. Stir in preserves and mustard. Reserve half the glaze for basting.

2. Cut the chicken along each side of the backbone with shears. Remove the backbone. Turn the chicken breast side up, and press to flatten. Sprinkle with salt and pepper.

3. Prepare grill for indirect medium heat. Place the chicken on greased grill grate, skin side down, covered, over direct heat until nicely browned, 10-15 minutes. Turn the chicken and place over indirect heat until a thermometer in the thickest part of the thigh reads 170°-175°, brushing occasionally with reserved glaze mixture, about 30 minutes.

4. Remove chicken from grill. Let stand 15 minutes before carving; serve with remaining glaze.

5 OZ. COOKED CHICKEN: 437 cal., 17g fat (5g sat. fat), 104mg chol., 458mg sod., 35g carb. (23g sugars, 0 fiber), 34g pro.

FRIED LASAGNA

One of my favorite dishes at Olive Garden is their fried lasagna. On a whim, I tried to recreate it at home. After a few tries, I think I got it pretty close to the original.
—*Jolene Martinelli, Fremont, NH*

PREP: 45 min. + freezing • **COOK:** 10 min./batch
MAKES: 10 servings

- 20 uncooked lasagna noodles
- 1 carton (32 oz.) whole-milk ricotta cheese
- 2½ cups shredded Italian cheese blend, divided
- 2 cups shredded part-skim mozzarella cheese
- 6 large eggs, beaten, divided use
- 4 tsp. Italian seasoning, divided
  Oil for deep-fat frying
- 2½ cups panko bread crumbs
- 1 jar (24 oz.) marinara sauce, warmed
- 1 jar (15 oz.) Alfredo sauce, warmed

1. Cook lasagna noodles according to package directions for al dente. In a large bowl, combine ricotta, 1¼ cups Italian cheese blend, mozzarella, 2 eggs and 3 tsp. Italian seasoning. Drain noodles. If desired, cut off ribboned edges (discard or save for another use). Spread about ¼ cup filling on each noodle. Starting with a short side, fold each in thirds. Place all on a parchment-lined baking sheet, seam side down. Freeze just until firm, about 1 hour.
2. In an electric skillet or deep fryer, heat oil to 375°. In a shallow bowl, mix bread crumbs, ⅔ cup Italian cheese blend and the remaining 1 tsp. Italian seasoning. Place remaining 4 eggs in a separate shallow bowl. Dip lasagna bundles into eggs, then into crumb mixture, patting to help coating adhere.
3. Fry bundles in batches until golden brown, 8-10 minutes, turning once. Drain on paper towels. Serve with marinara, Alfredo, the remaining Italian cheese blend and, if desired, additional Italian seasoning.
2 LASAGNA ROLLS: 876 cal., 54g fat (19g sat. fat), 195mg chol., 1011mg sod., 61g carb. (11g sugars, 4g fiber), 37g pro.

FRIED
LASAGNA

MIGHTY NICE
CURRIED CHICKEN
WITH RICE

MIGHTY NICE CURRIED CHICKEN WITH RICE

This was one of the first chicken recipes I prepared for my husband more than 54 years ago. His exclamation? Mighty nice! That's how it got its name. Sometimes I add extra broth to make more of the yummy sauce.
—*Kay Stansberry, Athens, TN*

PREP: 15 min. • **COOK:** 45 min. • **MAKES:** 4 servings

- 1 broiler/fryer chicken (3 to 4 lbs.), cut up
- 1 tsp. salt
- ½ tsp. pepper
- ¼ cup butter
- 2 medium tart apples, peeled and sliced
- 1 large onion, finely chopped
- 2 Tbsp. all-purpose flour
- 2 Tbsp. curry powder
- 1 can (14½ oz.) chicken broth
- 3 Tbsp. golden raisins
- ½ tsp. grated orange zest
- 2 Tbsp. slivered almonds, toasted
  Hot cooked rice

1. Sprinkle chicken with salt and pepper. In a large skillet, heat butter over medium heat. Brown chicken on both sides; remove from pan.
2. In the same pan, add apples and onion; cook and stir until softened, 2-3 minutes. Stir in flour and curry powder until blended; cook an additional 2 minutes. Gradually stir in chicken broth. Add chicken back to pan along with raisins and orange zest. Reduce heat; simmer, covered, until a thermometer reads 165°, 30-35 minutes. Sprinkle with almonds; serve with hot cooked rice.
7 OZ. COOKED CHICKEN WITH 1½ CUPS SAUCE: 657 cal., 39g fat (15g sat. fat), 187mg chol., 1210mg sod., 23g carb. (13g sugars, 4g fiber), 52g pro.

HERBY CHICKEN
WITH APRICOTS
& FETA

SLOW-COOKER PORK CHOPS

Everyone will enjoy these fork-tender pork chops with a creamy, light gravy. Serve with a green vegetable, mashed potatoes and coleslaw or a salad.

—*Sue Bingham, Madisonville, TN*

- -

PREP: 15 min. • **COOK:** 2 hours • **MAKES:** 4 servings

- ½ cup all-purpose flour, divided
- ½ tsp. ground mustard
- ½ tsp. garlic pepper blend
- ¼ tsp. seasoned salt
- 4 boneless pork loin chops (4 oz. each)
- 2 Tbsp. canola oil
- 1 can (14½ oz.) chicken broth

1. In a shallow bowl, combine ¼ cup flour, mustard, garlic pepper and seasoned salt. Add pork chops, 1 at a time, and dredge to coat. In a large skillet, brown chops in oil on both sides.

2. Transfer to a 5-qt. slow cooker. Pour broth over the chops. Cook, covered, on low for 2-3 hours or until meat is tender.

3. Remove pork to a serving plate and keep warm. Whisk remaining flour into cooking juices until smooth; cook, covered, on high until gravy is thickened.

1 PORK CHOP: 279 cal., 14g fat (3g sat. fat), 57mg chol., 606mg sod., 12g carb. (1g sugars, 0 fiber), 24g pro. **DIABETIC EXCHANGES:** 3 lean meat, 1½ fat, 1 starch.

HERBY CHICKEN WITH APRICOTS & FETA

Mix up your weeknight menu with an herby braised chicken dish with Middle Eastern flair. I love to serve it with couscous.

—*Sally Sibthorpe, Shelby Township, MI*

- -

PREP: 20 min. • **COOK:** 25 min. • **MAKES:** 8 servings

- 1½ tsp. salt
- 1 tsp. dill weed
- ½ tsp. dried oregano
- ½ tsp. dried thyme
- ½ tsp. pepper
- 8 boneless skinless chicken thighs (about 2 lbs.)
- 3 Tbsp. canola oil
- 1 small onion, chopped
- 8 dried apricots
- 8 pitted dates
- ½ cup chicken stock
- ¼ cup lemon juice
- 1 cup crumbled feta cheese
- 2 green onions, thinly sliced
  Hot cooked couscous, optional

1. Combine the first 5 ingredients; sprinkle over chicken. In a large skillet, heat oil over medium heat. Brown the chicken in batches; return all to skillet. Add onion, apricots and dates; cook 5 minutes longer.

2. Stir in stock and lemon juice; bring to a boil. Reduce heat; simmer, covered, until a thermometer reads 170°, 5-7 minutes. Uncover and top with feta and green onions. If desired, serve with couscous.

1 CHICKEN THIGH WITH ¼ CUP APRICOT MIXTURE: 282 cal., 16g fat (4g sat. fat), 83mg chol., 674mg sod., 10g carb. (7g sugars, 2g fiber), 24g pro. **DIABETIC EXCHANGES:** 3 lean meat, 2 fat, ½ starch.

SLOW-COOKER
PORK CHOPS

LOW-CARB LASAGNA

I love this recipe because you don't miss the pasta in the lasagna. It looks, smells and tastes like the real deal! You can add ricotta cheese or any other kind of cheese you like for variation.

—*Tammy Kirk, Raleigh, NC*

PREP: 25 min. • **BAKE:** 45 min. + standing
MAKES: 12 servings

- 2 Tbsp. olive oil
- 12 oz. ground beef
- 12 oz. bulk Italian sausage
- 1 medium onion, chopped
- 2 garlic cloves, minced
- 1 jar (24 oz.) pasta sauce
- 8 oz. thinly sliced deli chicken (12 slices)
- ½ lb. thinly sliced deli pepperoni
- 2 cups shredded mozzarella cheese
- 2 cups shredded cheddar cheese

1. Preheat oven to 425°. In a large skillet heat oil over medium heat. Cook beef, sausage, onion and garlic until meat is no longer pink, 6-8 minutes, breaking it into crumbles; drain, return to pan. Stir in pasta sauce; heat through.

2. Spread 1 cup sauce into a greased 13x9-in. baking dish. Layer with half the sliced chicken, half the sliced pepperoni, 2 cups sauce and half of each cheese. Repeat layers.

3. Bake, covered, 25 minutes. Uncover; bake until cheese is browned and lasagna is bubbling, 20-25 minutes longer. Let stand 15 minutes before serving.

1 PIECE: 419 cal., 32g fat (13g sat. fat), 95mg chol., 1106mg sod., 8g carb. (5g sugars, 1g fiber), 25g pro.

READER REVIEW

"I was actually surprised by how good it was. I added a little salt and pepper to the meat. I added 15 oz. of ricotta cheese. Give it a try—it's really quite tasty. I didn't miss the noodles at all."

—DEBBIE549, TASTEOFHOME.COM

ITALIAN
PAN-FRIED
CHICKEN

ITALIAN PAN-FRIED CHICKEN

I love this recipe for many reasons, but mostly because it is both simple and delicious. It was passed down from my Italian grandmother, and I modified it only slightly. I have used it and enjoyed it for years.

—*Karen Mahlke, Estero, FL*

PREP: 15 min. • **COOK:** 40 min.
MAKES: 6 servings

- 6 bone-in chicken thighs (about 2¼ lbs.)
- ½ tsp. pepper
- 1½ tsp. minced fresh rosemary or ½ tsp. dried rosemary, crushed
- ¾ tsp. minced fresh oregano or ¼ tsp. dried oregano
- ¼ tsp. minced fresh basil or ⅛ tsp. dried basil
- 2 Tbsp. olive oil
- 9 garlic cloves, minced and divided
- ¾ cup red wine vinegar
- ¼ cup balsamic vinegar
- 1 Tbsp. chicken base
- ½ cup chardonnay or chicken broth
- 1 Tbsp. heavy whipping cream
- 1 Tbsp. cold butter

1. Sprinkle chicken with pepper. Combine rosemary, oregano and basil; sprinkle half the herb mixture over chicken. In a large skillet over medium heat, place chicken, skin side down, in oil. Brown chicken on both sides. Add 8 garlic cloves; cook 1 minute longer. Stir in the vinegars and chicken base. Cook, covered, on low heat until a thermometer reads 170°-175°, 15-20 minutes.

2. Remove chicken to a serving platter; keep warm. Add chardonnay to pan; increase heat to medium-high. Bring to a boil; cook, uncovered, until liquid is reduced by half, 8-10 minutes, stirring to loosen browned bits from pan. Strain sauce. Return to pan. Add remaining garlic clove and herb mixture; heat through. Stir in cream; remove from heat. Whisk in butter until creamy. If needed, return pan briefly to very low heat to soften butter. (Do not allow butter to melt completely or sauce may separate.) Serve with chicken thighs. If desired, garnish with additional rosemary and basil.

1 SERVING: 317 cal., 22g fat (6g sat. fat), 89mg chol., 425mg sod., 8g carb. (3g sugars, 0 fiber), 23g pro.

SWEET & SPICY CHICKEN
WITH PUMPKIN WAFFLES

SEARED SCALLOPS WITH MINTED PEA PUREE

I'm always in the mood for mint, whether it's in a mojito or alongside a roasted leg of lamb. As a seafood lover, I came up with this blend of my favorite herb and shellfish.
—Teerawat Wiwatpanit, Chicago, IL

PREP: 20 min. • **COOK:** 15 min.
MAKES: 4 servings

- 4 cups fresh or frozen peas, thawed (about 16 oz.)
- ½ cup vegetable broth or water
- 3 Tbsp. sherry
- 2 garlic cloves, minced
- ½ tsp. salt, divided
- ¼ tsp. pepper, divided
- ⅓ cup minced fresh mint
- ¼ cup half-and-half cream
- 16 sea scallops (about 2 lbs.)
- 1 tsp. smoked paprika
- 1 Tbsp. canola oil
  Optional: Sliced fresh sugar snap peas and pea sprouts

1. In a large saucepan, cook peas and broth over medium-high heat until peas are bright green and tender, 3-4 minutes. Drain, reserving cooking liquid. Set aside 1 cup peas; keep warm. Transfer the remaining peas to a blender. Add sherry, garlic, ¼ tsp. salt, ⅛ tsp. pepper and reserved cooking liquid. Puree mixture until smooth. Cool. Add mint and cream; puree until smooth.

2. Pat scallops dry with paper towels; sprinkle with paprika and remaining ¼ tsp. salt and ⅛ tsp. pepper. In a large nonstick skillet, heat oil over medium-high heat. Add scallops in batches; cook until golden brown and firm, 2-3 minutes on each side. Serve with pea puree and reserved peas. Top with additional mint, sugar snap peas and pea sprouts if desired.

4 SCALLOPS WITH ½ CUP PEA PUREE: 351 cal., 7g fat (2g sat. fat), 62mg chol., 1355mg sod., 32g carb. (9g sugars, 9g fiber), 36g pro.

SWEET & SPICY CHICKEN WITH PUMPKIN WAFFLES

Whether you're indulging for brunch or dinner, these chicken and waffles do it all. The Sriracha syrup adds a special touch, but maple syrup would do the trick too.
—Trisha Kruse, Eagle, ID

PREP: 35 min. • **COOK:** 35 min.
MAKES: 6 servings

- 1 tsp. salt
- 1 tsp. onion powder
- 1 tsp. smoked paprika
- 12 chicken tenderloins (about 1½ lbs.)
- 12 bacon strips
- ⅓ cup packed brown sugar
- 1 Tbsp. chili powder

WAFFLES
- 1 cup self-rising flour
- 2 tsp. pumpkin pie spice
- ¼ tsp. salt
- ¼ tsp. chili powder
- 1 cup buttermilk
- ¼ cup packed brown sugar
- ¼ cup canned pumpkin
- 2 tsp. canola oil
- 1 large egg

SRIRACHA SYRUP
- 1 cup maple syrup
- 2 Tbsp. butter
- 2 to 4 tsp. Sriracha chili sauce

1. Preheat oven to 375°. In a small bowl, mix the salt, onion powder and paprika; sprinkle over chicken tenders. Wrap each tender with a strip of bacon; tuck ends under. In another small bowl, mix brown sugar and chili powder. Roll each wrapped chicken tender in sugar mixture, pressing to adhere.

2. Place a wire rack over a foil-lined baking sheet; place chicken on the rack. Bake until chicken is cooked and bacon is crisp, 20-25 minutes.

3. Preheat waffle maker. For waffles, in a large bowl, mix flour, pie spice, salt and chili powder. In a small bowl, combine buttermilk, brown sugar, pumpkin, oil and egg. Add to dry mix; stir just until moistened. Bake waffles according to manufacturer's directions until golden brown.

4. Meanwhile, place Sriracha syrup ingredients in a small saucepan. Heat until butter is melted and sauce is heated through, stirring occasionally. Serve waffles with chicken and warmed syrup.

2 CHICKEN TENDERS WITH 1 WAFFLE AND ABOUT 1 TBSP. SYRUP: 547 cal., 15g fat (5g sat. fat), 115mg chol., 1325mg sod., 70g carb. (49g sugars, 2g fiber), 37g pro.

SEARED SCALLOPS WITH
MINTED PEA PUREE

TWICE-COOKED
FRIED CHICKEN

2. In a small bowl, whisk buttermilk and hot sauce until blended. Pour into a shallow dish. Add chicken; turn to coat. Refrigerate for 1 hour. Drain chicken, discarding buttermilk mixture.
3. In a bowl or shallow dish, mix flour and seasonings. Add chicken, a few pieces at a time; turn to coat. Shake off excess.
4. In a deep skillet, heat 2 in. oil to 375°. Fry chicken pieces, a few at a time, until chicken is golden brown and juices run clear, 4-6 minutes on each side. Drain on paper towels.
5 OZ. COOKED CHICKEN: 571 cal., 44g fat (7g sat. fat), 105mg chol., 524mg sod., 9g carb. (1g sugars, 0 fiber), 35g pro.
AIR-FRIED OPTION: Preheat air fryer to 350°. In batches, arrange chicken pieces in a single layer on greased tray in air-fryer basket; spritz with cooking spray. Cook 5 minutes. Flip, spritz with cooking spray. Cook until browned, 5-6 minutes longer.

PEPPER JACK MEAT LOAF

This is a quick way to put a zesty twist on a traditional main dish. The meat loaf is stuffed with pepper jack cheese and has even more melted on top.
—*Debra Hartze, Zeeland, ND*

PREP: 20 min. • **BAKE:** 55 min. + standing • **MAKES:** 6 servings

1   large egg, lightly beaten
1   cup seasoned bread crumbs
¼   cup chopped onion
½ to 1 tsp. salt
½   tsp. pepper
1½ lbs. lean ground beef (90% lean)
1   cup (4 oz.) pepper jack cheese, divided
1   cup salsa, optional

1. In a large bowl, combine egg, bread crumbs, onion, salt and pepper. Crumble beef over mixture and mix well. Press half of the beef mixture onto the bottom and halfway up the sides of a greased 8x4-in. loaf pan. Sprinkle ¾ cup cheese over meat to within ½ in. of sides. Pat remaining beef mixture over cheese.
2. Bake, uncovered, at 350° for 50-55 minutes or until meat is no longer pink and a thermometer reads 160°. Sprinkle with remaining cheese. Bake 5 minutes longer or until cheese is melted. Let stand for 10 minutes before slicing. Serve with salsa if desired.
1 SERVING: 331 cal., 16g fat (7g sat. fat), 111mg chol., 681mg sod., 15g carb. (1g sugars, 1g fiber), 30g pro.

READER REVIEW

"Very good. The pepper jack cheese gave it a nice kick. I also topped it with a little salsa for extra flavor."

—GUNSLINGER, TASTEOFHOME.COM

TWICE-COOKED
FRIED CHICKEN

Fried chicken is my favorite food, so it's no surprise that I've tried dozens of recipes looking for the perfect batch. This one is the result of my mission to create my own foolproof rendition.
—*Audrey Alfaro, Rapid City, SD*

PREP: 25 min. + chilling. • **COOK:** 3½ hours • **MAKES:** 6 servings

1   broiler/fryer chicken (3 to 4 lbs.), cut up
3   cups chicken broth
1   tsp. crushed red pepper flakes
1   tsp. garlic powder
1   tsp. paprika
1   tsp. lemon-pepper seasoning
2   cups buttermilk
½   cup Louisiana-style hot sauce
COATING
1½ cups all-purpose flour
2   tsp. paprika
2   tsp. seasoned salt
1   tsp. garlic powder
1   tsp. lemon-pepper seasoning
1   tsp. onion powder
1   tsp. ground cumin
1   tsp. kosher salt
½   tsp. pepper
     Oil for deep-fat frying

1. In a 5- or 6-qt. slow cooker, combine the first 6 ingredients. Cook, covered, on low until meat is tender, 3-4 hours. Remove chicken from slow cooker; discard liquid.

MEDITERRANEAN
BRAISED
CHICKEN THIGHS

MEDITERRANEAN BRAISED CHICKEN THIGHS

This chicken and artichoke dish was inspired by a once-in-a-lifetime trip to Santorini for my parents' 40th anniversary. It's cooked in a big skillet until the chicken basically falls of the bone and all the flavors meld together into a sauce that will literally have you spooning into your mouth. It's really a showstopper!
—Grace Vallo, Salem, NH

- -

PREP: 15 min. • **COOK:** 30 min. • **MAKES:** 6 servings

- 2 Tbsp. butter
- 2 Tbsp. olive oil
- 6 bone-in chicken thighs (about 2 lbs.)
- 1 can (14 oz.) water-packed small artichoke hearts, drained
- 3 shallots, halved
- ⅓ cup dry white wine
- ½ cup pitted Greek olives
- ⅓ cup reduced-sodium chicken broth
- 1 Tbsp. lemon juice
- 1 garlic clove, thinly sliced
- 1 Tbsp. drained capers
- 1 tsp. ground sumac or za'atar seasoning

1. Preheat oven to 375°. In a 12-in. cast-iron or other ovenproof skillet, heat butter and oil over medium-high heat. Brown chicken, skin side down. Turn thighs over; arrange artichokes and shallots around chicken. Cook 1 minute longer. Add wine to pan; cook 1 minute longer, stirring to loosen browned bits from pan.
2. Add remaining ingredients to pan. Bake until a thermometer inserted in chicken reads 170°-175°, 15-20 minutes.
1 CHICKEN THIGH WITH ⅓ CUP ARTICHOKE MIXTURE: 378 cal., 26g fat (7g sat. fat), 91mg chol., 551mg sod., 10g carb. (1g sugars, 0 fiber), 25g pro.

VEGETABLE PAD THAI

Classic flavors of Thailand abound in this fragrant and flavorful dish featuring peanuts, tofu and noodles. Tofu gives the entree its satisfying protein.
—Sara Landry, Brookline, MA

- -

PREP: 25 min. • **COOK:** 15 min. • **MAKES:** 6 servings

- 12 oz. uncooked thick rice noodles
- ¼ cup rice vinegar
- 3 Tbsp. reduced-sodium soy sauce
- 2 Tbsp. brown sugar
- 2 Tbsp. fish sauce or additional reduced-sodium soy sauce
- 1 Tbsp. lime juice
  Dash Louisiana-style hot sauce
- 3 tsp. canola oil, divided
- 1 pkg. (12 oz.) extra-firm tofu, drained and cut into ½-in. cubes
- 2 medium carrots, grated
- 2 cups fresh snow peas
- 3 garlic cloves, minced
- 2 large eggs, lightly beaten
- 2 cups bean sprouts
- 3 green onions, chopped
- ½ cup minced fresh cilantro
- ¼ cup unsalted peanuts, chopped

1. Cook noodles according to package directions. Meanwhile, in a small bowl, combine vinegar, soy sauce, brown sugar, fish sauce, lime juice and hot sauce until smooth; set aside.
2. In a large skillet or wok, heat 2 tsp. oil over medium-high heat. Add tofu; cook and stir until golden brown, 4-6 minutes. Remove and keep warm. Cook and stir carrots and snow peas in remaining 1 tsp. oil until crisp-tender, 3-5 minutes. Add garlic; cook 1 minute longer. Add eggs; cook and stir until set.
3. Drain pasta; add to vegetable mixture. Stir vinegar mixture and add to the skillet. Bring to a boil. Add tofu, bean sprouts and onions; heat through. Sprinkle with cilantro and peanuts.
1⅓ CUPS: 402 cal., 10g fat (2g sat. fat), 62mg chol., 1054mg sod., 63g carb. (12g sugars, 4g fiber), 15g pro.

VEGETABLE
PAD THAI

ZUCCHINI-WRAPPED
CHICKEN ENCHILADAS

ZUCCHINI-WRAPPED CHICKEN ENCHILADAS

Thin planks of zucchini are the perfect low-carb substitute for tortillas when making enchiladas. It's a healthy and delicious alternative and also looks so pretty on a plate.
—*Donna Kelly, Lehi, UT*

PREP: 40 min. + standing
BAKE: 35 min. • **MAKES:** 4 servings

- 1 Anaheim pepper
- 3 cups cooked chicken, shredded
- 2 cups shredded pepper jack cheese, divided
- 2 oz. cream cheese, softened
- 3 green onions, thinly sliced
- 1 tsp. hot pepper sauce
- 2 cans (10 oz. each) enchilada sauce
- 2 Tbsp. tomato paste
- 6 large zucchini (about 4 lbs.)

1. Cut pepper lengthwise in half; remove stems and seeds. Place pepper on a foil-lined baking sheet, skin side up. Broil 4 in. from heat until skin blisters, about 5 minutes. Immediately place pepper in a small bowl; let stand, covered, 20 minutes. Reduce oven setting to 350°.
2. Peel off and discard charred skin; finely chop pepper and place in a large bowl. Add chicken, 1 cup pepper jack cheese, cream cheese, green onions and pepper sauce. In a small bowl, combine enchilada sauce and tomato paste; set aside.
3. Slice zucchini lengthwise into thirty-two ⅛-in.-thick slices. Place zucchini slices in an ungreased 13x9 microwave-safe dish. Cover and microwave on high 2 minutes or until crisp-tender; drain well on paper towels and set aside.
4. Spread half the sauce mixture into a 13x9-in. baking dish; set aside. Layer 4 slices of zucchini, slightly overlapping. Place ⅓ cup chicken mixture off center on top. Roll up zucchini, starting with the short side; place into the prepared dish, seam side down. Repeat with remaining zucchini and chicken mixture. Top with remaining sauce and cheese.
5. Bake, uncovered, until heated through, 35-40 minutes.

2 ENCHILADAS: 590 cal., 33g fat (18g sat. fat), 169mg chol., 957mg sod., 24g carb. (13g sugars, 5g fiber), 53g pro.

PULLED PORK TATERS

PULLED PORK TATERS

This recipe is as hearty as it gets—part barbecued pork, part baked potatoes, but completely delicious. My family can't get enough of this comforting, warm-you-up baked potato dish.
—*Shannon Harris, Tyler, TX*

PREP: 15 min. • **COOK:** 6 hours
MAKES: 6 servings

- 1 boneless pork loin roast (2 to 3 lbs.)
- 1 medium onion, chopped
- 1 cup ketchup
- 1 cup root beer
- ¼ cup cider vinegar
- 2 Tbsp. Worcestershire sauce
- 1 Tbsp. Louisiana-style hot sauce
- 2 tsp. salt
- 2 tsp. pepper
- 1 tsp. ground mustard
- 6 large russet potatoes
- 1 Tbsp. cornstarch
- 1 Tbsp. cold water
- 6 Tbsp. butter
- 6 Tbsp. sour cream
- 1½ cups shredded cheddar cheese
  Thinly sliced green onions, optional

1. Place roast in a 5-qt. slow cooker. Top with onion. Combine the ketchup, root beer, vinegar, Worcestershire, hot sauce, salt, pepper and mustard; pour over top. Cover and cook on low until meat is tender, 6-8 hours.
2. Meanwhile, scrub and pierce potatoes. Bake at 400° until tender, 50-55 minutes.
3. Remove pork; shred meat with 2 forks and set aside. Skim fat from cooking juices; transfer juices to a large saucepan. Bring liquid to a boil. Combine cornstarch and water until smooth; gradually stir into the pan. Return to a boil; cook and stir until thickened, 2 minutes. Return shredded meat to cooking juices; heat through.
4. With a sharp knife, cut an "X" in each potato; fluff with a fork. Top each with butter, pork mixture and sour cream. Sprinkle with cheese and, if desired, green onions.

1 SERVING: 795 cal., 29g fat (18g sat. fat), 145mg chol., 1677mg sod., 89g carb. (24g sugars, 7g fiber), 44g pro.

WHITE BEAN, SWEET POTATO & PEPPER RAGOUT

I try to serve a meatless meal two or three nights a week. It's a great way to keep up our vegetable intake-along with all the fiber and nutrients they provide. It even helps save money! This hearty dish is a family favorite.
—*Heather Savage, Wood River Junction, RI*

PREP: 20 min. • **COOK:** 25 min. • **MAKES:** 4 servings

- 1 large sweet red pepper, cut into 1-in. pieces
- 1 large green pepper, cut into 1-in. pieces
- 1 Tbsp. olive oil
- 1 large sweet potato, peeled, quartered and sliced
- ½ tsp. minced fresh rosemary or ¼ tsp. dried rosemary, crushed
- 3 garlic cloves, minced
- ½ cup water
- ¼ tsp. pepper
- 2 cans (15 oz. each) cannellini beans, rinsed and drained
- 1 can (14½ oz.) diced tomatoes, undrained
- ¼ tsp. salt

1. In a Dutch oven over medium heat, cook and stir peppers in oil until tender. Add the sweet potato and rosemary; cook for 4-5 minutes. Add garlic; cook 1 minute longer.
2. Stir in water and pepper. Bring to a boil. Reduce heat; cover and simmer for 5-7 minutes or until sweet potato is tender. Stir in the beans, tomatoes and salt; heat through.
FREEZE OPTION: Cool before placing in a freezer container. Cover and freeze for up to 3 months. Thaw in the refrigerator overnight. Place in a Dutch oven; heat through.
1¾ CUPS: 286 cal., 5g fat (0 sat. fat), 0 chol., 551mg sod., 51g carb. (10g sugars, 13g fiber), 11g pro.

WHITE BEAN, SWEET POTATO & PEPPER RAGOUT

LEMON-GARLIC CREAM FETTUCCINE

LEMON-GARLIC CREAM FETTUCCINE

I've been making this for my family for years. It's both simple and indulgent enough to make it a go-to recipe.
—*Anne Miller, Glenfield, NY*

PREP: 25 min. • **COOK:** 15 min. • **MAKES:** 4 servings

- 3 tsp. grated lemon zest
- 2 tsp. minced fresh parsley
- 2 garlic cloves, minced
- 8 oz. uncooked fettuccine

SAUCE

- ¼ cup butter
- 1 small onion, chopped
- 2 garlic cloves, minced
- 1 tsp. grated lemon zest
- ½ cup heavy whipping cream
- ¼ tsp. salt
- ⅛ tsp. pepper
- 4 oz. cream cheese, cubed
- 2 Tbsp. lemon juice
- 2 plum tomatoes, chopped
- 2 tsp. minced fresh parsley
  Grated Parmesan cheese, optional

1. In a small bowl, mix lemon zest, parsley and garlic. Cook fettuccine according to package directions; drain.
2. For sauce, in a large skillet, heat butter over medium-high heat. Add onion; cook and stir 2-3 minutes or until tender. Add garlic and lemon zest; cook 1 minute longer. Stir in cream, salt and pepper. Whisk in cream cheese until melted. Remove from heat; cool slightly. Stir in lemon juice.
3. Add pasta, tomatoes and parsley to skillet; toss to combine. Serve immediately with lemon zest mixture and, if desired, Parmesan cheese.
1 CUP: 518 cal., 34g fat (21g sat. fat), 102mg chol., 346mg sod., 46g carb. (4g sugars, 3g fiber), 11g pro.

SHEET-PAN NEW ENGLAND CLAMBAKE

This recipe transports you to hot summer nights on the beach enjoying fresh seafood, corn on the cob, spicy sausage and tender potatoes any time of the year! Bathed in garlicky, spicy butter, this one-pan wonder is beautiful, delicious and easy on cleanup! You could mix up the seafood and add pieces of salmon or haddock, use other quick-cooking veggies like cherry tomatoes or asparagus or substitute kielbasa for the chorizo. It's so versatile!
—Pamela Gelsomini, Wrentham, MA

PREP: 25 min. • BAKE: 45 min.
MAKES: 6 servings

- 1 lb. assorted baby potatoes
- 2 Tbsp. olive oil
- 2 tsp. Italian seasoning
- 6 half-ears frozen corn on the cob, thawed
- 2 lbs. fresh mussels, scrubbed and beards removed
- 1½ dozen fresh littleneck clams, scrubbed
- 1 lb. uncooked shrimp (26-30 per lb.), peeled and deveined
- ½ lb. fully cooked Spanish chorizo links, cut into ½-in. pieces
- ¼ cup dry white wine or chicken broth
- 1 medium lemon, cut into wedges
- ½ cup butter, melted
- 4 garlic cloves, chopped
- 2 tsp. seafood seasoning
- 1¼ tsp. Cajun seasoning
- ¼ tsp. pepper
- 2 Tbsp. minced fresh parsley
  French bread, optional

1. Preheat oven to 400°. Place potatoes in a 15x10x1-in. baking pan. Drizzle with oil and sprinkle with Italian seasoning; toss to coat. Bake until tender, 25-30 minutes. Using a potato masher, flatten potatoes to ½-in. thickness; remove and keep warm.
2. Add corn, mussels, clams, shrimp and chorizo to same pan; top with potatoes. Pour wine into pan. Squeeze lemon wedges over top; add to pan.
3. Combine melted butter, garlic, seafood seasoning and Cajun seasoning. Pour half the butter mixture over top. Bake until the shrimp turn pink and mussels and clams open, 20-25 minutes. Discard any unopened mussels or clams.
4. Drizzle with remaining butter mixture. Sprinkle with pepper; top with parsley. If desired, serve with bread.

1 SERVING: 639 cal., 35g fat (15g sat. fat), 214mg chol., 1302mg sod., 37g carb. (4g sugars, 3g fiber), 46g pro.

SHEET-PAN
NEW ENGLAND CLAMBAKE

4. In a small bowl, combine cornstarch and water. Remove ginger slices and garlic cloves from sauce; slowly stir in cornstarch mixture. Simmer, stirring constantly, until thickened, 1-2 minutes.
5. Add chicken and basil; stir to coat. Remove from heat; garnish with green onions. Serve with rice.

1 CUP: 456 cal., 22g fat (4g sat. fat), 76mg chol., 775mg sod., 33g carb. (14g sugars, 1g fiber), 25g pro.

KOREAN BULGOGI FRIES

I saw a version of this recipe made on the TV show *Diners, Drive-Ins and Dives* at the Crowbar & Grill in Laramie, Wyoming. I decided to make it using purchased shortcut ingredients.
—*Ann R. Sheehy, Lawrence, MA*

PREP: 35 min. + marinating
COOK: 15 min.
MAKES: 6 servings

- 2 lbs. lean ground beef (90% lean)
- 1 cup kimchi, chopped
- 1 small onion, chopped
- 3 garlic cloves, minced
- 2 Tbsp. gluten-free tamari soy sauce
- 2 Tbsp. honey
- 1 Tbsp. white vinegar
- 1 Tbsp. sesame oil
- 1 tsp. pepper
- 6 cups frozen shoestring potatoes
- 1 tsp. salt
- 3 Tbsp. minced fresh chives
- 3 Tbsp. minced fresh parsley
- ¾ cup Sriracha mayonnaise

1. In a large bowl, combine the first 9 ingredients. Refrigerate, covered, at least 4 hours. Prepare potatoes according to package directions. In a large nonstick skillet, cook beef mixture over medium heat, breaking into crumbles, until no longer pink, 12-15 minutes; drain. Stir in salt.
2. Divide potatoes among 6 large bowls; top with beef mixture. Sprinkle with chives and parsley. Serve with the Sriracha mayonnaise.

1 CUP BEEF MIXTURE WITH ABOUT 1 CUP FRIES: 645 cal., 40g fat (9g sat. fat), 114mg chol., 1150mg sod., 40g carb. (7g sugars, 4g fiber), 33g pro.

THREE-CUP BUTTERMILK FRIED CHICKEN

THREE-CUP BUTTERMILK FRIED CHICKEN

This recipe combines my Chinese roots with the southern-style fried chicken I've eaten over the past few years in Oklahoma. Three-cup chicken gets its name from the quintessential ingredients: soy sauce, Shaoxing wine and sesame oil.
—*Edward Chiu, Broken Arrow, OK*

PREP: 20 min. + marinating
COOK: 30 min. • **MAKES:** 6 servings

- 1½ lbs. boneless skinless chicken thighs, cut into 1-in. cubes
- 1 cup buttermilk
- 2 green onions
- 1 Tbsp. sesame oil
- 15 garlic cloves
- 1 piece fresh gingerroot (2 in.), peeled and sliced
- 1 cup Chinese cooking wine or sherry
- 6 Tbsp. brown sugar
- 6 Tbsp. reduced-sodium soy sauce
     Oil for deep-fat frying
- 2 cups all-purpose flour
- 1 Tbsp. cornstarch
- 1 Tbsp. water
- 1 cup fresh Thai basil leaves
     Hot cooked rice

1. Place chicken and buttermilk in a shallow dish, turning once to coat. Refrigerate 1 hour or overnight. Drain chicken, discarding buttermilk. Meanwhile, thinly slice green part of onions; reserve for garnish. Slice white part into ¼-in. pieces.
2. In a large skillet, heat sesame oil over medium-high heat. Add white part of green onions, garlic and ginger; stir-fry until fragrant and slightly browned, 3-4 minutes. Add wine, brown sugar and soy sauce, stirring until sugar dissolves. Reduce heat; simmer 10-15 minutes, stirring occasionally.
3. In a deep fryer or electric skillet, heat 2 in. oil to 375°. Place flour in a shallow dish. Add chicken, several pieces at a time, and toss to coat; shake off excess. Fry the chicken, several at a time, until golden brown, 3-4 minutes. Drain on paper towels.

KOREAN
BULGOGI FRIES

TURKEY CLUB PIZZA
AND EASY CAESAR
SALAD, PAGE 117

Meal Planner

Smart cooks always have some go-to tricks that make meal planning a breeze. Pick up a few of your own new favorites from these timesaving ideas.

MOST-REQUESTED RECIPES

On the Ball

Get ahead of this week's dinners (yes, even Meatless Monday!) with nifty meatball recipes that multiply into nine easy options.

SERVE 'EM UP!

+ **Traditional Spaghetti & Meatballs:** Add meatballs to cooked spaghetti, then coat in marinara sauce. Garnish with Parmesan cheese.

+ **Buffalo Meatballs:** Toss meatballs with Buffalo hot wing sauce; sprinkle with blue cheese.

+ **Meatball Sliders:** Cut meatballs in half and place on Hawaiian rolls. Top with barbecue sauce, cheddar cheese and pickled red onions.

QUICK & SIMPLE MEATBALLS

QUICK & SIMPLE MEATBALLS

Keep a batch of these meatballs in your freezer for an easy weeknight meal. This simple meatball recipe can be used for pizzas, sub sandwiches, soups and more.
—Taste of Home *Test Kitchen*

- -

PREP: 20 min. • **BAKE:** 15 min.
MAKES: 48 meatballs

- 2   lbs. ground beef
- 2   large eggs
- ¼   cup water
- 1   small onion, finely chopped
- 1⅓ cups soft bread crumbs
- ⅔   cup grated Parmesan cheese
- 2   garlic cloves, minced
- 2   tsp. Italian seasoning
- 1½ tsp. salt

Preheat oven to 375°. In a large bowl, crumble beef. Add eggs, water, onion, bread crumbs, Parmesan cheese, garlic and seasonings; mix lightly but thoroughly. Shape into 1½-in. balls. Place meatballs on greased racks in shallow baking pans. Bake, uncovered, until no longer pink, 15-18 minutes.

FREEZE OPTION: Freeze cooled meatballs in freezer containers. To use, partially thaw in refrigerator overnight. Heat through in the microwave.

3 MEATBALLS: 276 cal., 17g fat (7g sat. fat), 122mg chol., 533mg sod., 6g carb. (1g sugars, 0 fiber), 24g pro.

TEST KITCHEN TIP

To make soft bread crumbs, tear several slices of fresh white, French or whole wheat bread into 1-in. pieces. Place in a food processor or blender; cover and push the pulse button several times to make coarse crumbs. One slice of bread makes about ½ cup crumbs.

CHICKPEA MEATBALLS

CHICKPEA MEATBALLS

Being a vegetarian, it has been hard for me not to lean toward heavier, carb-laden foods. This recipe satisfies my cravings and doesn't leave me with a heavy feeling. Try the meatballs on top of spaghetti squash, zoodles or your favorite pasta.
—Sara Willen, Cypress, TX

PREP: 30 min. • **COOK:** 15 min./batch • **MAKES:** 4 servings

- 1 can (15 oz.) chickpeas or garbanzo beans, rinsed and drained
- ½ cup chopped sweet onion
- ⅓ cup grated Parmesan cheese
- 1 large egg
- 4 fresh basil leaves, torn
- 3 garlic cloves, halved
- ¼ tsp. fine sea salt
- ¼ tsp. pepper
- 1 cup dry bread crumbs
  Cooking spray

1. Place first 8 ingredients in a food processor; add ⅓ cup bread crumbs. Process until combined (mixture will be soft). Shape into 1½-in. balls. Place remaining ⅔ cup bread crumbs in a shallow bowl. Gently add balls, a few at a time, and toss to coat; shake off excess.
2. Preheat air fryer to 375°. In batches, place balls in a single layer in greased air fryer; spritz with cooking spray. Cook until golden brown, 11-13 minutes. If desired, top with additional fresh torn basil leaves.
4 BALLS: 252 cal., 7g fat (2g sat. fat), 52mg chol., 562mg sod., 36g carb. (5g sugars, 6g fiber), 11g pro.

BAKED CHICKEN MEATBALLS

My family loves these meatballs, so they're on the menu often. They're wonderful as an appetizer or when we're watching the game, but I love to turn them into easy dinner options as well. Try adding them to soups, tucking them into a hoagie bun or tossing them on top of spaghetti!
—Haley Herridge, Columbus, IN

PREP: 20 min. • **BAKE:** 20 min. • **MAKES:** 4 servings

- ½ cup shredded Parmesan cheese
- ½ cup dry bread crumbs
- 1 large egg, lightly beaten
- 2 Tbsp. olive oil
- ½ tsp. salt
- ½ tsp. garlic powder
- ½ tsp. paprika
- 2 tsp. minced fresh parsley or ½ tsp. dried parsley flakes
- ½ tsp. pepper
- 1 lb. ground chicken

Preheat oven to 400°. In a large bowl, combine the first 9 ingredients. Add the chicken; mix lightly but thoroughly. Shape into 1½-in. balls. Place meatballs on a greased rack in a 15x10x1-in. baking pan. Bake 20-25 minutes or until cooked through. If desired, top with additional chopped fresh parsley.
FREEZE OPTION: Freeze cooled meatballs in freezer containers. To use, partially thaw in refrigerator overnight. Microwave, covered, on high in a microwave-safe dish until heated through.
5 MEATBALLS: 326 cal., 20g fat (6g sat. fat), 129mg chol., 647mg sod., 11g carb. (1g sugars, 1g fiber), 25g pro.

BAKED CHICKEN MEATBALLS

Soup du Jar

Fix a mix for yourself or a friend by layering favorite soup starters in a glass container. Then just pull it from the pantry when you need dinner in a pinch!

WILD RICE & BARLEY SOUP MIX

Let loved ones warm up on frosty nights with this hearty, stick-to-the-ribs soup. Layered in pretty bow-tied jars, the mix looks just as good as the soup tastes.
—Taste of Home *Test Kitchen*

- -

PREP: 10 min. • **COOK:** 1 hour
MAKES: 6 servings

- 1 Tbsp. brown sugar
- 2 tsp. Italian seasoning
- ½ tsp. dried minced garlic
- ½ tsp. ground celery seed
- ½ tsp. pepper
- ½ cup medium pearl barley
- 2 Tbsp. dried parsley flakes
- 1 Tbsp. dried celery flakes
- 1 Tbsp. dried chives
- 3 Tbsp. chicken bouillon granules
- ½ cup uncooked wild rice
- ½ cup dried minced onion

ADDITIONAL INGREDIENTS

- 8 cups water
  Optional: Bacon bits and torn basil leaves

In a small bowl, combine the first 5 ingredients. In a pint-size jar with a tight-fitting lid, layer the barley, parsley flakes, celery flakes, chives, brown sugar mixture, bouillon granules, rice and onion, packing each layer tightly (do not mix). Cover and store in a cool, dry place for up to 4 months.

TO PREPARE SOUP: Pour mix into a large saucepan. Add water and bring to a boil. Reduce heat; cover and simmer for 1 hour or until rice is tender. Sprinkle with bacon bits and basil leaves if desired.

1 CUP: 150 cal., 1g fat (0 sat. fat), 1mg chol., 1267mg sod., 33g carb. (6g sugars, 4g fiber), 5g pro.

WILD RICE & BARLEY
SOUP MIX

45-60 minutes or until beans are tender. Stir in the tortellini and seasonings, broth, tomatoes, carrots and celery. Bring to a boil. Reduce heat; simmer, uncovered, for 8-10 minutes or until pasta and vegetables are tender. Serve with cheese if desired.

1 CUP: 103 cal., 1g fat (1g sat. fat), 6mg chol., 741mg sod., 18g carb. (3g sugars, 5g fiber), 6g pro.

CLASSIC CHILI MIX

This full-flavored chili seasoning will heat up your holiday gift-giving. The mix is on the mild side, which is nice for those who aren't partial to extra-spicy food.
—*Bernice Morris, Marshfield, MO*

PREP: 10 min. • **COOK:** 40 min.
MAKES: 6 batches (4 servings per batch)

- 1 cup plus 2 Tbsp. all-purpose flour
- ¾ cup dried minced onion
- 4 to 6 Tbsp. chili powder
- ¼ cup paprika
- 2 Tbsp. salt
- 1 Tbsp. ground cumin
- 1 Tbsp. dried minced garlic
- 1 Tbsp. sugar

ADDITIONAL INGREDIENTS (FOR EACH BATCH)

- 1 lb. ground beef
- 1 can (15 oz.) pinto beans, rinsed and drained
- 1 can (14½ oz.) diced tomatoes, undrained
- 1 small green pepper, chopped
- ½ to ¾ cup water
  Sour cream, optional

Combine the first 8 ingredients; divide into 6 batches (a scant ½ cup each). Store in airtight containers.

TO PREPARE CHILI: In a large saucepan, cook beef over medium heat until no longer pink; drain. Stir in one batch of chili mix, beans, tomatoes, green pepper and water; bring to a boil. Reduce heat; simmer, uncovered, for 30 minutes. Garnish with sour cream if desired.

1 SERVING: 379 cal., 15g fat (6g sat. fat), 75mg chol., 931mg sod., 31g carb. (7g sugars, 7g fiber), 30g pro.

TORTELLINI BEAN SOUP MIX

I like to prep mixes for Christmas gifts. One year I gave this soup mix in a jar and included a kettle, a mug and a pint of my home-canned tomatoes.
—*Doris Simmons, Browning, IL*

PREP: 15 min. • **COOK:** 1 hour
MAKES: 15 servings (3¾ qt.)

- 1 cup dried great northern beans
- ¼ cup dried lentils
- ¼ cup dried green split peas
- ¾ cup uncooked dried tricolor tortellini
- 1 Tbsp. dried parsley flakes
- 1 Tbsp. chicken bouillon granules
- 2 tsp. dried minced garlic
- 1 tsp. dried thyme
- ½ tsp. salt

ADDITIONAL INGREDIENTS

- 8 cups water
- 1 can (49½ oz.) chicken broth
- 1 can (14½ oz.) diced tomatoes, drained
- 2 medium carrots, chopped
- 2 celery ribs, chopped
  Grated Parmesan cheese, optional

In a 3-cup jar or container with a tight-fitting lid, layer the beans, lentils and peas. In a small resealable plastic bag, combine the tortellini, parsley, bouillon, garlic, thyme and salt. Place bag in jar. Replace lid and store in a cool, dry place.

TO PREPARE SOUP: Remove bag of tortellini and seasonings; set aside. Rinse the beans, lentils and peas; drain. Place in a Dutch oven. Add 8 cups water. Bring to a boil. Reduce heat; cover and simmer for

FRIENDSHIP SOUP MIX

FRIENDSHIP SOUP MIX

I layer this pretty, delicious soup mix in glass jars to give as gifts. It is always well-received and appreciated.
—*Wendy Taylor, Mason City, IA*

- -

PREP: 15 min. • **COOK:** 1¼ hours
MAKES: 16 servings (4 qt.)

- ½ cup dried green split peas
- ⅓ cup beef bouillon granules
- ¼ cup medium pearl barley
- ½ cup dried lentils
- ¼ cup dried minced onion
- 2 tsp. Italian seasoning
- ½ cup uncooked long grain rice
- ½ cup uncooked alphabet pasta or other small pasta

ADDITIONAL INGREDIENTS
- 1 lb. ground beef
- 3 qt. water
- 1 can (28 oz.) diced tomatoes, undrained

In a 1½-pint jar, layer the first 7 ingredients in the order listed. Wrap pasta in a small sheet of plastic wrap; add to jar. Seal tightly. Store in a cool, dry place for up to 3 months.

TO PREPARE SOUP: Remove pasta from jar and set aside. In a Dutch oven over medium heat, cook and crumble the beef until no longer pink; drain. Add the water, tomatoes and soup mix; bring to a boil. Reduce heat; cover and simmer for 45 minutes. Stir in the reserved pasta; cover and simmer for 15-20 minutes or until the pasta, peas, barley and lentils are tender.

1 CUP: 166 cal., 4g fat (1g sat. fat), 18mg chol., 883mg sod., 23g carb. (3g sugars, 4g fiber), 10g pro.

PASTA E FAGIOLI SOUP MIX

This is what I call Italian chili. When artfully packaged, the dry ingredients make a heartwarming gift for friends and family during the holidays.
—*Tamra Duncan, Lincoln, AR*

- -

PREP: 20 min. + soaking • **COOK:** 1¾ hours
MAKES: 14 servings (3½ qt.)

- 1 cup small pasta shells
- ¾ cup dried great northern beans
- ¾ cup dried pinto beans
- ¾ cup dried kidney beans
- ¼ cup dried minced onion
- 3 Tbsp. dried parsley flakes
- 1 tsp. dried basil
- 1 tsp. dried oregano
- ½ tsp. dried rosemary, crushed
- ¼ tsp. dried minced garlic
- 1 bay leaf
     Dash crushed red pepper flakes

ADDITIONAL INGREDIENTS
- 14 cups water, divided
- 1 can (28 oz.) diced tomatoes, undrained
- 3 medium carrots, chopped
- 1 celery rib, chopped
- 1 tsp. salt
     Grated Parmesan cheese, optional

Place pasta in a small resealable plastic bag; place in a 1-qt. glass jar. Layer with beans. Place seasonings in another plastic bag; place in jar. Cover and store in a cool, dry place for up to 3 months.

TO PREPARE SOUP: Remove seasoning packet from jar. Remove beans; sort and rinse. Set pasta aside. Place beans in a Dutch oven; add 6 cups water. Bring to a boil; boil 2 minutes. Remove from heat; cover and let stand 1-4 hours or until beans are softened.

Drain and discard liquid. Return beans to the pan. Add contents of seasoning packet and remaining 8 cups water. Bring to a boil. Reduce heat; cover and simmer 1 hour or until beans are tender.

Add tomatoes, carrots, celery and salt; cover and simmer 30 minutes longer, stirring occasionally. Stir in pasta. Cover and simmer 5-10 minutes or until pasta and carrots are tender, stirring occasionally. Remove bay leaf before serving. Garnish with cheese if desired.

1 CUP: 148 cal., 0 fat (0 sat. fat), 0 chol., 256mg sod., 29g carb. (4g sugars, 7g fiber), 8g pro. **DIABETIC EXCHANGES:** 1½ starch, 1 vegetable, 1 lean meat.

Theme-Night Delights

Clear the calendar for your favorite dishes every weekday.
The what's-for-dinner dilemma is solved with these
ready-made menu ideas.

ITALIAN GRILLED CHEESE
SANDWICHES

ITALIAN GRILLED CHEESE SANDWICHES

I made up this recipe for the students in the foods and nutrition class I teach. The kids like it so much, they often go home and fix it for their families.
—*Beth Hiott, York, SC*

TAKES: 25 min. • **MAKES:** 4 servings

- 8 slices Italian bread
- 4 Tbsp. prepared pesto
- 4 slices provolone cheese
- 4 slices part-skim mozzarella cheese
- 5 tsp. olive oil
  Marinara sauce, warmed, optional

1. Spread 4 bread slices with pesto. Layer with cheeses; top with remaining bread. Brush outsides of sandwiches with oil.
2. Using a large cast-iron skillet or electric griddle, toast sandwiches over medium heat until cheese is melted, 3-4 minutes on each side. If desired, serve with marinara.

1 SANDWICH: 445 cal., 27g fat (10g sat. fat), 35mg chol., 759mg sod., 32g carb. (1g sugars, 2g fiber), 20g pro.

READER REVIEW

"This was very easy, tasty and fun. I made it with my 5- and 7- year-olds on a snow day, and it is perfect for kids learning to cook. We put pesto on both sides. I was worried 2 pieces of cheese would not be enough, but it was the just the right amount. The kids loved making these on their own."

—NATALIE140, TASTEOFHOME.COM

BROCCOLI WITH SAUTEED RED PEPPER

BROCCOLI WITH SAUTEED RED PEPPER

Slivered almonds and sweet red peppers add crunch to fresh broccoli.
—Taste of Home *Test Kitchen*

TAKES: 20 min. • **MAKES:** 4 servings

- 1 cup chicken broth
- 1 lb. fresh broccoli florets
- 1 cup julienned sweet red pepper
- 2 Tbsp. chopped shallot
- 2 Tbsp. olive oil
- ⅓ cup slivered almonds
- ½ tsp. lemon-pepper seasoning
- ¼ tsp. salt

1. In a large saucepan, bring broth to a boil; add broccoli florets. Reduce heat; cover and simmer for 5-8 minutes or until crisp-tender.
2. Meanwhile, in a large skillet, saute red pepper and shallot in oil for 5 minutes or until crisp-tender. Drain broccoli; add broccoli, almonds, lemon pepper and salt to skillet. Cook and stir for 2 minutes or until broccoli is tender.

¾ CUP: 157 cal., 12g fat (1g sat. fat), 0 chol., 468mg sod., 10g carb. (4g sugars, 5g fiber), 6g pro.

BLACK
BEANS
& RICE

SHORTCUT
FISH TACOS

1. Sprinkle fish with taco seasoning. In a large skillet, heat butter over medium heat; add fish. Cook until fish just begins to flake easily with a fork, 3-4 minutes on each side.

2. Meanwhile, in a small bowl, combine coleslaw, cilantro, mayonnaise, lime juice, sugar, salt and pepper.

3. Place fish in tortillas. Top with coleslaw mixture; serve with lime wedges.

2 TACOS: 510 cal., 37g fat (11g sat. fat), 109mg chol., 1170mg sod., 20g carb. (4g sugars, 3g fiber), 23g pro.

BLACK BEANS & RICE

I often serve this quick skillet side dish to delighted guests. Chock-full of beans, rice, peppers and cheddar cheese, it pleases everyone and is hearty enough to present as a meatless main course.

—*Bonnie Baumgardner, Sylva, NC*

- -

TAKES: 20 min. • **MAKES:** 4 servings

- 1 Tbsp. olive oil
- 1 medium onion, chopped
- 1 medium green pepper, chopped
- 1 medium sweet red pepper, chopped
- 1 garlic clove, minced
- 1 Tbsp. tomato sauce
- ½ tsp. dried basil
- ¼ tsp. pepper
- 1 can (15 oz.) black beans, rinsed and drained
- 1 cup cooked long grain rice
- 1 Tbsp. red wine vinegar
- ¼ cup shredded cheddar cheese

Heat oil in a large, nonstick skillet over medium-high heat; saute onion, peppers and garlic until tender. Stir in tomato sauce, dried basil and pepper. Add the beans, rice and vinegar; heat through. Sprinkle with cheese before serving.

1 CUP: 217 cal., 5g fat (1g sat. fat), 5mg chol., 270mg sod., 33g carb. (4g sugars, 6g fiber), 9g pro. **DIABETIC EXCHANGES:** 2 starch, 1 fat.

SHORTCUT FISH TACOS

These fish tacos are an adaptation of a dish I was served in Bermuda. They're quick because there's so little prep work involved.

—*Jennifer Reid, Farmington, ME*

- -

TAKES: 20 min. • **MAKES:** 4 servings

- 1½ lbs. sole or cod fillets, cut into 1-in. strips
- 1 Tbsp. taco seasoning
- 3 Tbsp. butter, cubed
- 1 pkg. (10 oz.) angel hair coleslaw mix
- ½ cup minced fresh cilantro
- ½ cup mayonnaise
- 1 Tbsp. lime juice
- 1 tsp. sugar
- ¼ tsp. salt
- ¼ tsp. pepper
- 8 corn tortillas or taco shells, warmed
  Lime wedges

WHITE CHILI WITH CHICKEN

Folks who enjoy a change from traditional tomato-based chilis will enjoy this version. The flavorful blend has tender chunks of chicken, white beans and just enough zip.
—*Christy Campos, Richmond, VA*

TAKES: 30 min. • **MAKES:** 6 servings

- 1 Tbsp. canola oil
- 1 medium onion, chopped
- 1 jalapeno pepper, seeded and chopped, optional
- 2 garlic cloves, minced
- 4 cups chicken broth
- 2 cans (15½ oz. each) great northern beans, rinsed and drained
- 2 Tbsp. minced fresh parsley
- 1 Tbsp. lime juice
- 1 to 1¼ tsp. ground cumin
- 2 Tbsp. cornstarch
- ¼ cup cold water
- 2 cups shredded cooked chicken
  Optional: Chopped fresh cilantro, chopped red onion, sliced jalapenos and lime wedges

1. In a large saucepan, heat oil over medium heat; add onion and, if desired, jalapeno pepper. Cook and stir until tender, 3-5 minutes. Add garlic; cook 1 minute longer. Stir in broth, beans, parsley, lime juice and cumin. Bring to a boil. Reduce heat; cover and simmer for 10 minutes, stirring occasionally.

2. Combine cornstarch and water until smooth; gradually stir into chili. Bring to a boil; cook and stir until thickened, 1-2 minutes. Add chicken; heat through. If desired, serve with toppings and lime wedges.

NOTE: Wear disposable gloves when cutting hot peppers; the oils can burn skin. Avoid touching your face.

1¼ CUPS: 254 cal., 7g fat (1g sat. fat), 42mg chol., 820mg sod., 27g carb. (2g sugars, 8g fiber), 22g pro. **DIABETIC EXCHANGES:** 3 lean meat, 2 starch, ½ fat.

BACON CORNBREAD

Central Illinois is one of the major corn- and pork- producing areas of the country, so this bread is naturally a favorite here. I dress up the batter with corn, onion and cheese, then top it with poppy seeds and bacon.
—*Carol Roper, Litchfield, Illinois*

PREP: 30 min. • **BAKE:** 20 min.
MAKES: 9 servings

- 1 package (8½ ounces) cornbread/muffin mix
- 1 large egg, room temperature
- ½ cup frozen corn, thawed
- ⅓ cup 2% milk
- ¼ cup shredded cheddar cheese
- ¼ cup grated onion
- 5 bacon strips, cooked and crumbled
- ½ tsp. poppy seeds, optional
- ⅛ tsp. paprika

1. In a bowl, mix the first 6 ingredients just until blended. Pour into a greased 8-in. square baking dish. Sprinkle with bacon, poppy seeds if desired and paprika.

2. Bake at 375° for 20-25 minutes or until a toothpick inserted in the center comes out clean. Cut into squares; serve warm.

1 PIECE: 163 calories, 6g fat (2g sat. fat), 37mg cholesterol, 309mg sodium, 22g carbohydrate (7g sugars, 1g fiber), 5g protein.

BACON CORNBREAD

WHITE CHILI WITH CHICKEN

BEEF STIR-FRY WITH PEANUT SAUCE

The flavor of this stir-fry is very similar to restaurant-style dishes. A pleasant peanut sauce coats the meat and vegetables, giving the entree Thai flair.
—*Janet Lowe, Kennewick, WA*

TAKES: 25 min. • **MAKES:** 6 servings

- 2 **Tbsp. cornstarch**
- ¾ **cup water**
- 2 **Tbsp. plus 1½ tsp. chunky peanut butter**
- 4 **Tbsp. reduced-sodium soy sauce, divided**
- 2 **Tbsp. olive oil**
- 1½ **lbs. beef top sirloin steak, thinly sliced**
- ¼ **tsp. pepper**
- 1 **each medium green, sweet red and yellow pepper, julienned**
- 1 **can (8 oz.) bamboo shoots, drained**
- ½ **cup julienned carrot**
- ½ **tsp. crushed red pepper flakes**
- 1½ **tsp. minced garlic**
  Hot cooked rice

1. In a small bowl, combine cornstarch and water until smooth. Stir in peanut butter and 3 Tbsp. soy sauce; set aside.
2. In a large skillet or wok, heat oil over medium-high heat. Add beef, pepper and remaining 1 Tbsp. soy sauce. Cook and stir until meat is no longer pink, 4-6 minutes; remove and keep warm. Add peppers, bamboo shoots, carrot and pepper flakes; cook and stir until peppers are crisp-tender, 2-3 minutes. Add garlic; cook 1 minute longer.
3. Stir cornstarch mixture and add to pan. Bring to a boil; cook and stir until thickened, about 1 minute. Return beef mixture to pan. Serve with rice.
¾ CUP: 268 cal., 13g fat (3g sat. fat), 46mg chol., 708mg sod., 10g carb. (3g sugars, 2g fiber), 28g pro. **DIABETIC EXCHANGES:** 3 lean meat, 2 fat, 1 vegetable.

EFFORTLESS EGG ROLLS

Egg rolls are such a cinch with this recipe, you'll wonder why you haven't been making them all along! Look for a good dipping sauce in the Asian aisle of your supermarket.
—*Angel Randol, Apple Valley, CA*

TAKES: 30 min. • **MAKES:** 10 egg rolls

- ½ **lb. bulk pork sausage**
- 2½ **cups frozen stir-fry vegetable blend, thawed and chopped**
- 1 **Tbsp. teriyaki sauce**
- 10 **egg roll wrappers**
  Oil for frying

1. In a large skillet, cook sausage and vegetables over medium heat until meat is no longer pink; drain. Stir in teriyaki sauce.
2. Place 3 Tbsp. of sausage mixture in center of one egg roll wrapper. (Keep remaining wrappers covered with a damp paper towel until ready to use.) Fold bottom corner over filling. Fold sides toward center over filling. Moisten remaining corner with water; roll up tightly to seal. Repeat.
3. In an electric skillet, heat 1 in. of oil to 375°. Fry egg rolls in batches for 3-4 minutes on each side or until golden brown. Drain on paper towels.
1 EGG ROLL: 244 cal., 14g fat (2g sat. fat), 11mg chol., 349mg sod., 23g carb. (1g sugars, 2g fiber), 5g pro.

BEEF STIR-FRY WITH PEANUT SAUCE

EFFORTLESS EGG ROLLS

PIZZA FRIDAY

TURKEY CLUB PIZZA

EASY CAESAR SALAD

EASY CAESAR SALAD

My sister Jan deserves the credit for the wonderful Caesar dressing on this salad. This recipe is not only delicious but easy to prepare too. We all love it!
—*Dianne Nash, Kaslo, BC*

TAKES: 15 min. • **MAKES:** 8 servings

- ¼ cup grated Parmesan cheese
- ¼ cup mayonnaise
- 2 Tbsp. milk
- 1 Tbsp. lemon juice
- 1 Tbsp. Dijon-mayonnaise blend
- 1 garlic clove, minced
  Dash cayenne pepper
- 1 bunch romaine, torn
  Salad croutons and additional grated Parmesan cheese, optional

In a small bowl, whisk the first 7 ingredients. Place romaine in a large bowl. Drizzle with dressing and toss to coat. Serve with salad croutons and additional cheese if desired.
1 CUP: 73 cal., 6g fat (1g sat. fat), 5mg chol., 126mg sod., 2g carb. (0 sugars, 1g fiber), 2g pro. **DIABETIC EXCHANGES:** 1 vegetable, 1 fat.

READER RAVE

I did add a bit of Worcestershire sauce for some smokiness, but overall this is a really good, classic Caesar salad dressing recipe.

—RLLEWIS7, TASTEOFHOME.COM

TURKEY CLUB PIZZA

This easy pizza will be a hit with your family. And it'll keep you out of the kitchen! It's perfect for busy school nights, on hectic weekends or any time you just don't want to wait on dinner.
—*Pippa Milburn, Dover, OH*

TAKES: 20 min. • **MAKES:** 8 servings

- 1 prebaked 12-in. pizza crust
- ½ cup mayonnaise
- 1½ cups shredded Monterey Jack cheese, divided
- 1 cup chopped cooked turkey
- 8 bacon strips, cooked and crumbled
- 2 plum tomatoes, sliced
  Shredded lettuce, optional

Preheat oven to 450°. Place pizza crust on a baking sheet; spread with mayonnaise. Top with 1 cup cheese, turkey, bacon and tomatoes. Sprinkle with the remaining ½ cup cheese. Bake 10-12 minutes or until cheese is melted. If desired, top with lettuce.
1 PIECE: 367 cal., 22g fat (6g sat. fat), 42mg chol., 688mg sod., 23g carb. (1g sugars, 0 fiber), 18g pro.

The Morning Blend

Whirlwind mornings are no match for these super quick smoothie packs. Just prep ahead, stash in the freezer, then whip up breakfast in seconds.

MANGO-GINGER SMOOTHIES

MAKE IT AHEAD!
For freezer packs, divide mango, bananas and gingerroot evenly among 4 containers. Freeze. To make smoothies, add a frozen mixture to blender, then add ¼ portion each of the water, coconut oil and honey to make 1 serving.

BLUEBERRY-BANANA SMOOTHIES

Our ripest bananas go straight into the blender for this favorite beverage. This combo is fabulous for breakfast on the go or to top off a meal.
—*Lisa DeMarsh, Mount Solon, VA*

TAKES: 5 min. • **MAKES:** 3 servings

- 1 medium ripe banana, cut into chunks
- 1 cup frozen unsweetened blueberries
- 1 cup cherry juice blend
- ¾ cup vanilla yogurt
- ½ cup crushed ice
- Dash ground cinnamon

In a blender, combine all ingredients; cover and process for 30 seconds or until smooth. Pour into chilled glasses; serve immediately.
1 CUP: 164 cal., 2g fat (1g sat. fat), 6mg chol., 44mg sod., 33g carb. (26g sugars, 2g fiber), 4g pro

MANGO-GINGER SMOOTHIES

I blend smoothies every morning and change the flavors. My favorite version features mango with a spicy bite of ginger.
—*David Lee, Irvine, CA*

TAKES: 5 min. • **MAKES:** 4 servings

- 1½ cups cold water
- 1 pkg. (16 oz.) frozen mango chunks
- 2 medium ripe bananas, peeled and halved
- 1 Tbsp. coconut oil, melted
- 1 Tbsp. honey
- 1 to 2 tsp. minced fresh gingerroot

Place all ingredients in a blender; cover and process until smooth. Pour into chilled glasses; serve immediately.
1 CUP: 172 cal., 4g fat (3g sat. fat), 0 chol., 1mg sod., 37g carb. (29g sugars, 4g fiber), 1g pro.

BLUEBERRY-BANANA SMOOTHIES

MAKE IT AHEAD!
For freezer packs, divide banana, blueberries and ice evenly among 3 containers. Freeze. To make smoothies, add a frozen mixture to blender, then add 1/3 portion each of the cherry juice, yogurt and cinnamon to make 1 serving.

BANANA-MIXED BERRY
SMOOTHIES

MAKE IT AHEAD!
For freezer packs,
divide banana and
berries evenly among
3 containers. Freeze.
To make smoothies,
add a frozen mixture
to blender, then add
⅓ cup yogurt and ⅓ cup
milk to make 1 serving.

GINGER-KALE SMOOTHIES

Ever since I started drinking these green smoothies for breakfast
every day, I feel energized and healthy!. Substitute any fruit and
juice you'd like to make this recipe your own.
—*Linda Green, Kilauea, Kauai, HI*

- -

TAKES: 15 min. • **MAKES:** 2 servings

1¼ cups orange juice
1 tsp. lemon juice
2 cups torn fresh kale
1 medium apple, peeled and coarsely chopped
1 Tbsp. minced fresh gingerroot
4 ice cubes
⅛ tsp. ground cinnamon
⅛ tsp. ground turmeric or ¼-in. piece fresh turmeric, peeled
 and finely chopped
 Dash cayenne pepper

Place all ingredients in a blender; cover and process until
blended. Pour into chilled glasses; serve immediately.
1 CUP: 121 cal., 0 fat (0 sat. fat), 0 chol., 22mg sod., 29g carb.
(21g sugars, 2g fiber), 1g pro. **DIABETIC EXCHANGES:** 1½ fruit,
1 vegetable.

BANANA-MIXED BERRY SMOOTHIES

Bananas and berries are a no-brainer combo for a reason.
When you want to chill out in the morning, mix up a glass of this
freeze-y treat.
—*Brenda Strohm, Omaha, NE*

- -

TAKES: 5 min. • **MAKES:** 3 servings

1 cup vanilla yogurt
1 medium ripe banana, peeled, cut into chunks and frozen
¼ cup each frozen unsweetened strawberries, blueberries,
 raspberries and blackberries
1 cup 2% milk

In a blender or food processor, combine all ingredients;
cover and process until smooth. Pour into chilled glasses;
serve immediately.
1¼ CUPS: 170 cal., 3g fat (2g sat. fat), 11mg chol., 93mg sod.,
30g carb. (24g sugars, 3g fiber), 8g pro

GINGER-KALE
SMOOTHIES

MAKE IT AHEAD!
For freezer packs,
divide kale, apple,
gingerroot and ice cubes
evenly between
2 containers. Freeze.
To make smoothies,
add a frozen mixture to
blender, then add half
each of the orange juice,
lemon juice, cinnamon,
turmeric and cayenne
pepper to make
1 serving.

FREEZER
MASHED POTATOES
PAGE 125

Side Dishes & Condiments

No great menu is complete without delicious side dishes that perfectly complement the main course. On these pages, you will also find delightful homemade pickles, versatile condiments and 10 topping ideas for grilled corn on the cob.

DISHES WE LOVE

BALSAMIC
PURPLE
POTATOES

BREAD DUMPLINGS

I remember enjoying these dumplings as a kid with roast pork or *svickova*. My grandfather was Bohemian and this was one of his favorites. My mother gave me this recipe when I moved to college.
—*Peggy Woodward, Shullsburg, WI*

- -

PREP: 15 min. + standing • **COOK:** 25 min. • **MAKES:** 8 servings

- 2 cups all-purpose flour
- 2½ tsp. baking powder
- 1½ tsp. salt
- 1 tsp. caraway seeds
- 2 slices white bread, toasted and cut into ½-in. squares
- ½ cup 2% milk
- ¼ to ½ cup water
  Gravy, warmed
  Fresh thyme leaves, optional

1. In a large bowl, combine the first 5 ingredients. Stir in milk and enough water to be able to shape mixture into a loaf. Turn out onto a lightly floured surface. Shape into an 8x4-in. dumpling loaf. Cover and let stand 10 minutes.
2. Meanwhile, bring 12 cups water to a boil in a Dutch oven. Gently add the dumpling; return water to a simmer. Cover and simmer for 15 minutes. Turn dumpling over. Cover and simmer until a toothpick inserted in center comes out clean, 8-12 minutes longer. Gently remove to a cutting board using 2 slotted spoons. Using a serrated knife, cut into slices. Serve warm with gravy. If desired, sprinkle with thyme.
1 PIECE: 142 cal., 1g fat (0 sat. fat), 1mg chol., 636mg sod., 28g carb. (1g sugars, 1g fiber), 4g pro. **DIABETIC EXCHANGES:** 2 starch.

BALSAMIC PURPLE POTATOES

I volunteered at a local organic farm in exchange for fresh produce, and I was given purple potatoes. I wanted to cook something new and use herbs from our garden. I come from the Midwest, and adding vinegar to potato recipes has always been a hit here!
—*Kristin Schultz, Manor, TX*

- -

PREP: 20 min. • **BAKE:** 35 min. • **MAKES:** 8 servings

- ¼ cup olive oil
- 3 Tbsp. balsamic vinegar
- 3 garlic cloves, minced
- 1 Tbsp. minced fresh oregano or 1 tsp. dried oregano
- 1 Tbsp. coarsely chopped fresh thyme or 1 tsp. dried thyme
- 1 tsp. kosher salt
- ½ tsp. coarsely ground pepper
- ½ tsp. ground coriander
- 2 lbs. small purple potatoes, cut into ½-in. thick slices
- ½ cup chopped sweet onion
- ½ cup loosely packed basil leaves, chopped

1. Preheat oven to 350°. In a large bowl, whisk together the first 8 ingredients. Add potatoes and onion; toss to combine.
2. Transfer mixture to a greased 15x10x1-in. baking pan. Bake until potatoes start to brown and are tender, 35-40 minutes, turning once.
3. Transfer to a serving bowl. Top with basil and, if desired, additional balsamic vinegar.
¾ CUP: 155 cal., 7g fat (1g sat. fat), 0 chol., 248mg sod., 21g carb. (3g sugars, 2g fiber), 2g pro. **DIABETIC EXCHANGES:** 1½ starch, 1 fat.

TEST KITCHEN TIP

If you want to customize these potatoes to suit your taste, switch up the seasonings. Try using your favorite spice blend or a different assortment of fresh herbs.

BREAD
DUMPLINGS

SLOW-COOKED
RATATOUILLE

BASIL TOMATO TART

I received this recipe from a good friend. It's a great way to use up fresh tomatoes from the garden, and it tastes a lot like pizza.
—*Connie Stumpf, North Myrtle Beach, SC*

PREP: 20 min. • **BAKE:** 20 min. • **MAKES:** 8 servings

    Dough for a single-crust pie (9 in.)
1½ cups shredded part-skim mozzarella cheese, divided
5 to 6 fresh plum tomatoes
1 cup loosely packed fresh basil leaves
4 garlic cloves
½ cup mayonnaise
¼ cup grated Parmesan cheese
⅛ tsp. pepper

1. Roll dough to fit a 9-in. tart pan or pie plate; place in pan. Do not prick. Line crust with a double thickness of heavy-duty foil.
2. Bake at 450° for 5 minutes. Remove foil; bake 8 minutes more. Remove from the oven. Reduce the heat to 375°. Sprinkle ½ cup mozzarella over the hot crust.
3. Cut each tomato into 8 wedges; remove seeds. Arrange the tomato wedges over cheese.
4. In a food processor, process basil and garlic until coarsely chopped; sprinkle over tomatoes.
5. Combine mayonnaise, Parmesan, pepper and the remaining mozzarella; spoon over basil. Bake, uncovered, until the cheese is browned and bubbly, 20-25 minutes.
1 PIECE: 345 cal., 27g fat (12g sat. fat), 47mg chol., 413mg sod., 19g carb. (2g sugars, 1g fiber), 8g pro.
DOUGH FOR SINGLE-CRUST PIE: Combine 1¼ cups all-purpose flour and ¼ tsp. salt; cut in ½ cup cold butter until crumbly. Gradually add 3-5 Tbsp. ice water, tossing with a fork until dough holds together when pressed. Shape into a disk; wrap and refrigerate 1 hour.

🍎 🍲 ❄️

SLOW-COOKED RATATOUILLE

I get my son to eat eggplant by cooking this classic French veggie dish low and slow. A side of rice and some garlic cheese bread also help.
—*Diane Goedde, Red Lodge, MT*

PREP: 25 min. + standing • **COOK:** 5 hours • **MAKES:** 10 servings

1 medium eggplant, peeled and cut into 1-in. cubes
1 Tbsp. plus 1 tsp. salt, divided
2 medium onions, halved and thinly sliced
4 medium tomatoes, chopped
3 medium zucchini, cut into ¾-in. slices
2 celery ribs, chopped
3 Tbsp. olive oil
2 tsp. dried basil or 2 Tbsp. minced fresh basil
4 garlic cloves, minced
½ tsp. pepper
1 can (6 oz.) tomato paste
1 can (2¼ oz.) sliced ripe olives, drained
⅓ cup coarsely chopped fresh basil

1. Place eggplant in a strainer over a plate; sprinkle with 1 Tbsp. salt and toss. Let stand 45 minutes. Rinse and drain well; blot dry with paper towels.
2. Place eggplant and remaining vegetables in a 5- or 6-qt. slow cooker. Add oil, dried basil, garlic, pepper and remaining 1 tsp. salt; toss to combine.
3. Cook, covered, on low for 5-6 hours or until onions are tender. Stir in tomato paste, olives and fresh basil; heat through.
FREEZE OPTION: Freeze cooled ratatouille in freezer containers. To use, partially thaw in the refrigerator overnight. Microwave, covered, on high in a microwave-safe dish until heated through, stirring gently.
¾ CUP: 102 cal., 5g fat (1g sat. fat), 0 chol., 380mg sod., 13g carb. (7g sugars, 4g fiber), 3g pro. **DIABETIC EXCHANGES:** 2 vegetable, 1 fat.

BASIL
TOMATO
TART

GRANNY'S APPLE SCALLOPED POTATOES

2. In an 8- or 9-in. cast-iron or other ovenproof skillet, heat butter over medium heat. Add onion; cook and stir until crisp-tender, about 3 minutes. Remove from the heat.

3. Alternately arrange potato and apple slices in a single layer in the same skillet. Combine ¾ cup Parmesan cheese with cream, thyme, salt and pepper; pour over top.

4. Bake, uncovered, 50 minutes. Top with bacon and remaining 2 Tbsp. Parmesan. Bake until potatoes are tender and top is lightly browned, 5-10 minutes longer. Let stand for 10 minutes before serving. If desired, sprinkle with parsley.

1 SERVING: 376 cal., 25g fat (15g sat. fat), 70mg chol., 651mg sod., 27g carb. (7g sugars, 3g fiber), 13g pro.

GINGERED CARROTS & PARSNIPS

Guests at my holiday table are surprised to hear that this tasty side dish has just five ingredients!
—*Lucille Drake, Sherburne, NY*

TAKES: 25 min. • **MAKES:** 6 servings

- 4 medium carrots, peeled and julienned
- 4 medium parsnips, peeled and julienned
- 2 Tbsp. chopped crystallized ginger, divided
- 2 Tbsp. butter
- ¼ tsp. salt

1. Place carrots and parsnips in a steamer basket; place basket in a large saucepan over 1 in. water. Bring to a boil; cover and steam 15-20 minutes or until vegetables are crisp-tender.

2. In a large skillet, saute 1 Tbsp. ginger in butter for 1 minute. Add the carrots, parsnips and salt; toss to coat. Sprinkle with remaining 1 Tbsp. ginger.

½ CUP: 153 cal., 4g fat (2g sat. fat), 10mg chol., 165mg sod., 29g carb. (10g sugars, 5g fiber), 2g pro. **DIABETIC EXCHANGES:** 2 starch, 1 fat.

GRANNY'S APPLE SCALLOPED POTATOES

I created this dish because I love scalloped potatoes and apples. It is delicious with baked breaded pork chops, which you could cook at the same time in another cast-iron pan. My spouse and I are retired, so it's just the two of us, but you could easily double the recipe to serve more.
—*Shirley Rickis, The Villages, FL*

PREP: 25 min. • **BAKE:** 55 min. + standing
MAKES: 4 servings

- 1 medium Granny Smith apple, peeled and thinly sliced
- 1 tsp. sugar
- 1 tsp. lemon juice
- 2 Tbsp. butter
- ½ cup sliced sweet onion
- 4 medium red potatoes (about 1 lb.), thinly sliced
- ¾ cup plus 2 Tbsp. shredded Parmesan cheese, divided
- ½ cup heavy whipping cream
- ½ tsp. minced fresh thyme or ¼ tsp. dried thyme
- ¼ tsp. salt
- ¼ tsp. pepper
- 4 bacon strips, cooked and crumbled
  Chopped fresh parsley, optional

1. Preheat oven to 350°. In a small bowl, combine apple slices, sugar and lemon juice; toss to coat. Set aside.

ARUGULA PESTO

Arugula pesto is garden-fresh goodness. If your greens are too peppery, substitute spinach for half the arugula to balance it out beautifully.
—*Courtney Stultz, Weir, KS*

TAKES: 10 min. • **MAKES:** ¾ cup

- 4 cups fresh arugula
- 1 cup fresh basil leaves
- ½ cup grated Parmesan cheese
- ¼ cup pine nuts
- ½ tsp. minced garlic
- 1 tsp. sea salt
- ½ cup olive oil

Pulse first 6 ingredients in a food processor until chopped. While processing, gradually add oil in a steady stream until mixture is smooth. Store tightly covered in refrigerator; use within 5 days.
2 TBSP: 43 cal., 4g fat (0 sat. fat), 0 chol., 324mg sod., 1g carb. (0 sugars, 1g fiber), 1g pro. **DIABETIC EXCHANGES:** 1 fat.

FREEZER
MASHED
POTATOES

FREEZER MASHED POTATOES

Can you freeze mashed potatoes? You bet you can! I always make these potatoes and give them to my kids when they go away to school. All they have to do is keep it in freezer until it's mashed potato time!
—*Jessie Fortune, Pocahontas, AR*

PREP: 30 min. + freezing • **BAKE:** 30 min. • **MAKES:** 14 servings

- 5 lbs. potatoes (about 9 large), peeled and cut into chunks
- 2 Tbsp. butter, softened
- 1 cup sour cream
- 6 oz. cream cheese, cubed
- ½ tsp. onion powder
- ½ tsp. salt
- ¼ tsp. pepper

1. Place potatoes in a large saucepan and cover with water. Bring to a boil. Reduce heat; cover and cook 10-15 minutes or until tender. Drain.
2. In a large bowl, mash potatoes with butter. Beat in sour cream, cream cheese, onion powder, salt and pepper. Transfer to a greased 13x9-in. baking dish. Bake, uncovered, at 350° until heated through, 30-35 minutes. Or, transfer 1½-cup portions to greased 2-cup baking dishes. Cover and freeze up to 6 months.
3. To use frozen potatoes: Thaw in the refrigerator overnight. Bake at 350° until heated through, 30-35 minutes.
¾ CUP: 195 cal., 6g fat (4g sat. fat), 19mg chol., 173mg sod., 31g carb. (4g sugars, 3g fiber), 6g pro.

ARUGULA
PESTO

TEST KITCHEN TIP

Ideally, you should allow frozen mashed potatoes to thaw overnight in the refrigerator before reheating. In a pinch, you can thaw them on the stovetop. Just make sure to heat over low heat and stir occasionally so they don't scorch. In an airtight container, mashed potatoes can last up to 2 months in the freezer.

⑤ⁱ HOMEMADE PASTA DOUGH

Go for it. It's easier than you think, and once you try homemade pasta, you're hooked!

—*Kathryn Conrad, Milwaukee, WI*

- -

PREP: 15 min. + resting • **MAKES:** 6 servings

- 2 large eggs
- 1 large egg yolk
- ¼ cup water
- 1 Tbsp. olive oil
- ¼ tsp. salt
- ½ tsp. coarsely ground pepper, optional
- 1½ cups all-purpose flour
- ½ cup semolina flour

1. Whisk the first 5 ingredients and, if desired, pepper. On a clean work surface, mix the all-purpose and semolina flours, forming a mound. Make a large well in the center. Pour egg mixture into the well. Using a fork or your fingers, gradually mix flour mixture into egg mixture, forming a soft dough (dough will be slightly sticky).
2. Lightly dust the work surface with all-purpose flour; knead the dough gently 5 times. Divide into 6 portions; cover and let rest 30 minutes.
3. To make fettuccine, roll each ball into a 10x8-in. rectangle, dusting lightly with flour. Roll up jelly-roll style. Cut into ¼-in.-wide strips. Cook in boiling water 1-3 minutes.
1 SERVING: 217 cal., 5g fat (1g sat. fat), 93mg chol., 124mg sod., 34g carb. (0 sugars, 1g fiber), 8g pro.

GRILLED FRENCH ONIONS

HOMEMADE PASTA DOUGH

⑤ⁱ GRILLED FRENCH ONIONS

This savory delicacy lets you enjoy all the flavors of French onion soup during summertime. Serve it with toasty bread as another nod to a bowl of the beloved classic.

—*Krista Slack, Simi Valley, CA*

- -

PREP: 10 min. • **GRILL:** 35 min. • **MAKES:** 2 servings

- 2 large sweet onions
- 1 to 2 tsp. beef bouillon granules
- ½ cup butter, softened
- 2 slices Swiss cheese
  Minced fresh thyme, optional

1. Prepare grill for indirect heat. Cut ¼ in. from top and bottom of each onion; peel. Core onions, leaving the bottom fourth of the onions intact. Place each onion on a double thickness of heavy-duty foil (about 12 in. square). Place bouillon in each onion; top with butter and seal tightly.
2. Grill, covered, over medium heat 35-40 minutes or until onions are tender.
3. Carefully unwrap; top each onion with a cheese slice. If desired, top with fresh thyme. Serve immediately.
1 ONION: 556 cal., 49g fat (31g sat. fat), 132mg chol., 807mg sod., 26g carb. (17g sugars, 3g fiber), 6g pro.

PARMESAN RISOTTO

Risotto is a creamy Italian rice dish. In this version, the rice is briefly sauteed, then slowly cooked in wine and seasonings.
—Taste of Home *Test Kitchen*

PREP: 15 min. • **COOK:** 30 min. • **MAKES:** 12 servings

- 8 cups chicken broth
- ½ cup finely chopped onion
- ¼ cup olive oil
- 3 cups arborio rice
- 2 garlic cloves, minced
- 1 cup dry white wine or water
- ½ cup shredded Parmesan cheese
- ¼ tsp. salt
- ¼ tsp. pepper
- 3 Tbsp. minced fresh parsley

1. In a large saucepan, heat broth and keep warm. In a Dutch oven, saute onion in oil until tender. Add rice and garlic; cook and stir 2-3 minutes. Reduce heat; stir in wine. Cook and stir until all liquid is absorbed.
2. Add heated broth, ½ cup at a time, stirring constantly and allowing the liquid to absorb between additions. Cook just until risotto is creamy and rice is almost tender, about 20 minutes.
3. Add the remaining ingredients; cook and stir until heated through. Serve immediately.
¾ CUP: 260 cal., 6g fat (1g sat. fat), 2mg chol., 728mg sod., 41g carb. (1g sugars, 1g fiber), 6g pro.

SAUSAGE MUSHROOM RISOTTO: Use only 2 Tbsp. olive oil. In a large skillet, cook 1 lb. bulk Italian sausage over medium heat until meat is no longer pink; drain. Set aside and keep warm. Add onion, oil and ½ lb. quartered fresh mushrooms to skillet and cook until tender. Proceed as directed.
ASPARAGUS RISOTTO: Trim 1 lb. asparagus and cut into 2-in. pieces. Place asparagus in a large saucepan; add ½ in. water. Bring to a boil. Reduce heat; cover and simmer 3 minutes or until crisp-tender. Drain and set aside. After step 3, add asparagus; heat through.

PARMESAN RISOTTO

RHUBARB & ONION RELISH

RHUBARB & ONION RELISH

This makes a tasty chutney-like sauce you can use in place of steak sauce for basting or marinade. It goes well with beef, pork and poultry, and it's good even served over softened cream cheese for a really different appetizer. I entered it in the state fair and won first place in condiments!
—Jacalyn Margittay, Sturgeon Bay, WI

PREP: 2½ hours • **PROCESS:** 10 min. • **MAKES:** 4 half pints

- 4 cups chopped onion (about 4 large)
- 4 cups chopped fresh rhubarb
- 2 cups white vinegar
- 4½ cups packed brown sugar
- 1 Tbsp. salt
- 1 Tbsp. ground ginger
- 1 tsp. ground allspice
- 1 tsp. ground cinnamon
- 1 tsp. ground cloves
- 1 tsp. ground mace
- 1 tsp. ground nutmeg
- 1 tsp. pepper
- ¼ tsp. paprika
- ⅛ tsp. cayenne pepper

1. In a stockpot, combine all the ingredients; bring to a boil. Reduce the heat; simmer, uncovered, 2-2¼ hours or until slightly thickened.
2. Ladle the hot mixture into hot half-pint jars, leaving ½-in. headspace. Remove air bubbles and adjust headspace, if necessary, by adding more hot relish. Wipe rims. Center lids on jars; screw on bands until fingertip tight.
3. Place jars into the canner, ensuring they are completely covered with water. Bring to a boil; process 10 minutes. Remove jars and cool.
2 TBSP: 131 cal., 0 fat (0 sat. fat), 0 chol., 232mg sod., 33g carb. (31g sugars, 1g fiber), 0 pro.

ROASTED
BEET WEDGES

YUCA FRITA CON MOJO

Who doesn't love something fried? That's how I first got turned on to yuca, and now I cook it regularly. It is a starchy tuber, similar in texture to a potato, and is served with a lovely garlicky orange dipping sauce.
—*Deeanna Dickey, Denver, CO*

- -

PREP: 15 min. + chilling • **COOK:** 30 min. • **MAKES:** 6 servings

MOJO
- ¼ cup sour orange marinade
- ¼ cup olive oil
- 4 garlic cloves, minced
- ½ tsp. ground cumin
- ¼ tsp. salt
- ¼ tsp. dried oregano
- ⅛ tsp. pepper

FRIES
- 1½ lbs. yuca or cassava root, peeled, cored and cut into 3-in. pieces
- 1 tsp. salt
  Oil for frying

1. In a small bowl, whisk the mojo ingredients. Refrigerate, covered, at least 2 hours or overnight.
2. Place yuca and 1 tsp. salt in a Dutch oven; add water to cover. Bring to a boil. Reduce heat; cook, uncovered, until fork-tender, 20-25 minutes. Drain and pat yuca pieces dry.
3. In a deep skillet, heat 1 in. oil to 375°. Fry yuca, a few pieces at a time, until golden brown, 8-10 minutes. Drain on paper towels. Serve immediately with dipping sauce, or toss to coat in sauce if desired.
¾ CUP YUCA WITH 5 TSP. SAUCE: 344 cal., 18g fat (2g sat. fat), 0 chol., 154mg sod., 45g carb. (3g sugars, 2g fiber), 2g pro.

🍎 5ⁱ
ROASTED BEET WEDGES

This recipe makes ordinary beets taste tender and delicious with just a few sweet and good-for-you ingredients.
—*Wendy Stenman, Germantown, WI*

- -

PREP: 15 min. • **BAKE:** 1 hour • **MAKES:** 4 servings

- 1 lb. fresh beets (about 3 medium), peeled
- 4 tsp. olive oil
- ½ tsp. kosher salt
- 3 to 5 fresh rosemary sprigs

1. Preheat oven to 400°. Cut each beet into 6 wedges; place in a shallow dish. Add olive oil and salt; toss gently to coat.
2. Cut a piece of heavy-duty foil about 12 in. long; place in a 15x10x1-in. baking pan. Arrange beets on foil; top with rosemary. Fold foil around beets and seal tightly.
3. Bake until tender, about 1 hour. Open foil carefully to allow steam to escape. Discard rosemary sprigs.
3 WEDGES: 92 cal., 5g fat (1g sat. fat), 0 chol., 328mg sod., 12g carb. (9g sugars, 3g fiber), 2g pro. **DIABETIC EXCHANGES:** 1 vegetable, 1 fat.

TEST KITCHEN TIPS

- If you prefer a milder herb flavor, try using fresh thyme instead of rosemary.
- If you don't want to, you don't have to peel the beets before roasting. However, make sure you scrub them extra well to get rid of any residual dirt.
- You may make the beets a day ahead and either serve them cold or reheat in the microwave or in the oven. Once roasted, the beets can be kept in the refrigerator for 3-4 days.

YUCA FRITA
CON MOJO

CORN THIS WAY

Aw, shucks. Plain kernels won't cut it when you've got these 10 terrific toppings to try!

GRILLED HOISIN

ELOTE

HOT & SPICY

GRILLED ITALIAN-STYLE

MAPLE & BACON

TO PREP AND GRILL: Carefully peel back corn husks to within 1 in. of bottoms; remove silk. Brush corn with oil. Re-wrap corn in husks; secure with kitchen string. Place in a Dutch oven; cover with cold water. Soak 20 minutes; drain. Grill corn, covered, over medium heat 25-30 minutes or until tender, turning often.

GRILLED CURRY
Peel back husks. Spread cooked corn with a blend of **yogurt** and **curry powder**; sprinkle each ear with **cilantro**.

GARLIC WHIPPED CREAM
Puree **garlic** and **whipping cream** in a blender until smooth, about 20 seconds. Pour cream into a glass or copper bowl; whisk cream until soft peaks form. When corn is cooked, peel back husks; top with whipped cream, **lemon zest** and **oregano**.

ELOTE
Peel back husks. Spread **mayonnaise** over each ear; sprinkle with **chili powder**, **Cojita cheese** and **cilantro**. Squeeze **lime wedges** over **corn** before serving.

GRILLED HOISIN
Peel back husks. Top with **hoisin sauce**, **green onions** and **sesame seeds**.

GRILLED ITALIAN-STYLE
Peel back husks. Top with **pesto**, **mini pepperoni slices**, **Parmesan** and **basil**.

HOT & SPICY
Peel back husks. Drizzle with **Sriracha chili sauce**; top with **red pepper flakes** and **sliced jalapenos**.

MAPLE & BACON
Peel back husks. Brush corn with **maple syrup** and roll in **bacon**. Drizzle with additional syrup if desired.

CHEESY CORN ON THE COB
Peel back husks. Brush with melted **nacho cheese** and sprinkle with **blue cheese** and **shredded cheddar cheese**.

ONION LOVERS
Peel back husks. Brush with melted **butter** and top with **french-fried onions**, **chives**, **garlic** and **onion salt**.

SALT & PEPPER
Peel back husks. Brush with melted **butter** and sprinkle with **salt** and **pepper**.

VIOLET JELLY

DIJON-PARMESAN MAYONNAISE

Dijon mustard and grated Parmesan add just the right tang to mayonnaise. Try using this recipe on a sandwich, in potato salad or even on grilled salmon!
—*Taste of Home Test Kitchen*

- -

TAKES: 5 min. • **MAKES:** 10 servings (about ⅔ cup)

  ½ cup mayonnaise
  2 Tbsp. grated Parmesan cheese
  1 Tbsp. Dijon mustard
  ¼ tsp. dill weed

In a small bowl, combine all the ingredients.
1 TBSP.: 78 cal., 8g fat (1g sat. fat), 5mg chol., 110mg sod., 0 carb. (0 sugars, 0 fiber), 0 pro.

CREAMY BACON-CHEDDAR SPREAD

My mom was famous for her bacon dip. We love it with celery sticks or crackers, or spread on a sandwich!
—*Lynette Abderhalden, Salem, OR*

- -

PREP: 15 min. + chilling • **MAKES:** 16 servings (2 cups)

  1 pkg. (8 oz.) cream cheese, softened
  1 cup shredded cheddar cheese
  ½ cup Miracle Whip
  4 bacon strips, cooked and crumbled
  ¼ cup chopped almonds
  2 Tbsp. chopped fresh parsley
  1 tsp. Worcestershire sauce
  ½ tsp. onion powder
     Celery sticks and assorted crackers

In a small bowl, beat the first 8 ingredients. Refrigerate, covered, at least 1 hour before serving. Serve with celery and crackers.
2 TBSP.: 121 cal., 11g fat (5g sat. fat), 26mg chol., 181mg sod., 3g carb. (1g sugars, 0 fiber), 4g pro.

VIOLET JELLY

For a beautiful jelly to give as a gift or to enjoy yourself, this one can't be beat. It's impressive, but the floral flavor is also so refreshing.
—*Bernard Bellin, Franklin, WI*

- -

PREP: 40 min. + standing • **PROCESS:** 5 min.
MAKES: about 5 half pints

  4 cups fresh violet blossoms
 3½ cups boiling water
  ¼ cup lemon juice
  1 pkg. (1¾ oz.) powdered fruit pectin
  4 cups sugar

1. Rinse and drain blossoms; place in a large heat-resistant glass bowl. Pour boiling water over the blossoms and let stand 2 hours, stirring occasionally.
2. Strain and reserve violet liquid, pressing with a spatula to extract all possible color. Discard blossoms. Measure violet liquid; add enough water to measure 3½ cups (liquid will be blue-green).
3. In a Dutch oven, combine violet liquid, lemon juice and pectin (liquid will turn violet). Bring to a full rolling boil over high heat, stirring constantly. Stir in sugar; return to a full rolling boil. Boil and stir 1 minute.
4. Remove from heat; skim off foam. Ladle the hot mixture into 5 hot sterilized half-pint jars, leaving ¼-in. headspace. Adjust headspace, if necessary, by adding more hot mixture. Wipe the rims. Center lids on jars; screw on bands until fingertip tight.
5. Place jars in the canner with simmering water, ensuring that they are completely covered with water. Bring to a boil; process 5 minutes. Remove jars and cool.
NOTE: The processing time listed is for altitudes of 1,000 feet or less. Add 1 minute to the processing time for each 1,000 feet of additional altitude.
2 TBSP: 86 cal., 0 fat (0 sat. fat), 0 chol., 1mg sod., 22g carb. (21g sugars, 0 fiber), 0 pro.

CREAMY BACON-CHEDDAR SPREAD

SWEET
POTATO
CASSEROLE

SWEET POTATO CASSEROLE

I make this classic every Thanksgiving, but I also have been known to serve it with meat loaf and even grilled meat.
—*Eleanor Sherry, Highland Park, IL*

PREP: 10 min. • **BAKE:** 25 min. • **MAKES:** 8 servings

CASSEROLE
- 2¼ to 2½ lbs. sweet potatoes, cooked, peeled and mashed (about 4 cups)
- ⅓ cup butter, melted
- 2 large eggs, lightly beaten
- ½ cup 2% milk
- 1 tsp. vanilla extract
- ½ cup sugar

TOPPING
- ½ cup chopped nuts
- ½ cup sweetened shredded coconut
- ½ cup packed brown sugar
- 3 Tbsp. butter, melted

1. In a large bowl, combine mashed potatoes, butter, eggs, milk, vanilla and sugar. Spread into a greased 1½-qt. casserole dish.
2. Combine the topping ingredients and sprinkle over potatoes. Bake at 375° until a thermometer reads 160°, about 25 minutes.
¾ CUP: 445 cal., 21g fat (10g sat. fat), 80mg chol., 152mg sod., 62g carb. (42g sugars, 5g fiber), 6g pro.

TEST KITCHEN TIP

You can use canned sweet potatoes to make this casserole. Drain the sweet potatoes, then mash them with a potato masher or an electric mixer. If you're using canned sweet potatoes in syrup and you'd like to reduce added sugar, rinse them well before preparing this recipe, then plan to adjust the brown sugar to your tastes.

PICKLED GREEN ONIONS

Whether you grow your own green onions or get them from the farmers market, these pickled green onions provide an unusual and a tasty treat. They're a delicious alternative to ordinary pickles on a relish tray, or try them on hot dogs or in a sandwich.
—*Nancy Dentler, Greensboro, NC*

PREP: 20 min. + chilling • **MAKES:** 1½ qt.

- 4 cups cider vinegar
- 1 cup water
- ½ cup sugar
- 2 jalapeno peppers, seeded and chopped
- 3 garlic cloves, peeled and sliced
- 1 tsp. ground cinnamon
- 1 tsp. ground allspice
- 5 bunches green onions, trimmed

1. In a Dutch oven, combine the first 7 ingredients. Bring to a boil over medium heat; cook and stir 5 minutes. Place onions in heat-proof jar or bowl; pour brine over onion. Cool completely.
2. Cover and refrigerate 8 hours or overnight. Store in the refrigerator for up to 2 weeks.
NOTE: Wear disposable gloves when cutting hot peppers; the oils can burn skin. Avoid touching your face.
1 GREEN ONION: 2 cal., 0 fat (0 sat. fat), 0 chol., 1mg sod., 1g carb. (0 sugars, 0 fiber), 0 pro.

PICKLED
GREEN
ONIONS

ZUCCHINI
FRIES

ZUCCHINI FRIES

These aren't anything like potato fries—in a good way! They are air-fried to crispy perfection and so flavorful. Enjoy as an appetizer or a low-carb alternative to french fries. Don't have an air fryer? You can convection-bake for the same time.
—*Jen Pahl, West Allis, WI*

PREP: 20 min. • **COOK:** 10 min./batch • **MAKES:** 4 servings

- 2 medium zucchini
- 1 cup panko bread crumbs
- 2 tsp. dried basil, divided
- 1½ tsp. seasoned salt
- 1 tsp. garlic powder
- 1 tsp. dried oregano
- ½ cup plus 2 Tbsp. grated Parmesan cheese, divided
- 2 large eggs, lightly beaten
  Cooking spray
  Marinara sauce, warmed

1. Preheat the air fryer to 375°. Cut each zucchini in half lengthwise and then in half crosswise. Cut each piece lengthwise into ¼-in. slices.
2. In a shallow bowl, mix panko, 1 tsp. basil, salt, garlic powder, oregano and ½ cup Parmesan. Place eggs and the remaining 1 tsp. basil in a separate shallow bowl. Dip zucchini slices in the egg mixture and then in the crumb mixture, patting to help the coating adhere.
3. In batches, place zucchini in a single layer on a greased tray in the air-fryer basket; spritz with cooking spray. Cook until lightly browned, 6-8 minutes. Flip each piece; fry until golden brown, 3-5 minutes longer.
4. Sprinkle hot fries with remaining 2 Tbsp. Parmesan and serve with marinara sauce.
1 CUP: 91 cal., 4g fat (2g sat. fat), 52mg chol., 389mg sod., 9g carb. (2g sugars, 1g fiber), 6g pro. **DIABETIC EXCHANGES:** 1 vegetable, 1 fat.

HOW-TO

Clean the Air Fryer's Coil

Oil or residue on the heating coil can cause smoking and odors. Unplug the air fryer, then wipe the coil with a damp cloth—just as you would an electric stove's heating element.

THREE-CHEESE KETO CAULIFLOWER CASSEROLE

THREE-CHEESE KETO CAULIFLOWER CASSEROLE

This casserole is low on carbs but high on flavor. If you are trying to eat healthier, but miss eating macaroni and cheese, this casserole will hit the right spot!
—*Adrianna Cauthen, Decatur, GA*

PREP: 35 min. • **BAKE:** 20 min. + standing • **MAKES:** 6 servings

- 1 medium head cauliflower, cut into ½-in. pieces (about 10 cups)
- 4 Tbsp. butter, divided
- 1 Tbsp. canola oil
- 4 oz. cream cheese, cubed
- 3½ cups shredded cheddar cheese, divided
- 1½ cups shredded mozzarella cheese, divided
- 1 cup 2% milk

1. Preheat oven to 425°. Place cauliflower on a 15x10x1-in. baking sheet. Melt 1 Tbsp. butter; drizzle over cauliflower. Add oil; toss to coat. Roast until lightly browned and tender, 20-25 minutes.
2. In a large saucepan, melt cream cheese and remaining 3 Tbsp. butter over medium heat. Add 2 cups cheddar, 1 cup mozzarella and milk. Cook and stir until sauce begins to thicken, 1-2 minutes. Gently fold in cauliflower. Transfer to a greased 8-in. square baking dish. Sprinkle with the remaining 1½ cups cheddar and ½ cup mozzarella.
3. Bake, uncovered, until bubbly and cheese is melted, about 20 minutes. Let stand 10 minutes before serving.
⅔ CUP: 550 cal., 46g fat (26g sat. fat), 130mg chol., 775mg sod., 11g carb. (5g sugars, 2g fiber), 26g pro.

SPECTACULAR FINGERLING POTATOES

My children absolutely love these tender mini potatoes. Fingerling potatoes can be found at farmers markets and specialty grocery stores, though Yukon Gold potatoes would work too.
—*Michelle Herren, Las Vegas, NV*

TAKES: 30 min. • MAKES: 5 servings

- 1 lb. fingerling potatoes
- 3 Tbsp. grated Parmesan cheese
- 3 Tbsp. minced fresh parsley
- 2 Tbsp. olive oil
- 1 Tbsp. minced fresh rosemary or
  1 tsp. dried rosemary, crushed
- 1 Tbsp. butter, melted
- ¼ tsp. salt
- ¼ tsp. pepper

1. Preheat oven to 425°. Place potatoes in a large saucepan and cover with water. Bring to a boil. Reduce heat; cover and cook 10 minutes. Drain. Transfer to a greased 15x10x1-in. baking pan. Combine the remaining ingredients; drizzle over potatoes and toss to coat.
2. Bake, uncovered, 8-10 minutes or until tender, stirring once.
¾ CUP: 141 cal., 9g fat (3g sat. fat), 9mg chol., 184mg sod., 12g carb. (1g sugars, 2g fiber), 3g pro.

TEST KITCHEN TIP

You can interchange or add any of your favorite fresh herbs to this fingerling potato recipe. Add a tablespoon of minced fresh thyme and oregano, or use a teaspoon of dried herbs. If you're a big garlic fan, add a teaspoon or 2 of minced garlic to the mixture as well.

SPECTACULAR FINGERLING POTATOES

CRISPY FRIED ONION RINGS

CRISPY FRIED ONION RINGS

These crispy toppers add an extra element to already fantastic burgers. They're also perfect for giving your salads a little crunch.
—Taste of Home *Test Kitchen*

TAKES: 25 min. • MAKES: 12 servings

- ½ cup all-purpose flour
- ½ cup water
- 1 large egg, lightly beaten
- 1 tsp. seasoned salt
- ½ tsp. baking powder
- 1 large onion, very thinly sliced
  Oil for deep-fat frying

In a shallow bowl, whisk the first 5 ingredients. Separate the onion slices into rings. Dip rings into batter. In a deep-fat fryer, heat 1 in. oil to 375°. In batches, fry onion rings until golden brown, 1-1½ minutes on each side. Drain on paper towels. Serve immediately.
½ CUP: 71 cal., 5g fat (0 sat. fat), 16mg chol., 153mg sod., 5g carb. (1g sugars, 0 fiber), 1g pro.
BAKED ONION RINGS: Preheat oven to 425°. Beat egg in a shallow bowl. In another shallow bowl, mix ⅔ cup dry bread crumbs, ½ tsp. seasoned salt and ¼ tsp. pepper. Dip onion rings into egg, then roll in crumb mixture. Place on a baking sheet coated with cooking spray. Bake 15-18 minutes or until golden brown, turning once.
RED ONION RINGS: Use a red onion instead. With the flour mixture, whisk in ¼ tsp. cayenne.

BEST HUSH PUPPIES

Some years ago, when I was a cook on a large cattle ranch, I thought back to the hush puppies I'd had as a child on a southern trip. I created my own version of them for the ranchers. These go well as part of an old-fashioned fried chicken dinner with mashed potatoes and gravy, buttermilk biscuits, corn on the cob and watermelon pickles!
—*Karyl Goodhart, Geraldine, MT*

PREP: 15 min. • **COOK:** 20 min. • **MAKES:** 3 dozen

- 2 cups yellow cornmeal
- ½ cup all-purpose flour
- 2 Tbsp. sugar
- 2 tsp. baking powder
- 1 tsp. salt
- ½ tsp. baking soda
- 1 large egg, room temperature, lightly beaten
- ¾ cup 2% milk
- ¾ cup cream-style corn
  Oil for deep-fat frying

1. In a large bowl, whisk the cornmeal, flour, sugar, baking powder, salt and baking soda. Add egg, milk and corn; stir just until combined.

2. In a deep-fat fryer, heat oil to 375°. Drop batter by tablespoonfuls, a few at a time, into hot oil. Fry until golden brown on both sides. Drain on paper towels. Serve warm.

1 HUSH PUPPY: 66 cal., 2g fat (0 sat. fat), 6mg chol., 129mg sod., 10g carb. (1g sugars, 0 fiber), 1g pro.

BEST HUSH PUPPIES

AIR-FRYER HERB & LEMON CAULIFLOWER

AIR-FRYER HERB & LEMON CAULIFLOWER

A standout cauliflower side is easy to prepare with just a few ingredients. Crushed red pepper flakes add a touch of heat.
—*Susan Hein, Burlington, WI*

TAKES: 20 min. • **MAKES:** 4 servings

- 1 medium head cauliflower, cut into florets (about 6 cups)
- 4 Tbsp. olive oil, divided
- ¼ cup minced fresh parsley
- 1 Tbsp. minced fresh rosemary
- 1 Tbsp. minced fresh thyme
- 1 tsp. grated lemon zest
- 2 Tbsp. lemon juice
- ½ tsp. salt
- ¼ tsp. crushed red pepper flakes

1. Preheat air fryer to 350°. In a large bowl, combine cauliflower and 2 Tbsp. olive oil; toss to coat. In batches, arrange cauliflower in a single layer on tray in air-fryer basket. Cook until the florets are tender and edges are browned, 8-10 minutes, stirring halfway through.

2. In a small bowl, combine the remaining ingredients; stir in the remaining 2 Tbsp. oil. Transfer cauliflower to a large bowl; drizzle with the herb mixture and toss to combine.

¾ CUP: 161 cal., 14g fat (2g sat. fat), 0 chol., 342mg sod., 8g carb. (3g sugars, 3g fiber), 3g pro. **DIABETIC EXCHANGES:** 3 fat, 1 vegetable.

HAM CROQUETTES WITH MUSTARD SAUCE

3. Spread into an 8-in. square baking dish; cover and refrigerate at least 2 hours.
4. In a shallow bowl, combine egg and water. Place bread crumbs in a separate shallow bowl. Shape ham mixture into 12 balls (mixture will be soft); roll each ball in egg mixture, then in bread crumbs. Cover and refrigerate 2 hours longer.
5. In an electric skillet or deep fryer, heat oil to 375°. Fry croquettes, a few at a time, 2-3 minutes or until golden brown, turning once. Drain on paper towels.
6. Meanwhile, for the sauce, in a small saucepan, melt butter. Stir in flour, salt and pepper until smooth; gradually add milk. Bring to a boil; cook and stir until thickened, about 2 minutes. Stir in mustard. Serve with croquettes.

1 CROQUETTE WITH 2 TSP. SAUCE: 188 cal., 14g fat (5g sat. fat), 44mg chol., 503mg sod., 8g carb. (2g sugars, 0 fiber), 7g pro.

GINGER HONEY MUSTARD

This mustard tastes amazing with almost any meat, so slather it on ham, turkey or roast beef. It's also fantastic on pretzels!
—*Lynne Ellis, Lawrence, KS*

- -

PREP: 15 min. + chilling
MAKES: about ¾ cups

- ½   cup Dijon mustard
- ¼   cup honey
- ¾   tsp. ground ginger
- 1   tsp. lemon juice
- 1   tsp. canola oil

In a blender, combine all the ingredients; cover and process until smooth. Transfer to a jar or container. Refrigerate 2 hours before serving. Store in the refrigerator.
2 TBSP. 76 cal., 3g fat (0 sat. fat), 0 chol., 506mg sod., 14g carb. (11g sugars, 0 fiber), 1g pro.

HAM CROQUETTES WITH MUSTARD SAUCE

Whenever I have any leftover ham, I set it aside for these crispy croquettes. I shape them early in the day, then simply fry them at dinnertime. The mustard sauce is mild and pairs well with ham.
—*Kathy Vincek, Toms River, NJ*

- -

PREP: 35 min. + chilling
COOK: 5 min./batch
MAKES: 1 dozen

- 2   cups finely chopped fully cooked ham
- 1   Tbsp. finely chopped onion
- 1   tsp. minced fresh parsley
- ¼   cup butter, cubed
- ¼   cup all-purpose flour
- ¼   tsp. salt
- ⅛   tsp. pepper
- 1   cup 2% milk
- 1   large egg
- 2   Tbsp. water
- ¾   cup dry bread crumbs
      Oil for deep-fat frying

SAUCE
- 1½   tsp. butter
- 1½   tsp. all-purpose flour
- ¼   tsp. salt
      Dash pepper
- ½   cup 2% milk
- 4½   tsp. yellow mustard

1. In a small bowl, combine ham, onion and parsley; set aside.
2. In a small saucepan, melt butter. Stir in flour, salt and pepper until smooth; gradually add milk. Bring to a boil; cook and stir 1 minute or until thickened. Stir into the ham mixture.

CAPE COD CORN PUDDING

A family member passed along this recipe for corn baked with cheddar and ricotta. Don't skip the fresh basil—it adds a hint of sweet flavor reminiscent of mint and anise.
—*Melinda Messer, Benson, NC*

PREP: 20 min. • **BAKE:** 30 min. + standing • **MAKES:** 8 servings

- ¼ cup butter, cubed
- 5 cups frozen corn (about 24 oz.)
- 1 medium onion, finely chopped
- 4 large eggs, lightly beaten
- 2 cups whole milk
- 1 cup whole-milk ricotta cheese
- ½ cup cornmeal
- 1 Tbsp. sugar
- 1 tsp. salt
- ¾ tsp. pepper
- 1½ cups shredded cheddar cheese, divided
- 2 Tbsp. chopped fresh basil, optional

1. Preheat oven to 375°. In a 6-qt. stockpot, heat butter over medium-high heat. Add corn and onion; cook and stir until onion is crisp-tender, 6-8 minutes. Remove from heat.
2. In a large bowl, whisk eggs, milk, ricotta cheese, cornmeal, sugar, salt and pepper. Stir in ¾ cup cheddar cheese, corn mixture and, if desired, basil.
3. Transfer to a greased 11x7-in. baking dish. Sprinkle with the remaining cheddar cheese. Bake, uncovered, 30-35 minutes or until set. Let stand 10 minutes before serving.
1 SERVING: 378 cal., 21g fat (12g sat. fat), 148mg chol., 582mg sod., 34g carb. (9g sugars, 2g fiber), 17g pro.

CAPE COD
CORN PUDDING

DREAMY
POLENTA

DREAMY POLENTA

I grew up eating polenta, so it's a must at my holiday gatherings. Traditional recipes require constant stirring, but using my handy slow cooker allows me to turn my attention to the lineup of other foods on my spread.
—*Ann Voccola, Milford, CT*

PREP: 10 min. • **COOK:** 5 hours • **MAKES:** 12 servings

- 1 Tbsp. butter
- 5 cups whole milk
- 4 cups half-and-half cream
- 12 Tbsp. butter, cubed, divided
- 2 cups yellow cornmeal
- ¾ tsp. salt
- ½ tsp. minced fresh rosemary
- ¼ tsp. pepper
- 2 cups shredded Asiago cheese

1. Generously grease a 5-qt. slow cooker with 1 Tbsp. butter. Add milk, cream, 6 Tbsp. cubed butter, cornmeal, salt, rosemary and pepper; stir to combine.
2. Cook, covered, on low until polenta is thickened, 5-6 hours, whisking every hour. Just before serving, whisk again; stir in cheese and the remaining 6 Tbsp. cubed butter. Garnish with additional rosemary if desired.
¾ CUP: 444 cal., 29g fat (18g sat. fat), 100mg chol., 379mg sod., 29g carb. (9g sugars, 1g fiber), 13g pro.

BROWN
SUGAR SQUASH

PARMESAN FETTUCCINE

This simple side dish makes a pretty presentation. With only four ingredients, it's ready in no time. Try it with steak for a super treat!
—*Sundra Hauck, Bogalusa, LA*

TAKES: 20 min. • **MAKES:** 4 servings

- 8 oz. uncooked fettuccine
- ⅓ cup butter, cubed
- ⅓ cup grated Parmesan cheese
- ⅛ tsp. pepper

1. Cook fettuccine according to package directions; drain.
2. In a large skillet, melt butter over low heat. Add fettuccine and stir until coated. Sprinkle with cheese and pepper; toss to coat.
¾ CUP: 359 cal., 19g fat (11g sat. fat), 46mg chol., 260mg sod., 41g carb. (2g sugars, 2g fiber), 10g pro.

STRAWBERRY VINEGAR

This recipe is a wonderful start to a vinaigrette. It is so easy to infuse the vinegar with the strawberries, and it tastes wonderful.
—*Marilyn Nash, Orange City, FL*

PREP: 15 min. + chilling • **MAKES:** yield varies

- Whole strawberries
- Vinegar
- Sugar

Fill a large jar with rinsed strawberries (do not hull). Cover the berries with vinegar and seal jar. Refrigerate for 10 days. Strain and measure vinegar into pints; discard berries. For each pint of vinegar, add 3 cups sugar. Bring mixture to a boil; boil 2 minutes. Cool. Pour into sterile bottles or jars; seal.
2 TBSP: 84 cal., 0 fat (0 sat. fat), 0 chol., 0 sod., 22g carb. (22g sugars, 0 fiber), 0 pro.

STRAWBERRY
VINEGAR

BROWN SUGAR SQUASH

With brown sugar, butter and honey, what's not to love about this sweet and yummy fall side dish? It's ready in no time in the microwave.
—*Kara de la Vega, Santa Rosa, CA*

TAKES: 20 min. • **MAKES:** 4 servings

- 2 medium acorn squash
- ¼ cup packed brown sugar
- 2 Tbsp. butter
- 4 tsp. honey
- ¼ tsp. salt
- ¼ tsp. pepper

1. Cut squash in half; discard seeds. Place squash cut side down in a microwave-safe dish. Cover and microwave on high until tender, 10-12 minutes.
2. Turn squash cut side up. Fill centers of squash with brown sugar, butter and honey; sprinkle with salt and pepper. Cover; microwave on high until heated through, 2-3 minutes more.
½ FILLED SQUASH: 216 cal., 6g fat (4g sat. fat), 15mg chol., 200mg sod., 43g carb. (25g sugars, 3g fiber), 2g pro.

TEST KITCHEN TIP

This acorn squash recipe is sweet, but try making it sweet and spicy by adding cayenne or red pepper flakes. Or amp up the umami with cooked bacon bits. You can also skip the sugar and butter, and mash and eat it on its own.

PARMESAN
FETTUCCINE

BACON PRETZEL
FURY, PAGE 149

Breads, Rolls & Muffins

Put the butter out to soften, because hot homemade bread is just pages away! Discover rich scones, pretty popovers, delicious muffin variations and more. There are even savory dinner breads that grace the table in 20 minutes flat.

BEST OF THE BEST RECIPES

Drop Doughnuts p. 143

All-Star Muffin Mix p. 150

Triple Tomato Flatbread p. 153

GARLIC & OREGANO BREAD

GARLIC & OREGANO BREAD

Homemade bread can be easy! Literally just stir up the dough. No kneading. No sweating. Use a rubber spatula for easy clean-up.
—*Megumi Garcia, Milwaukee, WI*

PREP: 30 min. + rising • **BAKE:** 50 min. • **MAKES:** 1 loaf (16 pieces)

1½ tsp. active dry yeast
1¾ cups water (70° to 75°)
3½ cups plus 1 Tbsp. all-purpose flour, divided
2 tsp. salt
1 Tbsp. cornmeal or additional flour
½ cup garlic cloves, peeled and quartered
¼ cup 2% milk
2 Tbsp. minced fresh oregano

1. In a small bowl, dissolve yeast in water. In a large bowl, mix 3½ cups flour and salt. Using a rubber spatula, stir in yeast mixture to form a soft, sticky dough. Do not knead. Cover and let rise at room temperature 1 hour.
2. Punch down dough. Turn onto a lightly floured surface. Pat into a 9-in. square. Fold dough into thirds, forming a 9x3-in. rectangle. Fold rectangle into thirds, forming a 3-in. square. Turn dough over; place in a greased bowl. Cover; let rise at room temperature until almost doubled, about 1 hour.
3. Punch down dough and repeat folding process. Return dough to bowl; refrigerate, covered, overnight.
4. Dust bottom of a disposable foil roasting pan with cornmeal. In a small microwave-safe bowl, combine the garlic and milk; microwave on high for 45 seconds. Drain garlic, discarding milk. Turn dough onto a floured surface; knead in garlic and oregano. Shape dough into a 6-in. round loaf.

5. Transfer to prepared pan; dust top with remaining 1 Tbsp. flour. Cover pan; let dough rise at room temperature until dough expands to a 7½-in. loaf, about 1¼ hours.
6. Preheat oven to 500°. Using a sharp knife, make a slash ¼ in. deep across top of loaf. Cover pan tightly with foil. Bake on lowest oven rack 25 minutes.
7. Reduce oven setting to 450°. Remove foil; bake 25-30 minutes longer or until deep golden brown. Remove loaf to a wire rack to cool.
1 PIECE: 112 cal., 0 fat (0 sat. fat), 0 chol., 297mg sod., 23g carb. (0 sugars, 1g fiber), 3g pro. **DIABETIC EXCHANGES:** 1½ starch.

MINI TOFFEE ROLLS

I found this delicious recipe in a magazine years ago and adapted the original to make it my own. The rich bite-sized treats are full of cinnamon flavor!
—*Carol Gillespie, Chambersburg, PA*

PREP: 20 min. • **BAKE:** 15 min. • **MAKES:** 4 dozen

6 Tbsp. butter, softened
½ cup packed brown sugar
1 tsp. ground cinnamon
⅓ cup milk chocolate English toffee bits
2 tubes (8 oz. each) refrigerated crescent rolls
1 cup confectioners' sugar
4½ tsp. 2% milk
¼ tsp. vanilla extract

1. In a small bowl, cream the butter, brown sugar and cinnamon until light and fluffy, 5-7 minutes. Stir in toffee bits.
2. Separate each tube of crescent dough into 4 rectangles; seal perforations. Spread evenly with butter mixture. Roll up each rectangle jelly-roll style, starting with a long side.
3. Cut each into six 1-in. slices; place cut side down into 2 greased 8-in. square baking dishes. Bake at 375° for 14-16 minutes or until golden brown.
4. In a small bowl, combine the confectioners' sugar, milk and vanilla until smooth. Drizzle over warm rolls.
1 MINI ROLL: 74 cal., 4g fat (2g sat. fat), 4mg chol., 91mg sod., 10g carb. (7g sugars, 0 fiber), 1g pro.

DID YOU KNOW?

Most vanilla comes from Madagascar and Reunion Island—formerly known as the Bourbon Islands—off the southeast coast of Africa. Bourbon vanilla has a strong, clear vanilla flavor and creamy finish. For an attractive look, use specky vanilla, which has tiny flecks of vanilla seeds.

RGHOST PEPPER
POPCORN
CORNBREAD

GHOST PEPPER POPCORN CORNBREAD

I love popcorn and lots of spice and heat. I have recently been dabbling with ghost peppers and came up with this twist on classic cornbread. Try adding corn kernels for more texture.
—*Allison Antalek, Cuyahoga Falls, OH*

PREP: 40 min. • **BAKE:** 25 min. • **MAKES:** 8 servings

- ⅓ cup popcorn kernels
- 1 Tbsp. coconut oil or canola oil
- 1 cup all-purpose flour
- ½ cup sugar
- 2 tsp. baking powder
- ½ tsp. baking soda
- ½ tsp. salt
- ½ tsp. crushed ghost chile pepper or cayenne pepper
- 2 large eggs, room temperature
- 1½ cups 2% milk
- 4 Tbsp. melted butter, divided
- ½ cup chopped seeded jalapeno peppers

1. Preheat oven to 400°. Heat a 10-in. cast-iron or other ovenproof skillet over medium heat. Add the popcorn and coconut oil; cook until oil begins to sizzle. Cover and shake until popcorn stops popping, 3-4 minutes. Remove from heat.
2. Place popcorn in a food processor; process until ground. Transfer 2 cups of ground popcorn to a large bowl (save remainder for another use). Stir in flour, sugar, baking powder, baking soda, salt and chile pepper. Add eggs, milk and 2 Tbsp. butter; beat just until moistened. Stir in jalapenos.
3. Add remaining 2 Tbsp. butter to skillet; place in oven to heat skillet. Carefully remove hot skillet from oven. Add batter; bake until top is golden brown and a toothpick inserted in center

comes out clean, 25-30 minutes. Cut into wedges; serve warm.
NOTE: Wear disposable gloves when cutting hot peppers; the oils can burn skin. Avoid touching your face.
1 PIECE: 241 cal., 10g fat (6g sat. fat), 65mg chol., 432mg sod., 34g carb. (15g sugars, 2g fiber), 6g pro.

DROP DOUGHNUTS

Remember this recipe after your next holiday dinner. I use any leftover mashed potatoes to make these light and fluffy doughnuts. The recipe was originally created by my neighbor's mother-in-law as a breakfast treat or snack.
—*Marilyn Kleinfall, Elk Grove Village, IL*

TAKES: 25 min. • **MAKES:** 3½ dozen

- ½ cup mashed potatoes (made with milk and butter)
- ¼ cup sugar
- 1 large egg, lightly beaten
- ½ cup sour cream
- ½ tsp. vanilla extract
- 1½ cups all-purpose flour
- ½ tsp. baking soda
- ¼ tsp. baking powder
  Oil for deep-fat frying
  Optional: Additional sugar or confectioners' sugar

1. In a large bowl, combine the potatoes, sugar, egg, sour cream and vanilla. Combine next 3 ingredients; stir in potato mixture.
2. Heat oil in an electric skillet or deep-fat fryer to 375°. Drop batter by teaspoonfuls, a few at a time, into hot oil. Fry until golden brown on both sides. Drain on paper towels. If desired, roll in sugar while warm.
1 DOUGHNUT: 42 cal., 2g fat (1g sat. fat), 5mg chol., 29mg sod., 5g carb. (1g sugars, 0 fiber), 1g pro.

DROP
DOUGHNUTS

DOLLYWOOD'S CINNAMON BREAD COPYCAT

before removing from pan to a wire rack. Serve warm.

1 PIECE: 215 cal., 7g fat (4g sat. fat), 27mg chol., 167mg sod., 34g carb. (6g sugars, 1g fiber), 5g pro.

SPEEDY CINNAMON BREAD: If you don't feel like making your own dough, you can substitute a thawed 1-lb. frozen bread loaf. Cut the topping ingredients by ¼ and slightly decrease the bake time.

MANGO BREAD

I live in Maui, and when it's mango season, everyone shares their crop so all get to try different varieties. I like the Hayden because it's big, but mangoes from the supermarket, diced from the refrigerated section or frozen can be used in this recipe.
—*Lillian Takaki, Wailuku, HI*

PREP: 20 min. • **BAKE:** 1¼ hours + cooling
MAKES: 24 servings

  4 **cups all-purpose flour**
2½ **cups sugar**
  4 **tsp. ground cinnamon**
  3 **tsp. baking soda**
  1 **tsp. salt**
  6 **large eggs**
1½ **cups canola oil**
  2 **tsp. vanilla extract**
  4 **cups chopped peeled mangoes**
  1 **cup chopped walnuts, optional**
  1 **cup raisins, optional**

1. Preheat oven to 325°. In a large bowl, whisk flour, sugar, cinnamon, baking soda and salt. In another bowl, whisk eggs, oil and vanilla until blended. Add to flour mixture; stir just until moistened. Fold in mango and, if desired, walnuts and raisins.

2. Transfer to a greased 13x9-in. baking dish lined with parchment. Bake until a toothpick inserted in center comes out clean, 1¼ -1½ hours. Cool completely in dish on a wire rack.

1 PIECE: 317 cal., 16g fat (1g sat. fat), 47mg chol., 274mg sod., 42g carb. (25g sugars, 1g fiber), 4g pro.

DOLLYWOOD'S CINNAMON BREAD COPYCAT

Whenever I go to Dollywood, the first thing I do is run to the Grist Mill to get in line for the cinnamon bread. It's that good! I tried making it at home and think I got pretty close. I prefer using pumpkin pie spice instead of just cinnamon to give it a little more flavor.
—*Amanda Singleton, Kingsport, TN*

PREP: 30 min. + rising
BAKE: 30 min. + cooling
MAKES: 1 loaf (16 pieces)

  1 **pkg. (¼ oz.) active dry yeast**
1¼ **cups warm 2% milk (110° to 115°)**
2½ **cups bread flour**
⅓ **cup butter, melted**
  2 **Tbsp. sugar**
  1 **large egg, room temperature**
¾ **tsp. salt**
  2 **to 2½ cups all-purpose flour**
TOPPING
¼ **cup sugar**
  2 **tsp. pumpkin pie spice, apple pie spice or ground cinnamon**
¼ **cup butter, melted**

1. In a large bowl, dissolve yeast in warm milk. Add bread flour, butter, sugar, egg and salt. Beat on medium speed for 3 minutes. Stir in enough all-purpose flour to form a firm dough.

2. Turn onto a floured surface; knead until smooth and elastic, 6-8 minutes. Place in a greased bowl, turning once to grease the top. Cover and let rise in a warm place until doubled, about 1 hour.

3. In a pie plate, combine sugar and pie spice. Pour melted butter into another pie plate. Punch dough down. Turn onto a lightly floured surface. Shape into a loaf. Using a sharp knife, make 4 very deep slits straight across bread dough (without cutting all the way through the loaf). Roll dough in butter, massaging butter onto all surfaces until dough is thoroughly coated. Roll dough in the sugar mixture, firmly pressing mixture onto dough. Place dough in a parchment-lined 9x5-in. loaf pan. Cover and let rise in a warm place until doubled, about 30 minutes. Meanwhile, preheat oven to 350°.

4. Bake until golden brown, 30-40 minutes. (Cover loosely with foil if top browns too quickly.) Cool 10 minutes

TRADITIONAL SCONES

CELERY-ONION POPOVERS

I found this handwritten recipe in a cookbook I received from my mom. With onion and celery, these pleasing popovers taste a little like stuffing.
—*Barbara Carlucci, Orange Park, FL*

PREP: 15 min. • **BAKE:** 40 min. • **MAKES:** 9 popovers

- 2 cups all-purpose flour
- 1 tsp. onion salt
- ⅛ tsp. celery salt
- 4 large eggs, room temperature
- 2 cups 2% milk
- ¼ cup grated onion
- ¼ cup grated celery
- 3 Tbsp. butter, melted

1. In a large bowl, combine the flour, onion salt and celery salt. Combine the eggs, milk, onion, celery and butter; whisk into the dry ingredients just until blended. Grease and flour the bottom and sides of 9 popover cups; fill two-thirds full with batter.
2. Bake at 450° for 15 minutes. Reduce heat to 350° (do not open oven door). Bake 25 minutes longer or until deep golden brown (do not underbake). Immediately cut a slit in the top of each popover to allow steam to escape.
1 POPOVER: 202 cal., 8g fat (4g sat. fat), 98mg chol., 306mg sod., 25g carb. (3g sugars, 1g fiber), 7g pro.

TRADITIONAL SCONES

When my wife and I hosted an English tea, I learned that making scones is very simple. These are light and very tasty.
—*Chuck Hinz, Parma, OH*

PREP: 20 min. • **BAKE:** 25 min. • **MAKES:** 1 dozen

- 2 cups all-purpose flour
- 2 Tbsp. sugar
- 3 tsp. baking powder
- ⅛ tsp. baking soda
- 6 Tbsp. cold butter, cubed
- 1 large egg, room temperature
- ½ cup buttermilk
  Jam of your choice, optional

1. Preheat oven to 350°. In a large bowl, combine the flour, sugar, baking powder and baking soda. Cut in butter until mixture resembles coarse crumbs. In a small bowl, whisk egg and buttermilk until blended; add to crumb mixture just until moistened.
2. Turn dough onto a lightly floured surface; gently knead 10 times. Divide the dough in half; pat each portion into a 5-in. circle. Cut each circle into 6 wedges.
3. Separate wedges and place 1 in. apart on an ungreased baking sheet. Bake until golden brown, 25-30 minutes. Serve warm, with jam if desired.
1 SCONE: 144 cal., 6g fat (4g sat. fat), 33mg chol., 170mg sod., 19g carb. (3g sugars, 1g fiber), 3g pro.

CELERY-ONION POPOVERS

SWEET POTATO-CRANBERRY DOUGHNUTS

SWEET POTATO-CRANBERRY DOUGHNUTS

I grew up near Idaho where they're famous for spudnuts, a doughnut made from mashed potatoes. These use sweet potatoes and tart cranberries!
—*Joni Hilton, Rocklin, CA*

- -

PREP: 25 min. + rising • **COOK:** 5 min./batch • **MAKES:** 2 dozen

- ¼ cup sugar
- 1½ tsp. active dry yeast
- 1 tsp. ground cinnamon
- ½ tsp. salt
- 4 to 4½ cups all-purpose flour
- 1 cup 2% milk
- ¼ cup shortening
- 2 Tbsp. water
- 2 large eggs, room temperature
- ½ cup mashed sweet potatoes
- ½ cup finely chopped dried cranberries
  Oil for deep-fat frying
- 1 cup confectioners' sugar
- 2 to 3 Tbsp. apple cider or juice

1. In a large bowl, combine the sugar, yeast, cinnamon, salt and 1½ cups flour. In a small saucepan, heat the milk, shortening and water to 120°-130°; add to dry ingredients. Beat on medium speed for 2 minutes. Add the eggs, mashed potatoes and cranberries; beat 2 minutes longer. Stir in enough remaining flour to form a firm dough.

2. Do not knead. Place in a greased bowl, turning once to grease the top. Cover and let rise in a warm place until doubled, about 1 hour.

3. Punch dough down. Turn onto a lightly floured surface; roll out to ½-in. thickness. Cut with a floured 2½-in. doughnut cutter; reroll scraps. Place 1 in. apart on greased baking sheets. Cover and let rise until doubled, about 30 minutes.

4. In an electric skillet or deep fryer, heat oil to 375°. Fry doughnuts, a few at a time, until golden brown on both sides. Drain on paper towels. Combine confectioners' sugar and apple cider; dip warm doughnuts in glaze.

1 GLAZED DOUGHNUT: 191 cal., 8g fat (1g sat. fat), 18mg chol., 63mg sod., 27g carb. (10g sugars, 1g fiber), 3g pro.

SOUR CREAM CHIVE BREAD

This savory loaf mildly flavored with chives is delicious when served warm with a meal, soup, salad or stew. It also tastes wonderful toasted the next day for breakfast.
—*Deborah Plank, West Salem, OH*

- -

PREP: 10 min. • **BAKE:** 3 hours • **MAKES:** 1 loaf (1½ lbs., 16 pieces)

- ⅔ cup 2% milk (70° to 80°)
- ¼ cup water (70° to 80°)
- ¼ cup sour cream
- 2 Tbsp. butter
- 1½ tsp. sugar
- 1½ tsp. salt
- 3 cups bread flour
- ⅛ tsp. baking soda
- ¼ cup minced chives
- 2¼ tsp. active dry yeast

In bread machine pan, place all ingredients in the order suggested by manufacturer. Select basic bread setting. Choose crust color and loaf size if available. Bake according to bread machine directions (check dough after 5 minutes of mixing; add 1 to 2 Tbsp. of water or flour if needed).

NOTE: We recommend you do not use a bread machine's time-delay feature for this recipe.

1 PIECE: 105 cal., 2g fat (2g sat. fat), 8mg chol., 253mg sod., 18g carb. (1g sugars, 1g fiber), 4g pro.

SOUR CREAM CHIVE BREAD

SIMITS

SIMITS

These bread treats from my Turkish heritage are commonly eaten for breakfast. They are not boiled as regular bagels are, but dipped in molasses and sesame seeds prior to baking. This gives them a chewy texture similar to that of the bagels we know and love.

—*Trisha Kruse, Eagle, ID*

PREP: 30 min. + rising • **BAKE:** 20 min.
MAKES: 8 servings

- 3¾ to 4¼ cups all-purpose flour
- 1 pkg. (¼ oz.) active dry yeast
- 1 tsp. salt
- ¾ cup 2% milk
- ¼ cup unsalted butter, cubed
- ¼ cup olive oil
- 1 large egg, room temperature
- 3 Tbsp. warm water (110° to 115°)
- 3 Tbsp. molasses
- ½ cup sesame seeds, toasted

1. In a large bowl, mix 2 cups flour, yeast and salt. In a small saucepan, heat the milk, butter and oil to 120°-130°. Add to dry ingredients; beat on medium speed 2 minutes. Add the egg; beat on high 2 minutes. Stir in enough remaining flour to form a stiff dough.

2. Turn onto a floured surface; knead until smooth and elastic, 6-8 minutes. Place dough in a greased bowl, turning once to grease top. Cover and let rise in a warm place until doubled, about 1 hour.

3. Preheat oven to 350°. Punch down dough. Divide and shape into 8 balls. Push thumb through center of each, stretching and shaping to form an even ring with a 2-in. hole. Place on a floured surface. Cover with a kitchen towel; let rest 15 minutes.

4. In a shallow bowl, whisk warm water and molasses. Place sesame seeds in a separate shallow bowl. Dip bagels in molasses mixture, then roll in seeds to coat.

5. Place 2 in. apart on parchment-lined baking sheets. Bake until golden brown, 20-25 minutes. Remove from pans to wire racks to cool.

1 SIMIT: 406 cal., 19g fat (6g sat. fat), 40mg chol., 319mg sod., 50g carb. (3g sugars, 3g fiber), 10g pro.
POPPY SEED VARIATION: Mix poppy seeds in with the sesame seeds for a variation.

BACON PRETZEL FURY

(SHOWN ON PAGE 140)

I tried a bacon pretzel fury the last time I was at Busch Gardens, and afterward I ferociously tried to re-create it at home. I don't live anywhere close to the amusement park, so this version curbs my hankerings when back in the Midwest.
—*Alvin Ciepluch, Kenosha, WI*

PREP: 40 min. + rising • **BAKE:** 15 min. • **MAKES:** 6 pretzels

- 12 thick-sliced bacon strips
- 1 pkg. (¼ oz.) active dry yeast
- 1½ cups warm water (110° to 115°)
- 2 Tbsp. sugar
- 2 Tbsp. butter, melted
- 1½ tsp. salt
- 4 to 4½ cups all-purpose flour
- 8 cups water
- ⅓ cup baking soda
- 1 large egg yolk
- 1 Tbsp. cold water
- 1 tsp. coarse salt
- ¼ cup butter, melted
- 6 wooden skewers

1. In a large skillet, cook bacon over medium heat until partially cooked but not crisp. Remove to paper towels to drain; set aside.
2. In a large bowl, dissolve yeast in warm water. Add sugar, butter, salt and 2 cups flour. Beat until smooth. Stir in enough remaining flour to form a soft dough (dough will be sticky).
3. Turn dough onto a floured surface; knead until smooth and elastic, 6-8 minutes. Place in a greased bowl, turning once to grease top. Cover and let rise in a warm place until doubled, about 1 hour.
4. Preheat oven to 425°. In a Dutch oven, bring 8 cups water and baking soda to a boil. Punch dough down; divide into 6 portions. Roll each portion into a 32-in. rope. Fold each rope in half, creating an upside-down V shape. Place 1 bacon strip over the top of each "V"; braid dough around the bacon, layering in a second bacon strip halfway. Pinch ends to seal; tuck under. Add to boiling water, 1 at a time; cook 30 seconds. Remove with 2 slotted spoons; drain on paper towels.
5. Place on greased baking sheets. Lightly beat egg yolk and cold water; brush over pretzels. Sprinkle with coarse salt. Bake until golden brown, 12-15 minutes. Brush with melted butter; sprinkle with additional coarse salt if desired. Remove from pans to wire racks. Insert skewers; serve warm.
1 PRETZEL: 533 cal., 21g fat (9g sat. fat), 61mg chol., 1699mg sod., 68g carb. (4g sugars, 3g fiber), 17g pro.

CHEESE-FILLED
GARLIC ROLLS

CHEESE-FILLED GARLIC ROLLS

To change up plain old dinner rolls, I added mozzarella. Now my family wants them at every gathering. I don't mind, even in a time crunch.
—*Rosalie Fittery, Philadelphia, PA*

PREP: 20 min. + rising • **BAKE:** 15 min. • **MAKES:** 2 dozen

- 1 loaf (1 lb.) frozen bread dough, thawed
- 24 cubes part-skim mozzarella cheese (¾ in. each, about 10 oz.)
- 3 Tbsp. butter, melted
- 2 tsp. minced fresh parsley
- 1 garlic clove, minced
- ½ tsp. Italian seasoning
- ½ tsp. crushed red pepper flakes
- 2 Tbsp. grated Parmigiano-Reggiano cheese

1. Divide dough into 24 portions. Shape each portion around a cheese cube to cover completely; pinch to seal. Place each roll in a greased muffin cup, seam side down. Cover with kitchen towels; let rise in a warm place until doubled, about 30 minutes. Preheat oven to 350°.
2. In a small bowl, mix butter, parsley, garlic, Italian seasoning and pepper flakes. Brush over rolls; sprinkle with cheese. Bake until golden brown, 15-18 minutes.
3. Cool 5 minutes before removing from pans. Serve warm.
1 ROLL: 103 cal., 5g fat (2g sat. fat), 12mg chol., 205mg sod., 10g carb. (1g sugars, 1g fiber), 5g pro.

READER REVIEW

"Amazing rolls. I always get compliments on them every time I make them. Tonight I will be making them for guests. I will double the recipe and only put cheese in half for those who don't want the cheese."

—DBBURRUS19, TASTEOFHOME.COM

Morning Glory

Do you know the muffin plan? Start with one brilliant base, add your fave flavors, then pop 'em in the oven to make your breakfast blossom.

RHUBARB-ORANGE MUFFINS

CAPPUCCINO MUFFINS

APRICOT-CHERRY MUFFINS

APPLE-CHEESE MUFFINS

FIG-PISTACHIO MUFFINS

ALL-STAR MUFFIN MIX

In a large bowl, whisk 8 cups **all-purpose flour**, 3 cups **sugar**, 3 Tbsp. **baking powder**, 2 tsp. **salt**, 2 tsp. **ground cinnamon** and 2 tsp. **ground nutmeg** until well blended. Store in airtight containers in a cool, dry place or in the freezer up to 6 months. **Makes: 4 batches.**

To prepare plain muffins:
Preheat oven to 400°. Whisk together 1 large room temperature **egg**, 1 cup **2% milk** and ½ cup melted **butter**. Add 2¾ cups **muffin mix**, stirring just until moistened. Fill paper-lined muffin cups three-fourths full. Bake until a toothpick inserted in center comes out clean, 18-21 minutes. Cool 5 minutes before removing from pan to a wire rack. Serve warm. **Makes: 1 dozen.**

—Nancy Mackey, Madison, OH

Blueberry Muffins:
Prepare muffins as directed, folding 1 cup **fresh or frozen blueberries** into prepared batter.

Banana Muffins:
Prepare muffins as directed, adding 1 cup mashed **ripe bananas** to egg mixture.

Cranberry-Pecan Muffins:
Prepare muffins as directed, tossing 1 cup chopped **fresh or frozen cranberries**, ½ cup chopped **pecans** and 3 Tbsp. **sugar** with muffin mix before adding to egg mixture.

Rhubarb-Orange Muffins:
Prepare muffins as directed, adding ⅓ cup **orange marmalade** to egg mixture and folding ¾ cup diced **fresh or frozen rhubarb** into prepared batter.

Cappuccino Muffins:
Prepare muffins as directed, tossing 1 cup **miniature semisweet chocolate chips** and 2 tsp. **instant coffee granules** with muffin mix before adding to egg mixture.

Carrot-Raisin Muffins:
Prepare muffins as directed, tossing ¾ cup shredded **carrots** and ⅓ cup **golden raisins** with muffin mix before adding to egg mixture.

Apricot-Cherry Muffins:
Prepare muffins as directed, tossing ½ cup each chopped **dried apricots** and **dried cherries** with muffin mix before adding to egg mixture.

Zucchini-Pineapple Muffins:
Prepare muffins as directed, tossing ½ cup each shredded peeled **zucchini** and drained **pineapple tidbits** with muffin mix before adding to egg mixture.

Apple-Cheese Muffins:
Prepare muffins as directed, tossing ½ cup each shredded peeled **apple** and **shredded Colby-Monterey Jack cheese** with muffin mix before adding to egg mixture.

Fig-Pistachio Muffins:
Prepare muffins as directed, tossing 1 cup chopped **dried figs** and ⅓ cup chopped, toasted **pistachios** with muffin mix before adding to egg mixture.

NONNI'S FRITOLE

My Italian grandmother was famous for her fritole and made these treats for her family and friends. Later we found her recipe card and tried making them without success for several years. We finally figured out the missing part of this recipe —the self-rising flour! Now we can have these as often as we like. It brings back so many wonderful memories.
—Ann Marie Eberhart, Gig Harbor, WA

- -

PREP: 15 min. • **COOK:** 5 min./batch • **MAKES:** 4 dozen

- 4 cups self-rising flour
- ½ cup sugar
- 3 large eggs, room temperature
- 1 cup 2% milk
- 3 oz. whiskey, rum or orange juice
- 2 medium apples, peeled and grated
- 8 tsp. grated orange zest
  Oil for deep-fat frying
  Confectioners' sugar

1. In a large bowl, whisk flour and sugar. In another bowl, whisk eggs, milk and whiskey until blended. Add to dry ingredients, stirring just until moistened. Fold in apples and zest.
2. In an electric skillet or deep fryer, heat oil to 375°. Drop batter by tablespoonfuls, a few at a time, into hot oil. Fry until golden brown, about 2 minutes on each side. Drain on paper towels. Dust with confectioners' sugar.
NOTE: As a substitute for each cup of self-rising flour, place 1½ tsp. baking powder and ½ tsp. salt in a measuring cup. Add all-purpose flour to measure 1 cup.
1 FRITOLE: 69 cal., 2g fat (0 sat. fat), 12mg chol., 131mg sod., 11g carb. (3g sugars, 0 fiber), 2g pro.

NONNI'S
FRITOLE

SPICED
INDIAN
RUSKS

SPICED INDIAN RUSKS

Indian cake rusks, or delicious soft cakes, use traditional warm spices and can have add-ins like fruit or nuts. They can also be dipped in chocolate for a special treat. This plain version is a favorite of my friends and family.
—Mary Lou Timpson, Centennial Park, AZ

- -

PREP: 25 min. • **BAKE:** 40 min. + cooling • **MAKES:** 14 servings

- ½ cup unsalted butter, softened
- ½ cup sugar
- 1 tsp. vanilla extract
- 2 large eggs, room temperature
- 1 cup all-purpose flour
- 1 tsp. baking powder
- 1 tsp. each ground ginger, cardamom, coriander, fenugreek, turmeric and cumin

1. Preheat oven to 325°. Line an 8-in. square baking pan with parchment, letting ends extend up sides. In a large bowl, cream butter, sugar and vanilla until light and fluffy, 5-7 minutes. Add eggs, 1 at a time, beating well after each addition. In another bowl, whisk remaining ingredients; gradually beat into creamed mixture. Transfer to prepared pan.
2. Bake until edges pull away from the sides or a toothpick inserted in center comes out clean, 30-32 minutes. Cool in pan on a wire rack for 10 minutes. Lifting with parchment, remove from pan. Transfer to a cutting board. Using a serrated knife, cut into fourteen 4x1-in. slices. Place on baking sheets, cut side down.
3. Bake until golden brown, 8-10 minutes on each side. Remove from pans to wire racks to cool completely.
1 PIECE: 132 cal., 7g fat (4g sat. fat), 44mg chol., 46mg sod., 15g carb. (7g sugars, 0 fiber), 2g pro.

STRAWBERRIES
& CREAM SCONES

STRAWBERRIES & CREAM SCONES

When it comes to a special treat from the oven, these scones are hard to beat. I can never eat just one!
—*Agnes Ward, Stratford, ON*

TAKES: 30 min. • **MAKES:** 8 scones

- 2 cups all-purpose flour
- ⅓ cup sugar
- 2¼ tsp. baking powder
- 1 tsp. grated lemon zest
- ¾ tsp. salt
- ¼ tsp. ground cinnamon
- ¼ cup cold butter, cubed
- ⅔ cup half-and-half cream
- ½ cup coarsely chopped fresh strawberries
- 1 large egg, lightly beaten
- 2 tsp. coarse sugar

1. In a large bowl, combine flour, sugar, baking powder, lemon zest, salt and cinnamon. Cut in butter until mixture resembles coarse crumbs. Stir in cream just until moistened.

2. Turn onto a lightly floured surface; knead 5 times. Gently knead in the strawberries, about 5 times. Pat into an 8-in. circle; brush with egg and sprinkle with coarse sugar. Cut into 8 wedges.

3. Separate wedges and place 2 in. apart on a greased baking sheet. Bake at 425° for 9-12 minutes or until golden brown. Serve warm.

1 SCONE: 233 cal., 8g fat (5g sat. fat), 33mg chol., 387mg sod., 35g carb. (11g sugars, 1g fiber), 4g pro.

HOW-TO

Make Strawberry Scones

A few ingredients and a gentle hand are all you need to bake up these classics.

Step 1: Layer Flavors
A dusting of cinnamon adds depth of flavor and coziness, while lemon zest brightens the taste of fresh berries.

Step 2: Add Cream
Stir in half-and-half until the mix is just combined. Don't overmix the dough or you'll lose the scones' tender texture.

Step 3: Fold In the Fruit
Be gentle as you fold the sliced berries into the scone dough. A few turns is all it takes to incorporate them.

Step 4: Brush
An egg wash is an easy way to add shine and a professional-level finish to homemade scones. A wash will also help the coarse sugar in Step 5 adhere better.

Step 5: Sprinkle
Add a little extra to your scones with coarse sugar. A pinch scattered over the top of your scones adds crunch and a little sweetness.

Step 6: Divide and Bake
Use a bench scraper to divide the scones into 8 wedges. You can also use this tool to help shuttle each scone to the baking tray.

TRIPLE
TOMATO
FLATBREAD

TRIPLE TOMATO FLATBREAD

Tomatoes are the reason I have a vegetable garden, and I developed this recipe as a way to show off my garden's plum, sun-dried and cherry tomatoes. The dish is easy and will impress.
—*Rachel Kimbrow, Portland, OR*

- -

TAKES: 20 min. • **MAKES:** 8 pieces

- 1 tube (13.8 oz.) refrigerated pizza crust
  Cooking spray
- 3 plum tomatoes, finely chopped (about 2 cups)
- ½ cup soft sun-dried tomato halves (not packed in oil), julienned
- 2 Tbsp. olive oil
- 1 Tbsp. dried basil
- ¼ tsp. salt
- ¼ tsp. pepper
- 1 cup shredded Asiago cheese
- 2 cups yellow and/or red cherry tomatoes, halved

1. Unroll and press dough into a 15x10-in. rectangle. Transfer dough to an 18x12-in. piece of heavy-duty foil coated with cooking spray; spritz dough with cooking spray. In a large bowl, toss plum tomatoes and sun-dried tomatoes with oil and seasonings.

2. Carefully invert dough onto grill rack; remove foil. Grill, covered, over medium heat 2-3 minutes or until bottom is golden brown. Turn; grill 1-2 minutes longer or until second side begins to brown.

3. Remove from grill. Spoon plum tomato mixture over crust; top with cheese and cherry tomatoes. Return flatbread to grill. Grill, covered, 2-4 minutes or until crust is golden brown and cheese is melted.

1 PIECE: 235 cal., 9g fat (3g sat. fat), 12mg chol., 476mg sod., 29g carb. (7g sugars, 3g fiber), 8g pro. **DIABETIC EXCHANGES:** 1½ starch, 1½ fat, 1 vegetable.

TO BAKE FLATBREAD: Preheat oven to 425°. Unroll and press dough onto bottom of a 15x10x1-in. baking pan coated with cooking spray. Bake 6-8 minutes or until lightly browned. Assemble flatbread as directed. Bake 8-10 minutes longer or until crust is golden and cheese is melted.

AIR-FRYER ONION CRESCENT ROLLS

French-fried onions aren't just for green bean casserole. Sprinkle them onto crescent roll dough before rolling up and you'll end up with a crunchy treat inside flaky pastry.
—*Barbara Nowakowski, North Tonawanda, NY*

- -

TAKES: 20 min. • **MAKES:** 8 servings

- 1 tube (8 oz.) refrigerated crescent rolls
- 1⅓ cups french-fried onions, divided
- 1 large egg
- 1 Tbsp. water

1. Do not preheat air fryer. Unroll crescent dough and separate into triangles. Sprinkle each with about 2 Tbsp. onions. Roll up each from the wide end. Curve ends down to form crescents.

2. In batches, place crescents in a single layer on greased tray in air-fryer basket. Beat egg and water; brush over dough. Sprinkle with remaining onions. Cook at 325° until golden brown, 7-8 minutes. Serve warm.

NOTE: In our testing, we find cook times vary dramatically among brands of air fryers. As a result, we give wider than normal ranges on suggested cook times. Begin checking at the first time listed and adjust as needed.

1 ROLL: 170 cal., 10g fat (4g sat. fat), 23mg chol., 301mg sod., 16g carb. (3g sugars, 0 fiber), 3g pro.

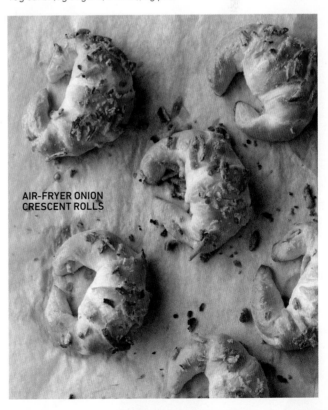

AIR-FRYER ONION
CRESCENT ROLLS

MORNING CRISPIES
PAGE 158

Breakfast & Brunch

Everyone will want to rise and shine when these wholesome specialties are on the menu. Here you'll find the makings for lazy weekend mornings, holiday company and every day in between.

GREEK TOFU
SCRAMBLE

PROSCIUTTO EGG PANINI

Change up the usual bacon and egg sandwich by piling on prosciutto instead. It's a breakfast worth waking up for!
—*Erin Mylroie, Santa Clara, UT*

TAKES: 30 min. • **MAKES:** 8 servings

- 3 large eggs
- 2 large egg whites
- 6 Tbsp. fat-free milk
- 1 green onion, thinly sliced
- 1 Tbsp. Dijon mustard
- 1 Tbsp. maple syrup
- 8 slices sourdough bread
- 8 thin slices prosciutto or deli ham
- ½ cup shredded sharp cheddar cheese
- 8 tsp. butter

1. In a small bowl, whisk the eggs, egg whites, milk and green onion. Coat a large skillet with cooking spray and place over medium heat. Add egg mixture; cook and stir until completely set.
2. Combine mustard and syrup; spread over 4 bread slices. Layer with scrambled eggs, prosciutto and cheese; top with the remaining bread. Butter outsides of the sandwiches.
3. Cook on a panini maker or indoor grill for 3-4 minutes or until bread is browned and cheese is melted. Cut each panini in half to serve.

½ SANDWICH: 228 cal., 10g fat (5g sat. fat), 111mg chol., 640mg sod., 21g carb. (3g sugars, 1g fiber), 13g pro. **DIABETIC EXCHANGES:** 1½ starch, 1½ fat, 1 lean meat.

READER REVIEW

"I used deli ham instead of prosciutto and loved these. Great weekend breakfast for the family."
—KRASMUSS, TASTEOFHOME.COM

GREEK TOFU SCRAMBLE

I created this recipe over a decade ago when I was in college, and it was the first time I ever had tofu. I wanted to eat tofu and be earthy like all my cool vegetarian friends. Well, the vegetarian diet may not have stuck with me, but this recipe is still popular with my family!
—*Jennifer Garcia, Franklin, MA*

TAKES: 25 min. • **MAKES:** 2 servings

- 1 pkg. (9 oz.) fresh spinach (about 10 cups)
- 1 Tbsp. butter
- ⅔ lb. firm tofu, drained and crumbled
- ¼ cup coarsely chopped pitted kalamata olives
- 2 Tbsp. fresh lemon juice
- 2 tsp. minced fresh oregano or 1 tsp. dried oregano
- ¼ tsp. pepper
- ¼ cup crumbled feta cheese
  Optional: Grated lemon zest and diced tomatoes

1. Place spinach and 1 Tbsp. water in a large skillet. Cook over medium-high heat until spinach is wilted, 2-3 minutes. Transfer to a colander; drain, pressing out as much liquid as possible. Coarsely chop.
2. In same skillet, melt the butter over medium-high heat. Add tofu, olives, lemon juice, oregano, pepper and spinach. Cook, stirring frequently, until heated through, 3-4 minutes. Add feta; cook until slightly melted. Serve immediately; sprinkle with lemon zest and tomatoes if desired.
1½ CUPS: 240 cal., 17g fat (6g sat. fat), 23mg chol., 481mg sod., 9g carb. (2g sugars, 3g fiber), 17g pro.

SLOW-COOKER OATMEAL

Waking up to this wonderful aroma and piping hot meal is a fantastic way to start the day!
—*Brandy Schaefer, Glen Carbon, IL*

PREP: 10 min. • **COOK:** 3 hours • **MAKES:** 4 servings

- 2 cups 2% milk
- 1 cup old-fashioned oats
- 1 cup chopped peeled tart apple
- ½ cup raisins
- ¼ cup packed brown sugar
- ¼ cup chopped walnuts
- 1 Tbsp. butter, melted
- ½ tsp. ground cinnamon
- ¼ tsp. salt

In a 1½-qt. slow cooker coated with cooking spray, combine all ingredients. Cover and cook on low for 3-4 hours or until liquid is absorbed and oatmeal is tender. If desired, serve with additional milk, walnuts and cinnamon.

1 CUP: 340 cal., 13g fat (5g sat. fat), 20mg chol., 225mg sod., 51g carb. (32g sugars, 3g fiber), 10g pro.

TEST KITCHEN TIP

Add seasonal fruits and berries to your oatmeal for sweetness. Reach for nuts and seeds (such as chia, flax or sunflower) to add texture and more protein. To really mix things up, skip the sugar, spices and fruit and treat your oatmeal as a savory breakfast grain bowl topped with a soft-cooked egg, spinach and bacon.

SLOW-COOKER OATMEAL

REUBEN & RYE STRATA

REUBEN & RYE STRATA

This make-ahead dish is wonderful for brunch, lunch, supper or as a potluck meal that is so easy to prepare. If you prefer it, substitute turkey pastrami for the corned beef.
—*Mary Louise Lever, Rome, GA*

PREP: 25 min. + chilling • **BAKE:** 50 min. + standing
MAKES: 10 servings

- 10 slices rye bread, cubed (about 6 cups)
- 1¼ lbs. thinly sliced deli corned beef, chopped
- 2 cups shredded Gruyere cheese or Swiss cheese
- 1 cup sauerkraut, rinsed, drained and patted dry
- ¼ cup chopped dill pickles
- 6 large eggs
- 2 cups 2% milk
- ⅔ cup Thousand Island salad dressing
  Dash garlic powder
- ¼ cup shredded Parmesan cheese
  Chopped fresh parsley

1. Place bread cubes in a greased 13x9-in. baking dish. Top with corned beef, Gruyere, sauerkraut and pickles. In a large bowl, whisk eggs, milk, dressing and garlic powder. Pour over bread. Refrigerate, covered, overnight.
2. Preheat oven to 350°. Remove strata from refrigerator while oven heats. Bake, uncovered, 45 minutes. Sprinkle with Parmesan. Bake until a knife inserted in the center comes out clean, 5-10 minutes longer. Let stand 10-15 minutes before cutting. Sprinkle with parsley.

1 PIECE: 382 cal., 22g fat (9g sat. fat), 175mg chol., 1377mg sod., 21g carb. (6g sugars, 2g fiber), 25g pro.

MORNING CRISPIES

(SHOWN ON PAGE 154)

These large cinnamon-sugar pastries make quite an impression on the table. Serve them with brunch or as an afternoon treat.
—*Emily Goad, Franklin, IN*

PREP: 30 min. + rising • **BAKE:** 15 min. + cooling
MAKES: 1½ dozen

- 1 pkg. (¼ oz.) active dry yeast
- ½ cup warm water (110° to 115°)
- 1 cup warm whole milk (110° to 115°)
- 2 cups sugar, divided
- ½ cup canola oil
- 1¼ tsp. salt
- 2 large eggs, room temperature
- 1½ tsp. lemon extract
- 5½ to 6 cups all-purpose flour
- 6 Tbsp. butter, softened, divided
- 1 Tbsp. ground cinnamon

1. In a large bowl, dissolve yeast in water; let stand for 5 minutes. Add milk, ½ cup sugar, oil, salt, eggs, extract and 2 cups flour; beat well. Stir in enough remaining flour to make a soft dough.
2. Turn onto a floured surface; knead until smooth and elastic, 6-8 minutes. Place in a greased bowl, turning once to grease top. Cover and let rise in a warm place until doubled, about 1 hour.
3. Punch down dough. Turn onto a floured surface, roll out into a ¼-in.-thick rectangle. Spread with 2 Tbsp. butter and sprinkle with ⅓ cup sugar. Fold dough in half lengthwise; roll out to ¼-in. thickness. Spread with 2 Tbsp. butter and sprinkle with ⅓ cup sugar.
4. Fold in half widthwise; roll to ¼-in. thickness. Spread with remaining butter and sprinkle with ⅓ cup sugar. Fold in half lengthwise; roll out to an 18x10-in. rectangle. Combine cinnamon and remaining ½ cup sugar; sprinkle half over the dough to within ¼ in. of all edges.
5. Roll up jelly-roll style, starting with a short side; pinch seam to seal. Cut into ½-in. slices and place on greased baking sheets (4 to 6 slices per sheet). Cover with waxed paper and flatten with palm of hand. Sprinkle with remaining cinnamon sugar. Let stand for 30 minutes.
6. Preheat oven to 400°. Bake until golden brown, 12-15 minutes. Immediately remove from pans to wire racks to cool completely.
1 PASTRY: 334 cal., 11g fat (3g sat. fat), 32mg chol., 209mg sod., 53g carb. (23g sugars, 1g fiber), 5g pro.

TEST KITCHEN TIP

If you don't have lemon extract, you can substitute 3 tsp. of finely grated lemon zest when making these pastries. Or use orange extract for a sun-kissed variation.

SHEET-PAN YELLOW BELLS & EGGS

This recipe is healthful and versatile—just add your favorite veggies, or even fruit. I love sweet potato and apple tossed into the mix.
—*Marina Castle-Kelley, Canyon Country, CA*

PREP: 15 min. • **BAKE:** 20 min. • **MAKES:** 2 servings

- ½ medium zucchini, halved lengthwise and cut into ¼-in. slices
- 1 cup fresh sliced Brussels sprouts
- 1 shallot, sliced
- ¼ tsp. salt
- ¼ tsp. pepper
- 2 Tbsp. olive oil
- 1 large sweet yellow pepper, cut into 4 rings
- 4 large eggs
- ¼ cup shredded Parmesan cheese

1. Preheat oven to 350°. Place first 5 ingredients in a large bowl. Drizzle with oil; toss to coat. Place pepper rings on a baking sheet. Arrange vegetable mixture around peppers. Bake for 12 minutes.
2. Break and slip an egg into center of each pepper ring; sprinkle with Parmesan. Bake until whites are set and yolks begin to thicken, 8-10 minutes.
2 PEPPER RINGS WITH 1½ CUP VEGETABLES: 373 cal., 26g fat (7g sat. fat), 379mg chol., 626mg sod., 16g carb. (3g sugars, 3g fiber), 20g pro.

SHEET-PAN YELLOW BELLS & EGGS

GREEN
SHAKSHUKA

COUNTRY CORNCAKES

Although we live in a suburban area, we are lucky to have plenty of farms nearby where we can purchase fresh homegrown corn. When it's out of season, though, I do substitute canned or frozen corn in this favorite recipe.
—Anne Frederick, New Hartford, NY

PREP: 15 min. • COOK: 20 min. • MAKES: 14 corncakes

- 1½ cups yellow cornmeal
- ¼ cup all-purpose flour
- 1 Tbsp. sugar
- 1 tsp. baking soda
- ½ tsp. salt
- 1 large egg, room temperature
- 1½ cups buttermilk
- 2 Tbsp. butter, melted
- 1½ cups fresh or frozen corn
  Optional: Sour cream, 6 cooked and crumbled bacon strips, and 2 Tbsp. minced chives

1. In a bowl, combine the first 5 ingredients; make a well in the center. In another bowl, beat the egg, buttermilk and butter; pour into well and stir just until blended. Gently stir in corn; do not overmix. Cover and let stand for 5 minutes.

2. Pour batter by ¼ cupfuls onto a greased cast-iron skillet or griddle over medium-high heat. Turn when bubbles form on the top, 2-3 minutes. Cook until second side is golden brown. Top with sour cream, bacon and chives if desired.

2 CORNCAKES: 220 cal., 5g fat (3g sat. fat), 41mg chol., 451mg sod., 37g carb. (6g sugars, 3g fiber), 7g pro.

GREEN SHAKSHUKA

This breakfast recipe is packed with healthy green vegetables as well as eggs and feta cheese for protein to start your day. The Italian parsley adds a lot of flavor to the fresh green vegetables. Try making this dish with lemon-infused olive oil if you can find it in your grocery store.
—Carrie Dault, Baxter, TN

PREP: 20 min. • COOK: 20 min. • MAKES: 4 servings

- 1 Tbsp. olive oil
- ½ lb. fresh Brussels sprouts, quartered
- 1 medium green pepper, chopped
- 1 tsp. kosher salt, divided
- ¼ cup reduced-sodium chicken broth or vegetable broth, divided
- 3 garlic cloves, minced
- 1 small bunch kale, trimmed and chopped (about 8 cups)
- 9 oz. fresh baby spinach, chopped (about 7 cups)
- ¼ cup fresh parsley leaves, minced
- 4 large eggs
- ¼ cup crumbled feta cheese
- 1 tsp. grated lemon zest

1. In a large skillet, heat oil over medium-high heat. Add Brussels sprouts, green pepper and ½ tsp. salt; cook and stir until lightly browned, 10-12 minutes. Add 2 Tbsp. broth and the garlic; cook 1 minute longer. In batches if needed, add kale, spinach and parsley; cook and stir until wilted, 3-4 minutes. Stir in remaining 2 Tbsp. broth and ½ tsp. salt.

2. With back of spoon, make 4 wells in vegetable mixture; break an egg into each well. Sprinkle with feta and lemon zest. Cook, covered, until egg whites are completely set and yolks begin to thicken but are not hard, 4-6 minutes.

1 EGG WITH 1 CUP VEGETABLE MIXTURE: 209 cal., 10g fat (3g sat. fat), 190mg chol., 756mg sod., 18g carb. (2g sugars, 6g fiber), 15g pro. **DIABETIC EXCHANGES:** 1 starch, 1 medium-fat meat, ½ fat.

COUNTRY
CORNCAKES

HAM & CHEESE BREAKFAST SLIDERS

I turned one of my favorite sliders into a breakfast sandwich, then exchanged the regular mustard for spicy brown to give it more zip. The recipe is now a mainstay. When we host overnight guests, I make these little sandwiches the night before and finish them in the morning before popping them into the oven to bake.
—*Jill Landis, Shinnston, WV*

TAKES: 30 min. • BAKE: 10 min. • MAKES: 1 dozen

- ½ cup butter, cubed, plus 1 Tbsp. butter, divided
- 2 Tbsp. brown sugar
- 2 Tbsp. spicy brown mustard, divided
- 1 tsp. Worcestershire sauce
- 12 dinner rolls, split
- 6 slices deli ham, halved
- 6 large eggs
- 2 Tbsp. 2% milk
- 6 slices cheddar cheese, halved

1. Preheat oven to 350°. In a small saucepan, combine ½ cup butter, brown sugar, 1 Tbsp. mustard and Worcestershire sauce; bring to a boil. Cook and stir until sugar is dissolved, 1-2 minutes. Remove from the heat.
2. Place roll bottoms, cut side up, in an ungreased 13x9-in. baking dish. Top each with 1 piece of ham.
3. In a large bowl, whisk the eggs, milk and remaining 1 Tbsp. mustard until blended. In a large nonstick skillet, heat remaining 1 Tbsp. butter over medium heat. Pour in egg mixture; cook and stir until eggs are thickened and no liquid egg remains. Spoon scrambled eggs evenly over ham. Top with cheese. Replace bun tops. Brush butter mixture over bun tops. Bake, uncovered, until cheese is melted, 10-15 minutes.
1 SLIDER: 299 cal., 18g fat (10g sat. fat), 154mg chol., 524mg sod., 22g carb. (4g sugars, 1g fiber), 12g pro.

HAM & CHEESE BREAKFAST SLIDERS

QUINOA BREAKFAST BOWL

QUINOA BREAKFAST BOWL

This is such a bright and healthy way to start the day! The basil, tomatoes and avocado add a nice fresh taste to the dish.
—*Karen Kelly, Germantown, MD*

TAKES: 30 min. • MAKES: 1 serving

- ⅔ cup water
- ⅓ cup quinoa, rinsed
- ¼ tsp. salt, divided
- ¼ tsp. pepper, divided
- 1 large egg
- ½ cup grape tomatoes, halved
- ¼ cup loosely packed basil leaves
- ½ medium ripe avocado, peeled and sliced
  Balsamic glaze

1. Place water in a small saucepan. Bring to a boil; add quinoa and ⅛ tsp. each salt and pepper. Reduce heat; cover and simmer until tender, 12-15 minutes.
2. Meanwhile, heat a small nonstick skillet over medium-high heat. Break egg into pan; reduce heat to low. Sprinkle with remaining ⅛ tsp. salt and pepper. Cook until white is set and yolk begins to thicken, turning once if desired.
3. Fluff quinoa with a fork; place in a serving bowl. Top with tomatoes, basil, avocado and cooked egg. Serve with balsamic glaze.
1 BOWL: 411 cal., 19g fat (3g sat. fat), 186mg chol., 674mg sod., 46g carb. (4g sugars, 10g fiber), 17g pro.

CORNED BEEF HASH & EGGS

Sunday breakfasts have always been special in our house. It's fun to get in the kitchen and cook with the kids. No matter how many new recipes we try, the kids always rate this No. 1!
—*Rick Skildum, Maple Grove, MN*

PREP: 15 min. • **BAKE:** 20 min.
MAKES: 8 servings

- 1 pkg. (32 oz.) frozen cubed hash browns
- 1½ cups chopped onion
- ½ cup canola oil
- 4 to 5 cups chopped cooked corned beef
- ½ tsp. salt
- 8 large eggs
  Salt and pepper to taste
- 2 Tbsp. minced fresh parsley

1. In a large ovenproof skillet, cook hash browns and onion in oil until potatoes are browned and onion is tender. Remove from the heat; stir in corned beef and salt.
2. Make 8 wells in the hash browns. Break 1 egg into each well. Sprinkle with salt and pepper. Cover and bake at 325° for 20-25 minutes or until eggs reach desired doneness. Garnish with parsley.

1 SERVING: 442 cal., 30g fat (6g sat. fat), 242mg chol., 895mg sod., 24g carb. (3g sugars, 2g fiber), 20g pro.

CORNED BEEF
HASH & EGGS

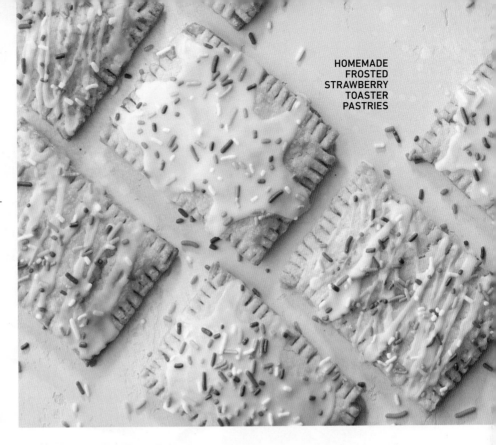

HOMEMADE
FROSTED
STRAWBERRY
TOASTER
PASTRIES

HOMEMADE FROSTED STRAWBERRY TOASTER PASTRIES

I love this classic treat from childhood! Homemade Pop-Tarts are, of course, awesome for breakfast, but they are also a satisfying dessert since they are really similar to hand pies. These pastries are worth the extra effort.
—*Andrea Potischman, Menlo Park, CA*

PREP: 45 min. + chilling
BAKE: 15 min. + cooling
MAKES: 8 servings

- 2 cups all-purpose flour
- 2 Tbsp. sugar
  Dash salt
- 1 cup cold unsalted butter, cubed
- 1 large egg
- 2 to 4 Tbsp. 2% milk
- ½ tsp. vanilla extract

FILLING
- ½ cup seedless strawberry jam
- 1 Tbsp. cornstarch
- ¼ tsp. vanilla extract
- 1 large egg

FROSTING
- 1¼ cups confectioners' sugar
- 2 Tbsp. 2% milk
  Nonpareils, optional

1. Place flour, sugar and salt in a food processor; pulse until blended. Add the butter; pulse until butter is the size of peas. In a small bowl, whisk egg, 2 Tbsp. milk and vanilla. While pulsing, add the egg mixture to form moist crumbs. If needed, add more milk, 1 tsp. at a time, to form moist crumbs. Divide dough in half. Shape each into a disk; wrap and refrigerate 1 hour or overnight.
2. For the filling, in a small bowl, combine jam, cornstarch and vanilla extract.
3. Preheat oven to 375°. On a lightly floured surface, roll half the dough into a 12x8-in. rectangle. Cut into eight 4x3-in. rectangles. Transfer to a parchment-lined baking sheet. Whisk egg; brush over rectangles all the way to edges. Spoon about 1 Tbsp. filling over each pastry to within ½ in. of edges. Roll remaining dough into a 12x8-in. rectangle; cut into eight 4x3-in. rectangles and place over filling. Press edges with a fork to seal.
4. Bake until edges are golden brown and filling is bubbly, 15-18 minutes. Remove from baking sheet to a wire rack to cool. For frosting, mix confectioners' sugar and milk until smooth. Spread on pastries. If desired, sprinkle with nonpareils. Let stand until set.

1 PASTRY: 475 cal., 24g fat (15g sat. fat), 97mg chol., 40mg sod., 60g carb. (34g sugars, 1g fiber), 5g pro.

POWER
BREAKFAST
SANDWICH

❄ POWER BREAKFAST SANDWICH

When I'm looking for a quick breakfast on the go, I always love to have these made and waiting in the freezer. I can grab one, pop it in the microwave and then head out the door with something nutritious.
—Jolene Martinelli, Fremont, NH

PREP: 20 min. • **BAKE:** 15 min.
MAKES: 6 servings

- 1 tsp. olive oil
- ¼ cup chopped onion
- ¼ cup chopped sweet red or orange pepper
- ¼ cup chopped fresh baby spinach
- 6 large eggs
- ¼ tsp. salt
- ¼ tsp. pepper
- 6 Italian turkey sausage links, casings removed
- 1 pkg. (12 oz.) multigrain sandwich thins, split
- 6 slices cheddar, Swiss or pepper jack cheese

1. Preheat oven to 350°. In a large nonstick skillet, heat oil over medium-high heat. Add onion and sweet pepper; cook and stir until tender, 3-4 minutes. Add spinach; cook 1 minute longer. Remove from heat; let cool 5 minutes. In a large bowl, whisk eggs, salt, pepper and onion mixture. Divide egg mixture among 6 greased 4-in. muffin top tins. Bake until the eggs are set, 12-15 minutes.

2. Meanwhile, shape sausage into six 5-in. patties. In the same skillet, cook patties over medium heat until a thermometer reads 160°, 4-5 minutes on each side. Drain if necessary on paper towels. Layer sandwich bottoms with sausage patties, egg rounds and cheese; replace tops.

FREEZE OPTION: Wrap sandwiches in waxed paper and then in foil; freeze in a freezer container. To use, remove foil. Microwave a waxed paper-wrapped sandwich at 50% power until thawed, 1-2 minutes. Turn sandwich over; microwave at 100% power until hot and a thermometer reads at least 165°, 30-60 seconds. Let stand 2 minutes before serving.

1 SANDWICH: 434 cal., 23g fat (9g sat. fat), 257mg chol., 1026mg sod., 31g carb. (3g sugars, 7g fiber), 30g pro.

How to Make Burrata Toast

*Spread toasted **bread** with 1 tsp. **extra virgin olive oil**. Spread 2 oz. **burrata cheese** over toast. Sprinkle with ⅛ tsp. **sea salt** and freshly **ground pepper**. If desired, drizzle with additional olive oil.*

Roasted Cherry Tomato Burrata Toast

Toss 1/2 cup **cherry tomatoes** with ½ tsp. **olive oil**. Place on a rimmed baking sheet. Roast at 400° until tomatoes begin to burst, about 10 minutes. Spread tomatoes over **burrata**; sprinkle with **salt** and **pepper**.

A Lotta Burrata

This rich, creamy, spreadable cheese is our new favorite way to start the day. Try these combos and thank us later!

Avocado Burrata Toast

Top **burrata** with ¼ medium ripe sliced **avocado**. Drizzle with additional 1 tsp. **olive oil**; sprinkle with **salt** and **pepper**.

Hot Honey Lemon Burrata Toast

Drizzle **burrata** with 2 tsp. **hot honey**. Sprinkle with ½ tsp. grated **lemon zest**, **salt** and **pepper**.

Apricot Almond Burrata Toast

Top **burrata** with 2 tsp. **apricot preserves**. Sprinkle with 2 tsp. toasted **sliced almonds**, **salt** and **pepper**.

Strawberry Basil Burrata Toast

Top **burrata** with 2 sliced **fresh strawberries**. Drizzle with 1 tsp. **balsamic** glaze. Sprinkle with chopped **fresh basil**, **salt** and **pepper**.

Original Burrata Toast

Spread toast with **extra virgin olive oil**. Spread **burrata** over toast. Sprinkle with **salt** and **pepper**. If desired, drizzle with additional **olive oil**.

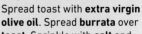

KETOLICIOUS CHEESY BISCUITS WITH TURKEY SAUSAGE

If you're craving a serious comfort food breakfast, look no further. These keto-friendly breakfast sandwiches check all the boxes!
—*Trisha Kruse, Eagle, ID*

PREP: 25 min. • **BAKE:** 15 min. • **MAKES:** 8 servings

- 2 cups almond flour
- 3 tsp. baking powder
- ¼ tsp. salt
- ¼ tsp. onion powder
- ¼ tsp. pepper
- 4 large eggs, room temperature
- 2½ cups shredded cheddar cheese
- ¼ cup heavy whipping cream

SAUSAGE

- ¼ cup finely chopped onion
- 1½ tsp. pepper
- 1 tsp. dried sage leaves
- ¾ tsp. salt
- 2 lbs. ground turkey
- 1 Tbsp. olive oil

1. Preheat oven to 350°. In a large bowl, whisk flour, baking powder, salt, onion powder and pepper. In another bowl, whisk the eggs, cheddar cheese and cream. Stir into flour mixture just until moistened. Drop dough by rounded ⅓ cupfuls 2 in. apart onto parchment-lined baking sheets. Bake 15-20 minutes or until golden.

2. Meanwhile, for sausage, in a large bowl, combine onion, pepper, sage and salt. Add turkey to mixture; mix lightly but thoroughly. Shape into eight 5-in. patties. Heat oil in a large nonstick skillet over medium heat. In batches, add patties. Cook until a thermometer reads 165°, 5-6 minutes on each side. Split biscuits in half; fill each with a sausage patty.

1 SANDWICH: 546 cal., 37g fat (12g sat. fat), 211mg chol., 806mg sod., 12g carb. (3g sugars, 2g fiber), 42g pro.

KETOLICIOUS CHEESY BISCUITS WITH TURKEY SAUSAGE

GOAT CHEESE & HAM OMELET

GOAT CHEESE & HAM OMELET

As a busy working mom, my breakfast needs to require minimal prep. I often combine the egg mixture beforehand and refrigerate overnight. Then all I have to do in the morning is heat up my skillet. My favorite part is the goat cheese filling, which gets nice and creamy from the heat of the omelet.
—*Lynne Dieterle, Rochester, MI*

TAKES: 20 min. • **MAKES:** 1 serving

- 4 large egg whites
- 2 tsp. water
- ⅛ tsp. pepper
- 1 slice deli ham, finely chopped
- 2 Tbsp. finely chopped green pepper
- 2 Tbsp. finely chopped onion
- 2 Tbsp. crumbled goat cheese
  Minced fresh parsley, optional

1. In a small bowl, whisk egg whites, water and pepper until blended; stir in ham, green pepper and onion. Heat a large skillet coated with cooking spray over medium-high heat. Pour in egg white mixture. Mixture should set immediately at edges. As egg whites set, push cooked portions toward the center, letting uncooked egg flow underneath.

2. When no liquid egg remains, sprinkle goat cheese on 1 side. Fold omelet in half; slide onto a plate. If desired, sprinkle with parsley.

1 OMELET: 143 cal., 4g fat (2g sat. fat), 27mg chol., 489mg sod., 5g carb. (3g sugars, 1g fiber), 21g pro. **DIABETIC EXCHANGES:** 3 lean meat, ½ fat.

OVERNIGHT YEAST WAFFLES

These easy, fluffy waffles are so delicious. I freeze them so I can enjoy them on busy mornings for breakfast.
—*Mary Balcomb, Florence, OR*

PREP: 15 min. + chilling
COOK: 5 min./batch • **MAKES:** 10 servings

- 1 pkg. (¼ oz.) active dry yeast
- ½ cup warm water (110° to 115°)
- 1 tsp. sugar
- 2 cups warm 2% milk (110° to 115°)
- ½ cup butter, melted
- 2 large eggs, room temperature, lightly beaten
- 2¾ cups all-purpose flour
- 1 tsp. salt
- ½ tsp. baking soda

1. In a large bowl, dissolve yeast in warm water. Add sugar; let stand 5 minutes. Add milk, butter and eggs; mix well. Combine flour and salt; stir into milk mixture. Cover and refrigerate overnight.

2. Stir batter; sift in baking soda and stir well. Bake waffles in a preheated waffle maker according to manufacturer's directions until golden brown.

2 WAFFLES: 220 cal., 12g fat (7g sat. fat), 74mg chol., 366mg sod., 22g carb. (3g sugars, 1g fiber), 6g pro.

⏱ 5i EASY STRAWBERRY BUTTER

After picking strawberries for the first time, I developed this fruity, spreadable butter. Try making other fruit spreads using raspberries or blackberries, or a seedless jam like apricot—my favorite.
—*Julie Herrera-Lemler, Rochester, MN*

TAKES: 5 min. • **MAKES:** 2¼ cups

- 6 large fresh strawberries, stems removed, room temperature
- 1 cup butter, softened
- ¾ to 1 cup confectioners' sugar

Pulse strawberries in a food processor until chopped. Add butter and ½ cup confectioners' sugar; process until blended. Add enough of the remaining confectioners' sugar to reach a spreading consistency and the desired level of sweetness. Store in the refrigerator for up to 1 week.

1 TBSP: 56 cal., 5g fat (3g sat. fat), 14mg chol., 41mg sod., 3g carb. (3g sugars, 0 fiber), 0 pro.

OVERNIGHT YEAST WAFFLES

EASY STRAWBERRY BUTTER

CREAMY
STRAWBERRY
CREPES

cooked, 15-20 seconds longer. Remove to a wire rack. Repeat with remaining batter, greasing pan as needed. When cool, stack crepes between pieces of waxed paper or paper towels.

3. For filling, in a small bowl, beat cream cheese, confectioners' sugar, lemon juice and zest, and vanilla until smooth. Fold in 2 cups berries and the whipped cream. Spoon about ⅓ cup filling down the center of each crepe; roll up. Garnish with remaining berries and, if desired, additional confectioners' sugar. Cover and refrigerate or freeze remaining crepes in an airtight container, unfilled, for another use.

2 CREPES: 415 cal., 26g fat (16g sat. fat), 115mg chol., 163mg sod., 40g carb. (28g sugars, 2g fiber), 7g pro.

BERRY BREAKFAST SMOOTHIES

Smooth out the morning rush with a boost of berries. It's tart, tangy and sweet, so there's no reason to add any extra sugar to this delightfully balanced beverage.
—*Elisabeth Larsen, Pleasant Grove, UT*

TAKES: 5 min. • **MAKES:** 5 servings

- 2 cups cranberry juice
- 2 containers (6 oz. each) raspberry yogurt
- 1 cup frozen unsweetened raspberries
- 1 cup frozen unsweetened blueberries
- 8 ice cubes

In a blender, combine all ingredients; cover and process until blended, 30-45 seconds. Pour mixture into chilled glasses; serve immediately.

1 CUP: 141 cal., 1g fat (1g sat. fat), 3mg chol., 39mg sod., 31g carb. (29g sugars, 2g fiber), 4g pro.

CREAMY STRAWBERRY CREPES

Wrap summer-ripe strawberries and creamy filling into these delicate crepes for an elegant brunch entree.
—*Kathy Kochiss, Huntington, CT*

PREP: 15 min. + chilling • **COOK:** 35 min. • **MAKES:** 7 servings

- 4 large eggs
- 1 cup 2% milk
- 1 cup water
- 2 Tbsp. butter, melted
- 2 cups all-purpose flour
- ¼ tsp. salt

FILLING

- 1 pkg. (8 oz.) cream cheese, softened
- 1¼ cups confectioners' sugar
- 1 Tbsp. lemon juice
- 1 tsp. grated lemon zest
- ½ tsp. vanilla extract
- 4 cups fresh strawberries, sliced, divided
- 1 cup heavy whipping cream, whipped

1. In a large bowl, whisk eggs, milk, water and butter. In another bowl, mix flour and salt; add to egg mixture and mix well. Refrigerate, covered, 1 hour.

2. Heat a lightly greased 8-in. nonstick skillet over medium heat. Stir batter. Fill a ¼-cup measure halfway with batter; pour into center of pan. Quickly lift and tilt pan to coat bottom evenly. Cook until top appears dry; turn crepe over and cook until bottom is

BERRY BREAKFAST
SMOOTHIES

OVERNIGHT BAKED OATMEAL

LIME-HONEY FRUIT SALAD

Nothing is more refreshing to me than a seasonal fruit salad enhanced with this simple lime-honey dressing.
—*Victoria Shevlin, Cape Coral, FL*

PREP: 20 min. + chilling • **MAKES:** 12 servings

- 1 tsp. cornstarch
- ¼ cup lime juice
- ¼ cup honey
- ½ tsp. poppy seeds
- 3 medium gala or Red Delicious apples, cubed
- 2 medium pears, cubed
- 2 cups seedless red grapes
- 2 cups green grapes

1. In a small microwave-safe bowl, combine cornstarch and lime juice until smooth. Microwave, uncovered, on high for 20 seconds; stir. Cook until slightly thickened, 10-15 seconds longer. Stir in honey and poppy seeds.
2. In a large bowl, combine the apples, pears and grapes. Pour dressing over fruit; toss to coat. Cover and refrigerate overnight.
¾ CUP: 96 cal., 0 fat (0 sat. fat), 0 chol., 2mg sod., 25g carb. (21g sugars, 2g fiber), 1g pro. **DIABETIC EXCHANGES:** 1½ fruit.

OVERNIGHT BAKED OATMEAL

My husband and I spent a long weekend at a bed-and-breakfast not far from our home. The owners shared this delicious recipe with me, which I made my own after a couple of simple changes.
—*Jennifer Cramer, Lebanon, PA*

PREP: 10 min. + chilling • **BAKE:** 40 min. • **MAKES:** 8 servings

- 2 large eggs, lightly beaten
- 3 cups 2% milk
- ¾ cup packed brown sugar
- ¼ cup canola oil
- 1½ tsp. ground cinnamon
- 1 tsp. salt
- 2 cups old-fashioned oats
- ¼ cup dried blueberries
- ¼ cup dried cherries
- ¼ cup sliced almonds

1. In a large bowl, whisk together first 6 ingredients. Stir in oats, blueberries and cherries. Transfer to a greased 8-in. square baking dish. Refrigerate, covered, 8 hours or overnight.
2. Preheat oven to 350°. Remove the oatmeal from refrigerator while oven heats. Stir oatmeal; sprinkle with almonds. Bake, uncovered, until golden brown and a thermometer reads 160°, 40-50 minutes. Serve warm.
½ CUP: 331 cal., 13g fat (2g sat. fat), 54mg chol., 364mg sod., 46g carb. (30g sugars, 4g fiber), 8g pro.

LIME-HONEY FRUIT SALAD

MAPLE
PANCAKES

MEXICALI QUICHE WITH AVOCADO CRUST

You've heard of avocado toast, but what about avocado crust? New Mexican cuisine is my go-to, so I created this quiche with my family's favorite ingredients: chorizo, tomatoes, avocado, green chiles and more.

—*Johnna Johnson, Scottsdale, AZ*

PREP: 30 min. • **BAKE:** 30 min. + standing • **MAKES:** 12 servings

- 6 oz. fresh chorizo
- 1½ cups all-purpose flour
- 1½ cups crushed Ritz crackers (about 38 crackers)
- ½ tsp. salt
- ⅔ cup butter-flavored shortening
- ½ cup cubed ripe avocado
- 2 cups shredded Swiss cheese
- 1 plum tomato, seeded and chopped
- 1 can (4 oz.) chopped green chiles, drained
- 5 large eggs
- 1 cup heavy whipping cream
- 1 cup half-and-half cream
- ½ tsp. ground cumin
  Additional ripe avocado, peeled and sliced, optional

1. Preheat oven to 400°. In a small skillet, cook chorizo over medium heat until cooked through, 4-5 minutes, breaking into crumbles; drain. Meanwhile, in a large bowl, mix flour, crackers and salt. Cut in shortening and avocado; toss with a fork until dough holds together when pressed. Press dough onto bottom of a greased 13x9-in. baking dish; prick with a fork.

2. Spoon chorizo over crust; top with cheese, tomato and chiles. In a large bowl, whisk eggs, heavy cream, half-and-half and cumin until blended; pour over top.

3. Bake on a lower oven rack until a knife inserted near the center comes out clean, about 30 minutes. Let stand 10 minutes before cutting. If desired, serve with additional avocado.

1 PIECE: 475 cal., 36g fat (15g sat. fat), 139mg chol., 481mg sod., 22g carb. (2g sugars, 1g fiber), 14g pro.

MAPLE PANCAKES

Our family looks forward to tapping the maple trees in March—and then enjoying the pure maple syrup year-round. This is just one of the recipes I like to make that has maple syrup as an ingredient.

—*Mary Colbath, Concord, NH*

TAKES: 30 min. • **MAKES:** 6 servings

- 3 cups all-purpose flour
- 4½ tsp. baking powder
- 1½ tsp. salt
- 3 large eggs
- 2¼ cups 2% milk
- ⅓ cup canola oil
- 3 Tbsp. maple syrup
  Optional: Additional maple syrup, butter and fresh blueberries

1. In a large bowl, combine flour, baking powder and salt. In another bowl, whisk eggs, milk, oil and syrup; stir into dry ingredients just until blended.

2. Preheat griddle over medium heat. Lightly grease griddle. Pour batter by ¼ cupfuls onto griddle; cook until bubbles on top begin to pop and bottoms are golden brown. Turn; cook until second side is golden brown (pancakes will be thin). Serve with additional maple syrup, butter and blueberries as desired.

3 PANCAKES: 445 cal., 17g fat (3g sat. fat), 100mg chol., 1031mg sod., 59g carb. (11g sugars, 2g fiber), 13g pro.

HOW-TO

Ripen Avocados Fast

When life hands you hard, less-than-ripe avocados, here's how to quickly ripen them. Place avocados in a paper bag with an apple or banana. Poke the bag a few times with a toothpick or scissors, and let ripen at room temperature for a day or two. The more fruits (and ethylene gas they give off), the faster the results.

MEXICALI QUICHE
WITH AVOCADO CRUST

**BACON POTATO
WAFFLES WITH
APPLESAUCE**

BACON POTATO WAFFLES WITH APPLESAUCE

My mother used to add bacon to a lot of recipes for extra flavor, so I modified this potato waffle by doing just that. It's the perfect recipe for using up leftover mashed potatoes, and the waffles go so well with applesauce.

—Laura Fall-Sutton, Buhl, ID

- -

PREP: 15 min. • **BAKE:** 5 min./batch
MAKES: 12 waffles

- 1 cup all-purpose flour
- 2 Tbsp. sugar
- 2 tsp. baking powder
- 1 tsp. salt
- 2 large eggs
- 1½ cups mashed potatoes
- 1 cup 2% milk
- 5 Tbsp. bacon drippings or canola oil
- 4 bacon strips, cooked and crumbled
- ¼ cup finely chopped onion
   Chunky applesauce

1. In a large bowl, combine flour, sugar, baking powder and salt. In another bowl, whisk eggs, mashed potatoes, milk and bacon drippings. Stir into dry ingredients just until moistened. Fold in the bacon and onion.

2. Bake mixture in a preheated waffle iron according to manufacturer's directions until golden brown. Serve with applesauce.

2 WAFFLES: 316 cal., 17g fat (6g sat. fat), 81mg chol., 895mg sod., 32g carb. (7g sugars, 1g fiber), 9g pro.

SUNNY-SIDE-UP HERBED TART

Feel free to be creative with this versatile egg tart. Try Canadian bacon or ham as the meat ingredient, and add toppings such as thyme, chopped spinach or goat cheese.

—Diana Neves, Lafayette, CA

- -

PREP: 30 min. • **BAKE:** 20 min.
MAKES: 4 servings

- 4 slices pancetta or 4 bacon strips
- 1 Tbsp. olive oil
- 1 cup sliced fresh mushrooms
- 2 Tbsp. chopped shallot
- 1 Tbsp. minced fresh tarragon or
   1 tsp. dried tarragon
- 1 tsp. sherry, optional
- ¼ cup shredded Gruyere or Swiss cheese
- ¼ cup shredded cheddar cheese
- 3 Tbsp. sour cream
- ⅛ tsp. salt
   Dash pepper
   TART
- 1 sheet frozen puff pastry, thawed
- 5 large eggs, divided use
- 1 tsp. water
- 1 Tbsp. minced chives
   Dash each salt and pepper

1. Preheat oven to 425°. In a large skillet, cook pancetta over medium heat until partially cooked but not crisp. Remove to paper towels to drain. In a small skillet, heat oil over medium heat; add mushrooms and shallot. Cook and stir until tender, 5-7 minutes. Add tarragon and, if desired, sherry; cook 1 minute longer.

2. Remove from heat; stir in cheeses, sour cream, salt and pepper. Set aside.

3. On a lightly floured surface, unfold puff pastry. Roll into a 10x9-in. rectangle. Transfer to a parchment-lined 15x10x1-in. baking pan. Prick with a fork.

4. Spread mushroom mixture over pastry to within 1 in. of edges. Top with pancetta (place pancetta near the edges of the mushroom mixture). Score edges of pastry with a fork. Beat 1 egg and water; brush over pastry edges. Bake until pastry is golden brown, 10-12 minutes.

5. Carefully crack the remaining eggs off-center into each corner. Bake until eggs are set, 8-10 minutes. Sprinkle with chives, salt and pepper. Cut into 4 pieces. Serve warm.

1 SERVING: 585 cal., 40g fat (13g sat. fat), 305mg chol., 893mg sod., 37g carb. (1g sugars, 5g fiber), 21g pro.

**SUNNY-SIDE-UP
HERBED TART**

OVERNIGHT OATMEAL

Because you make this convenient breakfast the night before, you can get some extra sleep in the morning. My husband adds coconut to his, and I stir in dried fruit.
—June Thomas, Chesterton, IN

- -

PREP: 10 min. + chilling • **MAKES:** 1 serving

- ⅓ cup old-fashioned oats
- 3 Tbsp. fat-free milk
- 3 Tbsp. reduced-fat plain yogurt
- 1 Tbsp. honey
- ½ cup assorted fresh fruit
- 2 Tbsp. chopped walnuts, toasted

In a small container or Mason jar, combine oats, milk, yogurt and honey. Top with fruit and nuts. Seal; refrigerate overnight.

NOTE: To toast nuts, bake in a shallow pan in a 350°; oven for 5-10 minutes or cook in a skillet over low heat until lightly browned, stirring occasionally.

1 SERVING: 345 cal., 13g fat (2g sat. fat), 4mg chol., 53mg sod., 53g carb. (31g sugars, 5g fiber), 10g pro.

HONEY COFFEE

For a soothing pick-me-up, sip this pleasantly sweet coffee, inspired by the taste of a traditional Spanish latte.
—Taste of Home *Test Kitchen*

- -

TAKES: 10 min. • **MAKES:** 4 servings

- 2 cups hot strong brewed coffee (French or other dark roast)
- ½ cup whole milk
- ¼ cup honey
- ⅛ tsp. ground cinnamon
  Dash ground nutmeg
- ¼ tsp. vanilla extract

In a small saucepan, combine the coffee, milk, honey, cinnamon and nutmeg. Cook and stir until heated through. (Do not boil.) Remove from the heat; stir in vanilla. Pour into cups or mugs; serve immediately.

½ CUP: 86 cal., 1g fat (1g sat. fat), 4mg chol., 18mg sod., 19g carb. (18g sugars, 0 fiber), 1g pro.

❄ APPLE & SAUSAGE SHEET-PAN PANCAKES

After my daughter told me about sheet-pan pancakes, I thought it sounded like something I needed to try! Using my homegrown sweet potatoes as inspiration, I created this tasty breakfast dish. My husband and I thought it was delicious and I liked the fact that it was easier to make than traditional pancakes! I like to line the sheet pan with foil for easier clean up.
—Sue Gronholz, Beaver Dam, WI

- -

PREP: 25 min. • **BAKE:** 15 min.
MAKES: 8 servings

- 1 pkg. (7 oz.) frozen fully cooked breakfast sausage links
- 1½ cups all-purpose flour
- 2 Tbsp. brown sugar
- 2 tsp. baking powder
- 1½ tsp. pumpkin pie spice
- ½ tsp. baking soda
- ½ tsp. salt
- 1½ cups buttermilk
- ½ cup mashed sweet potato
- 2 large eggs, room temperature
- 2 Tbsp. butter, melted
- 1 tsp. vanilla extract
- ¾ cup shredded peeled apple
  Maple syrup and butter

1. Preheat oven to 425°. Spray a 15x10x1-in. baking pan with cooking spray. Arrange sausages in pan and bake until heated through, about 10 minutes. Cool sausages slightly. Remove to a cutting board; cut into ½-in. slices. Wipe any excess oil from pan with a paper towel.
2. Meanwhile, in a large bowl, whisk together flour, brown sugar, baking powder, pie spice, baking soda and salt. In a separate bowl, whisk together buttermilk, sweet potatoes, eggs, butter and vanilla; stir in shredded apple.
3. Pour buttermilk mixture into flour mixture and stir until just combined. Stir in half the sliced sausages. Spread batter into same baking pan; top with remaining sausages. Bake 12-15 minutes or until pancake is set, Cut into pieces and serve with maple syrup and butter.

1 PIECE: 285 cal., 14g fat (6g sat. fat), 71mg chol., 718mg sod., 30g carb. (9g sugars, 2g fiber), 9g pro.

APPLE & SAUSAGE SHEET-PAN PANCAKES

VEGGIE
FRITTATA

SALSA SHAKSHUKA WITH AVOCADOS

I was watching a cooking show and the host put several ingredients into a pan for her *shakshuka*. I realized those ingredients were essentially the makings for salsa, so that's how I ended up with this fresh morning meal.
—Patty Crouse, Warren, PA

PREP: 10 min. • **GRILL:** 25 min. • **MAKES:** 6 servings

- 1 jar (24 oz.) salsa
- 6 large eggs
- ¼ tsp. salt
- ⅛ tsp. pepper
- 6 whole pita breads
- 1 medium ripe avocado, peeled and sliced
  Optional: Cotija cheese, sliced radishes and fresh cilantro leaves

1. Spread salsa into a large cast-iron or other heavy skillet; place on grill rack. Grill, covered, over medium heat until bubbly, 13-15 minutes, stirring occasionally.
2. With back of spoon, make 6 wells in salsa; break an egg into each well. Sprinkle with salt and pepper. Grill, covered, until egg whites are completely set and yolks begin to thicken but are not hard, 6-8 minutes. Serve with pita bread, avocado and toppings of your choice.

1 SERVING: 312 cal., 9g fat (2g sat. fat), 186mg chol., 946mg sod., 43g carb. (5g sugars, 3g fiber), 12g pro.

VEGGIE FRITTATA

I was impressed with myself that I could omit dairy and still create something so good! Use any vegetables in this recipe, then add a salad, fruit cup or yogurt on the side.
—Kizmet Byrd, FORT WAYNE, IN

TAKES: 30 min. • **MAKES:** 6 servings

- 9 large eggs, room temperature
- ½ tsp. salt, divided
- ¼ tsp. pepper, divided
- 1 Tbsp. olive oil
- ½ cup chopped carrot
- ½ cup chopped sweet red pepper
- ⅓ cup chopped red onion
- ½ cup sliced zucchini
- 2 Tbsp. chopped fresh basil, divided
- 2 garlic cloves, minced
- ½ cup grape tomatoes, halved

1. Preheat broiler. In a large bowl, whisk eggs, ¼ tsp. salt and ⅛ tsp. pepper until blended.
2. In a 10-in. broiler-safe skillet, heat oil over medium-high heat. Add carrot; cook and stir until crisp-tender, 4-5 minutes. Add red pepper and red onion; cook and stir 1-2 minutes or until crisp-tender. Add zucchini, 1 Tbsp. basil, garlic, remaining ¼ tsp. salt and ⅛ tsp. pepper; cook and stir until vegetables are tender.
3. Reduce heat to medium-low; pour in egg mixture. Cook, covered, until nearly set, 4-6 minutes. Add tomatoes; cook, uncovered, until edge begins to pull away from the pan, about 3 minutes.
4. Broil 3-4 in. from heat 1-2 minutes or until eggs are completely set. Let stand 5 minutes. Sprinkle with remaining 1 Tbsp. basil; cut into wedges.

1 WEDGE: 145 cal., 10g fat (3g sat. fat), 279mg chol., 313mg sod., 4g carb. (2g sugars, 1g fiber), 10g pro. **DIABETIC EXCHANGES:** 1 vegetable, 1 medium-fat meat, 1 fat.

SALSA
SHAKSHUKA WITH
AVOCADOS

MUFFULETTA FRITTATA

MUFFULETTA FRITTATA

Two of my favorite things are Italian sub sandwiches and olives. I wanted those flavors together but in a low-carb dish, so I created this frittata. Use fresh spinach in place of arugula if you don't love its peppery flavor like I do.
—*Donna Gribbins, Shelbyville, KY*

PREP: 25 min. • COOK: 25 min. • MAKES: 8 servings

- 1   Tbsp. canola oil
- 12 large eggs
- 1   cup half-and-half cream
- 3   Tbsp. grated Parmesan cheese
- ½   tsp. pepper
- 8   oz. fresh arugula, roughly chopped
- 2   oz. sliced capicola, chopped
- 2   oz. hard salami, chopped
- 2   oz. mortadella, chopped
- 1   cup shredded mozzarella and provolone cheese blend

OLIVE SALAD TOPPING

- 1   cup chopped assorted olives
- 1   cup chopped giardiniera
- ¼   cup olive oil
- 2   Tbsp. red wine vinegar
- 2   Tbsp. minced fresh parsley
- 1   garlic clove, minced

1. Preheat oven to 375°. In a 12-in. cast-iron or ovenproof skillet, heat oil over medium heat.
2. In a large bowl, whisk the eggs, half-and-half, Parmesan and pepper. Pour into skillet. Layer with arugula, capicola, salami and mortadella; top with cheese blend. Cook for 3-5 minutes or until eggs start to set on sides.
3. Transfer to oven; bake for 20-25 minutes or until eggs are set and top is browned.
4. In a small bowl, mix the olive salad topping ingredients together. Cut frittata into wedges; serve with olive topping.
1 PIECE WITH ¼ CUP OLIVE SALAD: 384 cal., 31g fat (10g sat. fat), 323mg chol., 1391mg sod., 6g carb. (2g sugars, 1g fiber), 20g pro.

APPLE BUTTER BREAD PUDDING

This is one of my mother's best recipes! I'm sure your family will be delighted with it too. Serve it as a dessert or a very special breakfast treat.
—*Jerri Gradert, Lincoln, NE*

PREP: 20 min. + standing • BAKE: 50 min. • MAKES: 12 servings

- ⅓   cup raisins
- 1   cup apple butter
- 6   croissants, split

CUSTARD

- 8   large eggs
- 3   cups 2% milk
- 1½ cups sugar
- 2   tsp. vanilla extract
- ¼   tsp. salt

STREUSEL

- ½   cup all-purpose flour
- ½   cup packed brown sugar
- ¼   tsp. salt
- ¼   cup cold butter

1. Place raisins in a small bowl. Cover with boiling water; let stand for 5 minutes. Drain and set aside.
2. Combine apple butter and raisins. Spread over croissant bottoms; replace tops. Cut each croissant into 3 pieces; place in a greased 13x9-in. baking dish.
3. In a large bowl, combine the eggs, milk, sugar, vanilla and salt. Pour over croissants; let stand for 30 minutes or until bread is softened.
4. In a small bowl, combine the flour, brown sugar and salt. Cut in butter until mixture resembles coarse crumbs. Sprinkle over top.
5. Bake, uncovered, at 350° for 50-60 minutes or until a knife inserted in the center comes out clean. Serve warm.
NOTE: This recipe was tested with commercially prepared apple butter.
1 SERVING: 433 cal., 14g fat (7g sat. fat), 175mg chol., 422mg sod., 68g carb. (51g sugars, 1g fiber), 9g pro.

APPLE BUTTER BREAD PUDDING

HASH BROWN NESTS WITH
PORTOBELLOS & EGGS

HASH BROWN NESTS WITH PORTOBELLOS & EGGS

Hash browns make a fabulous crust for these individual egg quiches. They look fancy but are actually easy to make. They've been a favorite at holiday brunches and other special occasions.
—Kate Meyer, Brentwood, TN

PREP: 30 min. • **BAKE:** 15 min. • **MAKES:** 1 dozen

- 2 Tbsp. butter
- ½ lb. sliced baby portobello mushrooms, chopped
- ¼ cup chopped shallots
- 1 garlic clove, minced
- ½ tsp. salt
- ¼ tsp. pepper
  Dash cayenne pepper
- 2 Tbsp. sour cream
- 1 Tbsp. minced fresh basil or 1 tsp. dried basil
- 4 cups frozen shredded hash brown potatoes (about 1 lb.), thawed
- 7 large eggs, lightly beaten
- ¼ cup shredded Swiss cheese
- 2 bacon strips, cooked and crumbled

1. Preheat oven to 400°. In a large skillet, heat the butter over medium-high heat; saute mushrooms and shallots until tender. Add garlic and seasonings; cook and stir 1 minute. Remove from heat; stir in sour cream and basil.
2. Press about ¼ cup potatoes onto bottom and up side of each of 12 greased muffin cups. Fill each with about 2 Tbsp. beaten egg. Top with mushroom mixture, cheese and bacon.
3. Bake until eggs are set, 15-18 minutes.
1 SERVING: 105 cal., 7g fat (3g sat. fat), 118mg chol., 191mg sod., 6g carb. (1g sugars, 1g fiber), 6g pro. **DIABETIC EXCHANGES:** 1 medium-fat meat, ½ starch, ½ fat.

READER REVIEW

"I served these at a tea party I host each year for five friends, and they were a hit. I do not enjoy cooking nor do I consider myself handy in the kitchen, but the recipe sounded simple and tasty, so I gave it a try. I'm so glad I did. My guests thoroughly enjoyed the dish, each had seconds, and all of them wanted the recipe. Can't wait to make it again!"
—CVFRANCOIS, TASTEOFHOME.COM

CHEDDAR & CHORIZO STRATA

Stratas are a wonderful way to use up bits and pieces of leftovers you have on hand. You can make them meatless, substitute the cheeses, the meats, etc. This can be made a day before baking. If you like more heat, use pepper jack cheese.
—Kallee Krong-McCreery, Escondido, CA

PREP: 20 min. + chilling • **BAKE:** 40 min. • **MAKES:** 8 servings

- 7 cups day-old French bread cut into 1-in. cubes
- 2 cups shredded cheddar cheese
- 1 pkg. (10 oz.) frozen chopped spinach, thawed and squeezed dry
- 6 oz. fresh chorizo, crumbled
- ⅓ cup chopped onion
- 6 large eggs
- 2¼ cups 2% milk
- 1 tsp. garlic salt
- 1 tsp. prepared mustard

1. Place 4 cups bread cubes in a single layer in a greased 13x9-in. baking dish. Sprinkle with 1 cup cheese and the spinach. Layer with chorizo and onion; top with remaining bread and cheese.
2. In a large bowl, whisk eggs, milk, garlic salt and mustard. Pour over bread. Refrigerate, covered, several hours or overnight.
3. Preheat oven to 350°. Remove strata from refrigerator while oven heats. Bake, uncovered, until golden brown and a knife inserted near the center comes out clean, 40-45 minutes. Let stand 5-10 minutes before serving.
1 PIECE: 370 cal., 22g fat (10g sat. fat), 192mg chol., 946mg sod., 21g carb. (6g sugars, 2g fiber), 22g pro.

CHEDDAR & CHORIZO STRATA

CHEWY OATMEAL COOKIES
PAGE 179

Cookies, Bars & Candies

There's no simpler, sweeter way to treat yourself than with a little hand-held goodie. You'll love discovering a fantastic array of cookie-tin favorites in this chapter. Find easy drop cookies, fruity bars and truffles galore!

CHECK OUT THESE SPECIALTIES

LOW-CARB
CHOCOLATE CHIP
CHEESECAKE BARS

mixture resembles coarse crumbs.
Sprinkle over chips.

3. Bake until center is just set and edges are golden brown, 40-45 minutes. Cool completely on a wire rack. Refrigerate, covered, at least 4 hours or overnight before serving. Refrigerate leftovers.

NOTE: This recipe was tested with Lakanto Golden Monk Fruit Sweetener and Lakanto Classic Monk Fruit Sweetener.

1 BAR: 293 cal., 25g fat (13g sat. fat), 78mg chol., 135mg sod., 21g carb. (2g sugars, 2g fiber), 7g pro.

TENDER ITALIAN SUGAR COOKIES

These traditional cookies are so lovely and unbelievably tender!

—*Weda Mosellie, Phillipsburg, NJ*

PREP: 20 min.
BAKE: 10 min./batch + cooling
MAKES: 3 dozen

- ¾ cup shortening
- ¾ cup sugar
- 3 large eggs, room temperature
- 1 tsp. vanilla extract
- 3 cups all-purpose flour
- 3 tsp. baking powder
- ⅛ tsp. salt

ICING

- ¼ cup 2% milk
- 2 Tbsp. butter, melted
- ½ tsp. vanilla extract
- 2½ cups confectioners' sugar
  Optional: Food coloring and coarse sugar

1. Preheat oven to 400°. In a large bowl, cream shortening and sugar until light and fluffy, 5-7 minutes. Beat in eggs and vanilla. Combine flour, baking powder and salt; gradually add to creamed mixture and mix well.

2. Shape dough into 1½-in. balls. Place 1 in. apart on ungreased baking sheets. Bake for 8-10 minutes or until lightly browned. Remove to wire racks to cool.

3. For icing, in a small bowl, combine the first 4 icing ingredients until smooth. Tint with food coloring if desired. Dip tops of cookies in icing; allow excess to drip off. Sprinkle with coarse sugar if desired. Place on waxed paper; let stand until set.

1 COOKIE: 136 cal., 5g fat (2g sat. fat), 20mg chol., 54mg sod., 21g carb. (12g sugars, 0 fiber), 2g pro.

LOW-CARB CHOCOLATE CHIP CHEESECAKE BARS

These cheesecake bars have four delectable layers: a buttery crust, a creamy cheesecake filling, chocolaty morsels and a crumbly topping. It's guilt free and low in sugar.

—*Rachel Sanders, Salem, OH*

PREP: 30 min.
BAKE: 40 min. + chilling
MAKES: 15 servings

- 1 cup almond flour
- ½ cup granulated golden monk fruit sugar substitute
- 2 large eggs, room temperature
- ½ cup butter, melted
- 1 tsp. vanilla extract

CHEESECAKE LAYER

- 1 pkg. (8 oz.) cream cheese, softened
- ¼ cup granulated monk fruit sugar substitute
- 2 Tbsp. sour cream
- ½ tsp. vanilla extract
- 1 large egg, room temperature, lightly beaten
- ½ cup sugar-free white baking chips
- ½ cup sugar-free chocolate baking chips

CRUMBLE LAYER

- ½ cup almond flour
- ¼ cup granulated golden monk fruit sugar substitute
- ¼ cup cold butter

1. Preheat oven to 325°. In a small bowl, whisk the flour and sugar substitute. In another bowl, whisk eggs, melted butter and vanilla until blended. Add to flour mixture; stir just until moistened. Pour into a greased 11x7-in. baking dish.

2. For cheesecake layer, in a large bowl, beat cream cheese and sugar substitute until smooth. Beat in sour cream and vanilla. Add egg; beat on low speed just until blended. Pour over crust. Sprinkle with white and chocolate baking chips. For crumble layer, mix almond flour and sugar substitute. Cut in butter until

CHEWY OATMEAL COOKIES

I pack chocolate chips, raisins, nuts and cinnamon into my oatmeal cookies. Our kids love them!
—*Janis Plageman, Lynden, WA*

- -

PREP: 15 min. • **BAKE:** 10 min./batch
MAKES: about 5 dozen

- 1 cup butter, softened
- 1 cup sugar
- 1 cup packed brown sugar
- 2 large eggs, room temperature
- 1 Tbsp. molasses
- 2 tsp. vanilla extract
- 2 cups all-purpose flour
- 2 cups quick-cooking oats
- 1½ tsp. baking soda
- 1 tsp. ground cinnamon
- ½ tsp. salt
- 1 cup each raisins and chopped pecans
- 1 cup semisweet chocolate chips

1. In a large bowl, cream butter and sugars until light and fluffy, 5-7 minutes. Add the eggs, molasses and vanilla; beat well.
2. Combine the flour, oats, baking soda, cinnamon and salt; gradually add to creamed mixture and mix well. Stir in the raisins, pecans and chocolate chips. Drop by tablespoonfuls 2 in. apart onto greased baking sheets.
3. Bake at 350° for 9-10 minutes or until lightly browned. Cool on pans for 2 minutes before removing to wire racks.
1 COOKIE: 103 cal., 4g fat (3g sat. fat), 15mg chol., 77mg sod., 16g carb. (10g sugars, 1g fiber), 1g pro.

CHEWY OATMEAL COOKIES

LARA'S TENDER GINGERSNAPS

LARA'S TENDER GINGERSNAPS

Soft gingersnaps herald the tastes and smells of the Christmas season, but they are perfect for any fall or winter gathering. I enjoy the flavors of molasses, cloves, cinnamon and ginger blended into one delicious cookie.
—*Lara Pennell, Mauldin, SC*

- -

PREP: 15 min. + chilling • **BAKE:** 10 min./batch + cooling
MAKES: 3 dozen

- 1 cup packed brown sugar
- ¾ cup butter, melted
- 1 large egg, room temperature
- ¼ cup molasses
- 2¼ cups all-purpose flour
- 1½ tsp. ground ginger
- 1 tsp. baking soda
- 1 tsp. ground cinnamon
- ½ tsp. ground cloves
- ¼ cup sugar or coarse sugar

1. In a large bowl, beat brown sugar and butter until blended. Beat in egg and molasses. Combine the flour, ginger, baking soda, cinnamon and cloves; gradually add to brown sugar mixture and mix well (dough will be stiff). Cover and refrigerate for at least 2 hours.
2. Preheat oven to 350°. Shape dough into 1-in. balls. Roll in sugar. Place 2 in. apart on greased baking sheets.
3. Bake until set, 9-11 minutes. Cool for about 1 minute; remove from pans to wire racks to cool completely.
1 COOKIE: 100 cal., 4g fat (2g sat. fat), 15mg chol., 70mg sod., 15g carb. (9g sugars, 0 fiber), 1g pro.

WHOOPIE
PIES

CHERRY WALNUT BARS

Send holiday cheer with these nutty little fruit bars that travel extremely well. Since our cookie-loving son joined the Air Force, I've shipped them as far away as England and Italy.
—*Margaret Zuber, Marietta, GA*

- -

PREP: 15 min. • **BAKE:** 40 min. + cooling • **MAKES:** 4 dozen

  2¼ cups all-purpose flour
   ½ cup sugar
   1 cup cold butter, cubed
   2 large eggs
   1 cup packed brown sugar
   ½ tsp. salt
   ½ tsp. baking powder
   ½ tsp. vanilla extract
   1 jar (6 oz.) maraschino cherries
   ½ cup chopped walnuts

ICING
   1 cup confectioners' sugar
   1 Tbsp. butter, softened
   ½ cup sweetened shredded coconut, toasted, optional

1. In a large bowl, combine flour and sugar. Cut in butter until mixture resembles coarse crumbs. Pat into an ungreased 13x9-in. baking pan. Bake at 350° for 18-22 minutes or until edges are lightly browned.
2. Meanwhile, in a small bowl, combine the eggs, brown sugar, salt, baking powder and vanilla. Drain cherries, reserving 2 Tbsp. juice; set juice aside. Chop cherries; add to brown sugar mixture. Stir in walnuts. Pour over crust and spread evenly. Bake until set, 20-25 minutes longer. Cool completely on a wire rack.
3. For icing, combine confectioners' sugar and butter in a bowl. Add enough reserved cherry juice to reach desired consistency; drizzle over bars. Sprinkle with coconut if desired.
1 BAR: 108 cal., 5g fat (3g sat. fat), 19mg chol., 66mg sod., 15g carb. (10g sugars, 0 fiber), 1g pro.

CHERRY
WALNUT BARS

WHOOPIE PIES

These soft cupcakelike treats have been a favorite of mine for many years. They're especially fun to assemble with kids.
—*Ruth Ann Stelfox, Raymond, AB*

- -

PREP: 15 min. • **BAKE:** 5 min./batch + cooling • **MAKES:** 4 dozen

   1 cup butter, softened
  1½ cups sugar
   2 large eggs, room temperature
   2 tsp. vanilla extract
   4 cups all-purpose flour
   ¾ cup baking cocoa
   2 tsp. baking soda
   ½ tsp. salt
   1 cup water
   1 cup buttermilk

FILLING
   3 cups confectioners' sugar
   2 cups marshmallow creme
   ½ cup butter, softened
   2 tsp. vanilla extract

1. In a large bowl, cream butter and sugar until light and fluffy, 5-7 minutes.
2. Beat in eggs and vanilla. Combine the flour, cocoa, baking soda and salt; add to creamed mixture alternately with water and buttermilk, beating well after each addition.
3. Drop by tablespoonfuls 2 in. apart onto greased baking sheets. Bake at 375° for 5-7 minutes or until set. Remove to wire racks to cool completely.
4. In a small bowl, beat filling ingredients until fluffy. Spread on the bottoms of half of the cookies; top with remaining cookies.
1 SANDWICH COOKIE: 167 cal., 6g fat (4g sat. fat), 23mg chol., 139mg sod., 26g carb. (17g sugars, 1g fiber), 2g pro.

BUGLE CONES

BUGLE CONES

It's OK to play with your food when it resembles a tiny ice cream cone. Serve these crunchy morsels at a barbecue or share them as a novelty gift.

—*Dianne Conway, London, ON*

- -

TAKES: 20 min. • **MAKES:** 2½ dozen

- 2 Tbsp. butter, softened
- 1⅓ cups confectioners' sugar
- ¼ tsp. salt
- ¼ tsp. vanilla extract
- 2 Tbsp. sweetened condensed milk
- 1 pkg. (6 oz.) Bugles
- ½ cup semisweet chocolate chips, melted, optional
  Assorted sprinkles and/or ground nuts

1. In a small bowl, beat butter and confectioners' sugar until crumbly. Beat in salt and vanilla. Add milk and mix well (mixture will be stiff).

2. Shape into ½-in. balls. Place 1 ball on top of each Bugle. Dip tops of some or all in melted chocolate if desired. Decorate with sprinkles and/or nuts.

1 CONE: 54 cal., 1g fat (1g sat. fat), 2mg chol., 65mg sod., 10g carb. (6g sugars, 0 fiber), 1g pro.

READER REVIEW

"These cookies came out very cute and tasty. I used a jalapeno popper holder to place them in while the chocolate set."

—PAUL3303, TASTEOFHOME.COM

VEGAN TROPICAL MAGIC BARS

Magic bars are one of the easiest treats you can make and I decided to give them a couple of twists. By using a plant-based butter and condensed coconut milk, I've made them completely vegan. I also added some dried pineapple, mango and macadamia nuts, giving it a tropical spin.

—*James Schend, Pleasant Prairie, WI*

- -

PREP: 10 min. • **BAKE:** 30 min. + chilling • **MAKES:** 16 bars

- ½ cup vegan butter-style sticks
- 1 cup graham cracker crumbs
- 1 cup sweetened shredded coconut
- 1 cup dairy-free white baking chips
- 1 cup macadamia nuts, chopped
- ½ cup dried pineapple, chopped
- ½ cup dried mangoes, chopped
- 1 can (11.6 oz.) sweetened condensed coconut milk

Preheat oven to 350°. Melt butter in a 9-in. square baking pan. On top of melted butter, sprinkle crumbs, then coconut, then baking chips, then macadamias, then pineapple and then mango. Pour well-stirred coconut milk over all. Do not stir. Bake until a toothpick inserted in center comes out clean, 30-35 minutes. Refrigerate at least 4 hours or overnight. Cut into bars and serve.

1 BAR: 323 cal., 20g fat (9g sat. fat), 2mg chol., 188mg sod., 34g carb. (27g sugars, 2g fiber), 2g pro.

VEGAN TROPICAL MAGIC BARS

WINNING APRICOT BARS

This recipe is down-home baking at its best, and it really represents all regions of the country. It's won blue ribbons at county fairs and cookie contests in several states! Easy to make, it's perfect for potluck suppers, bake sales, lunchboxes or just plain snacking.
—*Jill Moritz, Irvine, CA*

PREP: 15 min. • **BAKE:** 30 min. + cooling • **MAKES:** 2 dozen

- ¾ cup butter, softened
- 1 cup sugar
- 1 large egg, room temperature
- ½ tsp. vanilla extract
- 2 cups all-purpose flour
- ¼ tsp. baking powder
- 1⅓ cups sweetened shredded coconut
- ½ cup chopped walnuts
- 1 jar (10 to 12 oz.) apricot preserves

1. Preheat oven to 350°. In a large bowl, cream butter and sugar until light and fluffy, 5-7 minutes. Beat in egg and vanilla. In a small bowl, whisk flour and baking powder; gradually add to creamed mixture, mixing well. Fold in coconut and walnuts.
2. Press two-thirds of dough onto the bottom of a greased 13x9-in. baking pan. Spread with preserves; crumble remaining dough over preserves. Bake 30-35 minutes or until golden brown. Cool completely in pan on a wire rack. Cut into bars.
1 BAR: 195 cal., 10g fat (6g sat. fat), 23mg chol., 72mg sod., 27g carb. (16g sugars, 1g fiber), 2g pro.

TEST KITCHEN TIP

To soften butter super quick, partially unwrap the butter (use the wrapped half as a handle to keep your hand clean) and shred it using the largest holes of your box grater. The butter will reduce to a fluffy heap and soften faster. Shredded butter is ready to use in your recipe right away.

WINNING APRICOT BARS

MAPLE PRALINES

🄑 MAPLE PRALINES

This recipe rekindles memories of my grandfather and his love for making maple syrup. When I was in college, my mother would send me a package of her pralines during sugaring season. They were so popular with my friends that I barely managed to tuck away a few for myself.
—*Mary Beth Cool, Canajoharie, NY*

PREP: 10 min. • **COOK:** 10 min. + cooling • **MAKES:** about 1 lb.

- 1 cup sugar
- ⅔ cup heavy whipping cream
- ½ cup maple syrup
- 2 Tbsp. butter
- ¾ cup coarsely chopped pecans, toasted

1. In a heavy 1-qt. saucepan, combine sugar, cream and syrup. Cook and stir over medium heat until mixture boils. Reduce heat to medium-low. Cook, uncovered, until a candy thermometer reads 234° (soft-ball stage), stirring occasionally.
2. Remove from the heat. Add butter; do not stir. Cool, without stirring, to 160°. Stir in pecans. Beat vigorously with a wooden spoon until mixture just begins to thicken but is still glossy. Quickly drop by spoonfuls onto waxed paper. Cool completely. Store in an airtight container.
1 OZ.: 144 cal., 7g fat (3g sat. fat), 11mg chol., 4mg sod., 20g carb. (19g sugars, 0 fiber), 1g pro.

❄ DUTCH SPECULAAS

These spice cookies taste like the windmill cookies we enjoy in the United States. In Holland, it's tradition to mold the dough into the shape of St. Nicholas and serve the cookies on Sinterklaas (St. Nicholas Day).
—Taste of Home *Test Kitchen*

PREP: 40 min. + chilling
BAKE: 10 min./batch
MAKES: about 2½ dozen

- 1 cup butter, softened
- 1 cup packed dark brown sugar
- 2 large eggs, room temperature
- 1 Tbsp. molasses
- 2 tsp. grated orange zest
- 3½ cups all-purpose flour
- ½ cup finely ground almonds
- 3 tsp. ground cinnamon
- 1 tsp. baking powder
- ½ tsp. each ground nutmeg and cloves
- ¼ tsp. white pepper
- ¼ tsp. ground ginger
- ¼ tsp. ground cardamom

1. In a large bowl, cream butter and brown sugar until light and fluffy, 5-7 minutes. Beat in the eggs, molasses and orange zest. Combine the flour, ground almonds, cinnamon, baking powder, nutmeg, cloves, pepper, ginger and cardamom. Gradually add to creamed mixture and mix well. Cover and refrigerate for at least 4 hours or until easy to handle.
2. Preheat oven to 350°. On a parchment-lined surface, roll a small amount of dough to ⅛-in. thickness. Use a floured cookie stamp to press design into dough, then cut with floured 3-in. cookie cutters, leaving 1 in. between cookies. Remove excess dough, and reroll scraps if desired.
3. Transfer parchment with dough to cookie sheet. If dough has warmed, place baking sheet in refrigerator until it firms up, 10-15 minutes. Bake until edges are lightly browned, 8-10 minutes. Remove from pans to wire racks to cool.

TO MAKE AHEAD: Dough can be made 2 days in advance. Let stand at room temperature 30 minutes before rolling out. Baked cookies may be stored 1 week in an airtight container at room temperature or frozen for up to 1 month.
1 COOKIE: 151 cal., 7g fat (4g sat. fat), 30mg chol., 65mg sod., 19g carb. (8g sugars, 1g fiber), 2g pro.

DUTCH SPECULAAS

MAPLE NUT
TRUFFLES

BIRTHDAY CAKE
TRUFFLES

CHAMPAGNE
TRUFFLES

COCONUT
TRUFFLES

DARK CHOCOLATE
TRUFFLES

THE TRUFFLE SHUFFLE

Treat your sweetie—or
your sweet tooth—to these
ever-so-clever confections

MAPLE NUT TRUFFLES

In a small bowl, beat 4 oz. softened **cream cheese**, 1½ cups **confectioners' sugar** and ¾ tsp. **maple flavoring** until smooth. Gradually beat in 1½ cups melted and slightly cooled **semisweet chocolate chips**. Cover and refrigerate until firm, about 15 minutes. Shape into 1-in. balls; roll in 1 cup chopped **walnuts**.

BIRTHDAY CAKE TRUFFLES

Prepare and bake 1 regular-size **funfetti cake mix** according to package directions, using a greased 13x9-in. baking pan. Cool completely on a wire rack. Crumble cake into a large bowl. Add one 15.6-oz. can **funfetti** vanilla frosting with candy bits and mix well. Shape into 1¼-in. balls. Place on baking sheets. Freeze until firm, at least 2 hours. Dip in 1 lb. melted **white candy coating**. Place on waxed paper; sprinkle with **jimmies or nonpareils**.

CHAMPAGNE TRUFFLES

Simmer 1 cup **champagne** until reduced to ⅓ cup; cool slightly. Place 2 lbs. chopped **semisweet chocolate** in a bowl. Heat 1½ cups **heavy whipping cream** just to a boil. Pour over chocolate; stir until smooth. Stir in ½ cup cubed **unsalted butter** and the cooled champagne. Cool to room temperature, stirring occasionally. Refrigerate until firm, about 3 hours. Shape into 1-in. balls. Cover and refrigerate for at least 1 hour. Dip truffles in 1 lb. melted **dark chocolate candy coating**. Place them on waxed paper; let stand until set. Brush with **edible gold glitter or sprinkles**.

COCONUT TRUFFLES

In a large bowl, combine 6 cups **confectioners' sugar**, one 14-oz. can **sweetened condensed milk**, 4 Tbsp. melted **butter**, ½ tsp. **coconut extract** and 1 cup **sweetened shredded coconut**. Refrigerate until firm, about 2 hours. Shape into 1-in. balls; roll in additional coconut.

DARK CHOCOLATE TRUFFLES

Place 1 lb. **dark chocolate chips** in a bowl. Heat 1 cup **heavy whipping cream** and 2 Tbsp. **corn syrup** just to a boil. Pour over chocolate; stir until smooth. Stir in 2 Tbsp. softened **butter**. Cool to room temperature, stirring occasionally. Refrigerate until firm, about 3 hours. Shape into 1-in. balls; roll in **baking cocoa**.

EASY COOKIE TRUFFLES

Process one 15.5-oz. pkg. **Oreo cookies** in a food processor until finely crushed. Add one 8-oz. pkg. cubed **cream cheese**; process until blended. Roll into 1-in. balls. Roll in 1 cup **chocolate wafer crumbs**.

RED VELVET TRUFFLES

Prepare and bake 1 regular-size **red velvet cake mix** according to package directions, using a greased 13x9-in. baking pan. Cool completely on a wire rack. Crumble cake into a large bowl. Add one 16-oz. can **cream cheese frosting** and mix well. Shape into 1¼-in. balls. Place on baking sheets. Freeze until firm, at least 2 hours. Dip a third of the cake balls in each 1 lb. melted **white candy coating**, 1 lb. melted **milk chocolate** and 1 lb. melted **dark chocolate candy coating**; place on waxed paper. If desired, drizzle with any remaining chocolate or candy coating.

NUTTER BUTTER TRUFFLES

Process one 1-lb. pkg. **Nutter Butter cookies** in a food processor until finely crushed. Add one 8-oz. pkg. softened **cream cheese**; process until blended. Roll into 1-in. balls. Dip half the balls in 8 oz. melted **milk chocolate**. Place on waxed paper. Repeat with remaining balls and 8 oz. melted **white candy coating**. Drizzle 3 oz. melted **bittersweet chocolate** over truffles.

STRAWBERRY CHOCOLATE TRUFFLES

Process four 7-oz. **milk chocolate candy bars** in a food processor until chopped. Heat 1 cup **heavy whipping cream** just to a boil. Pour over chocolate; process until smooth. Stir in ¼ cup **strawberry spreadable fruit** and 1½ tsp. **vanilla** until combined. Transfer to a small bowl; cool to room temperature, stirring occasionally. Refrigerate until firm, about 3 hours. Shape into 1-in. balls. Roll in 1¼ cups toasted chopped **almonds**.

CHOCOLATE RUM TRUFFLES

Place 12 oz. chopped **semisweet chocolate** in a bowl. Heat 1 cup **heavy whipping cream** just to a boil. Pour over chocolate; stir until smooth. Stir in ⅓ cup cubed **butter** and 1 tsp. **rum extract**. Cool to room temperature, stirring occasionally. Cover and refrigerate until firm, about 6 hours. Shape into 1-in. balls. Cover and refrigerate for at least 1 hour. Combine ½ cup toasted finely chopped **pecans** and 2 oz. grated **semisweet chocolate**. Roll truffles in nut mixture.

FOR ALL TRUFFLES, STORE IN AN AIRTIGHT CONTAINER IN THE FRIDGE.

MOIST CHOCOLATE CAKE
PAGE 197

Cakes & Pies

Whether you need a showstopper for a special event or simply want a treat to surprise the family, you'll find just the thing in these pages of pies, cakes, tarts and more.

MOST-REQUESTED RECIPES

CLASSIC PINEAPPLE UPSIDE-DOWN CAKE

CLASSIC PINEAPPLE UPSIDE-DOWN CAKE

A classic recipe like this never goes out of style! It's delicious with the traditional pineapple, but try it with peaches or a combination of cranberries and orange.
—*Bernardine Melton, Paola, KS*

PREP: 20 min.
BAKE: 30 min. + standing
MAKES: 9 servings

⅓ cup butter, melted
⅔ cup packed brown sugar
1 can (20 oz.) sliced pineapple
½ cup chopped pecans
3 large eggs, separated, room temperature
1 cup sugar
1 tsp. vanilla extract
1 cup all-purpose flour
1 tsp. baking powder
¼ tsp. salt
9 maraschino cherries

1. Preheat oven to 375°. In an ungreased 9-in. square baking pan, combine butter and brown sugar. Drain the pineapple, reserving ⅓ cup juice. Arrange 9 slices of pineapple in a single layer over sugar (save remaining slices for another use). Sprinkle pecans over top; set aside.
2. In a large bowl, beat egg yolks until thick and lemon-colored. Gradually add sugar, beating well. Blend in vanilla and reserved pineapple juice. Combine flour, baking powder and salt; add to batter, beating well.
3. In a small bowl with clean beaters, beat egg whites on high speed until stiff peaks form; fold into batter. Spoon into pan.
4. Bake 30-35 minutes or until a toothpick inserted in center comes out clean. Let stand 10 minutes before inverting onto serving plate. Place a cherry in the center of each pineapple slice.
1 PIECE: 361 cal., 13g fat (5g sat. fat), 88mg chol., 193mg sod., 58g carb. (46g sugars, 2g fiber), 4g pro.

HOW-TO

Make Pineapple Upside-Down Cake
This vintage beauty is all about perfect timing.

Step 1: Make Your Mosaic
Get creative as you arrange your fruit in the bottom of the pan. Cherries can be added before or after baking—you choose! Nestle pecans into any gaps.

Step 2: Batter Up
Start the cake batter by beating the egg yolks and sugar until thickened. Next, beat in the vanilla and pineapple juice, and then the dry ingredients.

Step 3: Whisk The Whites
In a clean bowl, beat egg whites until they form stiff peaks. You're at the right stage when you pull out the beaters and the egg whites stand straight up—no drooping!

Step 4: Gently Fold
Take your time to fold in the egg whites. Be mindful not to deflate them. You worked hard to create that airy texture; don't lose it by rushing this part of the process.

Step 5: Lay It On Thick
Spread the batter evenly into the pan. Be careful not to disturb your beautiful fruit design.

Step 6: Time To Flip
After baking, let the cake cool for 10 minutes on a wire rack. Then it's time to flip. Be quick!

PLUM POPPY SEED CAKE

You can also use nectarines or even apricots in this recipe, but plums and poppy seeds are the most traditional Polish version of this dessert. One tip: Do not push the plums into the batter. Just let them sit on top. They will sink in a bit as they bake.
—*Lisa Kaminski, Wauwatosa, WI*

PREP: 20 min. • **BAKE:** 40 min. • **MAKES:** 15 servings

- 1 cup sugar
- 4 large eggs
- 1 cup canola oil or grapeseed oil
- 1 Tbsp. grated orange zest
- 1 tsp. vanilla extract
- 2 cups all-purpose flour
- 2 tsp. baking powder
- 1 tsp. ground cinnamon
- ½ tsp. salt
- 3 Tbsp. poppy seeds
- 5 small plums (about 1 lb.), sliced
  Confectioners' sugar

1. Preheat oven to 350°. In a large bowl, beat sugar, eggs and oil until lemon-colored and fluffy, about 5 minutes. Beat in orange zest and vanilla.

2. In another bowl, whisk flour, baking powder, cinnamon and salt; fold into egg mixture. Stir in poppy seeds. Transfer to a greased 13x9-in. baking pan, spreading evenly. Arrange plum slices over batter (do not press into batter).

3. Bake until a toothpick inserted in center comes out clean, 40-45 minutes. Cool in pan on a wire rack. Sprinkle with confectioners' sugar and additional cinnamon before serving.

1 PIECE: 284 cal., 17g fat (2g sat. fat), 50mg chol., 163mg sod., 30g carb. (16g sugars, 1g fiber), 4g pro.

PLUM POPPY SEED CAKE

PEANUT BUTTER ZUCCHINI SHEET CAKE

PEANUT BUTTER ZUCCHINI SHEET CAKE

I was so tired of the same zucchini dessert recipes and I love peanut butter, so I decided to try something different. The result was amazing, and it freezes well. Even people who do not like zucchini enjoy this recipe. I bet you can't eat just one piece!
—*Candy Scholl, West Sunbury, PA*

PREP: 25 min. • **BAKE:** 25 min. • **MAKES:** 24 servings

- 1¾ cups sugar
- 1 cup canola oil
- 1 cup creamy peanut butter
- 3 large eggs
- 1 Tbsp. vanilla extract
- 2½ cups all-purpose flour
- 1 tsp. baking soda
- ½ tsp. baking powder
- ¼ tsp. salt
- ½ cup 2% milk
- 2 cups peeled and shredded zucchini

FROSTING
- ½ cup creamy peanut butter
- 6 Tbsp. butter, softened
- 6 Tbsp. 2% milk
- 1 Tbsp. vanilla extract
- 4 cups confectioners' sugar
  Chopped salted peanuts, optional

1. Preheat oven to 350°. Grease a 15x10x1-in. baking pan.

2. In a large bowl, beat sugar, oil and peanut butter until smooth. Add eggs, 1 at a time, beating well after each addition. Beat in vanilla. In another bowl, whisk flour, baking soda, baking powder and salt; add to batter alternately with milk, beating well after each addition. Fold in zucchini.

3. Transfer to prepared pan. Bake until a toothpick inserted in center comes out clean, 25-28 minutes. Cool on a wire rack until warm.

4. Meanwhile, for frosting, in a large bowl, beat peanut butter and butter until creamy. Beat in milk and vanilla. Gradually beat in confectioners' sugar until smooth. Spread over warm cake. If desired, sprinkle with peanuts. Serve warm.

1 PIECE: 404 cal., 21g fat (5g sat. fat), 32mg chol., 193mg sod., 49g carb. (37g sugars, 1g fiber), 6g pro.

APPALACHIAN STACK CAKE WITH APPLE-BOURBON SAUCE

RECIPE PHOTO BY KANDI ZADEL PHOTOGRAPHY

APPALACHIAN STACK CAKE WITH APPLE-BOURBON SAUCE

My version of a completely traditional Appalachian stack cake was inspired by the way my ancestors would have made it many moons ago. All the ingredients are there: dried apples, a stiff dough, molasses and apple butter. My only flair is adding a bourbon sauce to drip over the edges and right into your heart.
—Lauren May, Pikeville, KY

- -

PREP: 30 min. + chilling
BAKE: 25 min. + cooling
MAKES: 8 servings

- 1 cup unsalted butter, softened
- 1 cup packed dark brown sugar
- ¾ cup molasses
- 2 large eggs, room temperature
- 5 cups all-purpose flour
- 1 tsp. baking soda
- 1 tsp. baking powder
- 1 tsp. salt
- 1 tsp. ground cinnamon
- ½ tsp. ground ginger
- 1½ cups buttermilk

APPLE & BOURBON SAUCE
- 4 cups dried apples
- 2 cups packed dark brown sugar
- 1½ cups water
- ⅓ cup bourbon
- 3 Tbsp. unsalted butter
- 2 cups apple butter

1. Preheat oven to 350°. Line bottoms of 5 greased 6-in. round baking pans with parchment. In a large bowl, cream butter, brown sugar and molasses until light and fluffy, 5-7 minutes. Add eggs, 1 at a time, beating well after each addition (mixture may appear curdled). In another bowl, whisk flour, baking soda, baking powder, salt, cinnamon and ginger; add to creamed mixture alternately with buttermilk, beating well after each addition.
2. Transfer to prepared pans. Bake until a toothpick inserted in center comes out clean, 25-30 minutes. Cool in pans 10 minutes before removing to wire racks; remove paper. Cool completely.
3. For the sauce, in a large heavy saucepan, combine apples, brown sugar, water and bourbon. Cook, covered, over medium-low heat until apples are soft and pliable, about 20 minutes, stirring occasionally. Add butter. Cook and stir, uncovered, until sauce is thin and syrupy, 5-10 minutes longer. Remove from heat; cool completely.
4. Using a long serrated knife, trim tops of the cakes if domed. Spread 1 Tbsp. apple butter on a rimmed serving plate; top with 1 cake layer. Spread with about ⅓ cup apple butter. Top with ⅔ cup apple and bourbon sauce. Repeat layers. Drizzle any remaining sauce from apple mixture over top of cake. Refrigerate, covered, at least 24 hours before serving.
NOTE: This recipe was tested with commercially prepared apple butter.
1 PIECE: 1195 cal., 30g fat (18g sat. fat), 121mg chol., 705mg sod., 223g carb. (154g sugars, 7g fiber), 12g pro.
CAKE LAYER SIZES: Appalachian stack cakes usually have a lot of cake layers stacked on top of each other. You can also make this version using 9-in. cake pans for a 4-layer cake.

LEMON SHEET CAKE

Lemon pie filling lends a splash of citrus flavor to a convenient cake mix, and a rich cream cheese frosting gives the cake sweetness. My family likes this dessert cold, so I cut it into squares and freeze it before serving.
—Alyce Dubisar, North Bend, OR

- -

PREP: 10 min. • **BAKE:** 20 min. + cooling
MAKES: 24 servings

- 1 pkg. lemon cake mix (regular size)
- 4 large eggs, room temperature
- 1 can (15¾ oz.) lemon pie filling
- 3 oz. cream cheese, softened
- ½ cup butter, softened
- 2 cups confectioners' sugar
- 1½ tsp. vanilla extract
- 1 to 2 Tbsp. 2% milk
  Optional: Assorted yellow sprinkles and colored sugar

1. In a large bowl, beat the cake mix and eggs until well blended. Fold in pie filling.
2. Spread into a greased 15x10x1-in. baking pan. Bake at 350° until a toothpick inserted in the center comes out clean, 18-20 minutes. Cool on a wire rack.
3. In a small bowl, beat the cream cheese, butter and confectioners' sugar until smooth. Stir in vanilla and enough milk to reach desired consistency. Spread over cake. If desired, top with sprinkles and colored sugar. Store cake in the refrigerator.
1 PIECE: 205 cal., 7g fat (4g sat. fat), 45mg chol., 242mg sod., 34g carb. (24g sugars, 0 fiber), 2g pro.

HAWAIIAN DREAM CAKE

Get a little taste of Hawaii when you
take a short trip to the kitchen.
—Mary Hudak-Collins, Bluff City, TN

- -

PREP: 20 min. • **BAKE:** 15 min. + cooling
MAKES: 20 servings

- 1   can (20 oz.) unsweetened crushed
     pineapple
- 1   pkg. yellow cake mix (regular size)
- 3   large eggs
- ½   cup canola oil
- ¼   cup water
- 1   pkg. (8 oz.) cream cheese, softened
- 1   cup cold 2% milk
- 1   pkg. (3.4 oz.) instant vanilla pudding
     mix
- 1   carton (8 oz.) frozen whipped
     topping, thawed
- ½   cup chopped walnuts
- ⅓   cup flaked coconut

1. Preheat oven to 350°. Drain pineapple,
reserving 1 cup juice. Set pineapple aside.
In a large bowl, combine cake mix, eggs,
oil, water and reserved pineapple juice;
beat on low speed for 30 seconds. Beat
on medium for 2 minutes. Transfer to a
greased 15x10x1-in. baking pan.
2. Bake until a toothpick inserted near the
center comes out clean, 15-18 minutes;
cool completely on a wire rack.
3. In a large bowl, beat cream cheese until
fluffy. Gradually beat in milk and pudding
mix until blended; fold in the reserved
pineapple. Spread over cake; top with
whipped topping. Sprinkle with walnuts
and coconut. Store in the refrigerator.
1 PIECE: 296 cal., 16g fat (6g sat. fat), 40mg
chol., 273mg sod., 36g carb. (24g sugars,
1g fiber), 3g pro.

PEACH & BLUEBERRY GALETTE

My husband's favorite pie is blueberry,
made with fresh-picked northern Ontario
blueberries. Adding peaches and a rustic
crust creates a bit of summer fun.
—Christine Kropp, London, ON

- -

PREP: 30 min. + chilling
BAKE: 50 min. + cooling
MAKES: 8 servings

- 1½ cups all-purpose flour
- 1   Tbsp. sugar
- ½   tsp. salt
- 10 Tbsp. cold unsalted butter
- 4   Tbsp. 2% milk
- 1   large egg yolk, room temperature

FILLING
- 1   lb. medium peaches, peeled and cut
     into ½-in. slices (about 3 cups)
- 2   cups fresh or frozen blueberries
- ¼   cup packed light brown sugar
- 2   Tbsp. all-purpose flour
- ¼   tsp. ground cinnamon
- ⅛   tsp. salt
- 1   large egg, beaten
- 2   Tbsp. demerara sugar

1. In a large bowl, mix flour, sugar and salt;
cut in butter until crumbly. Combine the
milk and egg yolk; gradually add to flour
mixture, tossing with a fork until dough
holds together when pressed. Shape into
a disk; cover and refrigerate for 1 hour
or overnight.
2. Preheat oven to 350°. On a lightly
floured surface, roll dough to a 13-in.
circle. Transfer to a parchment-lined
14-in. pizza pan. Refrigerate, covered,
while preparing filling.
3. For filling, combine the peach slices,
blueberries, brown sugar, flour, cinnamon
and salt. Arrange over crust to within
1½ in. of edge. Fold crust edge over the
filling, pleating as you go and leaving an
opening in the center. Brush beaten
egg over folded crust; sprinkle with
demerara sugar.
4. Bake until crust is golden and filling is
bubbly, 50-55 minutes. Transfer tart to a
wire rack to cool for 10 minutes before
cutting. Serve warm.
1 PIECE: 319 cal., 16g fat (9g sat. fat), 68mg
chol., 196mg sod., 42g carb. (20g sugars,
2g fiber), 4g pro.

PEACH & BLUEBERRY
GALETTE

RED VELVET
CUPCAKES
WITH COCONUT
FROSTING

RED VELVET CUPCAKES WITH COCONUT FROSTING

There's no better way to celebrate being together than with these fun-loving cupcakes.

—Marie Rizzio, Interlochen, MI

PREP: 25 min. • BAKE: 20 min. + cooling • MAKES: 2 dozen

- ¾ cup butter, softened
- 1½ cups sugar
- 2 large eggs, room temperature
- 1 Tbsp. red food coloring
- 1 tsp. vanilla extract
- 1¾ cups all-purpose flour
- ¼ cup baking cocoa
- ¾ tsp. baking soda
- ¾ tsp. salt
- 1 cup buttermilk
- 1 tsp. white vinegar

FROSTING
- 2 pkg. (8 oz. each) cream cheese, softened
- ¼ cup butter, softened
- 1½ cups confectioners' sugar
- 1 tsp. vanilla extract
- 2 cups sweetened shredded coconut, divided

1. Preheat oven to 350°. In a large bowl, cream butter and sugar until light and fluffy, 5-7 minutes. Add eggs, 1 at a time, beating well after each addition. Stir in food coloring and vanilla. Combine flour, cocoa, baking soda and salt. Combine the buttermilk and vinegar. Add dry ingredients to creamed mixture alternately with buttermilk mixture, beating well after each addition.
2. Fill foil or paper-lined muffin cups two-thirds full. Bake until a toothpick inserted in center comes out clean, 18-22 minutes. Cool 10 minutes before removing from pans to wire rack to cool completely.
3. For frosting, in a large bowl, beat cream cheese and butter until fluffy, 3-5 minutes. Add confectioners' sugar and vanilla; beat until smooth. Stir in 1 cup coconut. Frost cupcakes.
4. Toast remaining 1 cup coconut; sprinkle over cupcakes. Store in the refrigerator.
1 CUPCAKE: 296 cal., 18g fat (12g sat. fat), 59mg chol., 260mg sod., 32g carb. (23g sugars, 1g fiber), 4g pro.

MINI BLUEBERRY BUNDT CAKES

These pretty little blueberry cakes are topped with a yummy lemon-flavored glaze. The recipe makes 12 tiny cakes, so one batch gives you plenty of sweet treats to share with friends.
—Cathy Isaak, Rivers, MB

PREP: 20 min. • BAKE: 30 min. + cooling • MAKES: 1 dozen

- 1 cup butter, softened
- 2 cups sugar
- 4 large eggs, room temperature
- 2 tsp. vanilla extract
- 4 cups all-purpose flour
- 1 tsp. baking powder
- 1 tsp. salt
- 1 cup 2% milk
- 4 cups fresh blueberries

LEMON ICING
- 2 cups confectioners' sugar
- 2 Tbsp. 2% milk
- 4 tsp. lemon juice

1. Preheat oven to 350°. In a large bowl, cream butter and sugar until light and fluffy, 5-7 minutes. Beat in the eggs and vanilla. In another bowl, combine flour, baking powder and salt; add to creamed mixture alternately with milk, beating well after each addition. Fold in blueberries.
2. Scoop into 12 greased 4-in. fluted tube pans. Place pans on a large baking sheet. Bake until a toothpick inserted in the center comes out clean, 30-35 minutes. Cool for 10 minutes before removing from tube pans to wire racks to cool completely.
3. For icing, in a small bowl, combine the confectioners' sugar, milk and lemon juice; drizzle over cakes. If desired, garnish with additional blueberries.
1 MINI CAKE: 560 cal., 18g fat (11g sat. fat), 105mg chol., 395mg sod., 94g carb. (59g sugars, 2g fiber), 8g pro.

MINI BLUEBERRY
BUNDT CAKES

Make Pecan Pie

This recipe will take a little longer than the one on the back of a syrup bottle, but the extra steps yield mouthwatering results.

Stir. Keep the mix of pecans and butter moving so it doesn't burn.

Temper. Prevent the eggs from scrambling by whisking in a few tablespoons of the warm syrup. Once tempered, this mix is ready to mingle with the other ingredients.

Transfer. Fill the prepared crust with the pecan mix. Be sure to get every bit of the buttery syrup into the shell.

Test. Check if the pecan pie is done by piercing the center with a knife. If the blade comes away clean, the pie is fully baked. If the knife is sticky, give the pie another few minutes.

THE BEST PECAN PIE

THE BEST PECAN PIE

Pecan pie is a Thanksgiving tradition in my household, and I was on a quest to create the ultimate version. I think this might be it!
—*James Schend, Pleasant Prairie, WI*

PREP: 15 min. • **BAKE:** 55 min. + cooling
MAKES: 8 servings

    Dough for single-crust pie
½   cup butter
2½ cups coarsely chopped pecans
¾   cup packed brown sugar
¾   cup maple syrup
½   tsp. salt
3   large eggs, beaten
2   Tbsp. whiskey or bourbon, optional
2   tsp. vanilla extract
    Optional: Whipped cream and
    ground cinnamon

1. Preheat oven to 350°. On a lightly floured surface, roll dough to a ⅛-in.-thick circle; transfer to a 9-in. pie plate. Trim crust to ½ in. beyond rim of plate; flute edge. Refrigerate while preparing filling.
2. In a Dutch oven or large saucepan, melt butter over medium heat. Add pecans; cook, stirring constantly, until very fragrant and pecans start to brown, 4-5 minutes. Remove pecans with a slotted spoon, reserving butter in pan. Stir in brown sugar, maple syrup and salt; bring to a boil. Reduce heat; simmer for 2 minutes. Remove from the heat. In a bowl, whisk a small amount of the hot mixture into eggs; return all to the pan, whisking constantly. Stir whiskey, if desired, and vanilla into brown sugar mixture; stir in pecans. Pour into crust.
3. Bake until a knife inserted in the center comes out clean, 55-60 minutes. Cover edge with foil during the last 30 minutes to prevent overbrowning if necessary. Cool completely on a wire rack. If desired, top with whipped cream and cinnamon. Refrigerate leftovers.
DOUGH FOR SINGLE-CRUST PIE:
Combine 1¼ cups all-purpose flour and ¼ tsp. salt; cut in ½ cup cold butter until crumbly. Gradually add 3-5 Tbsp. ice water, tossing with a fork until dough holds together when pressed. Shape into a disk; wrap and refrigerate 1 hour.
1 PIECE: 695 cal., 49g fat (17g sat. fat), 130mg chol., 430mg sod., 60g carb. (40g sugars, 4g fiber), 8g pro.

APPLE
SNICKERDOODLE
DUMP CAKE

APPLE SNICKERDOODLE DUMP CAKE

With an apple farm just down the road, I'm always looking for creative ways to use up those bushels. We love this cozy cake with caramel drizzle and a scoop of vanilla ice cream.
—*Rachel Garcia, Honolulu, HI*

PREP: 15 min. • **BAKE:** 35 min. • **MAKES:** 10 servings

    6   cups sliced, peeled tart apple (about 8 medium)
    ⅓   cup packed brown sugar
    ¼   cup sugar
    ¼   cup orange juice
    1   Tbsp. lemon juice
    1   pkg. (17.9 oz.) snickerdoodle cookie mix
    ½   cup butter, melted
    1   cup coarsely chopped pecans or walnuts
        Whipped cream, optional

1. Preheat oven to 350°. Toss apples with sugars and fruit juices; spread into a greased 11x7-in. baking dish.
2. Place cookie mix in a bowl; stir in contents of cinnamon sugar packet. Sprinkle over apples. Drizzle with butter. Top with pecans.
3. Bake until golden brown and apples are tender, 35-40 minutes. Serve warm and, if desired, top with whipped cream.
1 SERVING: 475 cal., 23g fat (7g sat. fat), 24mg chol., 193mg sod., 67g carb. (48g sugars, 3g fiber), 3g pro.

TEST KITCHEN TIP

Pears will also work in this recipe, since they have a similar moisture level as apples. Canned apple pie filling is an option if you don't have fresh. Try throwing in a handful of dried cranberries or other fruit as a nice way to switch things up.

HONEY BERRY SHEET CAKE

I adapted a traditional honey cake recipe for this dessert. I wanted something that would show off all our amazing local honey as well as tasty summer berries. This also works perfectly as a Fourth of July cake, with the blueberries in the top corner and the raspberries in stripes—you wouldn't need as many blueberries, but you would need more raspberries.
—*Elisabeth Larsen, Pleasant Grove, UT*

PREP: 25 min. • **BAKE:** 45 min. + cooling • **MAKES:** 15 servings

    1   cup sugar
    1   cup canola oil
    1   cup honey
    3   large eggs
    ½   cup orange juice
    1   tsp. vanilla extract
    3½   cups all-purpose flour
    1   tsp. baking powder
    1   tsp. baking soda
    ½   tsp. salt
    1   cup fresh or frozen raspberries
    1   cup fresh or frozen blueberries
GLAZE
    1   cup confectioners' sugar
    2   Tbsp. honey
    2   Tbsp. 2% milk

1. Preheat oven to 350°. Grease a 13x9-in. baking pan. In a large bowl, beat sugar, oil, honey, eggs, orange juice and vanilla until well blended. In another bowl, whisk flour, baking powder, baking soda and salt; gradually beat into sugar mixture.
2. Transfer to prepared pan. Bake for 15 minutes. Sprinkle top of cake with raspberries and blueberries. Bake until a toothpick inserted in center comes out clean, 30-35 minutes longer. Cool completely in pan on a wire rack.
3. Combine glaze ingredients; drizzle over cake. Serve with additional berries if desired.
1 PIECE: 427 cal., 16g fat (1g sat. fat), 37mg chol., 212mg sod., 68g carb. (44g sugars, 2g fiber), 5g pro.

HONEY BERRY
SHEET CAKE

**GINGERBREAD
BUNDT CAKE**

GINGERBREAD BUNDT CAKE

This gorgeous cake's light, airy, moist and forkworthy texture has made me a true gingerbread cake fan.
—Colleen Delawder, Herndon, VA

- -

PREP: 25 min. • **BAKE:** 45 min. + cooling • **MAKES:** 12 servings

- ½ cup unsalted butter, softened
- 4 oz. cream cheese, softened
- 1½ cups packed light brown sugar
- 2 large eggs, room temperature
- 1 tsp. vanilla extract
- ½ cup molasses
- 2½ cups all-purpose flour
- 2 tsp. ground ginger
- 2 tsp. ground cinnamon
- 1 tsp. baking powder
- ½ tsp. kosher salt
- ½ tsp. ground nutmeg
- ¼ tsp. baking soda
- 1 cup 2% milk

1. Preheat oven to 350°. Grease and flour a 10-in. fluted tube pan. In a large bowl, cream butter, cream cheese and sugar until light and fluffy, 5-7 minutes. Add eggs, 1 at a time, beating well after each addition. Beat in the vanilla and molasses. In another bowl, whisk flour, ginger, cinnamon, baking powder, salt, nutmeg and baking soda; add to creamed mixture alternately with milk, beating well after each addition.
2. Transfer to prepared pan. Bake until a toothpick inserted in center comes out clean, 45-50 minutes. Cool in pan 10 minutes before removing to a wire rack to cool completely.
1 PIECE: 365 cal., 12g fat (7g sat. fat), 63mg chol., 212mg sod., 59g carb. (38g sugars, 1g fiber), 5g pro.

MEXICAN HOT CHOCOLATE CUPCAKES

Mexican hot chocolate has some unique ingredients, including cinnamon and cayenne pepper. I created these delicious cupcakes with a similar flavor profile and my secret ingredient: mayonnaise. I like to use mayonnaise in my chocolate cupcakes because I think it keeps them extra moist. To make them easy, I use cake mix and prepared frosting.
—Michele Kusma, Columbus, OH

- -

PREP: 30 min. • **BAKE:** 15 min. + cooling • **MAKES:** 2 dozen

- 1 pkg. chocolate cake mix (regular size)
- 1 cup water
- 1 cup mayonnaise
- 3 large eggs, room temperature
- 2 tsp. ground cinnamon
- ½ tsp. cayenne pepper
- 1 container (16 oz.) marshmallow creme
- 1 can (16 oz.) chocolate frosting
- 24 miniature marshmallows

1. Preheat oven to 350°. Line 24 muffin cup with paper liners.
2. In a large bowl, combine cake mix, water, mayonnaise, eggs, cinnamon and cayenne; beat on low speed 30 seconds. Beat on medium speed 2 minutes. Divide batter among prepared cups. Bake until a toothpick inserted in center comes out clean, 14-19 minutes. Cool in pans 10 minutes before removing to wire racks to cool completely.
3. Using an apple corer or a melon baller, core centers of the cupcakes, leaving bottoms intact (save removed cake for another use). Using a pastry bag with a large round tip, fill cupcakes with marshmallow creme. Frost the cupcakes and top each with a miniature marshmallow.
1 CUPCAKE: 279 cal., 11g fat (3g sat. fat), 27mg chol., 239mg sod., 43g carb. (31g sugars, 0 fiber), 2g pro.

MEXICAN HOT CHOCOLATE CUPCAKES

GINGERED ALMOND TRUFFLE TART

Fresh ginger complements the chocolate truffle filling in this elegant, almost sinful tart. Small servings are best!
—Janice Elder, Charlotte, NC

PREP: 30 min. + chilling • **BAKE:** 15 min. + cooling
MAKES: 16 servings

- 1 cup heavy whipping cream
- 2 Tbsp. minced fresh gingerroot
- 1 cup all-purpose flour
- ½ cup chopped almonds
- ½ cup confectioners' sugar
- ⅓ cup baking cocoa
- 6 Tbsp. cold butter, cubed
- ½ cup amaretto, divided
- 8 oz. bittersweet chocolate, chopped
- ½ cup butter, softened

1. Preheat oven to 350°. In a small heavy saucepan, heat cream and ginger until bubbles form around sides of pan. Set aside
2. Place flour, almonds, confectioners' sugar and cocoa in a food processor; pulse until blended. Add cold butter; pulse until butter is the size of peas. While pulsing, add ¼ cup amaretto to form moist crumbs. Press onto bottom and up side of an ungreased 9-in. fluted tart pan with removable bottom. Bake 13-16 minutes or until set. Cool on a wire rack.
3. Place chocolate in a small bowl. Bring gingered cream just to a boil. Strain through a fine-mesh strainer over chocolate; discard ginger. Stir chocolate mixture with a spatula until smooth; stir in softened butter. Stirring constantly, gradually add the remaining ¼ cup amaretto until blended. Pour into cooled crust. Refrigerate, covered, at least 2 hours or until set.
1 PIECE: 309 cal., 24g fat (13g sat. fat), 47mg chol., 77mg sod., 22g carb. (12g sugars, 2g fiber), 3g pro.

GINGERED ALMOND TRUFFLE TART

POPPY SEED STRAWBERRY SHEET CAKE

POPPY SEED STRAWBERRY SHEET CAKE

I decided to create a strawberry cake one day when I had trouble finding a recipe that did not use a boxed mix. This simple yet fluffy cake has a summery berry flavor, a sprinkling of poppy seeds and a rich cream cheese frosting everyone enjoys.
—Lauren Reiff, East Earl, PA

PREP: 25 min. • **BAKE:** 20 min. + cooling • **MAKES:** 9 servings

- ½ cup sugar
- ½ cup 2% milk
- ¼ cup butter, melted
- 1 large egg, room temperature
- 1 tsp. strawberry extract
- ½ tsp. vanilla extract
- 1 cup all-purpose flour
- ½ tsp. baking powder
- ½ tsp. baking soda
- ¼ tsp. salt
- ½ cup crushed strawberries
- 1 tsp. poppy seeds
- 6 drops red food coloring, optional

FROSTING
- 3 Tbsp. butter, softened
- 3 oz. cream cheese, softened
- ¾ tsp. vanilla extract
- ½ tsp. strawberry extract
- 1½ cups confectioners' sugar
  3-4 drops red food coloring, optional
  Fresh strawberries

1. Preheat oven to 350°. Grease an 8-in. square baking pan. In a large bowl, beat sugar, milk, melted butter, egg and extracts until well blended. In another bowl, whisk flour, baking powder, baking soda and salt; gradually beat into sugar mixture. Stir in crushed strawberries, poppy seeds and, if desired, food coloring.
2. Transfer to prepared pan. Bake until a toothpick inserted in center comes out clean, 20-22 minutes. Cool completely in pan on a wire rack.
3. For frosting, in a small bowl, beat butter, cream cheese and extracts until blended. Gradually beat in confectioners' sugar until smooth. If desired, add red food coloring. Spread over cooled cake. Top with strawberries and additional poppy seeds.
1 PIECE: 308 cal., 13g fat (8g sat. fat), 55mg chol., 278mg sod., 44g carb. (33g sugars, 1g fiber), 3g pro.

MOIST CHOCOLATE CAKE

(SHOWN ON PAGE 186)

This cake was my grandma's specialty. I bake it for family parties, and the fond memories come flooding back for everyone. This layered dessert is light and airy but with a decadent chocolate taste.
—*Patricia Kreitz, Richland, PA*

PREP: 15 min. • **BAKE:** 25 min. + cooling
MAKES: 16 servings

- 2 cups all-purpose flour
- 2 cups sugar
- 2 tsp. baking soda
- ¾ cup baking cocoa
- 1 tsp. salt
- 1 tsp. baking powder
- 1 cup canola oil
- 1 cup brewed coffee
- 1 cup whole milk
- 2 large eggs
- 1 tsp. vanilla extract

FAVORITE ICING

- 5 Tbsp. all-purpose flour
- 1 cup whole milk
- ½ cup butter, softened
- ½ cup shortening
- 1 cup sugar
- 1 tsp. vanilla extract
- 2 to 4 Tbsp. sprinkles, optional

1. Preheat oven to 325°. Grease and flour two 9-in. round baking pans. Sift dry ingredients together into a large bowl. Add oil, coffee and milk; mix at medium speed 1 minute. Add eggs and vanilla; beat 2 minutes longer. (Batter will be thin.) Pour into prepared pans.
2. Bake until a toothpick inserted in the center comes out clean, 25-30 minutes. Cool in pans 10 minutes before removing to wire racks to cool completely.
3. Meanwhile, for the icing, in a small saucepan, whisk flour and milk until smooth. Bring to a boil over medium heat; cook and stir 1-2 minutes or until thickened. Transfer to a small bowl. Cover and refrigerate until chilled.
4. In a large bowl, beat butter, shortening, sugar and vanilla 3-4 minutes or until creamy. Add chilled milk mixture and beat 10 minutes. Stir in sprinkles if desired. Spread frosting between layers and over top and side of cake.

1 PIECE: 482 cal., 28g fat (7g sat. fat), 42mg chol., 404mg sod., 55g carb. (39g sugars, 1g fiber), 4g pro.

TURTLE TART WITH CARAMEL SAUCE

TURTLE TART WITH CARAMEL SAUCE

Between the creamy chocolate filling, crunchy nut crust and gooey caramel sauce, this tart has a whole lot to love.
—*Leah Davis, Morrow, OH*

PREP: 15 min. + chilling
BAKE: 15 min. + cooling
MAKES: 12 servings

- 2 cups pecan halves, toasted
- ½ cup sugar
- 2 Tbsp. butter, melted

FILLING

- 2 cups semisweet chocolate chips
- 1½ cups heavy whipping cream
- ½ cup finely chopped pecans, toasted

CARAMEL SAUCE

- ½ cup butter, cubed
- 1 cup sugar
- 1 cup heavy whipping cream

1. Preheat oven to 350°. Place the pecans and sugar in a food processor; pulse until finely ground. Add melted butter; pulse until combined. Press onto bottom and up the side of a 9-in. fluted tart pan with removable bottom. Bake 12-15 minutes or until golden brown. Cool completely on a wire rack.
2. For filling, place chocolate chips in a small bowl. In a small saucepan, bring cream just to a boil. Pour over chocolate; stir with a whisk until smooth. Pour into cooled crust; cool slightly. Refrigerate until slightly set, about 30 minutes.
3. Sprinkle pecans over filling. Refrigerate, covered, until set, about 3 hours.
4. For sauce, in a large heavy saucepan, melt butter over medium heat; stir in sugar until dissolved. Bring to a boil; cook 10-12 minutes or until deep golden brown, stirring mixture occasionally. Slowly whisk in cream until blended. Remove from heat; cool slightly. Serve with tart.

NOTE: To toast nuts, bake in a shallow pan in a 350° oven for 5-10 minutes or cook in a skillet over low heat until lightly browned, stirring occasionally.

1 PIECE WITH 2 TBSP. CARAMEL SAUCE: 632 cal., 51g fat (24g sat. fat), 82mg chol., 93mg sod., 47g carb. (43g sugars, 4g fiber), 5g pro.

DISNEY'S
DOLE WHIP
PAGE 208

Just Desserts

Dinner isn't complete without a final sweet treat! From cool and creamy frozen delights to rich fruit desserts served hot from the pan, your happily-ever-after delicacy resides in these pages.

DISHES WE LOVE

GRILLED PEACHES
& POUND CAKE

GRILLED PEACHES & POUND CAKE

If you don't have a grill wok or basket for this no-fuss dessert, use a disposable foil pan. Poke holes in the bottom of the pan with a meat fork to allow liquid to drain.
—Joy Pendley, Ortonville, MI

- -

TAKES: 20 min. • **MAKES:** 6 servings

- 3   medium peaches, sliced
- 1   Tbsp. balsamic vinegar
- 1   loaf (10¾ oz.) frozen pound cake, thawed
- ¼   cup packed brown sugar
- 2   Tbsp. butter, melted
- 3   cups vanilla ice cream

1. Brush peaches with vinegar and place in a grill wok or basket. Grill, uncovered, over medium heat for 10-12 minutes or until tender, stirring frequently.

2. Cut pound cake into 6 slices. In a small bowl, combine brown sugar and butter; brush over both sides of cake slices. Grill, uncovered, over medium heat for 1-2 minutes on each side or until light golden brown. Place cake slices on serving plates, and top with peaches and ice cream.

NOTE: If you do not have a grill wok or basket, use a disposable foil pan. Poke holes in the bottom of the pan with a meat fork to allow liquid to drain.

1 SERVING: 413 cal., 20g fat (12g sat. fat), 112mg chol., 269mg sod., 55g carb. (39g sugars, 1g fiber), 6g pro.

TROPICAL PARADISE MILKSHAKES

Slip away to paradise without leaving home with these fruity, coconutty shakes. A little pineapple rum or coconut rum would make them extra indulgent.
—Taste of Home *Test Kitchen*

- -

TAKES: 15 min. • **MAKES:** 6 servings

- 2   medium limes, divided
- ¼   cup unsweetened shredded coconut, toasted
- 1½   cups frozen pineapple chunks
- 1½   cups frozen mango chunks
- 1   medium banana, sliced and frozen
- 1½   cups vanilla ice cream
- 1   cup light coconut milk
- ½   cup fat-free milk
- 1   cup frozen unsweetened strawberries
     Optional: Fresh pineapple, kiwifruit, strawberries, mango, starfruit and edible blossoms

1. Cut 1 lime into wedges. Moisten rims of 6 glasses with a lime wedge. Sprinkle coconut on a plate; dip rims in coconut.

2. Zest and juice remaining lime. Place zest and juice in a blender. Add pineapple, mango, banana, ice cream and milks; cover and process until smooth. Pour ⅔ cup mixture into each prepared glass. Add strawberries to remaining mixture in blender; cover and process until smooth. Pour into glasses; garnish as desired.

1 CUP: 198 cal., 6g fat (4g sat. fat), 15mg chol., 44mg sod., 33g carb. (23g sugars, 3g fiber), 3g pro.

TROPICAL PARADISE
MILKSHAKES

COPYCAT CELEBRATION CHEESECAKE

Both of my children are born on the same day five years apart, so I like to make an elaborate dessert to celebrate the occasion. This seven-layered beauty is perfect. The baking and preparation are easy, but do set aside some time for the assembly. Everyone will be amazed when they see the final product. If you have extra time, freeze for half an hour before adding cheesecake to the top of the pudding layer.
—Kristyne Mcdougle Walter, Lorain, OH

- -

PREP: 1 hour + freezing
BAKE: 30 min. + cooling
MAKES: 16 servings

- 4 cups cold 2% milk
- 3 pkg. (3.4 oz. each) instant white chocolate pudding mix
- 1 pkg. white cake mix (regular size)
- 1⅓ cups rainbow sprinkles, divided
- 1 pkg. (1 oz.) freeze-dried strawberries
- 3 to 12 drops blue food coloring
- ¼ cup baking cocoa
- 2 cartons (24.3 oz. each) Philadelphia ready-to-serve cheesecake filling
- 2 cans (16 oz. each) cream cheese frosting
- 2 Tbsp. rainbow sequin sprinkles

1. Preheat oven to 350°. In each of 3 small bowls, whisk 1⅓ cups milk and 1 package pudding mix for 2 minutes. Refrigerate, covered, while baking cake layers.
2. Line bottoms of 2 greased 9-in. round baking pans with parchment; grease paper. Prepare cake mix batter according to package directions, folding ⅔ cup sprinkles into batter. Transfer to prepared pans. Bake and cool as package directs.
3. Using a long serrated knife, trim tops of cake layers to level. Crumble trimmings; transfer to a parchment-lined baking sheet. Bake at 350° until crisp but not browned, about 5 minutes. Cool completely on pan on wire rack.
4. Line two 9-in. springform pans with plastic wrap, letting ends extend over sides. Place strawberries in a food processor; process until ground. Stir ground strawberries into 1 bowl of pudding. To another bowl of pudding, whisk in blue food coloring. To the third bowl, whisk in cocoa; refrigerate chocolate pudding.

5. Place 1 cake layer in 1 prepared springform pan; spread with strawberry pudding. Place remaining cake layer in remaining prepared springform pan; spread with blue pudding. Freeze both pans at least 1 hour. Top each with 1 carton cheesecake filling. Freeze at least 1 hour longer.
6. Remove strawberry-layered pan from freezer; spread chocolate pudding over top. Return to freezer for 3 hours longer. Meanwhile, stir remaining ⅔ cup sprinkles into cooled cake crumbs.
7. Remove rims from springform pans; discard plastic. Place strawberry-layered cake on a serving plate; top with blue-layered cake. Frost top and sides with cream cheese frosting. Gently press crumb mixture into frosting on sides of cake; sprinkle with sequin sprinkles. Freeze until ready to serve. Remove 10 minutes before cutting.
NOTE: This recipe was tested with Hershey's white chocolate instant pudding mix.
1 PIECE: 871 cal., 43g fat (19g sat. fat), 120mg chol., 929mg sod., 114g carb. (90g sugars, 1g fiber), 9g pro.

COPYCAT CELEBRATION CHEESECAKE

APPLE PAN BETTY

I found this recipe soon after I was married 47 years ago. It uses few ingredients, which are usually on hand, and takes little time to put together. It's a favorite of ours during fall and winter, when apples are at their best.
—Shirley Leister, West Chester, PA

- -

TAKES: 15 min. • **MAKES:** 2 servings

- 1 medium apple, peeled and cubed
- 3 Tbsp. butter
- 1 cup bread cubes
- 3 Tbsp. sugar
- ¼ tsp. ground cinnamon
  Vanilla ice cream, optional

In a small skillet, saute apple in butter for 2-3 minutes or until tender. Add bread cubes. Sprinkle with sugar and cinnamon; toss to coat. Saute until bread is warmed. If desired, serve with ice cream.
½ CUP: 302 cal., 18g fat (11g sat. fat), 46mg chol., 268mg sod., 36g carb. (26g sugars, 2g fiber), 2g pro.

CREAM PUFF DESSERT

CREAM PUFF DESSERT

Instead of making individual cream puffs, create this rich crowd-sized dessert with a cream puff base and sweet toppings.
—*Lisa Nash, Blaine, MN*

- -

PREP: 20 min. + chilling
BAKE: 30 min. + cooling
MAKES: 12 servings

  1 cup water
  ½ cup butter
  1 cup all-purpose flour
  4 large eggs, room temperature
FILLING
  1 pkg. (8 oz.) cream cheese, softened
3½ cups cold 2% milk
  2 pkg. (3.9 oz. each) instant chocolate pudding mix
TOPPING
  1 carton (8 oz.) frozen whipped topping, thawed
  ¼ cup chocolate ice cream topping
  ¼ cup caramel ice cream topping
  ⅓ cup chopped almonds

1. In a large saucepan, bring the water and butter to a boil over medium heat. Add flour all at once; stir until a smooth ball forms. Remove from the heat; let stand for 5 minutes. Add eggs, 1 at a time, beating well after each addition. Continue beating until mixture is smooth and shiny.
2. Spread into a greased 13x9-in. baking dish. Bake at 400° for 30-35 minutes or until puffed and golden brown. Remove to a wire rack to cool completely.
3. For filling, beat the cream cheese, milk and pudding mix in a large bowl until smooth. Spread over puff; refrigerate for 20 minutes.

4. Spread with whipped topping; refrigerate until serving. Drizzle with the chocolate and caramel toppings; sprinkle with almonds. Refrigerate leftovers.
1 PIECE: 381 cal., 23g fat (14g sat. fat), 122mg chol., 354mg sod., 34g carb. (20g sugars, 1g fiber), 8g pro.

BERRY NECTARINE BUCKLE

I found this recipe in a magazine a long time ago and modified it over the years. We enjoy its combination of blueberries, raspberries, blackberries and nectarines, particularly when the dessert is served warm with low-fat frozen yogurt.
—*Lisa Sjursen-Darling, Scottsville, NY*

- -

PREP: 25 min. • **BAKE:** 35 min.
MAKES: 20 servings

  ⅓ cup all-purpose flour
  ⅓ cup packed brown sugar
  1 tsp. ground cinnamon
  3 Tbsp. cold butter
BATTER
  6 Tbsp. butter, softened
  ¾ cup plus 1 Tbsp. sugar, divided
  2 large eggs
1½ tsp. vanilla extract
2¼ cups all-purpose flour
2½ tsp. baking powder
  ½ tsp. salt
  ½ cup fat-free milk
  1 cup fresh blueberries
  1 lb. nectarines, peeled, sliced and patted dry or 1 pkg. (16 oz.) frozen unsweetened sliced peaches, thawed and patted dry
  ½ cup each fresh raspberries and blackberries

1. For topping, in a small bowl, combine the flour, brown sugar and cinnamon; cut in butter until crumbly. Set aside.
2. In a large bowl, cream the butter and ¾ cup sugar until light and fluffy, 5-7 minutes. Add eggs, 1 at a time, beating well after each addition. Beat in vanilla. Combine the flour, baking powder and salt; add to creamed mixture alternately with milk, beating well after each addition. Set aside ¾ cup batter. Fold blueberries into remaining batter.
3. Spoon into a 13x9-in. baking dish coated with cooking spray. Arrange nectarines on top; sprinkle with remaining sugar. Drop reserved batter by teaspoonfuls over nectarines. Sprinkle with raspberries, blackberries and reserved topping.
4. Bake at 350° for 35-40 minutes or until a toothpick inserted in the center comes out clean. Serve warm.
1 PIECE: 177 cal., 6g fat (3g sat. fat), 35mg chol., 172mg sod., 28g carb. (15g sugars, 1g fiber), 3g pro.

DID YOU KNOW?

Buckle gets its name from the heavy streusel topping that weighs the batter down while the dessert bakes, causing the top of the cake to buckle in spots.

BERRY
NECTARINE
BUCKLE

PUMPKIN SOPAPILLA CHEESECAKE

I love baking and trying new things. You can make so many things with pumpkin, so why not try something new? That's where this cheesecake comes in, because everyone loves warm fall spices mixed with pumpkin. I can guarantee you have never had anything like this! Quick and easy to make, it will always be a hit.
—*Vicky Zigmantaite, Monroe, MI*

PREP: 15 min. • BAKE: 30 min. + chilling • MAKES: 16 servings

- 2 pkg. (8 oz. each) cream cheese, softened
- 1½ cups sugar, divided
- 1 tsp. vanilla extract
- 1¼ cups canned pumpkin
- 2 tubes (8 oz. each) refrigerated crescent rolls
- ½ cup butter, melted
- 1 Tbsp. pumpkin pie spice

1. Preheat oven to 350°. In a large bowl, beat cream cheese, 1 cup sugar and vanilla until smooth. Stir in pumpkin until well combined.
2. Unroll 1 tube of crescent dough into the bottom of a greased 13x9-in. baking dish; seal seams and perforations. Spread cream cheese mixture over crust.
3. Unroll remaining crescent dough; place over filling, sealing seams. Pour butter over top. Combine pie spice and remaining ½ cup sugar; sprinkle over top.
4. Bake until golden brown, 30-35 minutes. Cool completely on a wire rack. Refrigerate, covered, at least 3 hours before serving.

1 PIECE: 333 cal., 21g fat (11g sat. fat), 44mg chol., 349mg sod., 34g carb. (24g sugars, 1g fiber), 4g pro.

PUMPKIN SOPAPILLA CHEESECAKE

APPLE-WALNUT BREAD PUDDING

APPLE-WALNUT BREAD PUDDING

You can throw everything but the kitchen sink into bread pudding. This recipe came about because I had stale bread and apples that needed to be used. No apples? Use dried fruit, such as cranberries or apricots.
—*Debra Keil, Owasso, OK*

PREP: 30 min. • BAKE: 50 min. • MAKES: 8 servings

- 5 Tbsp. butter, divided
- 2 medium Granny Smith apples, peeled and chopped
- 1 cup sugar, divided
- ½ tsp. ground cinnamon
- ¼ cup brandy or unsweetened apple juice
- 3 cups refrigerated unsweetened vanilla almond milk
- 4 large eggs, beaten
- ½ tsp. vanilla extract
- 8 cups cubed day-old bread
- ½ cup chopped walnuts

1. Preheat oven to 350°. In a large cast-iron or other ovenproof skillet, melt 2 Tbsp. butter over medium heat. Add apples and ¼ cup sugar. Cook and stir until apples are golden brown and soft, about 6 minutes. Stir in cinnamon. Remove from heat. Stir in brandy; cook over medium heat until liquid is syrupy, 1-2 minutes. Remove from heat.
2. In a large bowl, whisk milk, eggs, vanilla and remaining ¾ cup sugar until blended. Gently stir in bread; let stand until bread is softened, about 5 minutes. Stir in apple mixture and walnuts.
3. Add 1 Tbsp. remaining butter to the skillet; place in oven to heat skillet. Carefully remove hot skillet from oven once butter has melted.
4. Add bread mixture. Melt remaining 2 Tbsp. butter; drizzle over top. Bake until puffed, golden and a knife inserted in center comes out clean, 50-55 minutes. Serve warm.

1 SERVING: 367 cal., 17g fat (6g sat. fat), 112mg chol., 328mg sod., 48g carb. (31g sugars, 2g fiber), 8g pro.

RASPBERRY CREAM CHEESE ICE CREAM

I love ice cream and am always looking for ways to make unique flavors. Since I work for New Glarus Brewery, I've started using some of their interesting flavors into my recipes. This is one of my favorites!
—*Ryan Schwechel, New Glarus, WI*

PREP: 20 min. + chilling
PROCESS: 20 min./batch + freezing
MAKES: 2 qt.

- 1   bottle (12 oz.) raspberry or other fruit beer, such as New Glarus Raspberry Tart
- 2   large eggs, lightly beaten
- 1¼   cups sugar
- 2½   cups half-and-half cream
- 12   oz. cream cheese, cubed
- 1   Tbsp. lemon juice
- ¼   tsp. almond extract
- 2   cups fresh or frozen raspberries

1. In a small saucepan, bring beer to a boil over medium heat; reduce heat and simmer until reduced to 1 cup. Remove from heat; cool completely. Refrigerate, covered, several hours or overnight.
2. Meanwhile, in a large heavy saucepan, whisk eggs and sugar until blended; stir in cream. Cook over low heat until the mixture is just thick enough to coat a metal spoon and a thermometer reads at least 160°, stirring constantly. Do not allow to boil. Remove from heat immediately.
3. Whisk in cream cheese until smooth. Cool quickly by placing pan in a bowl of ice water; stir for 2 minutes. Stir in lemon juice and almond extract. Press waxed paper onto surface of custard. Refrigerate several hours or overnight.
4. Stir reduced beer into custard. Fill cylinder of ice cream freezer two-thirds full; freeze according to manufacturer's directions. Fold in the raspberries, reserving some for second batch if necessary. Transfer ice cream to freezer containers, allowing headspace for expansion. Freeze mixture until firm, 4-6 hours. Refrigerate the remaining custard mixture and raspberries until ready to freeze. If desired, serve with additional fresh raspberries.
½ CUP: 206 cal., 12g fat (7g sat. fat), 63mg chol., 95mg sod., 20g carb. (19g sugars, 1g fiber), 4g pro.

QUEBEC MAPLE SYRUP DUMPLINGS (GRANDS-PERES)

These quick and easy maple dumplings are so delicious! The classic French Canadian comfort food at its best.
—*Francine Lizotte, Langley, BC*

PREP: 15 min. • **COOK:** 15 min.
MAKES: 8 servings

- 2   cups all-purpose flour
- 2   Tbsp. sugar
- 4   tsp. baking powder
- ½   tsp. kosher salt
- 3   Tbsp. unsalted butter
- 1   cup 2% milk
- ½   tsp. vanilla extract

SAUCE

- 2½   cups water
- 2   cups packed brown sugar
- ½   cup unsalted butter, cubed
- ½   cup maple syrup
- ½   tsp. vanilla extract
     Vanilla ice cream

1. In a large bowl, combine flour, sugar, baking powder and kosher salt. Cut in butter until crumbly. Gradually add milk and vanilla, tossing with a fork until dough comes together; set aside.
2. In a Dutch oven, combine water, brown sugar, butter, syrup and vanilla. Cook on high until mixture reaches a simmer. Drop dough by tablespoonfuls on top of the simmering liquid. Reduce heat to low; cover and cook until a toothpick inserted in center of dumplings comes out clean, 13-15 minutes, spooning sauce over dumplings halfway through cooking.
3. Serve warm with ice cream.
2 DUMPLINGS WITH ⅓ CUP SAUCE:
544 cal., 17g fat (10g sat. fat), 44mg chol., 395mg sod., 96g carb. (70g sugars, 1g fiber), 4g pro.

QUEBEC MAPLE SYRUP DUMPLINGS (GRANDS-PERES)

COOKIES & CREAM

Pair up two sweet treats—plus some tempting toppings—to make these easy, freeze-y twists on an ice cream sandwich

MINI BAKED ALASKA

COOKIE OVERLOAD

MINT COOKIE

FROZEN S'MORE

COOKIE-BUTTER LOVER

TOTALLY TROPICAL

COOKIE-BUTTER LOVER
Place 1 scoop **coffee ice cream** between 2 **Biscoff biscuits**. Drizzle with ¼ cup melted **Biscoff creamy cookie butter**. Freeze until serving.

COOKIE OVERLOAD
Place 1 scoop **cookie dough ice cream** between 2 **chocolate chip cookies**. Roll in ¼ cup mixture of frozen **cookie dough bites** and **mini chocolate chips**. Freeze until serving.

MINT COOKIE
Place 1 scoop **mint chip ice cream** between 2 **mint Milano cookies**. Freeze until serving.

MINI BAKED ALASKA
Place 1 scoop **strawberry ice cream** onto 1 **shortbread cookie**. Spread ¼ cup **marshmallow creme** over the top, covering all ice cream. Blow-torch **marshmallow** until browned. Serve immediately.

FROZEN S'MORE
Place 1 scoop **s'mores ice cream** onto 1 **graham cracker half**. Spread ⅛ cup **marshmallow fluff** over ice cream; top with remaining graham cracker half. Freeze until solid. Dip half the sandwich into ½ cup **milk chocolate coating**. Freeze until serving.

POP TART

LEMON BLUEBERRY

CHOCOLATE CHERRY

SNICKERDOODLE

TOTALLY TROPICAL

Place 1 scoop **mango sorbet** between 2 **Keebler Coconut Dreams Fudge, Coconut & Caramel Cookies**. Roll in ⅛ cup **toasted sweetened shredded coconut**. Thread 1 **maraschino cherry** on a toothpick and place in the center. Freeze until serving.

CHOCOLATE CHERRY

Place 1 scoop **black cherry ice cream** between 2 **classic chocolate wafer cookies**. Freeze until serving.

SNICKERDOODLE

Place 1 scoop **cinnamon ice cream** between 2 **snickerdoodle cookies**. Roll in ½ cup **coarse sugar**. Freeze until serving.

POP TART

Place 1 scoop **blue moon ice cream** between 2 **Wild Berry Pop-Tarts**. Roll in **sprinkles**. Freeze until serving.

LEMON BLUEBERRY

Place 1 scoop **lemon bar ice cream** onto 1 **windmill cookie**. Drizzle with ⅛ cup warmed **blueberry preserves**. Top with second **windmill cookie**. Freeze until serving.

DISNEY'S
DOLE WHIP

🕐 🍎 5️⃣

DISNEY'S DOLE WHIP

Your kitchen will be the happiest place on earth when you serve this sweet-sour treat. The recipe comes directly from the Disneyland app and tastes just the same as real deal you'd order at the park.
—Taste of Home *Test Kitchen*

- -

TAKES: 10 min. • **MAKES:** 2 servings

- 2 cups frozen pineapple chunks
- 1 cup vanilla ice cream
- ½ cup unsweetened pineapple juice

Place all ingredients in a blender; cover and process until thick, stopping and scraping sides as needed. Pour into a glass, topping with a swirl.
1 CUP: 290 cal., 7g fat (4g sat. fat), 29mg chol., 87mg sod., 50g carb. (34g sugars, 1g fiber), 3g pro.

EGGNOG ICE CREAM WITH HOT BUTTERED RUM SAUCE

Why save your ice cream maker for summer? Serve Christmasy scoops featuring the flavor of eggnog and drizzle them with a delectable buttered rum sauce straight from the stovetop.
—*Deirdre Cox, Kansas City, MO*

- -

PREP: 30 min. + chilling
PROCESS: 20 min. + freezing
MAKES: 1½ qt. (1 cup sauce)

- 6 large egg yolks
- 1 cup sugar
- 3 cups heavy whipping cream
- 1 cup whole milk
- 1 vanilla bean
- ¼ cup spiced rum
- ¼ tsp. ground nutmeg

SAUCE

- 6 Tbsp. unsalted butter
- 1 cup packed brown sugar
- ⅓ cup heavy whipping cream
- 2 Tbsp. light corn syrup
- 2 Tbsp. spiced rum

1. In a small bowl, whisk egg yolks and sugar; set aside. In a large heavy saucepan, combine the cream and milk. Split vanilla bean in half lengthwise. With a sharp knife, scrape vanilla seeds into pan; add bean.

2. Heat cream mixture until bubbles form around sides of pan. Whisk a small amount of the hot mixture into the egg mixture. Return all to the pan, whisking constantly. Cook and stir over low heat until mixture is thickened and coats the back of a spoon.

3. Quickly transfer to a bowl; place in ice water and stir for 2 minutes. Stir in rum and nutmeg. Press waxed paper onto surface of custard. Refrigerate for several hours or overnight.

4. Discard vanilla bean. Fill cylinder of ice cream freezer two-thirds full; freeze according to the manufacturer's directions. When ice cream is frozen, transfer to a freezer container; freeze for 2-4 hours before serving.

5. For sauce, in a small saucepan, melt butter over medium heat. Stir in brown sugar, cream and corn syrup; cook and stir until sugar is dissolved. Remove from the heat; stir in rum. Serve with ice cream.
½ CUP WITH 1 TBSP. SAUCE: 477 cal., 33g fat (20g sat. fat), 185mg chol., 39mg sod., 41g carb. (40g sugars, 0 fiber), 4g pro.

TEST KITCHEN TIP

Try spooning some of the eggnog ice cream into your coffee or hot chocolate. Or add a scoop on top of your favorite pie. Pumpkin, pecan or apple pie? We're looking at you!

EGGNOG ICE CREAM
WITH HOT BUTTERED
RUM SAUCE

SKILLET CARAMEL-APPLE BUCKLE

My grandma used to bake a version of this for me when I was a little girl. She would make it using fresh apples from her tree in the backyard. I've adapted her recipe because I love the combination of apples, pecans and caramel.
—*Emily Hobbs, Springfield, MO*

- -

PREP: 35 min. • **BAKE:** 1 hour + standing
MAKES: 12 servings

- ½ cup butter, softened
- ¾ cup sugar
- 2 large eggs, room temperature
- 1 tsp. vanilla extract
- 2 cups all-purpose flour
- 2½ tsp. baking powder
- 1¾ tsp. ground cinnamon
- ½ tsp. ground ginger
- ¼ tsp. salt
- 1½ cups buttermilk

TOPPING

- ⅔ cup packed brown sugar
- ½ cup all-purpose flour
- ¼ cup cold butter
- ¾ cup finely chopped pecans
- ½ cup old-fashioned oats
- 6 cups thinly sliced peeled Gala or other sweet apples (about 6 medium)
- 18 caramels, unwrapped
- 1 Tbsp. buttermilk
  Optional toppings: Vanilla ice cream, whipped cream, additional chopped pecans and ground cinnamon

1. Preheat oven to 350°. In a large bowl, cream butter and sugar until light and fluffy, 5-7 minutes. Add eggs, 1 at a time, beating well after each addition. Beat in vanilla. In another bowl, whisk flour, baking powder, cinnamon, ginger and salt; add to creamed mixture alternately with buttermilk, beating well after each addition. Pour into a greased 12-in. cast-iron or other ovenproof skillet.
2. For topping, in a small bowl, mix the brown sugar and flour; cut in butter until crumbly. Stir in pecans and oats; sprinkle over batter. Top with apples. Bake until apples are golden brown, 60-70 minutes. Cool in pan on a wire rack.
3. In a microwave, melt caramels with buttermilk; stir until smooth. Drizzle over cake. Let stand until set. Serve with toppings as desired.

1 PIECE: 462 cal., 19g fat (9g sat. fat), 64mg chol., 354mg sod., 68g carb. (42g sugars, 3g fiber), 7g pro.

SKILLET
CARAMEL-APPLE BUCKLE

READER REVIEW

"I love all the ingredients, so I had to try it. Easy to make and delicious. I used a caramel dip on top, and it worked well. Impressive in the skillet!"

—SUSEY22, TASTEOFHOME.COM

BOURBON &
CORNFLAKES
ICE CREAM

BOURBON & CORNFLAKES ICE CREAM

Humphry Slocombe, a small San Francisco chain, serves scoops of Secret Breakfast—a rich and boozy vanilla-based ice cream. Even (and especially) if the shop isn't in your corner of the country, consider giving the recipe a try!
—*Andrea Potischman, Menlo Park, CA*

PREP: 45 min. + chilling
PROCESS: 30 min. + freezing
MAKES: 1 qt.

- 3 Tbsp. heavy whipping cream
- 3 Tbsp. unsalted butter, melted
- 2 Tbsp. sugar
- Dash salt
- 1½ cups cornflakes, coarsely crushed

VANILLA BOURBON ICE CREAM

- 5 large egg yolks
- ½ cup sugar
- Dash salt
- 1 cup whole milk
- 1½ cups heavy whipping cream
- 1 tsp. vanilla extract
- 3 Tbsp. bourbon

1. Preheat oven to 375°. In a small bowl combine cream, butter, sugar and salt. Stir in the cornflakes until well coated. Spread onto a parchment-lined baking sheet. Bake until golden brown, 12-15 minutes, stirring once. Cool completely.

2. For the ice cream, in a large heavy saucepan, whisk egg yolks, sugar and salt until blended; stir in milk. Cook over low heat until mixture is just thick enough to coat a metal spoon and a thermometer reads at least 160°, stirring constantly. Do not allow to boil. Remove from heat immediately.

3. Quickly transfer to a small bowl; place bowl in a pan of ice water. Stir gently and occasionally for 2 minutes. Stir in cream and vanilla. Press waxed paper onto surface of custard. Refrigerate several hours or overnight.

4. Stir bourbon into custard. Fill cylinder of ice cream maker no more than two-thirds full; freeze according to manufacturer's directions, adding cornflakes during the last 2 minutes of processing. (Refrigerate any remaining mixture until ready to freeze.)

5. Transfer ice cream to freezer containers, allowing headspace for expansion. Freeze until firm, 2-4 hours.

½ CUP: 353 cal., 26g fat (16g sat. fat), 187mg chol., 108mg sod., 23g carb. (19g sugars, 0 fiber), 5g pro.

APPLE CREME BRULEE

Here's the cream of the apple dessert crop. Fruit, caramel and cinnamon flavors enhance the rich, velvety custard. Served warm or chilled, it's a classic end to a meal.
—*Cheryl Perry, Hertford, NC*

PREP: 35 min. • **BAKE:** 1 hour + chilling • **MAKES:** 6 servings

APPLE
CREME BRULEE

- 3 medium tart apples, peeled and thinly sliced
- 6 Tbsp. caramel ice cream topping
- ¼ cup sugar plus 4 Tbsp. sugar, divided
- ¼ cup plus 2 Tbsp. packed brown sugar, divided
- ½ tsp. ground cinnamon
- 2 cups heavy whipping cream
- 5 large egg yolks, beaten
- 1 tsp. vanilla extract

1. Place apples in a microwave-safe dish; cover with water. Cover and microwave on high for 3-4 minutes or until tender. Drain apples and pat dry on paper towel. Arrange apples in the bottoms of six 6-oz. ramekins or custard cups. Top with caramel topping; set aside.

2. In a small saucepan, combine ¼ cup sugar, ¼ cup brown sugar and cinnamon; stir in cream. Heat over medium heat until bubbles form around sides of pan. Remove from the heat; stir a small amount of hot mixture into the egg yolks. Return all to the pan, stirring constantly. Stir in vanilla.

3. Pour into prepared ramekins. Place ramekins in a baking pan; add 1 in. of boiling water to pan. Bake, uncovered, at 325° until centers are just set (mixture will jiggle), 55-60 minutes. Remove ramekins from water bath; cool for 20 minutes. Cover and refrigerate overnight.

4. If using a creme brulee torch, sprinkle remaining 4 Tbsp. sugar evenly over custards. Heat sugar with the torch until caramelized. Serve immediately.

5. If broiling the custards, place ramekins on a baking sheet; let stand at room temperature for 15 minutes. Sprinkle remaining 4 Tbsp. sugar evenly over custards. Broil 8 in. from the heat for 4-7 minutes or until sugar is caramelized. Refrigerate for 1-2 hours or until firm.

1 SERVING: 504 cal., 33g fat (20g sat. fat), 280mg chol., 114mg sod., 50g carb. (33g sugars, 1g fiber), 4g pro.

CUCUMBER CANAPES
PAGE 218

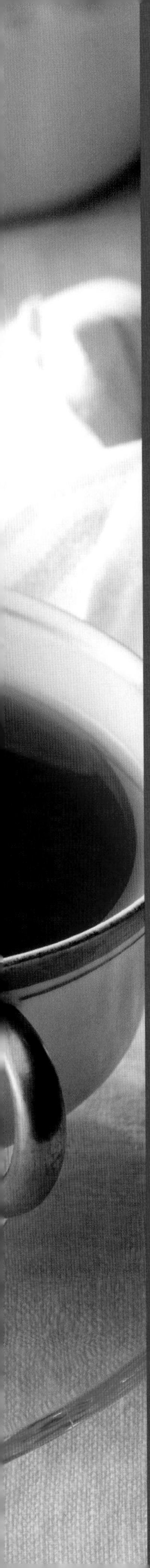

Potluck Pleasers

It's easy to feed a crowd when delicious big-batch recipes are on the menu. Serve up tempting appetizers, crowd-pleasing sweets, tasty pork sandwiches, vintage holiday ham and more.

BEST OF THE BEST DISHES

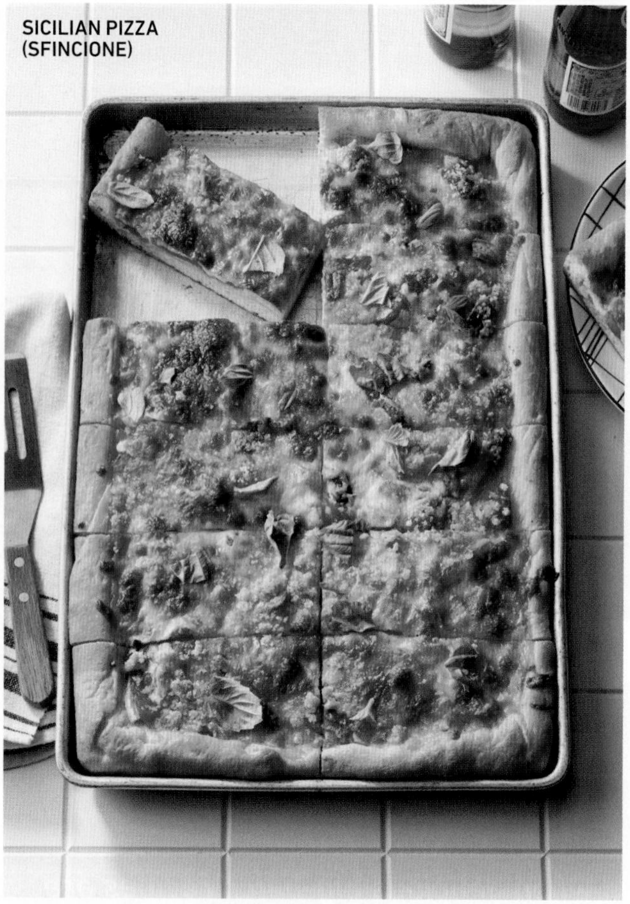

SICILIAN PIZZA (SFINCIONE)

SICILIAN PIZZA (SFINCIONE)

My favorite pizza from childhood is still my favorite today. The crunchy bread-crumb topping sets it apart from its American counterpart. I like to top this pie with torn fresh basil.
—Susan Falk, Sterling Heights, MI

PREP: 20 min. • **BAKE:** 20 min. • **MAKES:** 12 servings

- **2 loaves (1 lb. each) fresh or frozen pizza dough, thawed**
- **3 Tbsp. olive oil, divided**
- **1 can (28 oz.) whole tomatoes, drained and crushed**
- **1 medium onion, finely chopped**
- **1 can (2 oz.) anchovy fillets, drained and broken into ¼-in. pieces**
- **1 cup shredded mozzarella cheese**
- **½ cup soft bread crumbs**
- **Fresh torn basil leaves**

1. Preheat oven to 425°. Grease a 15x10x1-in. baking pan. Press dough to fit bottom and ½ in. up sides of pan. Brush with 2 Tbsp. oil; top with tomatoes, onion and anchovies. Sprinkle with the mozzarella. Combine bread crumbs and remaining 1 Tbsp. oil; sprinkle over pizza.
2. Bake pizza on a lower oven rack until edges are golden brown and cheese is melted, 20-25 minutes. Sprinkle with the basil before serving.
1 PIECE: 277 cal., 9g fat (2g sat. fat), 11mg chol., 527mg sod., 38g carb. (4g sugars, 3g fiber), 11g pro.

DOMINICAN GREEN AND YELLOW FRIED PLANTAINS

Fried plantains are a tradition in most Caribbean countries. In the Dominican Republic, they're served with almost everything. In our home, they are almost always served as a snack or an appetizer before dinner. The mojo dipping sauce adds extra flavor to the plantains so it is an absolute must!
—Belqui Ortiz-Millili, Mesa, Arizona

TAKES: 15 min. • **MAKES:** about 2 dozen (¼ cup sauce)

- **1 green plantain**
- **1 yellow plantain**
- **Oil for deep-fat frying**

MOJO SAUCE

- **¼ cup corn oil**
- **½ tsp. minced fresh cilantro**
- **¼ tsp. minced garlic**

1. In a deep cast-iron or electric skillet, heat oil to 375°. Peel the plantains. Cut green plantain into 1-in. slices. Cut yellow plantain into ½-in. slices. Add both plantains to oil, a few at a time, and cook until lightly browned, 30-60 seconds. Remove with a slotted spoon; drain on paper towels.
2. Place fried green plantain pieces between 2 sheets of aluminum foil. With the bottom of a glass, flatten to ½-in. thickness. Fry until golden brown, 2-3 minutes longer.
3. In a small bowl, combine the mojo sauce ingredients. Serve with plantains.
1 PIECE WITH ½ TSP. SAUCE: 50 cal., 4g fat (0 sat. fat), 0 chol., 1mg sod., 5g carb. (2g sugars, 0 fiber), 0 pro.

DOMINICAN GREEN AND YELLOW FRIED PLANTAINS

CHEESEBURGER
BOMBS

CHEESEBURGER BOMBS

Instead of enjoying your cheeseburger on a bun, have it in one!
These bundles are the perfect take-along option.
—Taste of Home *Test Kitchen*

PREP: 25 min. • **BAKE:** 20 min. • **MAKES:** 8 servings

½   lb. ground beef
¼   cup chopped onion
¼   cup crumbled cooked bacon
¼   cup ketchup
2   Tbsp. prepared mustard
2   Tbsp. chopped dill pickle or pickle relish
1   tube (16.3 oz.) large refrigerated buttermilk biscuits
½   cup shredded cheddar cheese
1   large egg, room temperature, beaten
½   tsp. sesame seeds

1. Preheat oven to 350°. In a large skillet, cook beef and onion
over medium heat until beef is no longer pink and onion is tender,
3-4 minutes, breaking up beef into crumbles; drain. Stir in bacon,
ketchup, mustard and pickles; cool slightly.
2. On a lightly floured surface, roll each biscuit into a 5-in. circle.
Add 1 Tbsp. cheese in the center of each biscuit; top with 2 Tbsp.
meat mixture. Bring biscuit dough over filling to center; pinch to
seal. Place seam side down on a parchment-lined baking sheet.
3. Brush tops with beaten egg; sprinkle with sesame seeds. Bake
until golden brown, 18-20 minutes. Serve warm.
1 SERVING: 276 cal., 13g fat (5g sat. fat), 27mg chol., 897mg sod.,
28g carb. (5g sugars, 1g fiber), 12g pro.

GRILLED LEEK DIP

Smoky leeks from the grill add punch to this creamy appetizer.
I like to serve it with fresh veggies and chips.
—Ramona Parris, Canton, GA

PREP: 10 min. • **GRILL:** 10 min. + chilling • **MAKES:** 2½ cups

2   medium leeks
2   tsp. olive oil
½   tsp. salt, divided
¼   tsp. pepper
2   cups reduced-fat sour cream
2   Tbsp. Worcestershire sauce
    Assorted fresh vegetables

1. Trim and discard dark green portions of leeks. Brush leeks
with oil; sprinkle with ¼ tsp. salt and pepper. Grill leeks, covered,
over medium-high heat 8-10 minutes or until lightly charred and
tender, turning occasionally. Cool slightly; chop leeks.
2. In a small bowl, combine sour cream, Worcestershire sauce
and remaining salt; stir in leeks. Refrigerate, covered, 2 hours
before serving. Serve with vegetables.
2 TBSP: 43 cal., 2g fat (1g sat. fat), 8mg chol., 93mg sod., 3g carb.
(2g sugars, 0 fiber), 2g pro.

TEST KITCHEN TIP

Switching up this dip to make it your own is simple. Add a
few dashes of hot pepper sauce, stir in a little lemon juice or
mix in freshly chopped chives. Replace the sour cream with
plain yogurt, or swap in soy, hoisin, teriyaki or steak sauce
for the Worcestershire sauce. Take the appetizer to another
level by folding in cooked, peeled and chopped shrimp.

GRILLED
LEEK DIP

CHIPOTLE CHICKEN

CHEESEBURGER NACHOS

Cheeseburger nachos are the perfect game-day graze. Load them up with all the toppings or let everyone claim part of the platter that they can top with their faves.
—Taste of Home *Test Kitchen*

TAKES: 25 min. • **MAKES:** 8 servings

1 pkg. (22 oz.) frozen waffle fries
1 lb. ground beef
⅔ cup water
1 envelope taco seasoning
1 cup shredded cheddar cheese
8 bacon strips, cooked and crumbled
½ cup dill pickle slices
¾ cup shredded lettuce
1 medium tomato, seeded and chopped
¼ cup secret burger sauce
¼ cup ketchup
1 Tbsp. prepared mustard

1. Bake fries according to package directions. Meanwhile, in a large skillet, cook beef over medium heat until no longer pink, 5-7 minutes, breaking into crumbles; drain. Return to pan. Add water and taco seasoning. Cook and stir until sauce thickens, about 3 minutes.
2. Transfer fries to a 10-in. cast-iron or other ovenproof skillet. Top with seasoned ground beef, shredded cheese and bacon. Return to oven until cheese is melted, about 5 minutes. Top with pickles, lettuce and tomato. Drizzle with secret sauce, ketchup and mustard.

1 CUP: 407 cal., 24g fat (11g sat. fat), 71mg chol., 1082mg sod., 27g carb. (3g sugars, 3g fiber), 22g pro.

TEST KITCHEN TIP

Try loading up your cheeseburger nachos with extra toppings, such as sesame seeds, sliced onions or other tasty burger garnishes.

No matter what extra toppings you choose, always add them after the cheese. Doing so will give the toppings a melty surface to stick to, so nothing will slide off during the nosh fest. Once the cheese is on, feel free to add the toppings in whatever order you'd like.

CHIPOTLE CHICKEN

No need to make a trip to the famous restaurant chain for its marinated chicken when you can whip up this flavor-packed dish at home. I experimented with different ingredients over several months to perfect the recipe, and I think I got it right! The savory marinade, with a spicy kick and a slightly sweet finish, serves up a full-flavored entree both kids and adults love. Try it in bowls, tacos and burritos. You can easily reheat leftovers in a skillet on medium-high heat.
—Kim Tower, Danville, CA

PREP: 20 min. + marinating
GRILL: 15 min. + resting
MAKES: 8 servings

¼ cup water
3 Tbsp. brown sugar
3 Tbsp. white vinegar
3 Tbsp. canola oil
1 Tbsp. chopped chipotle pepper in adobo sauce
5 garlic cloves, halved
1 Tbsp. ground chipotle pepper or ground ancho chile pepper
2½ tsp. ground cumin
2½ tsp. dried oregano
1½ tsp. kosher salt
1 tsp. smoked paprika
½ tsp. pepper
3 lbs. boneless skinless chicken thighs

1. Place the first 12 ingredients in a blender; cover and process until pureed. Transfer marinade to a large bowl or shallow dish. Add chicken; turn to coat. Refrigerate 8 hours or overnight.
2. Drain chicken, discarding marinade. Grill chicken, covered, over medium-high heat or broil 4 in. from the heat until a thermometer reads 170°, 6-8 minutes on each side. Let chicken rest 10 minutes before slicing.
FREEZE OPTION: Place cooled chicken in freezer containers. To use, partially thaw in refrigerator overnight. Microwave, covered, on high in a microwave-safe dish until heated through, stirring gently.
4 OZ. COOKED CHICKEN: 284 cal., 15g fat (4g sat. fat), 113mg chol., 297mg sod., 4g carb. (3g sugars, 0 fiber), 32g pro.
DIABETIC EXCHANGES: 4 lean meat, 2 fat.

CONTEST-WINNING HOLIDAY GLAZED HAM

I like to serve this juicy, mouthwatering ham with mashed potatoes and colorful vegetables. The apricot glaze is delicious, and the pineapple, cherries and cloves assure a lovely presentation.
—*Diane Freeman, Falkland, BC*

PREP: 20 min. • **BAKE:** 2 hours • **MAKES:** 16 servings

- 1 boneless fully cooked ham (about 6 lbs.)
- 1 Tbsp. whole cloves
- 1 can (20 oz.) sliced pineapple
- 1 cup apricot preserves
- 1 tsp. ground mustard
- ½ tsp. ground allspice
  Maraschino cherries

1. Preheat oven to 325°. Place the ham on a rack in a shallow roasting pan. Score the surface of ham, making diamond shapes ½ in. deep; insert a clove in each diamond. Bake, uncovered, 1½ hours.
2. Drain pineapple, reserving juice. In a small saucepan, combine pineapple juice, preserves, mustard and allspice. Bring to a boil; cook and stir for 10 minutes or until slightly thickened.
3. Spoon half the glaze over ham. Secure pineapple slices and cherries on top and sides of ham with toothpicks.
4. Bake 30-45 minutes longer or until a thermometer reads 140°, basting twice with remaining glaze.
5 OZ. HAM: 248 cal., 6g fat (2g sat. fat), 87mg chol., 1774mg sod., 18g carb. (13g sugars, 0 fiber), 32g pro.

CONTEST-WINNING
HOLIDAY GLAZED HAM

PEACH
COBBLER
COOKIES

PEACH COBBLER COOKIES

My sister brought me fresh peaches one year, and we decided to make these fruity cookies. A quick and easy change from pie, they're a wonderfully creative way to use fresh peaches.
—*Anna Miller, Churdan, IA*

PREP: 30 min. • **BAKE:** 15 min./batch + cooling
MAKES: about 4½ dozen

- 1 cup butter, softened
- 1 cup sugar
- ⅓ cup packed brown sugar
- 1 large egg, room temperature
- 1 tsp. vanilla extract
- ¼ tsp. almond extract
- 3 cups all-purpose flour
- 1½ tsp. ground cinnamon
- 1 tsp. cream of tartar
- 1 tsp. baking soda
- ½ tsp. salt
- ¼ tsp. ground nutmeg
- 1 cup chopped peeled fresh peaches

1. Preheat oven to 350°. In a large bowl, cream butter and sugars until light and fluffy, 5-7 minutes. Beat in egg and extracts. In another bowl, whisk flour, cinnamon, cream of tartar, baking soda, salt and nutmeg; gradually beat into creamed mixture. Stir in peaches.
2. Drop dough by tablespoonfuls 2 in. apart onto parchment-lined baking sheets. Bake until set, 14-16 minutes. Cool on pans 2 minutes. Remove cookies to wire racks to cool completely. Store in an airtight container.
1 COOKIE: 78 cal., 4g fat (2g sat. fat), 12mg chol., 74mg sod., 11g carb. (5g sugars, 0 fiber), 1g pro.

CUCUMBER CANAPES

I always get requests for the recipe whenever I serve these delicate finger sandwiches with a creamy herb spread and festive red and green garnishes.
—Nadine Whittaker, South Plymouth, MA

PREP: 20 min. + chilling • MAKES: 2 dozen

- 1 cup mayonnaise
- 3 oz. cream cheese, softened
- 1 Tbsp. grated onion
- 1 Tbsp. minced chives
- ½ tsp. cider vinegar
- ½ tsp. Worcestershire sauce
- 1 garlic clove, minced
- ¼ tsp. paprika
- ⅛ tsp. curry powder
- ⅛ tsp. each dried oregano, thyme, basil, parsley flakes and dill weed
- 1 loaf (1 lb.) white or rye bread
- 2 medium cucumbers, scored and thinly sliced
  Diced pimientos and additional dill weed

1. In a blender or food processor, combine the mayonnaise, cream cheese, onion, chives, vinegar, Worcestershire sauce, garlic and seasonings. Cover and process until blended. Cover and refrigerate for 24 hours.

2. Using a 2½-in. biscuit cutter, cut out circles from bread slices. Spread mayonnaise mixture over bread; top with cucumber slices. Garnish with pimientos and dill.

1 CANAPE: 120 cal., 9g fat (2g sat. fat), 7mg chol., 134mg sod., 8g carb. (1g sugars, 1g fiber), 2g pro.

SLOW-COOKER
TROPICAL ORANGE CAKE

SLOW-COOKER TROPICAL ORANGE CAKE

Inspired by the fruity tropical flavors of my all-time favorite yogurt, this makes for a fresh, fun and comforting treat. Try it for a beautiful dessert that is ridiculously easy to prepare.
—Lisa Renshaw, KS City, MO

PREP: 15 min. • COOK: 4 hours + standing • MAKES: 8 servings

- 3 cups cold 2% milk
- 1 pkg. (3.4 oz.) instant coconut cream pudding mix
- 1 pkg. orange cake mix (regular size)
- ¾ cup unsweetened pineapple tidbits
- 2 cups toasted coconut marshmallows, quartered

1. In a large bowl, whisk milk and pudding mix for 2 minutes. Transfer to a greased 5-qt. slow cooker. Prepare cake mix batter according to package directions, folding pineapple into batter. Pour into slow cooker.

2. Cook, covered, on low until edges of cake are golden brown, about 4 hours.

3. Remove slow-cooker insert; sprinkle cake with marshmallows. Let cake stand, uncovered, 10 minutes before serving.

1 SERVING: 518 cal., 20g fat (6g sat. fat), 77mg chol., 596mg sod., 73g carb. (50g sugars, 1g fiber), 9g pro.

TEST KITCHEN TIP

It's important to keep the lid on the slow cooker whenever simmering up a family favorite, but it's particularly true when using a slow cooker to "bake" a treat. When preparing this cake, avoid the temptation to sneak a peek and you're sure to enjoy sweet success in the end.

CUCUMBER
CANAPES

ELEGANT SMOKED SALMON STRATA

This fancy overnight egg bake is ideal for guests. In the morning, you can simply let it come to room temperature and whip up side dishes as it bakes. Then get ready for compliments!
—*Lisa Speer, Palm Beach, FL*

PREP: 30 min. + chilling • **BAKE:** 55 min. + standing
MAKES: 12 servings

- 4 cups cubed ciabatta bread
- 2 Tbsp. butter, melted
- 2 Tbsp. olive oil
- 2 cups shredded Gruyere or Swiss cheese
- 2 cups shredded white cheddar cheese
- 10 green onions, sliced
- ½ lb. smoked salmon or lox, coarsely chopped
- 8 large eggs
- 4 cups 2% milk
- 4 tsp. Dijon mustard
- ¼ tsp. salt
- ¼ tsp. pepper
  Creme fraiche or sour cream and minced chives

1. In a large bowl, toss bread cubes with butter and oil; transfer to a greased 13x9-in. baking dish. Sprinkle with cheeses, onions and salmon. In another bowl, whisk the eggs, milk, mustard, salt and pepper; pour over top. Cover and refrigerate overnight.
2. Remove from the refrigerator 30 minutes before baking. Preheat oven to 350°. Cover and bake for 30 minutes. Uncover; bake 25-30 minutes longer or until a knife inserted in the center comes out clean. Let stand for 10 minutes before serving. Serve with creme fraiche and chives.
1 PIECE: 359 cal., 21g fat (11g sat. fat), 194mg chol., 845mg sod., 21g carb. (6g sugars, 1g fiber), 22g pro.

ELEGANT SMOKED SALMON STRATA

MIDNIGHT CARIBBEAN PORK SANDWICHES

MIDNIGHT CARIBBEAN PORK SANDWICHES

These sandwiches are so tasty! They have depth of flavor—savory, sweet, piquant, subtle and sublime.
—*Elizabeth Bennett, Mill Creek, WA*

PREP: 25 min. • **COOK:** 6 hours • **MAKES:** 12 servings

- 1 Tbsp. canola oil
- 3 medium onions, cut into ½-in. slices
- 1 bottle (12 oz.) amber beer or 1½ cups chicken broth
- ¼ cup packed brown sugar
- 10 garlic cloves, minced and divided
- 2 Tbsp. ground cumin
- 7 tsp. minced chipotle peppers in adobo sauce, divided
- ½ tsp. salt
- ½ tsp. pepper
- 1 boneless pork shoulder butt roast (2 to 3 lbs.)
- 1 cup mayonnaise
- ½ cup minced fresh cilantro
- 12 Hawaiian sweet hamburger buns
- 2 medium ripe avocados, peeled and sliced

1. In a large skillet, heat oil over medium-high heat. Add onions; cook and stir until tender, 6-8 minutes. Add beer, brown sugar, 8 garlic cloves, cumin, 5 tsp. chipotle peppers, salt and pepper; cook and stir until combined.
2. Place roast in a 5- or 6-qt. slow cooker. Pour onion mixture over meat. Cook, covered, on low 6-8 hours, until pork is tender.
3. Meanwhile, combine mayonnaise, cilantro, remaining 2 garlic cloves and 2 tsp. chipotle peppers. Cover and refrigerate until serving.
4. Remove roast; shred with 2 forks. Strain cooking juices. Reserve vegetables and 1 cup juices; discard remaining juices. Skim fat from reserved juices. Return pork and reserved vegetables and cooking juices to slow cooker; heat through. Serve on buns with avocado slices and mayonnaise mixture.
FREEZE OPTION: Place shredded pork and vegetables in freezer containers; top with cooking juices. Cool and freeze. To use, partially thaw in refrigerator overnight. Heat through in a covered saucepan, stirring gently. Add broth or water if necessary.
1 SANDWICH: 484 cal., 29g fat (7g sat. fat), 71mg chol., 400mg sod., 36g carb. (15g sugars, 3g fiber), 18g pro.

MEATY ARUGULA PIZZAS

HARVEST PORK ROAST

I went to my crisper drawer for carrots and potatoes one night, but all I found was butternut squash and apples. I combined the fall favorites with some Craisins, brown sugar and, of course, the pork, and this recipe was born. The whole family raves about it each and every time I serve it.
—*Shirley Tuttle-Malone, Glenfield, NY*

PREP: 20 min.
BAKE: 1 hour 10 min. + standing
MAKES: 12 servings

- 1   boneless pork loin roast (about 4 lbs.)
- 1   Tbsp. plus ¼ cup olive oil, divided
- 1   tsp. salt
- ½   tsp. pepper
- 3   garlic cloves, peeled and sliced
- 1   medium butternut squash (3 to 4 lbs.), peeled and cut into ¾-in. cubes
- 4   large apples, peeled and each cut into 8 wedges
- 1   cup dried cranberries
- ½   cup packed brown sugar
    Optional: 1 tsp. each minced fresh rosemary and minced fresh thyme

1. Preheat oven to 350°. If desired, tie pork with kitchen twine. Rub pork with 1 Tbsp. olive oil; sprinkle with salt and pepper. In a large skillet over medium-high heat, sear the pork until it is browned on all sides, 7-9 minutes. Place in a large roasting pan; top with garlic slices. Cover and place in oven. Meanwhile, the combine squash, apples, dried cranberries, brown sugar, remaining olive oil and, if desired, minced fresh rosemary and thyme; toss to coat.
2. Remove the pork from oven after 30 minutes; add squash mixture to the roasting pan. Return to oven; roast, uncovered, until a thermometer reads 145°, 40-50 minutes. Let the pork stand 10 minutes before slicing. Drizzle pork with pan juices after slicing. Serve with roasted squash mixture. If desired, top with additional fresh rosemary and thyme.
4 OZ. PORK WITH ¾ CUP VEGETABLES: 395 cal., 13g fat (3g sat. fat), 75mg chol., 199mg sod., 41g carb. (28g sugars, 5g fiber), 31g pro.

MEATY ARUGULA PIZZAS

When I was growing up, my mom made homemade pizza every Friday night. We'd watch a movie as a family or invite over friends. Now that I'm married, I carry on the pizza tradition.
—*Morgan Harvey, Longview, WA*

PREP: 40 min. + rising • **BAKE:** 10 min.
MAKES: 2 pizzas (8 pieces each)

- 1   pkg. (¼ oz.) active dry yeast
- 1½   cups warm water (110° to 115°)
- 2   Tbsp. olive oil
- 2   tsp. salt
- 1   tsp. sugar
- 3½   to 4 cups bread flour
- 4   tsp. cornmeal
TOPPINGS
- 1   lb. bulk Italian sausage
- 2   Tbsp. olive oil
- 6   garlic cloves, minced
- 1½   cups shredded part-skim mozzarella cheese
- 1   pkg. (3½ oz.) sliced pepperoni
- 4   cups fresh arugula or baby spinach
- ½   cup grated Parmesan cheese

1. In a small bowl, dissolve yeast in warm water. In a large bowl, combine 2 Tbsp. oil, salt, sugar, yeast mixture and 1½ cups flour; beat on medium speed 3 minutes or until smooth. Stir in enough remaining flour to form a soft dough (dough will be sticky).
2. Turn dough onto a floured surface; knead 6-8 minutes or until smooth and elastic. Place in a greased bowl, turning once to grease the top. Cover and let rise in a warm place until doubled, about 1½ hours.
3. Preheat oven to 425°. Grease two 15x10x1-in. baking pans; sprinkle with cornmeal. Punch down dough. Turn onto a lightly floured surface; divide in half. Roll each half into a 15x10-in. rectangle; transfer to prepared pans, pinching edges to form a rim. Cover; let rest 10 minutes.
4. In a large skillet, cook sausage over medium heat 6-8 minutes or until no longer pink, breaking it into crumbles; drain. Mix the oil and garlic; spread over pizza crusts. Sprinkle each with ¼ cup mozzarella cheese. Top with pepperoni, arugula, cooked sausage and remaining 1 cup mozzarella cheese; sprinkle with Parmesan cheese.
5. Bake until crust and cheese are lightly browned, 10-15 minutes. If desired, top with additional arugula and Parmesan before serving.
1 PIECE: 310 cal., 17g fat (6g sat. fat), 34mg chol., 751mg sod., 25g carb. (1g sugars, 1g fiber), 14g pro.

HARVEST
PORK ROAST

SMOKED
PORK
BUTT

🔁 ❄️ SMOKED PORK BUTT

Low and slow is the best way to go when cooking pork butt, and it happens perfectly in a smoker. This has very little hands-on time, but you will need to plan for a long cook time. The fantastic thing is the meat freezes very well so you can make it ahead of time and have it ready to go.
—*James Schend, Pleasant Prairie, WI*

PREP: 10 min. + standing • **SMOKE:** 7 hours + resting
MAKES: 24 servings

- 1 bone-in pork shoulder roast (8 to 10 lbs.)
  Applewood chips or pellets
- 3 Tbsp. spicy brown mustard
- ¼ cup all-purpose meat seasoning or favorite spice rub
- ⅓ cup apple cider or juice
- 3 Tbsp. cider vinegar

1. Let roast stand at room temperature for 1 hour. Preheat a smoker to 275°. Add wood chips or pellets to smoker according to manufacturer's directions.
2. Trim excess fat from pork, leaving some exterior fat. Pat roast dry; rub with mustard and sprinkle with spice rub. Place pork in smoker. In a spray bottle, combine apple cider and vinegar; lightly spritz pork. Smoke, spritzing pork every hour, until pork reaches 165° and is a dark brown color, about 5 hours.
3. Transfer pork to a 13x9-in. baking pan or large cast iron skillet; liberally spritz with the cider mixture. Cover tightly with foil and return to smoker. Cook until pork reaches desired degree of doneness. For sliced pork, cook until pork reaches 190°-195°, 2-3 hours longer. For pulled pork, cook until 200°-205°. Remove roast and let rest at room temperature, covered, 45-60 minutes. For slices, cut around bone and cut roast into slices. For pulled pork, remove bone and shred pork. Skim fat from cooking juices; toss pork with cooking juices.
FREEZE OPTION: Freeze cooled meat mixture and juices in freezer containers. To use, partially thaw in refrigerator overnight. Heat through in a saucepan, stirring occasionally; add broth or water if necessary.
½ CUP MEAT MIXTURE: 186 cal., 11g fat (4g sat. fat), 67mg chol., 548mg sod., 0 carb. (0 sugars, 0 fiber), 19g pro.

❄️ TOMATO BASIL TORTELLINI SOUP

When my family tried this soup, they all had to have seconds. My husband is happy any time I put it on the table. Sometimes I include cooked, crumbled bacon and serve it with mozzarella cheese.
—*Christina Addison, Blanchester, Ohio*

PREP: 25 min. • **COOK:** 6 hours 15 min. • **MAKES:** 18 servings

- 2 Tbsp. olive oil
- 1 medium onion, chopped
- 3 medium carrots, chopped
- 5 garlic cloves, minced
- 3 cans (28 oz. each) crushed tomatoes, undrained
- 1 carton (32 oz.) vegetable broth
- 1 Tbsp. sugar
- 1 tsp. dried basil
- 1 bay leaf
- 3 packages (9 oz. each) refrigerated cheese tortellini
- ¾ cup half-and-half cream
  Shredded Parmesan cheese and minced fresh basil

1. In a large skillet, heat oil over medium-high heat. Add onion and carrots; cook and stir until crisp-tender, 5-6 minutes. Add garlic; cook 1 minute longer. Transfer to a 6- or 7-qt. slow cooker. Add the tomatoes, broth, sugar, basil and bay leaf. Cook, covered, on low until vegetables are tender, 6-7 hours.
2. Stir in tortellini. Cook, covered, on high 15 minutes. Reduce heat to low; stir in cream until heated through. Discard bay leaf. Serve topped with Parmesan cheese and basil.
TO FREEZE: Discard bay leaf. Before stirring in half-and-half, cool soup and freeze in freezer containers. To use, partially thaw in refrigerator overnight. Heat through in a saucepan, stirring occasionally; add half-and-half as directed.
1 CUP: 214 cal., 7g fat (3g sat. fat), 23mg cholesterol, 569mg sod., 32g carb. (9g sugars, 4g fiber), 9g pro. **DIABETIC EXCHANGES:** 2 starch, 1 fat.

TOMATO BASIL
TORTELLINI SOUP

BUTTERSCOTCH
MULLED CIDER

BUTTERSCOTCH MULLED CIDER

Five minutes of preparation result in this dynamite slow-cooked drink. You'll love the sweet taste of butterscotch and cinnamon in this hot apple cider.
—*Karen Mack, Webster, NY*

PREP: 5 min. • **COOK:** 3 hours • **MAKES:** 18 servings

- 1 gallon apple cider or juice
- 2 cups butterscotch schnapps liqueur
- 8 cinnamon sticks (3 in.)
  Optional: Apple pieces and additional cinnamon sticks

In a 6-qt. slow cooker, combine the first 3 ingredients. Cover and cook on low for 3-4 hours or until heated through. If desired, garnish with apple pieces and additional cinnamon sticks.
1 CUP: 128 cal., 0 fat (0 sat. fat), 0 chol., 22mg sod., 27g carb. (23g sugars, 0 fiber), 0 pro.

READER REVIEW

"This is so good and easy, throw it together ... instant signature drink with no effort. Warming, sweet, boozy & cinnamony. I have made it part of my Christmas Eve tradition."
—KREDHEAD, TASTEOFHOME.COM

ENGLISH MUFFIN BREAKFAST BAKLAVA

Classic baklava comes to breakfast courtesy of a lightly toasted cinnamon raisin English muffin with a buttery baklava topping of pistachios and walnuts. First it's broiled, then it's topped with a blend of mascarpone cheese and fig preserves and finished off with a light drizzle of honey. It's a delicious way to start the day and the perfect way to change up your breakfast routine. Serve with your choice of fresh fruit and lots of napkins.
—*Sharyn LaPointe Hill, Las Cruces, NM*

TAKES: 20 min. • **MAKES:** 8 servings

- ½ cup butter, softened
- ¼ cup shelled pistachios, coarsely chopped
- ¼ cup black walnuts, coarsely chopped
- 2 Tbsp. dark brown sugar
- 1 tsp. ground cinnamon
- ½ tsp. ground nutmeg
- ¼ tsp. ground cardamom
- 4 cinnamon raisin English muffins, split and lightly toasted
- ¼ cup mascarpone cheese
- ¼ cup fig preserves
- 2 Tbsp. honey

1. Preheat broiler. In a small bowl, mix butter, pistachios, walnuts, brown sugar and spices. Spread over split sides of muffin halves. Place on a baking sheet. Broil 3-4 in. from heat until just hot and bubbly, 1-2 minutes.
2. In another bowl, blend mascarpone cheese and fig preserves. Spread over muffin halves. Lightly drizzle each with honey; top with additional pistachios and walnuts.
1 MUFFIN HALF: 309 cal., 19g fat (9g sat. fat), 41mg chol., 202mg sod., 31g carb. (18g sugars, 1g fiber), 4g pro.

ENGLISH
MUFFIN
BREAKFAST
BAKLAVA

PROSCIUTTO SHRIMP
WITH TROPICAL
MANGO SALSA
PAGE 269

CHEESE PUFFS
PAGE 269

DEVILED CRAB
PAGE 269

Holiday & Seasonal Celebrations

Good cooks make the gathering even more special when they share their time-honored dishes. But they know that part of the fun is debuting new recipes too! Feast your eyes on these party favorites.

Fish Fry, USA

Join in the Friday night tradition—whichever shore is yours! Seasoned fillets and signature sides inspired by staples from the West Coast, South and Midwest are tasty enough to lure any seafood fan.

WEST COAST

SUNNY GRAPEFRUIT AVOCADO SALAD

PISTACHIO-CRUSTED FRIED FISH

A FISH FRY FAVE

Connie and Ted's

WEST HOLLYWOOD, CA

This delightfully out-of-place Southern California eatery, inspired by New England culture, opened in 2013. But the story of Connie and Ted started long before then. The restaurant is lovingly named after the late couple who inspired it. The duo moved up and down the Atlantic coastline during the 1940s and '50s, fishing and enjoying the same seafood dishes you'll find today at the chic-yet-cozy spot.

PISTACHIO-CRUSTED FRIED FISH

This nut-crusted fish is so novel compared to the standard breaded fillets. Plus, the pistachios give it a lovely color.
—Taste of Home *Test Kitchen*

TAKES: 30 min. • MAKES: 6 servings

- ½ cup dry bread crumbs
- ½ cup chopped pistachios
- ½ tsp. seafood seasoning
- ¼ tsp. salt
- ¼ tsp. garlic powder
- ¼ tsp. pepper
- ½ cup all-purpose flour
- ½ cup 2% milk
- 1½ lbs. whitefish or cod fillets
- 3 Tbsp. canola oil

1. In a shallow bowl, combine the first 6 ingredients. Place flour and milk in separate shallow bowls. Dip fillets in flour, then in milk; coat with pistachio mixture.
2. In a large nonstick skillet, heat oil over medium heat; add fish. Cook until fish just begins to flake easily with a fork, 4-5 minutes on each side.

3 OZ. COOKED FISH: 325 cal., 18g fat (2g sat. fat), 71mg chol., 260mg sod., 14g carb. (2g sugars, 1g fiber), 26g pro. **DIABETIC EXCHANGES:** 3 lean meat, 3 fat, 1 starch.

SUNNY GRAPEFRUIT AVOCADO SALAD

When you have the winter blues, brighten lettuce greens with the fresh, fruity tartness of pink grapefruit and orange juice. This citrus salad is a sunny and elegant pairing with most suppers.
—Mary Relyea, Canastota, NY

TAKES: 20 min. • MAKES: 6 servings

- 6 cups torn leaf lettuce
- 3 large pink grapefruit, peeled and sectioned
- 1 medium ripe avocado, peeled and sliced
- 1 small red onion, thinly sliced
- ¼ cup orange juice
- 3 Tbsp. olive oil
- 1 Tbsp. lemon juice
- ¾ tsp. ground cumin
- 1 garlic clove, minced
- Dash hot pepper sauce
  Toasted chopped pecans, optional

1. Arrange the lettuce on a large platter. Top with grapefruit, avocado and onion.
2. In a bowl, whisk orange juice, oil, lemon juice, cumin, garlic and pepper sauce; drizzle over salad. If desired, sprinkle with pecans.

1 SERVING: 167 cal., 11g fat (1g sat. fat), 0 chol., 13mg sod., 19g carb. (13g sugars, 4g fiber), 2g pro. **DIABETIC EXCHANGES:** 2 fat, 1 vegetable, ½ fruit.

FRESH STRAWBERRY PIE

Each year we can hardly wait for strawberry season because we believe ours are the best in the country! After plucking the berries from the bushes at a nearby farm, I fill my homemade pie crust.
—Mary Egan, Carney, MI

PREP: 45 min. + chilling
COOK: 5 min. + chilling
MAKES: 8 servings

- Classic butter pie pastry
- 2 cups sliced fresh strawberries
- 2 cups halved fresh strawberries, mashed
- 1 cup sugar
- 3 Tbsp. cornstarch

TOPPING
- 2 cups halved fresh strawberries
- 1 cup heavy whipping cream
- 2 Tbsp. sugar
- ¼ tsp. almond extract, optional

1. On a lightly floured surface, roll dough to a ⅛-in.-thick circle; transfer to a 9-in. pie plate. Trim to ½ in. beyond rim of plate; flute edge. Refrigerate for 30 minutes. Preheat the oven to 425°.
2. Line crust with a double thickness of foil. Fill with pie weights, dried beans or uncooked rice. Bake on a lower oven rack until edge is golden brown, 20-25 minutes. Remove the foil and weights; bake until bottom is golden brown, 3-6 minutes longer. Cool on a wire rack.
3. Arrange sliced strawberries over crust. In a saucepan over medium heat, combine the mashed strawberries, sugar and cornstarch. Bring to a boil; cook and stir until thickened, 1-2 minutes. Cool for 15 minutes; pour over sliced strawberries. Arrange strawberry halves over pie. Refrigerate until chilled, 2-3 hours.
4. Just before serving, in a large bowl, beat cream until it begins to thicken. Add sugar and, if desired, almond extract; beat until stiff peaks form. Serve with pie.

1 PIECE: 378 cal., 18g fat (10g sat. fat), 46mg chol., 113mg sod., 53g carb. (35g sugars, 3g fiber), 2g pro.

FRESH STRAWBERRY PIE

CLASSIC BUTTER PIE PASTRY
Combine 1¼ cups **all-purpose flour** and ¼ tsp. **salt.** Cut in ½ cup cold **butter** until crumbly. Gradually add 3-4 Tbsp. **ice water.** Toss with a fork until dough holds together when pressed. Shape dough into a disk; wrap and refrigerate until ready to use.

**FLAVORFUL
CATFISH
FILLETS**

DOWN-HOME HUSH PUPPIES

Hush puppies are a classic southern side. The sweet-spicy flavor of these fried bites has delighted friends and family for decades.
—*Gene Pitts, Wilsonville, AL*

PREP: 15 min. + standing • **COOK:** 20 min.
MAKES: 2½ dozen

- 1 cup cornmeal
- 1 cup self-rising flour
- 1½ tsp. baking powder
- ½ tsp. salt
- 1 large onion, chopped
- 2 jalapeno peppers, seeded and diced
- ¼ cup sugar
- 1 large egg
- 1 cup buttermilk
  Canola oil

1. In a large bowl, combine the first 7 ingredients. Add egg and buttermilk; stir just until moistened. Let stand at room temperature for 30 minutes. Do not stir again.
2. In an electric skillet or deep fryer, heat 2-3 in. oil to 375°. Drop batter by rounded tablespoonfuls, a few at a time, into hot oil. Fry until golden brown, about 1½ minutes on each side. Drain on paper towels.
NOTES: As a substitute for 1 cup of self-rising flour, place 1½ tsp. baking powder and ½ tsp. salt in a measuring cup. Add all-purpose flour to measure 1 cup. Wear disposable gloves when cutting hot peppers; the oils can burn skin. Avoid touching your face.
1 HUSH PUPPY: 73 cal., 3g fat (0 sat. fat), 7mg chol., 132mg sod., 10g carb. (2g sugars, 0 fiber), 1g pro.

FLAVORFUL CATFISH FILLETS

This is the best catfish ever! Cayenne adds zip, and the golden cornmeal coating feels traditional—but without all the fat that comes from deep-frying.
—*Ellen De Munnik, Chesterfield, MI*

TAKES: 15 min. • **MAKES:** 4 servings

- ¼ cup buttermilk
- 2 tsp. Dijon mustard
- ½ cup cornmeal
- 1 tsp. each salt, onion powder, garlic powder and paprika
- ½ tsp. dried thyme
- ½ tsp. pepper
- ¼ to ½ tsp. cayenne pepper
- 1 lb. catfish fillets
  Lemon wedges, optional

1. In a shallow bowl, whisk buttermilk and mustard until blended. In another bowl, combine cornmeal and seasonings. Dip fillets into buttermilk mixture, then into cornmeal mixture.
2. Place 1 in. apart on a wire rack coated with cooking spray. Place rack on a baking sheet. Broil 4 in. from the heat until fish just begins to flake easily with a fork, 3-4 minutes on each side. If desired, serve with lemon.
3 OZ. COOKED FISH: 204 cal., 7g fat (2g sat. fat), 63mg chol., 623mg sod., 14g carb. (1g sugars, 1g fiber), 19g pro. **DIABETIC EXCHANGES:** 3 lean meat, 1 starch.
TO COOK IN AIR FRYER: Preheat air fryer to 400°. Place fillets in a single layer on greased tray in air-fryer basket. Cook until fish just begins to flake easily with a fork, 6-8 minutes.

CABBAGE SLAW

Homemade slaw needn't be fussy, and this recipe proves it! I make it at a moment's notice to serve with many a main dish.
—*Johnnie McLeod, Bastrop, LA*

TAKES: 20 min. • **MAKES:** 6 servings

- 1 medium head cabbage (about 2½ lbs.)
- 1 carrot
- 1 cup mayonnaise
- 2 Tbsp. 2% milk
- 2 Tbsp. vinegar
- 3 Tbsp. sugar
- 1 tsp. salt
- ½ to 1 tsp. pepper
- ½ to 1 tsp. celery seed

In a food processor or by hand, coarsely chop cabbage and carrot. In a small bowl, combine the mayonnaise, milk, vinegar, sugar, salt, pepper and celery seed; stir into cabbage mixture. Cover and refrigerate until serving.
1 CUP: 319 cal., 27g fat (4g sat. fat), 14mg chol., 624mg sod., 19g carb. (13g sugars, 5g fiber), 3g pro.

CABBAGE
SLAW

FLAVORFUL
CATFISH
FILLETS

DOWN-HOME
HUSH PUPPIES

A FISH FRY FAVE

Barrow's Catfish

NEW ORLEANS, LA

Touted by many as the best catfish in the Big Easy, Barrow's Catfish, formerly known as Barrow's Shady Inn, was founded in 1943. The owners, William "Cap" Barrow Sr. and his wife, Mary, crafted a simple but masterful menu of fried catfish, Mary's potato salad, buttered white bread and sweet-tart lemonade. The menu has since expanded, but night after night, it's still those time-honored staples drawing people inside.

PRESSURE-COOKER
HOMEMADE
CHUNKY APPLESAUCE

ONION
POTATO
PANCAKES

FRIED
WALLEYE
WITH
TARTAR
SAUCE

A FISH FRY FAVE

The Ranch Supper Club

HAYWARD, WI

With food that's as rich as its history, the Ranch Supper Club has been a Northwoods go-to for more than 90 years. Attracting humble lumberjacks as well as Chicago gangsters in the 1930s, and curious tourists and loyal locals today, the haunt specializes in stellar surf and turf along with "honest" cocktails. As the current owners, Haley and Nathan Bochler, say, "Cheers to northern hospitality!"

FRIED WALLEYE WITH TARTAR SAUCE

I love to eat fish, especially walleye, and this is the way I love to make it. The homemade tartar sauce promotes this meal to restaurant grade.
—*Carolyn Turner, Reno, NV*

- -

PREP: 20 min. • **COOK:** 10 min./batch
MAKES: 6 servings (1¼ cups sauce)

- 1 cup mayonnaise
- ⅓ cup sweet pickle relish
- 4½ tsp. lemon juice
- ¼ tsp. salt
- ⅛ tsp. pepper

FISH

- 2 cups all-purpose flour
- 2 tsp. lemon-pepper seasoning
- 1 tsp. baking powder
- 1 tsp. garlic salt
- ½ tsp. dried parsley flakes
- 1½ cups ice water
- 2 Tbsp. canola oil
  Oil for deep-fat frying
- 2 lbs. walleye fillets, cut into 6 pieces
  Lemon wedges

1. In a small bowl, combine mayonnaise, pickle relish, lemon juice, salt and pepper; cover and refrigerate until serving.
2. For fish, in a shallow bowl, combine flour, lemon pepper, baking powder, garlic salt and parsley flakes. Combine ice water and 2 Tbsp. oil; whisk into dry ingredients just until smooth.
3. In an electric skillet or deep fryer, heat oil to 375°. Dip fillets in batter, turning to coat; allow excess batter to drip off. Fry fillets, a few at a time, until golden brown and fish just begins to flake easily with a fork, 5-7 minutes on each side. Drain on paper towels. Serve with sauce and lemon.
4 OZ. COOKED FISH WITH 3 TBSP. SAUCE: 754 cal., 55g fat (6g sat. fat), 143mg chol., 882mg sod., 30g carb. (4g sugars, 1g fiber), 32g pro.

TEST KITCHEN TIP

Walleye or walleye pike, a mild fish from the perch family, is flaky and delicate. If you're looking for a swap, opt for haddock, rockfish or snapper.

ONION POTATO PANCAKES

I make these pancakes for my family for breakfast often. I sometimes even serve them as a dish for light suppers.
—*Joan Hutter, Warwick, RI*

- -

TAKES: 20 min.• **MAKES:** 6 servings

- 2 large eggs
- 1 medium onion, quartered
- 2 Tbsp. all-purpose flour
- ¾ tsp. salt
- ¼ tsp. pepper
- ¼ tsp. baking powder
- 4 medium potatoes, peeled and cubed (about 1½ pounds)
- 2 tablespoons chopped fresh parsley
- 3 to 4 Tbsp. canola oil

1. Place the eggs, onion, flour, salt, pepper, baking powder and ½ cup potatoes in a blender or food processor. Cover and process on high until smooth. Add parsley and remaining potatoes; cover and pulse 2-4 times until potatoes are chopped.
2. Pour 1-2 Tbsp. oil onto a hot griddle or skillet. Pour batter by ⅓ cupfuls onto griddle; flatten slightly to a 4-to-5-in. diameter. Cook over medium heat until golden, 2-3 minutes on each side. Add oil to griddle as needed.
2 PANCAKES: 159 cal., 6g fat (1g sat. fat), 47mg chol., 262mg sod., 22g carb. (2g sugars, 3g fiber), 4g pro. **DIABETIC EXCHANGES:** 1½ starch, 1 fat.

PRESSURE-COOKER HOMEMADE CHUNKY APPLESAUCE

This homemade applesauce is simple and down-home delicious. My family loves the things I make from scratch, and it's so nice knowing exactly what I'm putting in the dishes!
—*Marilee Cardinal, Burlington, NJ*

- -

PREP: 10 min.• **COOK:** 5 min. + releasing
MAKES: 5 cups

- 7 medium McIntosh, Empire or other apples (about 3 lbs.)
- ½ cup sugar
- ½ cup water
- 1 Tbsp. lemon juice
- ¼ tsp. almond or vanilla extract

1. Peel, core and cut each apple into 8 wedges. Cut each wedge crosswise in half; place in a 6-qt. electric pressure cooker. Add the remaining ingredients.
2. Lock lid; close pressure-release valve. Adjust to pressure-cook on high for 3 minutes. Let pressure release naturally. Mash apples with a potato masher. Select saute setting and adjust for low heat. Simmer, stirring occasionally, until desired consistency.
¾ CUP: 139 cal., 0 fat (0 sat. fat), 0 chol., 0 sod., 36g carb. (33g sugars, 2g fiber), 0 pro.

BRANDY OLD-FASHIONED SWEET

Here in Wisconsin, we make this old-fashioned favorite using brandy in place of whiskey and soda instead of water for a milder sweet cocktail.
—*Taste of Home Test Kitchen*

- -

TAKES: 10 min. • **MAKES:** 1 serving

- 1 orange slice
- 1 maraschino cherry
- 1½ oz. maraschino cherry juice
- 1 tsp. bitters
- ¼ to ⅓ cup ice cubes
- 1½ oz. brandy
- 2 tsp. water
- 1 tsp. orange juice
- 3 oz. lemon-lime soda

In a rocks glass, muddle orange, cherry, cherry juice and bitters. Add ice. Pour in the brandy, water, orange juice and soda.
1 SERVING: 277 cal., 0 fat (0 sat. fat), 0 chol., 18mg sod., 36g carb. (17g sugars, 0 fiber), 0 pro.

BRANDY OLD-FASHIONED SWEET

Shamrockin' Snacks

Lucky you! We've packed this beauty of a board with sweet and savory surprises for your St. Paddy's Day celebration.

TIE-DYED CUPCAKES

SHAMROCK COOKIES

RAINBOW MARSHMALLOW SKEWERS

RAINBOW TOPPERS

Top each homemade or store-bought cupcake with 2 fluffs of white buttercream frosting. Cut Sour Power Quattro into 2-in. pieces; secure ends in the clouds, creating an arch.

Build a St. Patrick's Day Board

Use two round boards to create one sweet and one savory charcuterie for your favorite leprechauns to enjoy on St. Paddy's Day!

ITEMS TO INCLUDE

Sweet Items

- Chocolates in green and shamrock foil
- Chocolate coins
- Green-and-white striped hard candies
- Green apple gummy rings
- Green grapes
- Green licorice
- Hard candy wrapped in gold foil
- Lindor truffles
- Rainbow lollipops (variety)
- Rainbow Marshmallow Skewers
- Rolo candies
- Shamrock Cookies
- Tie-Dyed Cupcakes

Savory Items

- Corned beef
- Dark rye bread
- Green bell pepper "shamrocks"
- Sage Derby cheese
- Sauerkraut
- Crackers topped with herbed cream cheese, mini cucumber slices and dill sprigs
- Swiss cheese
- Thousand Island dressing

EASY ASSEMBLY

Step 1: Using the photo as a guide, arrange the sweet items on 1 of the boards.

Step 2: Arrange the savory items on the second board. Stack boards as shown at left if desired (adding support for stability if needed), or serve boards side by side.

SHAMROCK COOKIES

With a hint of mint flavor, these shamrock cookies are especially yummy with hot cocoa or chocolate milk.
—*Edna Hoffman, Hebron, IN*

PREP: 25 min. + chilling
BAKE: 10 min./batch
MAKES: 3 dozen

- 1 cup shortening
- 1 cup confectioners' sugar
- 1 large egg, room temperature
- 1 tsp. peppermint extract
- 2½ cups all-purpose flour
- 1 tsp. salt
  Green paste food coloring
  Green colored sugar, optional

1. Preheat oven to 375°. In a large bowl, cream the shortening and confectioners' sugar until light and fluffy, 3-4 minutes. Beat in egg and extract. Gradually add flour and salt. Tint with food coloring. Cover and refrigerate for 1 hour or until easy to handle.

2. On a lightly floured surface, roll out dough to ¼-in. thickness. Cut with a lightly floured 2-in. shamrock cookie cutter. Place cutouts 1 in. apart onto ungreased baking sheets. If desired, sprinkle with colored sugar.

3. Bake until edges are lightly browned, 10-12 minutes. Cool for 1 minute before removing to wire racks.

1 COOKIE: 96 cal., 6g fat (1g sat. fat), 5mg chol., 68mg sod., 10g carb. (3g sugars, 0 fiber), 1g pro.

🎱 TIE-DYED CUPCAKES

Take a trip back to the '60s with these sweetly psychedelic cupcakes. Each is a simple white cake, but tinting the batter all the colors of the rainbow makes them funky and fun!
—*Gwyndolyn Wilkerson, Kyle, TX*

PREP: 30 min. • **BAKE:** 20 min. + cooling
MAKES: 1½ dozen

- 1 pkg. white cake mix (regular size)
- 1½ cups (12 oz.) lemon-lime soda
  Neon food coloring
- 1 can (16 oz.) vanilla frosting
  Colored sprinkles

1. Preheat oven to 350°. In a large bowl, combine cake mix and soda. Beat on low speed 30 seconds. Beat on medium for 1 minute. Divide batter among 5 bowls. Add a few drops of food coloring to each bowl; stir just until combined.

2. Drop a spoonful of 1 color of batter into each of 18 paper-lined muffin cups. Layer with spoonfuls of remaining colored batter until muffin cups are two-thirds full.

3. Bake 18-20 minutes or until a toothpick inserted in the center comes out clean. Cool for 10 minutes before removing from pans to wire racks to cool completely.

4. Frost tops and decorate with sprinkles.

1 CUPCAKE: 235 cal., 9g fat (3g sat. fat), 0 chol., 258mg sod., 38g carb. (26g sugars, 0 fiber), 1g pro.

RAINBOW MARSHMALLOW SKEWERS

Place 1 package each of cherry, orange, lemon, lime, berry blue and grape gelatin in separate shallow dishes. Dip a handful of mini marshmallows into a bowl of water; allow excess to drip off. Place in the cherry gelatin. Turn to coat marshmallows evenly; remove from dish and place on a tray, separating any that have stuck together. Repeat with remaining colors. When marshmallows are dry, slide onto wooden skewers in proper color order (red, orange, yellow, green, blue and purple).

Kalo Pascha!

Nothing says "Happy Easter" like this celebratory spread that marries modern flavors with traditional Greek flair.

ROASTED GREEK
POTATOES WITH
FETA CHEESE
PAGE 236

GREEK
ROAST
LAMB

MINI
BAKLAVA
PAGE 240

GREEK ROAST LAMB

Growing up on the island of Cyprus, lamb was a common dinner for us, not just a meal for Easter. Here in the U.S., I don't cook lamb often, but I always make my mom's roast lamb for Easter.

—*Paris Paraskeva, San Francisco, CA*

- -

PREP: 20 min. • **BAKE:** 2 hours + standing.
MAKES: 12 servings

- 1 boneless leg of lamb (5 to 6 lbs.), trimmed
- 1 whole garlic bulb, peeled and separated
- 1 Tbsp. dried oregano
- 1½ tsp. kosher salt
- 1 lb. sliced mushrooms
- 2 medium onions, coarsely chopped
- 4 medium lemons
- 3 Tbsp. butter, cubed
- ½ cup water

1. Preheat oven to 500°. Tie lamb leg at 2-in. intervals with kitchen string. Cut slits into lamb; insert garlic cloves. Mix the oregano and salt; rub onto all sides of lamb. Place mushrooms and onions in a 13x9-in. baking pan; top with lamb. Squeeze lemons over lamb; top with butter cubes. Add water to pan.
2. Roast, uncovered, 30 minutes; reduce heat to 450° and cook 30 minutes longer. Reduce heat to 350°; continue cooking until meat reaches desired doneness (for medium-rare, a thermometer should read 135°; medium, 140°; medium-well, 145°), about 1 hour longer. Let stand 15 minutes before slicing. Cut string and slice. Serve lamb with mushrooms, onions and pan drippings.
5 OZ. COOKED LAMB WITH ABOUT 3 TBSP. MUSHROOM MIXTURE: 291 cal., 13g fat (6g sat. fat), 122mg chol., 517mg sod., 5g carb. (2g sugars, 1g fiber), 36g pro.

GREEK SHRIMP
CANAPES

3. Cut each cucumber into ¼-in.-thick slices. Scoop out centers, leaving bottoms intact. Pipe cream cheese onto each cucumber slice; top with shrimp and parsley.

1 CANAPE: 68 cal., 6g fat (2g sat. fat), 26mg chol., 139mg sod., 1g carb. (1g sugars, 0 fiber), 3g pro.

ROASTED GREEK POTATOES WITH FETA CHEESE
(SHOWN ON PAGE 234)

Lemony potatoes are a traditional Greek side dish. When they come out of the oven, we top them with feta for a little melty goodness.
—*Arge Salvatori, Waldwick, NJ*

PREP: 15 min. • **BAKE:** 40 min.
MAKES: 8 servings

- ⅔ cup water
- ½ cup olive oil
- 3 Tbsp. lemon juice
- 4 garlic cloves, minced
- 2 tsp. dried oregano
- 1 tsp. salt
- ½ tsp. pepper
- 3 lbs. Yukon Gold potatoes (about 6 medium), each cut into 8 wedges
- ¾ cup crumbled feta cheese

1. Preheat oven to 450°. In a small bowl, whisk the first 7 ingredients. Arrange potatoes evenly in a shallow roasting pan. Pour water mixture over top.
2. Roast until potatoes are golden brown and tender, 40-50 minutes. Sprinkle with cheese.

¾ CUP: 308 cal., 15g fat (3g sat. fat), 6mg chol., 405mg sod., 38g carb. (3g sugars, 3g fiber), 5g pro.

NANA'S DOLMATHES WITH AVGOLEMONO SAUCE

This recipe is special to me because while I was growing up, our family always had dolmathes for holidays and important events. They are fantastic for parties. You may also serve them as an entree.
—*Elizabeth Latsis, Tacoma, WA*

PREP: 45 min. • **COOK:** 45 min.
MAKES: about 6 dozen (2 cups sauce)

- 1 large sweet onion, finely chopped
- ¾ cup beef broth
- ½ cup uncooked long grain brown rice
- ½ cup chopped fresh parsley
- 1 large egg
- 3 Tbsp. tomato sauce
- 1 Tbsp. olive oil
- 1 Tbsp. butter, melted
- 2 tsp. minced fresh mint
- 2 tsp. kosher salt
- 2 tsp. pepper
- 1 lb. ground beef
- 1 jar (16 oz.) grape leaves, rinsed and drained

AVGOLEMONO SAUCE
- 2 cups beef broth
- 2 medium lemons
- 3 large eggs, beaten
  Dash kosher salt
  Dash pepper

1. In a large bowl, mix the onion, ¾ cup beef broth, rice, parsley, egg, tomato sauce, olive oil, butter, mint, salt and pepper; crumble beef over top and mix lightly but thoroughly. Pat grape leaves dry with paper towels.
2. Line the bottom of a Dutch oven with 8 grape leaves. Place about 1 Tbsp. beef mixture on each remaining grape leaf, shiny side down. Fold in long sides over filling; roll up. Repeat. Arrange dolmathes seam side down over grape leaves in Dutch oven. Place a heavy plate over dolmathes. Add enough water just to cover plate. Bring to a boil; reduce heat. Cook, covered, 45-50 minutes or until rice is tender.
3. Meanwhile, for avgolemono sauce, in a small saucepan, bring broth to a boil. Reduce heat to a simmer. Finely grate zest from lemons. Cut lemons crosswise in half; squeeze juice from lemons. Transfer zest and juice to a small bowl. Whisk in eggs, salt and pepper until blended. Gradually whisk egg mixture into broth. Cook and stir over low heat until slightly thickened, 4-5 minutes (do not boil). Remove plate from Dutch oven; remove dolmathes with tongs, draining excess liquid. Serve with sauce.

1 DOLMA WITH 1½ TSP. SAUCE: 35 cal., 2g fat (1g sat. fat), 18mg chol., 237mg sod., 2g carb. (0 sugars, 1g fiber), 2g pro.

GREEK SHRIMP CANAPES

I grew up by the ocean and then moved to a landlocked state. I wanted to show people in my area how to easily cook seafood, and this is the recipe I came up with. I think it's safe to say it has become a neighborhood favorite.
—*Amy Harris, Springville, UT*

PREP: 15 min. + marinating
COOK: 65 min. • **MAKES:** 2½ dozen

- 1½ cups olive oil
- ¾ cup lemon juice
- ⅔ cup dry white wine
- ¼ cup Greek seasoning
- 4 garlic cloves, minced
- 1 lb. uncooked shrimp (31-40 per lb.), peeled and deveined
- 2 large cucumbers
- 1 pkg. (8 oz.) cream cheese, softened
  Minced fresh parsley

1. In a large bowl, whisk the oil, lemon juice, wine, seasoning and garlic until blended. Pour 1½ cups marinade into a large bowl. Add shrimp and stir to coat. Cover and refrigerate 45 minutes.
2. Meanwhile, pour remaining marinade in a 4- or 5-qt. slow cooker. Cook, covered, on high 45 minutes. Drain shrimp, discarding marinade in bowl. Add shrimp to slow cooker. Cook, covered, on high until shrimp turn pink, about 20 minutes, stirring once; drain.

NANA'S DOLMATHES WITH
AVGOLEMONO SAUCE

NANA'S DOLMATHES WITH
AVGOLEMONO SAUCE
PAGE 236

ASPARAGUS
SPANAKOPITA

HALLOUMI
SAGANAKI

ASPARAGUS SPANAKOPITA

Fresh asparagus gives traditional Greek spinach pie a tasty twist in this recipe. Served with a mild dill sauce, these crispy light squares make a perfect first course for a special-occasion dinner.
—*Dean Paraskeva, La Mesa, CA*

PREP: 30 min. • **BAKE:** 30 min.
MAKES: 12 servings

- 2 cups fresh asparagus (cut into 1-in. pieces)
- 20 sheets phyllo dough (14x9 in.)
- ¾ cup butter, melted
- 2 cups torn fresh spinach
- 3 oz. crumbled feta cheese
- 2 Tbsp. butter
- 2 Tbsp. all-purpose flour
- 1½ cups half-and-half cream
- 3 Tbsp. lemon juice
- 1 tsp. dill weed
- ½ tsp. dried thyme
- ¼ tsp. salt

1. Place asparagus in a steamer basket. Place over 1 in. of water in a saucepan; bring to a boil. Cover and steam until crisp-tender, 5 minutes
2. Place 1 sheet of phyllo dough in a 13x9-in. baking dish coated with cooking spray; trim dough if necessary. Brush dough with melted butter. Repeat layers 9 times. Arrange spinach, feta cheese and asparagus over the top. Cover with a sheet of phyllo dough; brush with melted butter. Repeat, using remaining phyllo. Cut into 12 pieces. Bake, uncovered, at 350° for 30-35 minutes or until golden brown.
3. For sauce, melt 2 Tbsp. butter in a small saucepan. Stir in flour until smooth; gradually add cream. Stir in lemon juice, dill, thyme and salt. Bring to a boil; cook and stir for 1-2 minutes or until thickened. Serve spanakopita with sauce.
1 PIECE WITH ABOUT 2 TBSP. SAUCE:
239 cal., 18g fat (11g sat. fat), 54mg chol., 327mg sod., 14g carb. (2g sugars, 1g fiber), 5g pro.

HALLOUMI SAGANAKI

This show-stopping appetizer is a combination of a number of dishes I've had at various Greek restaurants. Be careful when you add the ouzo to the hot skillet as it can flame up before you grab the lighter. The flames burn off the alcohol, leaving an amazing slight licorice flavor that combines well with the cheese and olives.
—*James Schend, Pleasant Prairie, WI*

TAKES: 20 min. • **MAKES:** 6 servings

- 1 pkg. (7 to 8 oz.) Halloumi cheese
- 2 Tbsp. olive oil
- 1 cup cherry tomatoes, halved
- ¾ cup assorted Greek olives, pitted
- 3 fresh rosemary sprigs
- 2 fresh oregano sprigs
- ¼ cup ouzo
- 1 medium lemon, halved
  Coarsely ground pepper
  Optional: Baked pita chips, assorted crackers or vegetables

1. Cut Halloumi into ½-in.-thick slices. In a 10- or 12-in. cast-iron or flameproof skillet, heat olive oil over medium high heat. Add Halloumi and cook until golden brown on 1 side, 2-3 minutes. Turn; add tomatoes, olives, rosemary and oregano. Cook until Halloumi is golden brown, 2-3 minutes.
2. Remove pan from heat; immediately and carefully add ouzo. With a long match or long-handled lighter, ignite the ouzo. Let stand until flames extinguish. Squeeze lemon over mixture and sprinkle with freshly cracked pepper. Serve with chips, crackers or vegetables if desired.
1 SERVING: 209 cal., 18g fat (7g sat. fat), 25mg chol., 629mg sod., 3g carb. (1g sugars, 0 fiber), 8g pro.

EASTER EGG BREAD

I've made this Easter treat for 20 years! Colored hard-boiled eggs baked in the dough give this sweet bread such a festive look. Leave them out and it can be enjoyed any time of year. My husband especially enjoys this bread with baked ham.
—*Heather Durante, Wellsburg, WV*

PREP: 55 min. + rising • BAKE: 25 min
MAKES: 1 loaf (16 pieces)

- ½ cup sugar
- 1 pkg. (¼ oz.) active dry yeast
- 1 to 2 tsp. ground cardamom
- 1 tsp. salt
- 6 to 6½ cups all-purpose flour
- 1½ cups 2% milk
- 6 Tbsp. butter, cubed
- 3 large eggs, room temperature
- 3 to 6 hard-boiled large eggs, unpeeled
  Assorted food coloring
  Canola oil
- 1 Tbsp. heavy whipping cream
- 1 large egg yolk

1. In a large bowl, mix sugar, yeast, cardamom, salt and 2 cups flour. In a small saucepan, heat milk and butter to 120°-130°. Add to dry ingredients; beat on medium speed 2 minutes. Add 3 eggs; beat on high 2 minutes. Stir in enough remaining flour to form a soft dough (dough will be sticky).
2. Turn dough onto a floured surface; knead 6-8 minutes or until smooth and elastic. Place in a greased bowl, turning once to grease the top. Cover and let rise in a warm place until doubled, about 45 minutes.
3. Meanwhile, dye hard-boiled eggs with food coloring following package directions. Let stand until completely dry.
4. Punch down dough. Turn onto a lightly floured surface; divide into thirds. Roll each portion into a 24-in. rope. Place ropes on a greased baking sheet and braid. Bring ends together to form a ring. Pinch ends to seal. Lightly coat dyed eggs with oil; arrange on braid, tucking them carefully between ropes.
5. Cover dough with a kitchen towel; let rise in a warm place until doubled, about 20 minutes. Preheat oven to 375°.
6. In a bowl, whisk egg yolk and cream; gently brush over dough, avoiding eggs. Bake until golden brown, 25-30 minutes. Remove from pan to a wire rack to cool. Refrigerate leftovers.

1 PIECE: 281 cal., 8g fat (4g sat. fat), 107mg chol., 231mg sod., 44g carb. (8g sugars, 1g fiber), 9g pro.

MINI BAKLAVA

Baklava provides amazing memories for me: My best friend made it for my bridal and baby showers. And then she taught me how to make it! These delicious little miniatures give you the taste of baklava in a bite-sized package.
—*Margaret Guillory, Eunice, LA*

PREP: 20 min. • BAKE: 10 min. + cooling
MAKES: about 2½ dozen

- ½ cup butter
- ¼ cup sugar
- 1 tsp. ground cinnamon
- 1 cup finely chopped pecans
- 1 cup finely chopped walnuts
- 2 pkg. (1.9 oz. each) frozen miniature phyllo tart shells
  Honey

1. Preheat oven to 350°. In a small saucepan over medium heat, melt butter. Stir in sugar and cinnamon. Bring to a boil. Reduce heat; add pecans and walnuts, tossing to coat. Simmer, uncovered, until nuts are lightly toasted, 5-10 minutes.
2. Place phyllo shells on a parchment-lined baking sheet. Spoon the nut and butter sauce mixture evenly into shells. Bake until golden brown, 9-11 minutes. Cool completely on pan on a wire rack. Drizzle a drop of honey into each shell; let stand, covered, until serving. Serve with additional honey if desired.

1 FILLED PHYLLO CUP: 105 cal., 9g fat (2g sat. fat), 8mg chol., 33mg sod., 5g carb. (2g sugars, 1g fiber), 1g pro.

EASTER EGG BREAD

MINI
BAKLAVA

Easter Candy Board

A-tisket, a-tasket, put down that basket! Build a curated candy board for your bunch instead.

PINWHEEL MINTS

Build an Easter Candy Board

Let the Easter Bunny surprise your guests this year with a spectacular assortment of candies, mints and other sweet treats.

ITEMS TO INCLUDE

- Yellow Easter grass
- Pinwheel Mints
- Light blue M&M's
- Funfetti Jelly Beans
- Milk chocolate bunny
- Easter grass bubble gum
- Whoppers Robin Eggs
- Easter Bunny Peeps
- Yellow chick Peeps
- Shimmer pastel almond blend
- Bunny Grahams honey-baked snacks
- Hershey Kisses, pink foiled
- Foil-wrapped chocolate carrots
- Speckled fruit jelly beans
- Foil-wrapped chocolate eggs

EASY ASSEMBLY

Step 1: Line a rimmed tray with yellow Easter grass.

Step 2: Add two groupings of Pinwheel Mints to tray.

Step 3: Set two Easter-themed cookie cutters in tray; fill with blue M&M's and Funfetti Jelly Beans. Add chocolate bunny to tray.

Step 4: Shape bubble gum into a nest. Fill with Whoppers; set in the tray.

Step 5: Add two groupings of bunny and chick Peeps to the tray.

Step 6: Fill in gaps with groupings of remaining items.

PINWHEEL MINTS

Both my grandmother and my mom used to make these eye-catching confections as a replacement for ordinary mints at Christmas. When I offer them at parties, guests tell me the mints are wonderful, and then ask how I create the pretty swirl pattern.
—*Marilou Roth, Milford, NE*

PREP: 45 min. + chilling • **MAKES:** 4 dozen

- 1 pkg. (8 oz.) cream cheese, softened
- ½ to 1 tsp. mint extract
- 7½ to 8½ cups confectioners' sugar
  Red and green food coloring
  Additional confectioners' sugar

1. In a large bowl, beat cream cheese and extract until smooth. Gradually beat in as much confectioners' sugar as possible.
2. Turn onto a work surface dusted with confectioners' sugar; knead in remaining confectioners' sugar until smooth and sugar is absorbed (mixture will be stiff). Divide mixture in half. Using food coloring, tint 1 portion pink and the other portion light green, kneading until blended.
3. Divide each portion in half; shape each half into a 10-in. log to make 2 pink logs and 2 green logs. Place 1 log on a 12-in. piece of waxed paper lightly dusted with confectioners' sugar. Flatten log slightly; cover with a second piece of waxed paper. Roll out candy mixture into a 12-in. x 5-in. rectangle. Repeat with remaining logs.
4. Remove the top sheet of waxed paper from 1 pink and 1 green rectangle. Place 1 rectangle over the other. Roll up jelly-roll style, starting with a long side. Wrap in waxed paper; twist ends. Repeat with remaining rectangles. Chill overnight.
5. To serve, cut candy into ½-in. slices. Store in an airtight container in the refrigerator for up to 1 week.
1 PIECE: 90 cal., 2g fat (1g sat. fat), 5mg chol., 15mg sod., 19g carb. (19g sugars, 0 fiber), 0 pro.

EASTER SUGAR COOKIES

EASTER SUGAR COOKIES

Cream cheese contributes to the rich taste of these melt-in-your-mouth cookies. They have such nice flavor, you can skip the frosting and sprinkle them with colored sugar for a change.
—*Julie Brunette, Green Bay, WI*

PREP: 15 min. + chilling
BAKE: 10 min./batch + cooling
MAKES: 4 dozen

- 1 cup butter, softened
- 3 oz. cream cheese, softened
- 1 cup sugar
- 1 large egg yolk, room temperature
- ½ tsp. vanilla extract
- ¼ tsp. almond extract
- 2¼ cups all-purpose flour
- ½ tsp. salt
- ¼ tsp. baking soda
  Tinted frosting or colored sugar

1. In a bowl, cream the butter, cream cheese and sugar until light and fluffy, 5-7 minutes. Beat in egg yolk and extracts. Combine the flour, salt and baking soda; gradually add to creamed mixture. Cover and refrigerate for 3 hours or until easy to handle.
2. Preheat oven to 375°. On a lightly floured surface, roll out dough to ⅛-in. thickness. Cut with a 2½-in. cookie cutter dipped in flour. Place cutouts 1 in. apart on ungreased baking sheets. Bake until edges begin to brown, 8-10 minutes. Cool for 2 minutes before removing from pans to wire racks to cool completely. Decorate as desired.
1 COOKIE: 79 cal., 5g fat (3g sat. fat), 16mg chol., 67mg sod., 9g carb. (4g sugars, 0 fiber), 1g pro.

CHOCOLATE-COVERED
EGGS

CHOCOLATE-COVERED EGGS

These chocolatey eggs beat store-bought varieties hands down! The smiles you'll see when you serve these pretty candies make them worth the effort.
—*Louise Oberfoell, Bowman, ND*

- -

PREP: 1 hour + chilling • **MAKES:** 2 dozen

- ¼ cup butter, softened
- 1 jar (7 oz.) marshmallow creme
- 1 tsp. vanilla extract
- 3 cups plus 1 Tbsp. confectioners' sugar, divided
- 3 to 4 drops yellow food coloring
- 2 cups (12 oz.) white baking chips or semisweet chocolate chips
- 2 Tbsp. shortening
   Icing of your choice
   Assorted decorating candies

1. In a large bowl, beat the butter, marshmallow creme and vanilla until smooth. Gradually beat in 3 cups confectioners' sugar. Place ¼ cup butter mixture in a bowl; add yellow food coloring, and mix well. Shape into 24 small balls; cover and chill for 30 minutes. Wrap plain mixture in plastic wrap; chill for 30 minutes.

2. Dust work surface with remaining confectioners' sugar. Divide plain dough into 24 pieces. Wrap one piece of plain dough around each yellow ball and form into an egg shape. Place on a waxed paper-lined baking sheet; cover and freeze for 15 minutes or until firm.

3. In a microwave, melt chips and shortening; stir until smooth. Dip eggs in mixture; allow excess to drip off. Return eggs to waxed paper. Refrigerate for 30 minutes or until set. Decorate with icing and decorating candies as desired. Store in an airtight container in the refrigerator.

1 SERVING: 180 cal., 7g fat (4g sat. fat), 5mg chol., 22mg sod., 31g carb. (27g sugars, 1g fiber), 1g pro.

EASTER BUNNY TREATS

Our whole family had fun making these bunny-riffic treats together. They are just so cute!
—*Holly Jost, Manitowoc, WI*

- -

TAKES: 15 min. • **MAKES:** 1 dozen

- ⅓ cup vanilla frosting
- 36 large marshmallows
- 36 miniature marshmallows
   Red and pink heart-shaped decorating sprinkles
   Small black nonpareils
   White jimmies
   Pink colored sugar

Place frosting in a piping bag. For each bunny, cut 2 mini marshmallows in half and use the frosting to attach them to a large marshmallow to form arms and legs. For the face, attach 2 mini marshmallow halves for cheeks. Use white jimmies, black nonpareils and heart-shaped sprinkles to form whiskers, eyes and nose. For the ears, cut a large marshmallow in half diagonally. Dip each sticky side in colored sugar and use frosting to attach the ears to the top of the large marshmallow. Use frosting to connect the 2 large marshmallows; let stand until dry.
1 TREAT: 128 cal., 2g fat (1g sat. fat), 0 chol., 48mg sod., 27g carb. (20g sugars, 0 fiber), 0 pro.

EASTER BUNNY
TREATS

BIRD'S
NEST
TREATS

BIRD'S NEST TREATS

I make this birds nest recipe in the spring when the birds are starting to build their own nests. They are so easy to make and disappear fast.

—Pam Painter, Poseyville, IN

PREP: 25 min. • COOK: 15 min. • MAKES: 1 dozen

- ¼ cup butter, cubed
- 4½ cups miniature marshmallows
- ¼ cup creamy peanut butter
- ¼ cup semisweet chocolate chips
- 4 cups chow mein noodles
- 1 cup jelly beans or candy eggs

1. In a large saucepan over medium heat, melt butter and marshmallows until smooth, stirring occasionally. Add the peanut butter and chocolate chips; heat and stir for 2 minutes or until smooth. Remove from the heat; stir in chow mein noodles until well coated.

2. Divide into 12 mounds on a waxed paper-lined baking sheet. Using fingers, shape each into a nest; press an indentation in the center of nest. Fill each nest with 3 or 4 jelly beans or candy eggs. Cool.

1 TREAT: 296 cal., 12g fat (4g sat. fat), 10mg chol., 149mg sod., 46g carb. (27g sugars, 1g fiber), 3g pro.

MARSHMALLOW EASTER EGGS

I've been making this wonderful Easter candy for years. These eggs are a big hit with everyone who loves marshmallows.

—Betty Claycomb, Alverton, PA

PREP: 45 min. + standing • COOK: 15 min. • MAKES: 3 dozen

- 25 cups all-purpose flour (about 8 lbs.)
- 1 large egg
- 2 Tbsp. unflavored gelatin
- ½ cup cold water
- 2 cups sugar
- 1 cup light corn syrup
- ¾ cup hot water
- 2 tsp. vanilla extract
- 1 lb. dark chocolate candy coating, melted
  Candy coating disks, multiple colors, melted

1. Spread 7 cups flour in each of three 13x9-in. pans and 4 cups flour in a 9-in. square pan. Carefully wash the egg in a mild bleach solution (1 tsp. chlorine bleach to 1 qt. warm water); dry. Press washed egg halfway into the flour to form an impression. Repeat 35 times, 2 in. apart; set aside.

2. In a small bowl, sprinkle the gelatin over cold water. In a large saucepan, combine the sugar, ½ cup corn syrup and hot water. Bring to a boil over medium heat, stirring constantly, until a candy thermometer reads 238° (soft-ball stage). Remove from the heat; stir in remaining ½ cup corn syrup.

3. Pour into a large bowl. Add gelatin, 1 Tbsp. at a time, beating on high speed until candy is thick and has cooled to lukewarm, about 10 minutes. Beat in vanilla.

4. Spoon lukewarm gelatin mixture into egg depressions; dust with flour. Let stand for 3-4 hours or until set.

5. Brush excess flour off marshmallow eggs. Dip each egg in chocolate candy coating. Place flat side down on waxed paper. Let stand until set. Drizzle each colored candy coating over eggs.

NOTE: We recommend that you test your candy thermometer before each use by bringing water to a boil; the thermometer should read 212°. Adjust your recipe temperature up or down based on your test.

NOTE: For safety reasons, we recommend that you discard the egg and all of the flour.

1 PIECE: 147 cal., 4g fat (4g sat. fat), 0 chol., 7mg sod., 28g carb. (28g sugars, 0 fiber), 1g pro.

TEST KITCHEN TIP

Silicone egg molds are available and can be used instead of the flour.

MARSHMALLOW
EASTER EGGS

Hot Diggity Dog!

It's the Fourth of July! Link up with your pals for an evening filled with fireworks, franks and all-American fun.

VIDALIA ONION RELISH

FRESH TOMATO RELISH

GRILLED CORN RELISH

VIDALIA ONION RELISH

Let's be frank: Sausages and burgers are far tastier with this sweet onion topping. Bourbon adds a lovely caramel note, and the crushed pepper flakes turn up the heat.
—Janet Roth, Tempe, AZ

PREP: 20 min. • **COOK:** 1 hour
MAKES: 3 cups

- 4 large sweet onions, chopped
- 2 Tbsp. canola oil
- 3 garlic cloves, minced
- ⅓ cup bourbon
- 4 plum tomatoes, peeled, seeded and chopped
- ½ cup golden raisins
- ¼ cup sugar
- ¼ cup packed dark brown sugar
- ¼ cup cider vinegar
- 1 tsp. mustard seed
- ½ tsp. salt
- ½ tsp. ground turmeric
- ½ tsp. ground mustard
- ½ tsp. crushed red pepper flakes
- ¼ tsp. pepper
  Cooked sausage or meat of your choice

1. In a large saucepan, cook onions in oil over medium heat 40-45 minutes or until onions are golden brown, stirring occasionally. Add garlic; cook 1 minute longer. Remove from heat. Add bourbon, stirring to loosen browned bits from pan.
2. Stir in the next 11 ingredients; bring to a boil. Reduce heat; simmer, uncovered, 15-20 minutes or until thickened. Store in airtight containers in the refrigerator up to 1 week. Serve with cooked sausage or other meat.

2 TBSP.: 65 cal., 1g fat (0 sat. fat), 0 chol., 56mg sod., 12g carb. (9g sugars, 1g fiber), 1g pro. **DIABETIC EXCHANGES:** 1 starch.

FRESH TOMATO RELISH

My two grown sons eat this as a salad, but that's not my thing! Instead, I enjoy this fresh recipe from my late husband's mother as relish for grilled meats. I make a batch as soon as the first tomatoes of the season are ready.
—Lela Baskins, Windsor, MO

PREP: 30 min. + cooling
MAKES: about 6 pints

- 2 cups white vinegar
- ½ cup sugar
- 8 cups chopped tomatoes (about 11 large)
- ½ cup chopped onion
- 1 medium green pepper, diced
- 1 celery rib, diced
- ¼ cup prepared horseradish
- 2 Tbsp. salt
- 1 Tbsp. mustard seed
- 1½ tsp. pepper
- ½ tsp. ground cinnamon
- ½ tsp. ground cloves

1. In a large saucepan, bring vinegar and sugar to a boil. Remove from the heat; cool completely.
2. In a large bowl, combine remaining ingredients; add vinegar mixture and mix well. Spoon into storage containers, allowing ½ in. of headspace. Refrigerate up to 2 weeks or freeze up to 12 months. Serve with a slotted spoon.

2 TBSP.: 9 cal., 0 fat (0 sat. fat), 0 chol., 151mg sod., 2g carb. (2g sugars, 0 fiber), 0 pro.

GRILLED CORN RELISH

Upgrade from regular green relish! This colorful condiment is a great way to get kids to eat their veggies.
—Ellen Riley, Murfreesboro, TN

TAKES: 25 min. • **MAKES:** 2 cups

- 1 large sweet red pepper
- 2 medium ears sweet corn, husks removed
- 5 Tbsp. honey Dijon vinaigrette, divided
- 2 green onions, thinly sliced
- ½ tsp. coarsely ground pepper
- ¼ tsp. salt

1. Cut red pepper lengthwise in half; remove seeds. Grill red pepper and corn, covered, over medium heat 10-15 minutes or until tender, turning and basting occasionally with 3 Tbsp. vinaigrette.
2. Remove corn from cobs and chop red pepper; transfer to a small bowl. Add green onions, pepper, salt and remaining vinaigrette; toss to combine.

¼ CUP: 42 cal., 1g fat (0 sat. fat), 0 chol., 157mg sod., 8g carb. (4g sugars, 1g fiber), 1g pro. **DIABETIC EXCHANGES:** ½ starch.

DOGS 6 WAYS

❶ **SLOW-COOK:** Stand hot dogs upright in slow cooker; do not add water. Cook on low for 4 hours.
❷ **FLAME-ROAST:** Thread hot dogs lengthwise onto cooking fork; rotate constantly over fire until heated through, 2-4 minutes.
❸ **GRILL:** Grill hot dogs, placed diagonally on top of grates, over indirect heat for about 1 minute on each side.
❹ **BOIL:** Add water (1 cup per hot dog) to a large saucepan; bring to a boil. Add hot dogs, then let simmer over low heat for 3-6 minutes. Drain.
❺ **PAN-FRY:** Bring ½ in. water to a boil over medium-high heat. With tongs, add hot dogs to skillet and cook, flipping frequently, until all sides are browned.
❻ **BAKE:** Bake hot dogs at 400° for 10-15 minutes. If desired, broil a few additional minutes to crisp outsides.

QUICK BACON POTATO SALAD

My family was tired of the same old potato salad at family functions, so I created this with the ingredients I had on hand. Now I'm always asked to bring it to potluck gatherings.
—*Tami Gallagher, Eagan, MN*

PREP: 30 min. + chilling • **MAKES:** 8 servings

- 4 cups cubed red potatoes
- 1 cup chopped onion
- 7 bacon strips, cooked and crumbled
- 2 Tbsp. minced fresh parsley
- 1⅓ cups mayonnaise
- 3 Tbsp. grated Parmesan cheese
- 3 Tbsp. prepared ranch salad dressing
- 2 Tbsp. prepared mustard
- 4 tsp. white vinegar
- ½ tsp. minced garlic
- ¼ tsp. salt
- ¼ tsp. pepper

1. Place potatoes in a large saucepan and cover with water. Bring to a boil. Reduce heat; cover and cook until tender, 10-15 minutes. Drain.

2. In a large bowl, combine the potatoes, onion, bacon and parsley. In a small bowl, combine the remaining ingredients. Pour over potato mixture; toss to coat. Refrigerate for 1 hour or until chilled.

¾ CUP: 369 cal., 32g fat (6g sat. fat), 24mg chol., 523mg sod., 15g carb. (2g sugars, 2g fiber), 5g pro.

SMOKY BAKED BEANS

QUICK BACON POTATO SALAD

SMOKY BAKED BEANS

They'll be lining up for this saucy bean recipe full of that hard-to-capture campfire flavor. A combination of colorful calico beans makes it a lovely-looking dish alongside many summer entrees.
—*Lynne German, Buford, GA*

PREP: 25 min. • **COOK:** 7 hours • **MAKES:** 16 servings

- 1 lb. bulk spicy pork sausage
- 1 medium onion, chopped
- 2 cans (15 oz. each) pork and beans
- 1 can (16 oz.) kidney beans, rinsed and drained
- 1 can (16 oz.) butter beans, rinsed and drained
- 1 can (15½ oz.) navy beans, rinsed and drained
- 1 can (15 oz.) black beans, rinsed and drained
- 1 can (10 oz.) diced tomatoes and green chiles, drained
- ½ cup hickory smoke-flavored barbecue sauce
- ½ cup ketchup
- ½ cup packed brown sugar
- 1 tsp. ground mustard
- 1 tsp. steak seasoning
- 1 tsp. liquid smoke, optional

1. In a large skillet, cook sausage and onion over medium heat, breaking sausage into crumbles, until meat is no longer pink; drain.

2. In a 5-qt. slow cooker, combine the beans, tomatoes and sausage mixture. In a small bowl, combine the barbecue sauce, ketchup, brown sugar, mustard, steak seasoning and, if desired, liquid smoke. Stir into bean mixture.

3. Cover and cook on low for 7-8 hours or until heated through.

¾ CUP: 244 cal., 6g fat (2g sat. fat), 10mg chol., 896mg sod., 39g carb. (15g sugars, 8g fiber), 11g pro.

WALKING BANANA PUDDING

This is goodness on the go! A sweet take on walking tacos, mobile banana pudding combines all the beloved ingredients, including the quintessential vanilla wafers, in single personal-sized bags.
—Taste of Home *Test Kitchen*

PREP: 15 min. + chilling.
COOK: 20 min. + cooling
MAKES: 12 servings

- ½ cup sugar
- 2 Tbsp. cornstarch
- ⅛ tsp. salt
- 2½ cups 2% milk
- 2 large egg yolks, lightly beaten
- 1 Tbsp. butter
- 1 tsp. vanilla extract
- 12 pkg. (1 oz. each) miniature vanilla wafers
- 4 medium bananas, sliced
- ¾ cup frozen whipped topping, thawed

1. In a large heavy saucepan, mix sugar, cornstarch and salt. Whisk in milk. Cook and stir over medium heat until thickened and bubbly. Reduce heat to low; cook and stir 2 minutes longer. Remove from heat.
2. In a small bowl, whisk a small amount of hot mixture into egg yolks; return all to pan, whisking constantly. Bring to a gentle boil; cook and stir 2 minutes. Remove from heat. Stir in butter and vanilla. Cool 15 minutes, stirring occasionally.
3. Transfer to a large bowl. Press plastic wrap onto surface of pudding. Refrigerate until cold.
4. Just before serving, cut open packages of wafers. Spoon pudding into each package. Top with banana slices and whipped cream.

1 SERVING: 267 cal., 10g fat (4g sat. fat), 43mg chol., 165mg sod., 42g carb. (27g sugars, 1g fiber), 3g pro.

WALKING
BANANA
PUDDING

S'mores to Love

Pair your roasted 'mallow with a slew of sweet goodies to craft the ultimate campfire confection.

HOMEMADE HONEY GRAHAMS

Build a
S'mores Board

Get ready for fun when guests gather around the fire and you set out this sweet assortment of s'more fixings.

ITEMS TO INCLUDE

- Nutella
- Peanut butter
- Chocolate chip cookies
- Homemade Honey Grahams
- White chocolate-covered pretzels
- Peanut butter cups
- White chocolate squares
- Marshmallows
- Chocolate bars
- Strawberries, halved
- Oreo cookies
- Miniature marshmallows

EASY ASSEMBLY

Step 1: Spoon Nutella and peanut butter into small bowls and set on opposite ends of board.

Step 2: Line chocolate chip cookies and Homemade Honey Grahams in groupings on board.

Step 3: Add groupings of white chocolate-covered pretzels, peanut butter cups, white chocolate squares, marshmallows, chocolate bars, strawberries and Oreo cookies.

Step 4: Fill in gaps with miniature marshmallows.

Step 5: Add serving utensils.

HOMEMADE
HONEY
GRAHAMS

HOMEMADE HONEY GRAHAMS

The way my boys eat them, I would spend a fortune on honey graham crackers at the grocery store. So I decided to make a homemade version that is less processed—and less expensive. These are wonderful, although they still don't last long.
—*Crystal Jo Bruns, Iliff, CO*

- -

PREP: 15 min. + chilling
BAKE: 10 min./batch • **MAKES:** 32 crackers

1	cup whole wheat flour
¾	cup all-purpose flour
½	cup toasted wheat germ
2	Tbsp. dark brown sugar
1	tsp. baking powder
1	tsp. ground cinnamon
½	tsp. salt
½	tsp. baking soda
6	Tbsp. cold butter, cubed
¼	cup honey
4	Tbsp. ice water

1. In a bowl, whisk first 8 ingredients; cut in butter until crumbly. In another bowl, whisk honey and water; gradually add to dry ingredients, tossing with a fork until dough holds together when pressed.

2. Divide dough in half. Shape each into a disk; cover and refrigerate until firm enough to roll, about 30 minutes.

3. Preheat oven to 350°. On a lightly floured surface, roll each portion of dough to an 8-in. square. Using a knife or fluted pastry wheel, cut each portion into sixteen 2-in. squares. If desired, prick holes with a fork. Place 1 in. apart on parchment-lined baking sheets.

4. Bake 10-12 minutes or until edges are light brown. Remove graham crackers from pans to wire racks to cool. Store in an airtight container.

1 CRACKER: 60 cal., 2g fat (1g sat. fat), 6mg chol., 89mg sod., 9g carb. (3g sugars, 1g fiber), 1g pro. **DIABETIC EXCHANGES:** ½ starch, ½ fat.

Home Slices

You wanna pizza this? Homemade crusts, two kinds of sauces and loads of tempting toppings deliver parlor-style fun from the comfort of your kitchen.

HOMEMADE
PIZZA SAUCE

HOMEMADE PIZZA SAUCE

For years, I had trouble finding a pizza my family likes, so I started making my own. The evening I served it to company and they asked for my recipe, I knew I'd finally got it right! When I prepare my sauce, I usually fix enough for three to four pizzas and freeze it. Feel free to spice up the sauce to suit your own family's tastes.
—*Cheryl Kravik, Spanaway, WA*

PREP: 10 min. • **COOK:** 70 min.
MAKES: about 4 cups

- 2 cans (15 oz. each) tomato sauce
- 1 can (12 oz.) tomato paste
- 1 Tbsp. Italian seasoning
- 1 Tbsp. dried oregano
- 1 to 2 tsp. fennel seed, crushed
- 1 tsp. onion powder
- 1 tsp. garlic powder
- ½ tsp. salt

1. In a large saucepan over medium heat, combine tomato sauce and paste. Add remaining ingredients; mix well. Bring to a boil, stirring constantly. Reduce heat; cover and simmer for 1 hour, stirring occasionally. Cool.
2. Pour into jars or freezer containers, leaving ½ in. of headspace. Freeze up to 12 months. Thaw frozen sauce in refrigerator before serving.
¼ CUP: 26 cal., 0 fat (0 sat. fat), 0 chol., 189mg sod., 6g carb. (3g sugars, 2g fiber), 1g pro.

WHITE PIZZA SAUCE

If you favor the rich flavor of white pizzas, this sauce will become your new favorite. Add more garlic or your favorite herbs to give it more flavor.
—Taste of Home *Test Kitchen*

TAKES: 15 min. • **MAKES:** 2 cups

- 2 Tbsp. butter
- 2 garlic cloves, minced
- 2 Tbsp. all-purpose flour
- 2 cups half-and-half cream
- ⅓ cup grated Parmesan cheese
- ½ tsp. Italian seasoning, optional

In a small saucepan, melt butter over medium heat. Add garlic; cook and stir 1 minute. Stir in the flour until blended; gradually add cream. Bring to a boil; cook and stir 1-2 minutes or until thickened. Remove from heat. Stir in Parmesan cheese and, if desired, Italian seasoning.
¼ CUP: 128 cal., 10g fat (6g sat. fat), 41mg chol., 113mg sod., 4g carb. (2g sugars, 0 fiber), 3g pro.

WHITE PIZZA
SAUCE

HOW-TO

Posh Pies

Think outside of the (pizza) box with these tempting topping ideas.

RED-SAUCE PIZZAS:

Very Veggie: Red onion, mushrooms, broccoli, mini red peppers, fresh basil, shredded mozzarella.

Hog Wild: Sliced Italian sausage, crumbled bacon, sliced Canadian bacon, shredded mozzarella, fresh oregano.

Best-o Pesto: Pesto sauce, roasted cherry tomatoes, fresh basil, torn fresh mozzarella pieces, red pepper flakes.

WHITE-SAUCE PIZZAS:

Fig-geddabout It: Prosciutto slices, fresh quartered figs, arugula, drizzle of quality olive oil, shredded mozzarella.

Happy Hearts: Marinated artichoke hearts, red onion, salami slices, fresh thyme, shredded mozzarella.

Creamy Garlic: Roasted garlic slices, caramelized onions, spinach, basil, shredded mozzarella.

NO STOPPING THE TOPPINGS:

To help people build their perfect pie, fill a table or countertop with an assortment of fresh veggies, proteins, cheeses and more, including some kid-friendly items along with more grown-up picks.

You may want to add some dairy-free cheeses and ample vegetarian topping options too.

CANNOLI WAFER
SANDWICHES

BACON
CAESAR
SALAD

CANNOLI WAFER SANDWICHES

My family loves to visit a local Italian restaurant that has a wonderful dessert buffet. The cannoli is among our favorite choices, so I just had to come up with my own simple version. These sandwiches are best served the same day so the wafers remain nice and crisp.
—*Nichi Larson, Shawnee, KS*

PREP: 35 min. + standing
MAKES: 3½ dozen

- 1 cup whole-milk ricotta cheese
- ¼ cup confectioners' sugar
- 1 Tbsp. sugar
- ¼ tsp. vanilla extract
- 1 pkg. (11 oz.) vanilla wafers
- 12 oz. white candy coating, melted
- ½ cup miniature semisweet chocolate chips
  Additional confectioners' sugar

1. In a small bowl, mix ricotta cheese, confectioners' sugar, sugar and vanilla until blended. Spread 1 scant tsp. filling on bottoms of half the wafers; cover with remaining wafers.
2. Dip each sandwich cookie halfway into candy coating; allow excess to drip off. Place on waxed paper; sprinkle with chocolate chips. Let stand until set, about 10 minutes.
3. Serve within 2 hours or refrigerate until serving. Dust with additional confectioners' sugar just before serving.
1 SANDWICH COOKIE: 93 cal., 5g fat (3g sat. fat), 4mg chol., 38mg sod., 13g carb. (10g sugars, 0 fiber), 1g pro.

BACON CAESAR SALAD

Family and friends always say my Caesar salad rivals any restaurant version. The addition of bacon is a little untraditional, but it lends a slightly smoky flavor and makes it unique.
—*Sharon Tipton, Casselberry, FL*

TAKES: 20 min. • MAKES: 12 servings

- 2 Tbsp. olive oil
- 2 cups cubed day-old bread
- 3 garlic cloves, sliced
  DRESSING
- ½ cup olive oil
- ¼ cup lemon juice
- 1 Tbsp. Dijon mustard
- 3 garlic cloves, minced
- 1½ tsp. anchovy paste
  Dash pepper
  SALAD
- 1 large bunch romaine, torn
- 4 bacon strips, cooked and crumbled
- ½ cup shredded Parmesan cheese

1. For croutons, in a large skillet, heat oil over medium heat. Add bread cubes; cook and stir until golden brown, 4-5 minutes. Add garlic; cook 1 minute longer. Remove to paper towels; cool.
2. For dressing, in a small bowl, whisk oil, lemon juice, mustard, garlic, anchovy paste and pepper.
3. In a serving bowl, combine romaine and bacon. Drizzle with dressing; toss to coat. Sprinkle with croutons and cheese.
¾ CUP: 158 cal., 14g fat (3g sat. fat), 8mg chol., 229mg sod., 6g carb. (1g sugars, 1g fiber), 3g pro.
CHICKEN CAESAR SALAD: Top salad with slices of grilled chicken breast.

INDIVIDUAL PIZZA CRUSTS

This dough is great for parties. Everyone can pick their own toppings and it's always fun to do some cooking together. Or, use the dough to make two 12-inch pizzas.
—*Beverly Anderson, Sinclairville, NY*

PREP: 10 min. + resting • BAKE: 15 min.
MAKES: 10 servings

- 2 pkg. (¼ oz. each) active dry yeast
- 2 cups warm water (110° to 115°)
- ¼ cup canola oil
- 2 tsp. sugar
- ½ tsp. salt
- 5 to 5½ cups all-purpose flour
  Cornmeal
  Pizza toppings of your choice

1. In a large bowl, dissolve yeast in warm water. Add the oil, sugar, salt and 3 cups flour. Beat until smooth. Stir in enough remaining flour to form a firm dough. Turn onto a floured surface; cover and let rest for 10 minutes.
2. Divide dough into 10 pieces. Roll each portion into an 8-in. circle; prick each circle of dough several times with the tines of a fork. Transfer the dough to greased baking sheets lightly sprinkled with cornmeal, building up edges slightly. Do not let rise. Bake at 425° until lightly browned, 6-8 minutes. Add toppings; bake 8-12 minutes longer.
1 CRUST: 285 cal., 6g fat (1g sat. fat), 0 chol., 120mg sod., 49g carb. (1g sugars, 2g fiber), 7g pro.

TEST KITCHEN TIP

To keep things moving at the party, parbake a batch of pizza crusts ahead of time and stack them between sheets of parchment paper so guests can simply grab and get to topping. Once topped, the crusts get popped into the oven for the final bake.

INDIVIDUAL
PIZZA CRUSTS

The Great American Feast

Find your family's new favorite with the very best recipes for your Thanksgiving table, courtesy of our Community Cooks!

SOURDOUGH, SAUSAGE & BLUEBERRY DRESSING

I was looking in my pantry for raisins to make a Thanksgiving dressing just like my mom's. I was out, but I spied a bag of dried blueberries and decided to give them a try. Michigan is known for its blueberries, second only to cherries, so this is a delicious nod to my home state.
—*Teri Rasey, Cadillac, MI*

- -

PREP: 50 min. • **BAKE:** 45 min.
MAKES: 20 servings

1 cup dried blueberries
½ cup blueberry schnapps liqueur
6 Tbsp. butter, divided
5 tsp. minced garlic, divided
1 loaf (14½ oz.) sourdough bread, torn into ½-in. pieces
1 Tbsp. avocado oil or canola oil
3 celery ribs, chopped
1 medium onion, chopped
1 large carrot, peeled and grated

2 lbs. bulk pork sausage
1 pkg. (7 oz.) blueberry white cheddar cheese or sharp cheddar cheese, shredded
½ tsp. dried rosemary, crushed
½ tsp. rubbed sage
½ tsp. pepper
2½ cups reduced-sodium chicken broth
3 large eggs, beaten
Optional: Fresh blueberries and fresh sage

1. Preheat oven to 425°. In a small bowl, combine blueberries and schnapps; set aside.
2. In a small saucepan, heat 4 Tbsp. butter and 3 tsp. minced garlic until butter melts and mixture is fragrant, 2-3 minutes. In a large bowl, combine bread and the butter mixture; toss to coat. Spread onto a rimmed baking sheet. Bake, stirring occasionally, 12-15 minutes or until golden brown. Cool on a wire rack. Decrease oven temperature to 350°.

Meanwhile, in a large skillet, heat oil and remaining 2 Tbsp. butter over medium heat. Add celery, onion and carrot; cook until carrot is tender, 8-10 minutes, stirring occasionally. Add remaining 2 tsp. garlic; cook 1 minute. Add sausage; cook, breaking up sausage into crumbles, until sausage is no longer pink.

4. In a large bowl, combine toasted bread, sausage mixture, cheese, rosemary, sage and pepper. Drain blueberry mixture, reserving schnapps. Add blueberries to bread mixture. In a bowl, stir together broth, beaten eggs and reserved blueberry schnapps. Pour over bread mixture; toss to combine.

5. Transfer mixture to a lightly greased 4-qt. baking dish. Bake until top is golden brown and crispy, 45-50 minutes. If desired, garnish with fresh blueberries and sage.

¾ CUP: 290 cal., 19g fat (8g sat. fat), 71mg chol., 581mg sod., 18g carb. (4g sugars, 1g fiber), 11g pro.

SOURDOUGH, SAUSAGE & BLUEBERRY DRESSING

CHIPOTLE-CITRUS BRINED TURKEY

Our turkey recipe was getting a little tired, so I decided to use my trusty chipotle-citrus brine on the holiday bird. I've grilled, roasted and even deep-fried this turkey with equally excellent results.
—*Shawn Carleton, San Diego, CA*

PREP: 45 min. + chilling
BAKE: 2¾ hours + standing
MAKES: 18 servings

- 2   qt. water
- 1½ cups kosher salt
- 1½ cups sugar
- 2   medium oranges, sliced
- ¼   cup ground chipotle pepper
- 2   chipotle peppers in adobo sauce, minced
- 8   garlic cloves, halved
- 1   Tbsp. coarsely ground pepper
- 4   cups cold orange juice
- 2   large oven roasting bags
- 1   turkey (14 to 16 lbs.)

CHIPOTLE RUB
- ⅓   cup olive oil
- 2   Tbsp. grated orange zest
- 1   chipotle peppers in adobo sauce, minced
- 2   tsp. ground cumin
- 1½ tsp. coarsely ground pepper

SEASONED SALT RUB
- ¼   cup olive oil
- 1½ tsp. seasoned salt

In a 6-qt. stockpot, combine the first 8 ingredients. Bring to a boil. Remove from heat. Add cold juice to brine; cool to room temperature.

Place 1 oven roasting bag inside the other. Place turkey inside both bags; pour in cooled brine. Seal bags, pressing out as much air as possible, and turn to coat. Place turkey in a roasting pan or other large container. Refrigerate 8 hours or overnight, turning occasionally.

In a small bowl, mix rub ingredients. Remove turkey from brine; rinse and pat dry. Discard brine and bags. Place turkey, breast side up, on a rack in a roasting pan. With fingers, carefully loosen skin from turkey breast; spread rub under the skin. Secure skin to underside of breast with toothpicks. Tuck wings under turkey; tie drumsticks together. Refrigerate, covered, 18-24 hours.

Preheat oven to 425°. In a small bowl, mix oil and seasoned salt; brush over outside of turkey. Roast 15 minutes.

Reduce oven setting to 325°. Roast 2½-3 hours or until a thermometer inserted in the thickest part of the thigh reads 170°-175°, covering loosely with foil for the last 45 minutes. Remove turkey from oven; tent with foil. Let stand 20 minutes before carving.

8 OZ. COOKED TURKEY: 478 cal., 26g fat (7g sat. fat), 191mg chol., 350mg sod., 1g carb. (0 sugars, 0 fiber), 56g pro.

CHIPOTLE-CITRUS BRINED TURKEY

CARAWAY
BRUSSELS
SPROUTS

CARAWAY BRUSSELS SPROUTS

Brussels sprouts are a must on Thanksgiving. I like to make them my own with a variation on a recipe I found in a cooking magazine. I add bacon drippings, onion, caraway seeds, maple syrup, sherry vinegar, Dijon and more.
—*Ann Sheehy, Lawrence, MA*

PREP: 15 min. • **COOK:** 30 min.
MAKES: 8 servings

- 2 lbs. fresh Brussels sprouts, trimmed and halved
- 6 tsp. olive oil or bacon drippings
- 1 large sweet onion or large red onion, sliced
- 6 garlic cloves, thinly sliced
- 2 tsp. caraway seeds
- 1 tsp. dried thyme
- ½ tsp. kosher salt
- ½ tsp. coarsely ground pepper
- ¼ tsp. crushed red pepper flakes
- ¼ cup maple syrup
- 3 Tbsp. sherry vinegar
- 1 tsp. Dijon mustard

1. In a large skillet, place steamer basket over 1 in. water. Place Brussels sprouts in basket. Bring water to a boil. Reduce heat to maintain a simmer; steam, covered, 8-10 minutes or until crisp-tender. Remove from skillet; keep warm. Drain water.
2. In the same skillet, heat oil over medium heat. Add onion; cook and stir until tender, 4-5 minutes. Add the sliced garlic; cook 1 minute longer. Stir in Brussels sprouts, caraway seeds, thyme, salt, pepper and red pepper flakes. In a small bowl, whisk maple syrup, sherry vinegar and Dijon until blended. Pour over Brussels sprout mixture; stir until coated. Serve warm.
1 SERVING: 121 cal., 4g fat (1g sat. fat), 0 chol., 166mg sod., 20g carb. (10g sugars, 5g fiber), 4g pro.

ORANGE-MAPLE CRANBERRY SAUCE

During the holidays, I always have the five ingredients for this versatile cranberry sauce on hand. I add maple syrup and, of course, orange juice because it's so iconic to Florida. I serve it with ham or turkey but also on French toast or waffles.
—*Nancy Murphy, Mount Dora, FL*

TAKES: 30 min. • **MAKES:** 8 servings

- 2 cups fresh cranberries
- ½ cup orange juice
- ½ cup maple syrup
- ¼ cup golden raisins
- ¼ cup chopped walnuts, toasted
  Optional: Orange slices and minced fresh parsley

In a large saucepan, combine the first 5 ingredients over medium-high heat. Bring mixture to a boil; reduce heat. Simmer, uncovered, until cranberries start to burst and mixture thickens, about 20 minutes, stirring occasionally. If desired, garnish with orange slices, additional chopped walnuts and minced parsley.
NOTE: To toast nuts, bake in a shallow pan in a 350° oven for 5-10 minutes or cook in a skillet over low heat until lightly browned, stirring occasionally.
3 TBSP: 108 cal., 2g fat (0 sat. fat), 0 chol., 4mg sod., 22g carb. (17g sugars, 1g fiber), 1g pro.

ORANGE-MAPLE
CRANBERRY SAUCE

BEER-CHEESE GREEN BEAN CASSEROLE

Being from Wisconsin, where beer, cheese and snap beans abound, I thought I'd try a local spin on a beloved casserole. My mom deemed this even better than the original recipe. One point to America's dairyland!
—Sue Gronholz, Beaver Dam, WI

PREP: 25 min. • **BAKE:** 30 min.
MAKES: 8 servings

- 5 Tbsp. butter, divided
- ¼ cup all-purpose flour
- 1 cup 2% milk
- ½ cup lager beer or chicken broth
- 1½ cups shredded cheddar cheese
- ½ tsp. salt
- ½ tsp. Worcestershire sauce
- ⅛ tsp. cayenne pepper
- ⅛ tsp. smoked paprika
- 6 cups frozen cut green beans (about 24 oz.), thawed
- 1 Tbsp. finely chopped onion
- ½ cup dry bread crumbs

1. Preheat oven to 350°. In a large saucepan, melt 4 Tbsp. butter over medium heat. Stir in flour until smooth; gradually whisk in milk and beer. Bring to a boil, stirring constantly; cook and stir until thickened, 1-2 minutes. Stir in cheese, salt, Worcestershire sauce, cayenne and paprika until blended. Add green beans and onion; stir to combine.
2. Transfer to a greased 2-qt. baking dish. Melt remaining 1 Tbsp. butter; stir into bread crumbs. Sprinkle over casserole. Bake, uncovered, until bubbly and top is golden brown, 30-35 minutes.
¾ CUP: 235 cal., 15g fat (9g sat. fat), 43mg chol., 410mg sod., 16g carb. (4g sugars, 2g fiber), 9g pro.

BEER-CHEESE
GREEN BEAN
CASSEROLE

**HOLIDAY HOMINY,
TEXAS STYLE**

EASY CHEESY BISCUITS

I'm a big fan of homemade biscuits, but not the rolling and cutting that goes into making them. The drop biscuit method used in this recipe solves everything!
—*Christy Addison, Clarksville, OH*

TAKES: 30 min. • **MAKES:** 1 dozen

- 3 cups all-purpose flour
- 3 tsp. baking powder
- 1 Tbsp. sugar
- 1 tsp. salt
- ¾ tsp. cream of tartar
- ½ cup cold butter
- 1 cup shredded sharp cheddar cheese
- 1 garlic clove, minced
- ¼ to ½ tsp. crushed red pepper flakes
- 1¼ cups 2% milk

1. Preheat oven to 450°. In a large bowl, whisk flour, baking powder, sugar, salt and cream of tartar. Cut in butter until mixture resembles coarse crumbs. Stir in cheese, garlic and pepper flakes. Add milk; stir just until moistened.
2. Drop dough by heaping ¼ cupfuls 2 in. apart onto a greased baking sheet. Bake 18-20 minutes or until golden brown. Serve warm.

1 BISCUIT: 237 cal., 12g fat (7g sat. fat), 32mg chol., 429mg sod., 26g carb. (2g sugars, 1g fiber), 7g pro.

READER REVIEW

"I love to make these. As I take them out of oven, I like to brush on melted butter (ghee is best) mixed with salt and garlic."

—BRENDA860, TASTEOFHOME.COM

HOLIDAY HOMINY, TEXAS STYLE

This casserole, which can always be found on our Thanksgiving table, is a true Tex-Mex treat. Loaded with peppers, corn, Cotija cheese, tortilla chips and more, it's perfect for any potluck in need of a little spice.
—*Joan Hallford, North Richland Hills, TX*

PREP: 30 min. • **BAKE:** 20 min.
MAKES: 8 servings

- 1 small onion, chopped
- 2 Tbsp. canola oil
- 1 lb. yellow summer squash, chopped
- 1½ cups frozen or fresh corn
- 1 medium sweet red pepper, chopped
- 1 poblano pepper or jalapeno pepper, seeded and chopped
- ¼ tsp. dried oregano
- 1 can (15½ oz.) hominy, rinsed and drained
- ¼ cup whole milk
- ¼ cup sour cream
- 1 cup crushed corn tortilla chips
- ½ cup crumbled Cotija cheese or shredded pepper jack cheese
- ½ cup shredded sharp cheddar cheese
- ½ cup crumbled cooked bacon

1. Preheat oven to 350°. In a large skillet over medium heat, cook onion in oil until browned and crisp-tender, 5-7 minutes. Stir in squash, corn, peppers and oregano. Cook until vegetables are just tender, 3-5 minutes.
2. Remove from heat; cool slightly. Stir in hominy, milk and sour cream. Transfer to a lightly greased 13x9-in. baking dish. In a small bowl, combine tortilla chips, Cotija, cheddar and bacon; sprinkle over hominy mixture. Bake until mixture is bubbly and topping starts to brown, 20-25 minutes.
NOTE: Wear disposable gloves when cutting hot peppers; the oils can burn skin. Avoid touching your face.
¾ CUP: 252 cal., 14g fat (5g sat. fat), 26mg chol., 603mg sod., 25g carb. (4g sugars, 2g fiber), 10g pro.

EASY CHEESY BISCUITS

2. Bake 15 minutes. Reduce heat to 350°. Bake until crust is golden brown and top of pie is set, 45-50 minutes longer. Cover edge loosely with foil during the last 15 minutes if needed to prevent overbrowning. Remove foil. Cool on a wire rack for 1 hour. Refrigerate overnight or until set.

3. If desired, serve with whipped cream and sprinkle with cinnamon.

DOUGH FOR SINGLE-CRUST PIE: Combine 1¼ cups all-purpose flour and ¼ tsp. salt; cut in ½ cup cold butter until crumbly. Gradually add 3-5 Tbsp. ice water, tossing with a fork until dough holds together when pressed. Shape into a disk; wrap and refrigerate 1 hour.

1 PIECE: 461 cal., 27g fat (17g sat. fat), 126mg chol., 274mg sod., 47g carb. (30g sugars, 2g fiber), 6g pro.

PUMPKIN ICE CREAM

This recipe really captures the flavor of fall. It's good with or without the gingersnaps.
—Linda Young, Longmont, CO

TAKES: 30 min. • **MAKES:** 5 servings

> 1 cup canned pumpkin
> ¼ tsp. pumpkin pie spice
> 1 qt. vanilla ice cream, softened
> Gingersnaps, optional

In a large bowl, combine the pumpkin and pie spice until well blended. Stir in ice cream. Freeze until serving. Garnish with gingersnaps if desired.

1 CUP: 190 cal., 10g fat (6g sat. fat), 39mg chol., 72mg sod., 24g carb. (17g sugars, 2g fiber), 4g pro.

FIREBALL PUMPKIN PIE

FIREBALL PUMPKIN PIE

This pumpkin pie recipe takes the traditional fall dessert to a whole new level. Try adding whipped cream or cinnamon on top for some added sweetness.
—Taste of Home Test Kitchen

PREP: 25 min. • **BAKE:** 1 hour + chilling • **MAKES:** 8 servings

> Dough for single-crust pie
> 2 large eggs
> 1 can (15 oz.) pumpkin
> 1 cup half-and-half cream
> ¾ cup sugar
> ¼ cup packed brown sugar
> 3 Tbsp. Fireball cinnamon whiskey
> ½ tsp. pumpkin pie spice
> ¼ tsp. salt
> Optional: Sweetened whipped cream and cinnamon

1. Preheat oven to 425° On a lightly floured surface, roll dough to a ⅛-in.-thick circle; transfer to a 9-in. pie plate. Trim crust to ½ in. beyond rim of plate; flute edge. In a large bowl, combine eggs, pumpkin, cream, sugars, whiskey, pumpkin pie spice and salt; beat until smooth. Add filling to crust.

PUMPKIN ICE CREAM

CHOCOLATE-COVERED
STRAWBERRY TURKEYS

Make Turkey Treats

Slide a mini marshmallow onto the top portion of each of 24 pretzel halves. Because of the marshmallows' stickiness, they'll stay in place.

For best results, attach the drumsticks to strawberries straight from the refrigerator. The colder the strawberry, the faster the chocolate will set.

We recommend using wooden dowels or skewers when coating the prepared berries in chocolate. Compared with a toothpick, it is sturdier and longer, minimizing the chance of a mess.

Adding coconut oil to the two types of melted chips gives the chocolate a silky smooth texture and touch of shine without the hassle of tempering.

Birdy Bonbons

Spread your wings with this chocolate-dipped confection that the kids are sure to gobble up.

CHOCOLATE-COVERED STRAWBERRY TURKEYS

These chocolaty turkeys are too cute. The white chocolate is the finishing touch that takes them over the top.

—Audrey Rompon, Milwaukee, WI

- -

PREP: 45 min. + standing • **MAKES:** 1 dozen

- 12   pretzel sticks
- 24   miniature marshmallows
- 1½   cups milk chocolate chips
- 2   tsp. coconut oil, divided
- 12   fresh strawberries, hulled
- ¼   cup white baking chips

1. Snap pretzel sticks in half; slide a marshmallow onto the top of each of the pretzel halves to form the thighs (you will end up with 24 legs).
2. Combine the milk chocolate chips and 1 tsp. coconut oil in a microwave-safe bowl. Microwave on medium power until melted, stirring occasionally. Dip half of a marshmallow in chocolate, then stick to 1 side of a strawberry. Repeat on the other side with another pretzel and marshmallow. Hold for a few seconds until the legs stay in place on their own, then transfer to a waxed paper-lined sheet tray to set completely. Repeat with all pretzels, marshmallows and strawberries.
3. Stick a wooden dowel into the top of each assembled strawberry, then dip entirely in chocolate, turning a few times to ensure it's completely coated. Let the excess drip off, then return the strawberry to waxed paper to harden.
4. Combine the white chocolate chips and remaining 1 tsp. coconut oil; melt in the microwave until smooth. Once the dipped strawberries are hard to the touch, dip the ends of both turkey legs in white chocolate. Let stand until set.
1 TURKEY: 124 cal., 7g fat (4g sat. fat), 5mg chol., 26mg sod., 15g carb. (12g sugars, 1g fiber), 2g pro.

Appy Holidays!

Whether they're wrapped in prosciutto, coated in bread crumbs or stuffed in sweet peppers, these festive starters are the merriest way to trim your table.

CARAMELIZED ONION SPINACH DIP PAGE 266

CHEESY VEGETABLE GARDEN TART, PAGE 266

FRIED CHEESE RAVIOLI

Be sure to make enough of these crispy, coated ravioli. They're bound to be the hit of your party. The golden brown pillows are easy to pick up and dip in tomato sauce.

—*Kate Dampier, Quail Valley, CA*

PREP: 15 min. • COOK: 20 min. • MAKES: about 2½ dozen

- 1 pkg. (9 oz.) refrigerated cheese ravioli
- 1 large egg
- 1 cup seasoned bread crumbs
- ¼ cup shredded Parmesan cheese
- 1½ tsp. dried basil
- ½ cup canola oil, divided
  Additional shredded Parmesan cheese, optional
- 1 cup marinara sauce or meatless spaghetti sauce, warmed

1. Cook ravioli according to package directions; drain and pat dry. In a shallow bowl, lightly beat the egg. In another shallow bowl, combine the bread crumbs, cheese and basil. Dip ravioli in egg, then in bread crumb mixture.
2. In a large skillet or deep-fat fryer, heat ¼ cup oil over medium heat. Fry ravioli in batches for 30-60 seconds on each side or until golden brown and crispy; drain on paper towels. Halfway through frying, replace the oil; wipe out skillet with paper towels if necessary.
3. Sprinkle with additional cheese if desired. Serve ravioli with marinara sauce.

1 RAVIOLI: 58 cal., 2g fat (1g sat. fat), 11mg chol., 158mg sod., 7g carb. (1g sugars, 1g fiber), 2g pro.

DRIED CRANBERRY SHARP CHEDDAR CHEESE BALLS

DRIED CRANBERRY SHARP CHEDDAR CHEESE BALLS

These bite-sized cheese balls are a pleasure to pass around a party. They're much easier to eat than their large-scale counterparts. And with their bacon, pecans and berries, they're probably more delicious too!

—*DonnaMarie Ryan, Topsfield, MA*

TAKES: 30 min. • MAKES: about 4½ dozen

- 2 cups chopped pecans
- ⅔ cup dried cranberries
- ½ cup crumbled cooked bacon

FILLING
- 3 cups smoked sharp cheddar cheese, shredded
- 6 oz. cream cheese, softened
- ½ cup finely chopped pecans
- ½ cup crumbled cooked bacon
- ¼ cup minced fresh basil

1. Place pecans, cranberries and bacon in a food processor. Pulse until finely chopped. Transfer to a shallow bowl. Place remaining ingredients in the same food processor. Pulse until combined.
2. Shape cheese mixture into 1-in. balls; roll in pecan mixture. Store in an airtight container in the refrigerator.

1 APPETIZER: 83 cal., 7g fat (2g sat. fat), 11mg chol., 90mg sod., 3g carb. (2g sugars, 1g fiber), 3g pro.

FRIED CHEESE RAVIOLI

CARAMELIZED ONION SPINACH DIP

Spinach dip is at the top of just about everyone's favorite party-food list. I make it extra special with caramelized onions and a splash of white wine, so this is a recipe you can feel excited to serve.
—*Corrine Rupp, Statesville, NC*

PREP: 10 min. • **COOK:** 40 min.
MAKES: 2½ cups

- 1 sweet onion, chopped
- 2 tsp. olive oil
- 3 garlic cloves, minced
- ¼ cup reduced-sodium chicken broth
- ¼ cup white wine or additional reduced-sodium chicken broth
- 2 cups fat-free sour cream
- 1 pkg. (10 oz.) frozen chopped spinach, thawed and squeezed dry
- ¾ tsp. salt
  Tortilla chips and assorted fresh vegetables

1. In a large nonstick skillet coated with cooking spray, cook onion in oil over medium heat for 8 minutes, stirring frequently. Add garlic; cook 3 minutes longer.

2. Stir in broth and wine. Reduce heat to medium-low; cook for 25-30 minutes or until onions are golden brown and liquid is evaporated, stirring occasionally.

3. Transfer to a bowl. Stir in the sour cream, spinach and salt. Serve with tortilla chips and vegetables. Refrigerate leftovers.

¼ CUP: 73 cal., 1g fat (0 sat. fat), 7mg chol., 250mg sod., 11g carb. (4g sugars, 1g fiber), 4g pro. **DIABETIC EXCHANGES:** 1 starch.

CHEESY VEGETABLE GARDEN TART

Flower focaccia has been the rage recently, so I took this beautiful trend and applied it to a simple, savory vegetarian tart. I topped it with herbaceous Boursin and Parmesan, then decorated it with a medley of veggies.
—*Juls Palmer, Lebanon, NJ*

PREP: 30 min. • **BAKE:** 15 min. + cooling
MAKES: 12 servings

- 1 pkg. (5.2 oz.) Boursin garlic and fine herbs cheese
- 2 Tbsp. grated Parmesan cheese
- 2 Tbsp. sour cream
- 1 tsp. grated lemon zest
- 1 sheet frozen puff pastry, thawed
  Assorted fresh vegetables and herbs such as olives, sliced red onion, sliced miniature sweet peppers and rosemary
- 1 Tbsp. olive oil
- 1 large egg, beaten
  Sesame seeds, optional

1. Preheat oven to 400°. In a large bowl, mash Boursin cheese with a fork. Add Parmesan, sour cream and zest; beat until smooth and creamy.

2. On a lightly floured surface, unfold puff pastry. Roll into a 13x11-in. rectangle. Transfer to a parchment-lined baking sheet. Prick pastry several times with a fork. Using a sharp knife, score a ½ in. border around edges of pastry sheets (do not cut through). Spread Boursin mixture evenly over center of pastry.

3. Arrange vegetables and herbs over cheese mixture as desired. Brush vegetables with olive oil. Brush edges of pastry with egg; sprinkle with sesame seeds if desired. Bake until pastry is puffed and golden brown, 15-20 minutes. Cool 10 minutes before serving. Refrigerate leftovers.

1 PIECE: 171 cal., 13g fat (5g sat. fat), 20mg chol., 161mg sod., 12g carb. (1g sugars, 2g fiber), 3g pro.

CARAMELIZED ONION SPINACH DIP

**CHEESY VEGETABLE
GARDEN TART**

PROSCIUTTO SHRIMP
WITH TROPICAL
MANGO SALSA

CHEESE
PUFFS

DEVILED
CRAB

PROSCIUTTO SHRIMP WITH TROPICAL MANGO SALSA

Prosciutto and melon are a perfect pairing. I took things a few steps further by adding an assortment of other fresh ingredients, including mango, pineapple and papaya. Finally, add shrimp and you've got yourself one tasty starter.
—*Jane Whittaker, Pensacola, FL*

TAKES: 30 min. • **MAKES:** 24 servings

- 24 peeled and deveined cooked shrimp (16-20 per lb.)
- 5 Tbsp. lime juice

MANGO SALSA

- 2 medium ripe mangoes, peeled and chopped
- ¾ cup cubed fresh pineapple
- ¾ cup chopped peeled papaya
- ½ cup finely chopped red onion
- ½ cup finely chopped sweet red pepper
- 2 jalapeno peppers, seeded and minced
- 2 Tbsp. minced fresh cilantro
- 2 Tbsp. lime juice
- 24 thin slices cantaloupe
- 12 thin slices prosciutto, halved lengthwise

1. Place shrimp and lime juice in a large shallow bowl. Refrigerate, covered, while making salsa, turning once. In a large bowl, combine mangoes, pineapple, papaya, red onion, red pepper, jalapenos, cilantro and lime juice. Refrigerate, covered, until serving.

2. Drain shrimp, discarding lime juice. Place 1 cantaloupe slice on each prosciutto slice; top each with 1 shrimp. Fold both sides to close. If desired, secure with toothpicks. Serve with mango salsa.

NOTE: Wear disposable gloves when cutting hot peppers; the oils can burn skin. Avoid touching your face.

1 WRAPPED SHRIMP WITH 1 TBSP. SALSA: 65 cal., 1g fat (0 sat. fat), 37mg chol., 170mg sod., 7g carb. (6g sugars, 1g fiber), 7g pro.

CHEESE PUFFS

I based this appetizer on a recipe in one of my mother's old cookbooks and updated the flavor by adding cayenne and mustard. Tasty and quick for this busy season, these tender, golden puffs go together in minutes and simply disappear at parties!
—*Jamie Wetter, Boscobel, WI*

PREP: 15 min. • **BAKE:** 15 min./batch
MAKES: 4½ dozen

- 1 cup water
- 2 Tbsp. butter
- ½ tsp. salt
- ⅛ tsp. cayenne pepper
- 1 cup all-purpose flour
- 4 large eggs, room temperature
- 1¼ cups shredded Gruyere or Swiss cheese
- 1 Tbsp. Dijon mustard
- ¼ cup grated Parmesan cheese

1. In a large saucepan, bring the water, butter, salt and cayenne to a boil. Add flour all at once and stir until a smooth ball forms. Remove from the heat; let stand for 5 minutes. Add eggs, 1 at a time, beating well after each addition. Continue beating until mixture is smooth and shiny. Stir in Gruyere and mustard.

2. Drop 1-in. balls 2 in. apart on greased baking sheets. Sprinkle with Parmesan cheese. Bake at 425° for 15-20 minutes or until golden brown. Serve warm or cold.

FREEZE OPTION: Cheese puffs also freeze incredibly well After cooling completely, stack them on layers of waxed paper in a freezer container. You can freeze them up to 3 months.

1 PUFF: 30 cal., 2g fat (1g sat. fat), 18mg chol., 62mg sod., 2g carb. (0 sugars, 0 fiber), 2g pro.

DEVILED CRAB

Dip your spoon into this super rich comfort food, and you might think you're in heaven. Generous portions of crab are mixed with cream and eggs and are flavored with chives, onions and more. Yum!
—*Doris Prillaman, Wilmington, NC*

PREP: 30 min. • **BAKE:** 20 min.
MAKES: 6 servings

- ½ cup finely chopped onion
- 3 Tbsp. butter
- 3 Tbsp. all-purpose flour
- ½ tsp. salt
- 1½ cups half-and-half cream
- 2 large egg yolks, lightly beaten
- 3 cans (6 oz. each) crabmeat, drained, flaked and cartilage removed
- 1 Tbsp. Dijon mustard
- 2 tsp. Worcestershire sauce
- 1 tsp. minced chives

TOPPING

- 1 cup soft bread crumbs
- 1 Tbsp. butter, melted
  Additional minced chives, optional

1. Preheat oven to 375°. In a large skillet, saute onion in butter until tender. Stir in flour and salt until blended. Gradually stir in cream until smooth.

2. Bring to a boil; cook and stir until thickened and bubbly, about 2 minutes. Remove from heat.

3. Stir a small amount of hot mixture into the egg yolks. Return all to pan, stirring constantly. Bring to a gentle boil; cook and stir 2 minutes longer. Remove from heat. Stir in crab, mustard, Worcestershire sauce and chives.

4. Spoon into 6 greased 6-oz. ramekins or custard cups. Place on a baking sheet. Combine bread crumbs and melted butter; sprinkle over tops. Bake until topping is golden brown, 20-25 minutes. If desired, sprinkle with chives.

1 SERVING: 292 cal., 16g fat (10g sat. fat), 194mg chol., 697mg sod., 11g carb. (3g sugars, 1g fiber), 22g pro.

RIESLING & SWISS CHEESE FONDUE

Cheese lovers are sure to enjoy dipping into this rich and fancy fondue sparked with reisling. It makes a savory, no-fuss appetizer for the holidays. Don't be surprised when the pot is scraped clean!
—*Angela Spengler, Niceville, FL*

TAKES: 20 min. • **MAKES:** 3 cups

- 4 cups shredded Swiss cheese
- 2 Tbsp. all-purpose flour
- 1 cup dry riesling wine
- 1 garlic clove, minced
- 2 Tbsp. sherry
- 1 Tbsp. lemon juice
- ⅛ tsp. ground nutmeg
  Sliced smoked sausage, French bread baguette and roasted Brussels sprouts

1. In a large bowl, combine the cheese and flour. In a large saucepan, heat wine and garlic over medium heat until bubbles form around side of pan (do not boil).
2. Reduce heat to medium-low. Add ½ cup cheese mixture; stir constantly until almost completely melted. Continue adding cheese, ½ cup at a time, allowing cheese to melt almost completely between additions. Stir in the sherry, lemon juice and nutmeg.
3. Transfer to a heated fondue pot; keep fondue bubbling gently. Serve with sausage, bread cubes and Brussels sprouts. If fondue becomes too thick, stir in a little additional wine.
¼ CUP FONDUE: 167 cal., 11g fat (7g sat. fat), 33mg chol., 84mg sod., 3g carb. (0 sugars, 0 fiber), 10g pro.

TEST KITCHEN TIP

The dunking possibilities are endless for this fondue. Consider apples, pears, broccoli, cauliflower, roasted red potatoes, sauteed shrimp, roasted cubed chicken or slices of grilled steak.

RIESLING & SWISS CHEESE FONDUE

WARM CIDER CRANBERRY PUNCH

I first made this at an instructional cooking camp. My kids loved it so much that, for a time, they insisted we make it every day. Serve it hot in the winter or with ice during the summer.
—Carol Gehringer, Raleigh, NC

PREP: 10 min. • **COOK:** 3 hours
MAKES: 20 servings

- 1 bottle (64 oz.) cranberry juice
- 6 cups apple cider or juice
- 2 cans (12 oz. each) frozen lemonade concentrate, thawed
- 1 medium lemon, cut into wedges
- 4 cinnamon sticks (3 in.)
- 2 tsp. whole cloves
- 1 tsp. whole allspice
  Optional: Cranberries, lemon peel strips and additional cinnamon sticks

In a 6-qt. slow cooker, combine cranberry juice, apple cider, lemonade concentrate and lemon. Place cinnamon sticks, cloves and allspice on a double thickness of cheesecloth. Gather corners of cloth to enclose seasonings; tie securely with string. Place in slow cooker. Cook, covered, on low 3-4 hours or until heated through. Discard spice bag and lemon. If desired, garnish with cranberries, lemon peel and additional cinnamon sticks.
¾ CUP: 83 cal., 0 fat (0 sat. fat), 0 chol., 10mg sod., 21g carb. (20g sugars, 0 fiber), 0 pro.

PEPPER SHOOTERS

PEPPER SHOOTERS

Pop one of these savory peppers into your mouth for a tantalizing array of flavors. It's like an antipasto platter all in one bite.
—Taste of Home *Test Kitchen*

TAKES: 30 min. • **MAKES:** 2 dozen

- 24 pickled sweet cherry peppers
- 4 oz. fresh mozzarella cheese, finely chopped
- 2¾ oz. thinly sliced hard salami, finely chopped
- 3 Tbsp. prepared pesto
- 2 Tbsp. olive oil

Cut tops off peppers and remove seeds; set aside. In a small bowl, combine the cheese, salami and pesto; spoon into peppers. Drizzle with oil. Chill until serving.
1 APPETIZER: 55 cal., 4g fat (1g sat. fat), 7mg chol., 313mg sod., 2g carb. (1g sugars, 1g fiber), 3g pro.

READER REVIEW

"Brought these to a Christmas get-together and everyone enjoyed them. Next time, I'll add olives into the mix."
—BUNNY99, TASTEOFHOME.COM

WARM CIDER CRANBERRY PUNCH

RUBIES ON ICE

CHERRY-LIME SHRUB

This festive beverage is perfect for the holidays. The vinegar portion can be made up to one week ahead for ease.
—*Gina Nistico, Denver, CO*

- -

PREP: 20 min. • **COOK:** 10 min. + chilling • **MAKES:** 2 cups

1   medium lime
1½ cups fresh or frozen dark sweet cherries, pitted and crushed
1   cup cider vinegar
1½ cups sugar
½   cup water

SERVING SUGGESTION
  Ice cubes, sparkling water, fresh cherries, mint sprigs and lime slices

1. Finely grate zest from lime. Place zest and cherries in a sterilized pint jar. Bring vinegar just to a boil; pour over fruit, leaving ¼-in. headspace. Center lid on jar; screw on band until fingertip tight. Refrigerate for 1 week.
2. Strain vinegar mixture through a fine-mesh strainer into another sterilized pint jar. Press solids to extract juice; discard remaining fruit.
3. Bring sugar and water to a boil. Reduce heat; simmer until sugar is dissolved. Cool slightly. Stir into vinegar mixture; shake well. Store in the refrigerator up to 2 weeks.
4. To serve, drink 1-2 Tbsp. or add to a glass of ice, top with sparkling water and garnish with fresh cherries, mint and lime.

2 TBSP. SHRUB: 86 cal., 0 fat (0 sat. fat), 0 chol., 1mg sod., 21g carb. (20g sugars, 0 fiber), 0 pro.

RUBIES ON ICE

Ginger and pomegranate are made for each other, and the color of this beverage is tantalizing. If you're looking for a nonalcoholic option, you can easily leave out the vodka for a delicious and festive drink!
—*Tara Deshpande, New York, NY*

- -

PREP: 15 min. + freezing • **MAKES:** 4 servings

6   Tbsp. pomegranate seeds
½   cup vodka
4   Tbsp. pomegranate molasses
3   Tbsp. sweetened ginger syrup
2   Tbsp. lime juice
1   cinnamon stick (3 in.)
    Club soda, chilled
    Lime slices, optional
1   to 4 tsp. pomegranate seeds, optional

1. Scatter pomegranate seeds over an ice cube tray, about 1 tsp. per cube; fill with water and freeze.
2. Combine vodka, molasses, ginger syrup, lime juice and the cinnamon stick. Let steep 15 minutes. Strain; discard cinnamon stick. Place 4 pomegranate ice cubes in each of 4 tall glasses. Pour molasses mixture evenly into glasses; top off with chilled club soda. Stir well. Garnish with lime slices and additional pomegranate seeds if desired.

½ CUP: 148 cal., 0 fat (0 sat. fat), 0 chol., 3mg sod., 21g carb. (17g sugars, 0 fiber), 0 pro.

TEST KITCHEN TIP

Monin makes a ginger-flavored syrup. Look for it near the coffee syrups. Or make your own by combining 1 cup sugar, ½ cup water and sliced peeled fresh ginger (from a 2-in. piece). Bring to a boil. Cool completely, then strain out solids. Refrigerate up to 2 weeks.

CHERRY-LIME SHRUB

Champagne Wishes

When bubbles beckon on New Year's Day, these mimosa makeovers keep the celebration sparkling.

Blue Lagoon Mimosa

Ginger Mule Mimosa

Beermosa

Pomegranate Mimosa

Tequila Sunrise Mimosa

APPLE CIDER MIMOSA
Pour 2 oz. **spiced apple cider** into a champagne flute or wine glass; top with 3 oz. **champagne**.

BEERMOSA
Pour 2 oz. **orange juice** into a champagne flute or wine glass; top with 3 oz. **Belgian-style white beer**.

BLUE LAGOON MIMOSA
Pour 2 oz. **lemonade** and ½ oz. **blue Curacao** into a champagne flute or wine glass; top with 3 oz. **champagne**.

CLASSIC MIMOSA
Pour 2 oz. **orange juice** into a champagne flute or wine glass; top with 3 oz. **champagne**.

GINGER MULE MIMOSA
Pour 1 oz. **ginger liqueur** and ½ oz. **lime juice** into a champagne flute or wine glass; top with 4 oz. **champagne**.

HAWAIIAN MIMOSA
Pour 2 oz. **pineapple juice** and 1 oz. **coconut rum** into a champagne flute or wine glass; top with 2 oz. **champagne**.

PEACH MELBA BELLINI
Pour 2 oz. **peach nectar** and 1 oz. **raspberry liqueur** into a champagne flute or wine glass; top with 2 oz. **champagne**.

PEPPERMINT MIMOSA
Pour ½ oz. **peppermint schnapps** into a champagne flute or wine glass; top with 4½ oz. **champagne**.

POMEGRANATE MIMOSA
Pour 1 oz. **pomegranate juice** and 1 oz. **pomegranate liqueur** into a champagne flute or wine glass; top with 3 oz. **champagne**.

TEQUILA SUNRISE MIMOSA
Pour 2 oz. **orange juice** and 1 oz. **tequila** into a champagne flute or wine glass; top with 2 oz. **champagne**. Slowly pour ½ oz. **grenadine** on top.

✳ *To make nonalcoholic mimosas, swap in any dry sparkling white grape juice for the champagne and use nonalcoholic white ale in the Beermosa.*

Gourmet Gifts from the Kitchen

Share your love of cooking (and show you care too!) when you tuck a selection of these fresh favorites into their stockings.

FRENCH MACARONS

FRENCH MACARONS

Even decorated simply—a sprinkle of sugar, a drizzle of icing—these stylish beauties are part of our creative cookies collection. They will be the showstoppers on any Christmas cookie tray.
—Josh Rink, Milwaukee, WI

- -

PREP: 1 hour + standing
BAKE: 15 min./batch + cooling
MAKES: 30 macarons

MACARON SHELL
- 1⅓ cups almond flour
- 2¼ cups confectioners' sugar, divided
- 4 large egg whites, room temperature
- ⅛ tsp. salt
- 2 Tbsp. superfine sugar

BUTTERCREAM FILLING
- ¼ cup unsalted butter, softened
- 1 cup confectioners' sugar
- 2 Tbsp. heavy whipping cream
- ½ tsp. vanilla extract
- ⅛ tsp. salt

1. Place the almond flour and 1¾ cups confectioners' sugar in a food processor; pulse until thoroughly mixed to ensure almond flour is very fine. Pass almond flour mixture through a fine-mesh sieve; discard any large pieces that remain.

2. Place egg whites and salt in a very clean bowl of a stand mixer fitted with a whisk attachment; whisk on medium-low speed until frothy. Slowly add superfine sugar; whisk until dissolved, 1-2 minutes. Slowly add the remaining ½ cup confectioners' sugar; increase speed to high and whip until meringue is glossy and stiff peaks form, 1-2 minutes.

3. Gently fold the almond flour mixture into meringue, a third at a time. Using the side of a spatula, smooth batter up side of bowl several times to remove air bubbles and ensure there are no lumps; do not overmix. Run spatula down the center of the bowl; the line in the batter should remain visible for a moment before mixture runs back into itself.

4. Position rack in upper third of oven; preheat oven to 300°. Transfer batter into a pastry bag fitted with a #7 or #10 round tip. Pipe 1⅜-in. rounds onto a parchment-lined tray about 1 in. apart. Tap tray against counter 2-3 times to remove excess air bubbles. Let macarons rest until no longer wet or sticky to the touch, 30-60 minutes. Bake, 1 tray at a time, 14-16 minutes or until cookies rise about ⅛ in. to form feet, rotating tray halfway through baking. Remove tray and let macarons cool completely; repeat with remaining trays. Once macarons have cooled completely, remove from parchment.

5. To make the filling, cream butter in a stand mixer fitted with whisk attachment; slowly add confectioners' sugar until incorporated. Add heavy cream, vanilla and salt; mix until smooth. Pour frosting into a pastry bag fitted with a small round tip; pipe buttercream onto the bottoms of half the macarons. Top with remaining macaron shells. Refrigerate, covered, until ready to serve.

STRAWBERRY VARIATION: For macaron shells: Add pink gel food coloring (do not use liquid food coloring) to whipped meringue until desired color is reached. For filling: Add 1 Tbsp. strawberry powder to confectioners' sugar. If desired, add 2-3 drops strawberry flavoring to frosting. Pipe a circle of frosting onto bottoms of half the macaron shells. Place ¼ tsp. strawberry jam in center of each frosting circle. Top with remaining macaron shells.

CHOCOLATE VARIATION: For macaron shells: Add 2 Tbsp. dark cocoa powder to almond flour and confectioners' sugar before sifting.

1 MACARON: 101 cal., 4g fat (1g sat. fat), 5mg chol., 26mg sod., 16g carb. (14g sugars, 0 fiber), 2g pro.

HOW-TO

Make Macarons

Step 1: Whisk The Egg Whites
Meringue forms the foundation of these cookies. Beat egg whites and salt until frothy, then slowly add the superfine and confectioners' sugars. Whisk until you have stiff, glossy peaks.

Step 2: Fold In Almond Flour
Take your time to fold the almond flour mix into the meringue, adding a third of the flour at a time. Be careful not to deflate the egg whites; they give the cookies their texture and lift.

Step 3: Pipe Macaron Shells
Add the batter to a piping bag fitted with a round tip. Hold the bag perpendicular to your baking sheet and pipe circles. Use a mat with guides or draw them yourself with a template (a shot glass works!).

Step 4: Rest, Then Bake
After piping, don't rush to the oven. Let the shells dry out at room temperature. They're ready to bake when the tops of the cookies are no longer tacky to the touch. Be patient.

Step 5: Make The Buttercream
The filling for these cookies is a simple buttercream. Start by beating room-temperature butter and confectioners' sugar, then add cream, vanilla extract and salt. Make sure you're using a good quality vanilla for the best flavor.

Step 6: Fill With Buttercream
Lastly, use a pastry bag fitted with a round tip to pipe a generous dollop of buttercream filling on the bottoms of half the macaron shells. Then top with the remaining cookies for the perfect French confection.

PEANUT BUTTER CAROB CUPS

These peanut butter cups are dog-friendly since they use carob instead of chocolate. I had my own dogs, Emma and Abby, in mind when I made the recipe!
—Shannon Norris, Cudahy, WI

PREP: 30 min. + chilling • **MAKES:** 1 dozen

- 1 cup carob chips, divided
- 3 tsp. coconut oil, divided
- ⅓ cup all-natural creamy peanut butter
- 1 tsp. honey, optional

1. Combine ½ cup carob chips and 1 tsp. coconut oil in a microwave-safe bowl. Microwave, uncovered, on high for 30 seconds; stir. Microwave, stirring every 30 seconds, until the carob is melted and smooth, about 1 minute longer. Carob should not exceed 90°. Spoon 1 tsp. carob mixture into each of 12 silicone molds or foil-lined mini muffin cups; press spoon into center of each cup so mixture coats the sides of liners about halfway up. Freeze until set.

2. Combine peanut butter, 1 tsp. coconut oil and if using, honey, in a microwave-safe bowl. Microwave, uncovered, on high for 30 seconds; stir until smooth. Cool slightly. Drop 2 tsp. of peanut butter mixture over carob. Freeze until set.

3. Melt remaining ½ cup carob chips and 1 tsp. coconut oil in a microwave-safe bowl, stirring every 30 seconds. Spoon mixture by teaspoonfuls over the set peanut butter mixture. Freeze until set. Store in the refrigerator.

1 PIECE: 53 cal., 3g fat (3g sat. fat), 0 chol., 0 sod., 7g carb. (7g sugars, 0 fiber), 0 pro.

TEST KITCHEN TIP

Carob is a dog-safe alternative to chocolate that can be found at health food stores or online. You can keep these carob cups up to 1 month, tightly covered, in the refrigerator (if your dog doesn't eat them before then!)

PEANUT BUTTER CAROB CUPS

TRADITIONAL POPCORN BALLS

⑤i
DARK CHOCOLATE BOURBON BALLS

Here's an all-time chocolate classic made easy. The blended flavor of bourbon and pecans is always irresistible!
—Taste of Home *Test Kitchen*

- -

PREP: 30 min. + chilling • **MAKES:** 4 dozen

- 1¼ cups finely chopped pecans, divided
- ¼ cup bourbon
- ½ cup butter, softened
- 3¾ cups confectioners' sugar
- 1 lb. dark chocolate candy coating, melted

1. Combine 1 cup pecans and bourbon; let stand, covered, for 8 hours or overnight.

2. Cream butter and confectioners' sugar, ¼ cup at a time, until crumbly; stir in pecan mixture. Refrigerate, covered, until firm enough to shape, about 45 minutes. Shape into 1-in. balls; place on waxed paper-lined baking sheets. Refrigerate until firm, about 1 hour.

3. Dip in chocolate coating; allow excess to drip off. Sprinkle with remaining ¼ cup pecans. Let stand until set.

1 BOURBON BALL: 124 cal., 7g fat (4g sat. fat), 5mg chol., 15mg sod., 16g carb. (15g sugars, 0 fiber), 0 pro.

TRADITIONAL POPCORN BALLS

Having an old-fashioned popcorn ball will make you feel like a kid again. You'll find that one batch of this goes a long way.
—*Cathy Karges, Hazen, ND*

- -

TAKES: 20 min. • **MAKES:** 20 servings

- 7 qt. popped popcorn
- 1 cup sugar
- 1 cup light corn syrup
- ¼ cup water
- ¼ tsp. salt
- 3 Tbsp. butter
- 1 tsp. vanilla extract
  Food coloring, optional

1. Place the popcorn in a large baking pan; keep warm in a 200° oven.

2. In a heavy saucepan, combine the sugar, corn syrup, water and salt. Cook over medium heat until a candy thermometer reads 235° (soft-ball stage).

3. Remove from the heat. Add butter, vanilla and, if desired, food coloring; stir until butter is melted. Immediately pour over popcorn and stir until evenly coated.

4. When mixture is cool enough to handle, quickly shape into 3-in. balls, dipping hands in cold water to prevent sticking.

NOTE: We recommend that you test your candy thermometer before each use by bringing water to a boil; the thermometer should read 212°. Adjust your recipe temperature up or down based on your test.

1 POPCORN BALL: 177 cal., 6g fat (2g sat. fat), 5mg chol., 203mg sod., 31g carb. (18g sugars, 2g fiber), 1g pro.

DARK CHOCOLATE BOURBON BALLS

MOCHA COFFEE CREAMER

In a small saucepan, heat 1 cup **2% milk** until bubbles form around side of pan; remove from heat. Whisk in 1½ tsp. **coffee granules** until dissolved. Cool completely. Transfer to a small pitcher. Stir in one 14-oz. can **sweetened condensed milk**, 1 cup **heavy whipping cream**, 2 Tbsp. **chocolate syrup** and 1 tsp. **vanilla extract**. Cover and refrigerate up to 4 days. Stir before using. Makes 3¼ cups.
—*Andrea Price, Grafton, WI*

PUMPKIN PIE SPICE COFFEE CREAMER

In a small saucepan, whisk 2 cups **half-and-half cream,** ¼ cup **canned pumpkin**, 3 Tbsp. **sugar** and 2 tsp. **pumpkin pie** spice until blended. Add 1 **cinnamon stick**. Bring to a boil over medium heat. Remove from the heat; cool to room temperature, stirring occasionally. Transfer to a small pitcher. Cover and refrigerate up to 4 days. Stir before using. Makes 2 cups.
—*Ally Billhorn, Wilton, IA*

TRES LECHES COFFEE CREAMER

In a small pitcher, whisk 2 cups **heavy whipping cream**, one 14-oz. can **sweetened condensed milk**, one 12-oz. can **evaporated milk**, 1½ tsp. **vanilla extract** and 1 tsp. **rum extract** until blended. Cover and refrigerate up to 4 days. Stir before using. Makes 5 cups.
—*Marina Castle Kelley, Canyon Country, CA*

HOMEMADE GUMDROPS

Your friends and family will remember these chewy fruity candies long after they've licked the last bit of sugar off their fingers! They're a great gift any time of year.
—*Christin Holt, Kingsburg, CA*

PREP: 20 min. + chilling • **COOK:** 10 min. + standing
MAKES: About 1¾ lbs. (70 gumdrops)

2½ cups sugar, divided
1⅓ cups applesauce
2 pkg. (3 oz. each) red or green gelatin
2 envelopes unflavored gelatin
1 tsp. lemon juice

1. In a large saucepan, combine 2 cups sugar, applesauce, red or green gelatin, unflavored gelatin and lemon juice; let stand for 1 minute. Bring to a boil over medium heat, stirring constantly. Boil for 1 minute. Immediately pour into a cold 11x7-in. baking dish coated with cooking spray. Refrigerate 3 hours or until firm.
2. With a spatula, loosen gelatin from side of pan. To remove, invert onto waxed paper. Using kitchen scissors or small sharp cookie cutters dipped in hot water, cut into 1-in. squares or shapes.
3. Place on waxed paper. Dry at room temperature for 8 hours or until slightly sticky. Roll in remaining sugar. Store in an airtight container.
1 GUMDROP: 35 cal., 0 fat (0 sat. fat), 0 chol., 3mg sod., 9g carb. (8g sugars, 0 fiber), 0 pro.

CHERRY BOUNCE

CHERRY BOUNCE

Smooth and with the fragrant flavor of sweet cherries, this homemade libation makes a wonderful holiday gift. For an additional treat, the drained cherries are delicious over vanilla ice cream.
—*Matt Warren, Mequon, WI*

PREP: 5 min. • **COOK:** 25 min. + standing
MAKES: 5¼ cups

4½ lbs. fresh unpitted sweet cherries
2¼ cups sugar
½ tsp. ground allspice
1½ cups spiced rum
1½ cups brandy

1. Place cherries in a large saucepan. Bring to a boil. Reduce heat; simmer, uncovered, for 15-20 minutes or until soft. Strain juice through a cheesecloth-lined colander; divide cherries among six 1-pint jars.
2. Return juice to saucepan; add sugar and allspice. Bring to a boil. Reduce heat; simmer, uncovered, for 5 minutes. Transfer to a large bowl; cool completely.
3. Stir in rum and brandy; pour syrup into bottles over cherries. Cover and let stand for at least 1 month, stirring every week. Store in a cool, dry place up to 3 months.
1½ OZ.: 160 cal., 0 fat (0 sat. fat), 0 chol., 0 sod., 28g carb. (26g sugars, 2g fiber), 1g pro.

HOMEMADE GUMDROPS

General Index

Alphabetical Index

Mediterranean Braised Chicken
Thighs, 97
Mediterranean Shrimp Orzo
Salad, 32
Mexicali Quiche with Avocado
Crust, 168
Mexican Hot Chocolate Cupcakes, 195
Midnight Caribbean Pork
Sandwiches, 219
Mighty Nice Curried Chicken with
Rice, 91
Mini Baklava, 240
Mini Blueberry Bundt Cakes, 192
Mini Burgers with the Works, 23
Mini Reuben Casseroles, 87
Mini Toffee Rolls, 142
Mocha Coffee Creamer, 278
Moist Chocolate Cake, 197
Mojito Hazelnuts, 21
Morning Crispies, 158
Muffuletta Frittata, 173
Mushroom Corn Chowder, 48

N

Nana's Dolmathes with Avgolemono
Sauce, 236
Nonni's Fritole, 151
Nutter Butter Truffles, 185

O

Old Bay Mixed Nuts, 21
One-Pot Coconut Curry Lentil
Soup, 42
Onion Pakodas, 24
Onion Potato Pancakes, 231
Orange-Maple Cranberry Sauce, 258
Overnight Baked Oatmeal, 167
Overnight Oatmeal, 171
Overnight Yeast Waffles, 165

P

Parmesan-Crusted Tilapia, 67
Parmesan Fettuccine, 138
Parmesan Ranch Popcorn, 14
Parmesan Risotto, 127
Pasta & Veggies in Garlic Sauce, 65
Pasta e Fagioli Soup Mix, 111
Pasta with White Clam Sauce, 62
Peach & Blueberry Galette, 191
Peach Cobbler Cookies, 217
Peach Melba Bellini, 273
Peanut Butter Carob Cups, 276
Peanut Butter Zucchini Sheet
Cake, 189

Pecan Muhammara, 18
Pepper Jack Meat Loaf, 96
Pepper Shooters, 271
Peppermint Mimosa, 273
Pesto Corn Salad with Shrimp, 36
Pickled Green Onions, 131
Pinwheel Mints, 243
Pistachio & Date Ricotta Crostini, 26
Pistachio-Crusted Fried Fish, 227
Pizza on the Grill, 80
Pizza Potato Toppers, 88
Plum Poppy Seed Cake, 189
Polynesian Roast Beef, 88
Pomegranate Mimosa, 273
Poppy Seed Strawberry Sheet
Cake, 196
Pork & Bok Choy Udon Soup, 55
Pork & Chive Pot Stickers, 19
Pork Tenderloin with Sun-Dried
Tomato Cream Sauce, 79
Potato, Sausage & Kale Soup, 47
Power Breakfast Sandwich, 162
Pressure-Cooker Homemade Chunky
Applesauce, 231
Pressure-Cooker Italian Wedding
Soup, 47
Pressure-Cooker Jalapeno Popper
Chicken Chili, 55
Pressure-Cooker Lemon Chicken
Pasta, 72
Pressure-Cooker Penne with Meat
Sauce, 66
Prosciutto Egg Panini, 156
Prosciutto Shrimp with Tropical
Mango Salsa, 269
Pulled Pork Taters, 99
Pumpkin Ice Cream, 262
Pumpkin Pie Spice Coffee
Creamer, 278
Pumpkin Sopapilla Cheesecake, 204
Pumpkin Spice Pecans, 21

Q

Quebec Maple Syrup Dumplings
(Grands-Peres), 205
Quick & Simple Meatballs, 106
Quick Bacon Potato Salad, 248
Quinoa Breakfast Bowl, 160

R

Raspberry Cream Cheese Ice
Cream, 205
Red Velvet Cupcakes with Coconut
Frosting, 192
Red Velvet Truffles, 185

Reuben & Rye Strata, 157
Rhubarb & Onion Relish, 127
Riesling & Swiss Cheese Fondue, 270
Roasted Beet Wedges, 128
Roasted Greek Potatoes with Feta
Cheese, 235
Rosemary-Grapefruit Cashews, 21
Rubies on Ice, 272

S

Salsa Shakshuka with Avocados, 172
Salsa Verde Chicken Casserole, 65
San Francisco Cioppino, 54
Sausage & Bean Skillet with Crispy
Plantains, 61
Seared Scallops with Minted Pea
Puree, 94
Shamrock Cookies, 233
Sheet-Pan New England
Clambake, 101
Sheet-Pan Salmon with Simple
Bread Salad, 76
Sheet-Pan Yellow Bells & Eggs, 158
Shortcut Fish Tacos, 114
Shredded Green Chile Beef, 79
Shrimp Cocktail, 7
Shrimp Spaghetti with Cherry
Tomatoes, 74
Sicilian Pizza (Sfincione), 214
Simits, 148
Skillet Caramel-Apple Buckle, 209
Skillet Pork Chops in Pineapple-Soy
Sauce, 63
Slow-Cooked Ratatouille, 123
Slow-Cooker Garlic Clove Chicken, 73
Slow-Cooker Lasagna Soup, 51
Slow-Cooker Memphis-Style Ribs, 83
Slow-Cooker Oatmeal, 157
Slow-Cooker Pork Chops, 92
Slow-Cooker Tropical Orange
Cake, 218
S'mores Board, 251
Smoked Pork Butt, 222
Smoky Baked Beans, 248
Smoky Black-Eyed Pea Cakes, 18
Sopa Ajoblanco, 51
Sour Cream Chive Bread, 147
Sourdough, Sausage & Blueberry
Dressing, 256
Spectacular Fingerling Potatoes, 134
Speedy Salmon Patties, 67
Spiced Indian Rusks, 151
Spicy Sweet Potato Chips &
Cilantro Dip, 16
Spinach & Feta Bourekas, 8
Sriracha-Molasses Pecans, 21

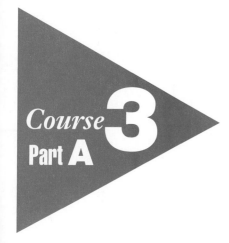

Course 3
Part A

Contemporary Mathematics in Context

A Unified Approach

Course Part A 3

Contemporary Mathematics in Context
A Unified Approach

Arthur F. Coxford
James T. Fey
Christian R. Hirsch
Harold L. Schoen
Gail Burrill
Eric W. Hart
Ann E. Watkins
with
Mary Jo Messenger
Beth E. Ritsema
Rebecca K. Walker

Glencoe
McGraw-Hill

New York, New York   Columbus, Ohio   Chicago, Illinois   Peoria, Illinois   Woodland Hills, California

Glencoe/McGraw-Hill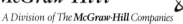

A Division of The **McGraw·Hill** Companies

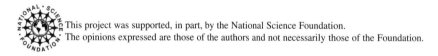 This project was supported, in part, by the National Science Foundation.
The opinions expressed are those of the authors and not necessarily those of the Foundation.

Send all inquiries to:
Glencoe/McGraw-Hill
8787 Orion Place
Columbus, OH 43240-4027

ISBN: 0-07-827545-8 (Part A)   Contemporary Mathematics in Context
ISBN: 0-07-827546-7 (Part B)   Course 3 Part A Student Edition

2   3   4   5   6   7   8   9   10   004/004   10   09   08   07   06   05   04   03

Core-Plus Mathematics Project Development Team

Project Directors

Christian R. Hirsch
Western Michigan University

Arthur F. Coxford
University of Michigan

James T. Fey
University of Maryland

Harold L. Schoen
University of Iowa

Senior Curriculum Developers

Gail Burrill
University of Wisconsin-Madison

Eric W. Hart
Western Michigan University

Ann E. Watkins
California State University, Northridge

Professional Development Coordinator

Beth E. Ritsema
Western Michigan University

Evaluation Coordinator

Steven W. Ziebarth
Western Michigan University

Advisory Board

Diane Briars
Pittsburgh Public Schools

Jeremy Kilpatrick
University of Georgia

Kenneth Ruthven
University of Cambridge

David A. Smith
Duke University

Edna Vasquez
Detroit Renaissance High School

Curriculum Development Consultants

Alverna Champion
Grand Valley State University

Cherie Cornick
Wayne County Alliance for Mathematics and Science

Edgar Edwards
(Formerly) Virginia State Department of Education

Richard Scheaffer
University of Florida

Martha Siegel
Towson University

Edward Silver
University of Michigan

Lee Stiff
North Carolina State University

Technical Coordinator

Wendy Weaver
Western Michigan University

Collaborating Teachers

Emma Ames
Oakland Mills High School, Maryland

Cheryl Bach Hedden
Sitka High School, Alaska

Mary Jo Messenger
Howard County Public Schools, Maryland

Valerie Mills
Ann Arbor Public Schools, Michigan

Jacqueline Stewart
Okemos High School, Michigan

Michael Verkaik
Holland Christian High School, Michigan

Marcia Weinhold
Kalamazoo Area Mathematics and Science Center, Michigan

Graduate Assistants

Judy Flowers
University of Michigan

Gina Garza-Kling
Western Michigan University

Robin Marcus
University of Maryland

Chris Rasmussen
University of Maryland

Bettie Truitt
University of Iowa

Roberto Villarubi
University of Maryland

Rebecca Walker
Western Michigan University

Production and Support Staff

James Laser
Kelly MacLean
Michelle Magers
Cheryl Peters
Angela Reiter
Jennifer Rosenboom
Anna Seif
Kathryn Wright
Teresa Ziebarth
Western Michigan University

Software Developers

Jim Flanders
Colorado Springs, Colorado

Eric Kamischke
Interlochen, Michigan

Core-Plus Mathematics Project Field-Test Sites

Special thanks are extended to these teachers and their students who participated in the testing and evaluation of Course 3.

Ann Arbor Huron High School
Ann Arbor, Michigan
 Ginger Gajar
 Brenda Garr

Ann Arbor Pioneer High School
Ann Arbor, Michigan
 Jim Brink
 Tammy Schirmer

Arthur Hill High School
Saginaw, Michigan
 Virginia Abbott

Battle Creek Central High School
Battle Creek, Michigan
 Teresa Ballard
 Steven Ohs

Bedford High School
Temperance, Michigan
 Ellen Bacon
 David J. DeGrace

Bloomfield Hills Andover High School
Bloomfield Hills, Michigan
 Jane Briskey
 Homer Hassenzahl
 Cathy King
 Linda Robinson
 Mike Shelley
 Roger Siwajek

Brookwood High School
Snellville, Georgia
 Ginny Hanley
 Marie Knox

Caledonia High School
Caledonia, Michigan
 Deborah Bates
 Jenny Diekevers
 Kim Drefcenski
 Larry Timmer
 Gerard Wagner

Centaurus High School
Lafayette, Colorado
 Gail Reichert

Clio High School
Clio, Michigan
 Bruce Hanson
 Lee Sheridan

Davison High School
Davison, Michigan
 Evelyn Ailing
 John Bale
 Dan Tomczak

Dexter High School
Dexter, Michigan
 Kris Chatas

Ellet High School
Akron, Ohio
 Marcia Csipke
 Jim Fillmore

Firestone High School
Akron, Ohio
 Barbara Crucs

Flint Northern High School
Flint, Michigan
 Al Wojtowicz

Goodrich High School
Goodrich, Michigan
 John Doerr
 Barbara Ravas
 Bonnie Stojek

Grand Blanc High School
Grand Blanc, Michigan
 Charles Carmody
 Maria Uhler-Chargo

Grass Lake Junior/Senior High School
Grass Lake, Michigan
 Brad Coffey
 Larry Poertner

Gull Lake High School
Richland, Michigan
  Dorothy Louden

Kalamazoo Central High School
Kalamazoo, Michigan
  Gloria Foster
  Amy Schwentor

Kelloggsville Public Schools
Wyoming, Michigan
  Nancy Hoorn
  Steve Ramsey
  John Ritzler

Midland Valley High School
Langley, South Carolina
  Ron Bell
  Janice Lee

North Lamar High School
Paris, Texas
  Tommy Eads
  Barbara Eatherly

Okemos High School
Okemos, Michigan
  Lisa Magee
  Jacqueline Stewart

Portage Northern High School
Portage, Michigan
  Pete Jarrad
  Scott Moore
  Jerry Swoboda

Prairie High School
Cedar Rapids, Iowa
  Dave LaGrange
  Judy Slezak

San Pasqual High School
Escondido, California
  Damon Blackman
  Ron Peet

Sitka High School
Sitka, Alaska
  Mikolas Bekeris
  Cheryl Bach Hedden
  Dan Langbauer
  Tom Smircich

Sturgis High School
Sturgis, Michigan
  Kathy Parkhurst
  Jo Ann Roe

Sweetwater High School
National City, California
  Bill Bokesch

Tecumseh High School
Tecumseh, Michigan
  Jennifer Keffer
  Elizabeth Lentz
  Carl Novak

Traverse City High School
Traverse City, Michigan
  Diana Lyon-Schumacher
  Ken May
  Diane Moore

Vallivue High School
Caldwell, Idaho
  Scott Coulter
  Kathy Harris

Ypsilanti High School
Ypsilanti, Michigan
  Keith Kellman
  Mark McClure
  Valerie Mills

Overview of Course 3

Part A

Unit ▶ 1 Multiple-Variable Models

Multiple-Variable Models develops student ability to construct and reason with linked quantitative variables and relations involving several variables and several constraints.

Topics include formulas, including the Law of Sines and the Law of Cosines, relating several variables by a single equation; systems of equations with several dependent variables or constraints; patterns of change in one or more variables in response to changes in others; solution of systems of equations and inequalities; and linear programming.

Lesson 1 *Linked Variables*
Lesson 2 *Algebra, Geometry, and Trigonometry*
Lesson 3 *Linked Equations*
Lesson 4 *Linear Programming*
Lesson 5 *Looking Back*

Unit ▶ 3 Symbol Sense and Algebraic Reasoning

Symbol Sense and Algebraic Reasoning develops student ability to represent and draw inferences about algebraic relations and functions using symbolic expressions and manipulations.

Topics include formalization of function concept, notation, domain, and range; use of polynomial, exponential, and rational expressions to model relations among quantitative variables; field properties of real numbers and their application to expression of algebraic relations in equivalent forms and to solution of equations and inequalities by methods including factoring and the quadratic formula; and algebraic proof.

Lesson 1 *Algebra and Functions*
Lesson 2 *Algebraic Operations: Part 1*
Lesson 3 *Algebraic Operations: Part 2*
Lesson 4 *Reasoning to Solve Equations and Inequalities*
Lesson 5 *Proof through Algebraic Reasoning*
Lesson 6 *Looking Back*

Unit ▶ 2 Modeling Public Opinion

Modeling Public Opinion develops student understanding of how public opinion can be measured. The situations analyzed include elections (where there are more than two choices) and sample surveys, including political polling.

Topics include preferential voting, vote-analysis methods, Arrow's theorem, fairness in social decision making; surveys, sampling, sampling distributions, relationship between a sample and a population, confidence intervals, margin of error; and critical analysis of elections and surveys.

Lesson 1 *Voting Models*
Lesson 2 *Surveys and Samples*
Lesson 3 *Sampling Distributions: From Population to Sample*
Lesson 4 *Confidence Intervals: From Sample to Population*
Lesson 5 *Looking Back*

Unit ▶ 4 Shapes and Geometric Reasoning

Shapes and Geometric Reasoning introduces students to formal reasoning and deduction in geometric settings.

Topics include inductive and deductive reasoning, counterexamples, the role of assumptions in proof; conclusions concerning supplementary and vertical angles and the angles formed by parallel lines and transversals; conditions insuring similarity and congruence of triangles and their application to quadrilaterals and other shapes; and necessary and sufficient conditions for parallelograms.

Lesson 1 *Reasoned Arguments*
Lesson 2 *Reasoning about Similar and Congruent Triangles*
Lesson 3 *Parallelograms: Necessary and Sufficient Conditions*
Lesson 4 *Looking Back*

Overview of Course 3

Part B

Unit 5 ▶ Patterns in Variation

Patterns in Variation extends student understanding of the measurement of variation, develops student ability to use the normal distribution as a model of variation, and introduces students to the probability and statistical inference involved in the control charts used in industry for statistical process control.

Topics include standard deviation and its properties, normal distribution and its relation to standard deviation, statistical process control, control charts, control limits, mutually exclusive events, and the Addition Rule of Probability.

Lesson 1 *Measuring Variation with the Standard Deviation*
Lesson 2 *The Normal Distribution*
Lesson 3 *Statistical Process Control*
Lesson 4 *Looking Back*

Unit 7 ▶ Discrete Models of Change

Discrete Models of Change extends student ability to represent, analyze, and solve problems in situations involving sequential and recursive change.

Topics include iteration and recursion as tools to model and analyze sequential change in real-world contexts; arithmetic, geometric, and other sequences; arithmetic and geometric series; finite differences; linear and nonlinear recurrence relations; and function iteration, including graphical iteration and fixed points.

Lesson 1 *Modeling Sequential Change Using Recursion*
Lesson 2 *A Discrete View of Function Models*
Lesson 3 *Iterating Functions*
Lesson 4 *Looking Back*

Unit 6 ▶ Families of Functions

Families of Functions reviews and extends student ability to recognize different function patterns in numerical and graphical data and to interpret and construct appropriate symbolic representations modeling those data patterns.

Topics include review of linear, polynomial, exponential, rational, and trigonometric functions (including effects of parameters on numeric and graphic patterns) and construction of function rules for function tables and graphs that are transformations of basic types (translation, reflection, stretch).

Lesson 1 *Function Models Revisited*
Lesson 2 *Customizing Models 1: Reflections and Vertical Transformations*
Lesson 3 *Customizing Models 2: Horizontal Transformations*
Lesson 4 *Looking Back*

Capstone ▶ Making the Best of It: Optional Forms and Strategies

Making the Best of It: Optimal Forms and Strategies is a thematic, two-week project-oriented activity that enables students to pull together and apply the important mathematical concepts and methods developed throughout the course.

Contents

x

Preface

The first three courses in the *Contemporary Mathematics in Context* series provide a common core of broadly useful mathematics for all students. They were developed to prepare students for success in college, in careers, and in daily life in contemporary society. Course 4 formalizes and extends the core program with a focus on the mathematics needed to be successful in college mathematics and statistics courses. The series builds upon the theme of *mathematics as sense-making*. Through investigations of real-life contexts, students develop a rich understanding of important mathematics that makes sense to them and which, in turn, enables them to make sense out of new situations and problems.

Each course in the *Contemporary Mathematics in Context* curriculum shares the following mathematical and instructional features.

- **Unified Content** Each year the curriculum advances students' understanding of mathematics along interwoven strands of algebra and functions, statistics and probability, geometry and trigonometry, and discrete mathematics. These strands are unified by fundamental themes, by common topics, and by mathematical habits of mind or ways of thinking. Developing mathematics each year along multiple strands helps students develop diverse mathematical insights and nurtures their differing strengths and talents.

- **Mathematical Modeling** The curriculum emphasizes mathematical modeling including the processes of data collection, representation, interpretation, prediction, and simulation. The modeling perspective permits students to experience mathematics as a means of making sense of data and problems that arise in diverse contexts within and across cultures.

- **Access and Challenge** The curriculum is designed to make more mathematics accessible to more students while at the same time challenging the most able students. Differences in student performance and interest can be accommodated by the depth and level of abstraction to which core topics are pursued, by the nature and degree of difficulty of applications, and by providing opportunities for student choice on homework tasks and projects.

- **Technology** Numerical, graphics, and programming/link capabilities such as those found on many graphing calculators are assumed and appropriately used throughout the curriculum. This use of technology permits the curriculum and instruction to emphasize multiple representations (verbal, numerical, graphical, and symbolic) and to focus on goals in which mathematical thinking and problem solving are central.

- **Active Learning** Instructional materials promote active learning and teaching centered around collaborative small-group investigations of problem situations followed by teacher-led whole-class summarizing activities that lead to analysis, abstraction, and further application of underlying mathematical ideas. Students are actively engaged in exploring, conjecturing, verifying, generalizing, applying, proving, evaluating, and communicating mathematical ideas.

- **Multi-dimensional Assessment** Comprehensive assessment of student understanding and progress through both curriculum-embedded assessment opportunities and supplementary assessment tasks supports instruction and enables monitoring and evaluation of each student's performance in terms of mathematical processes, content, and dispositions.

Unified Mathematics

Contemporary Mathematics in Context is a unified curriculum that replaces the traditional Algebra-Geometry-Advanced Algebra/Trigonometry-Precalculus sequence. Each course features important mathematics drawn from four strands.

The Algebra and Functions strand develops student ability to recognize, represent, and solve problems involving relations among quantitative variables. Central to the development is the use of functions as mathematical models. The key algebraic models in the curriculum are linear, exponential, power, polynomial, logarithmic, rational, and trigonometric functions. Modeling with systems of equations, both linear and nonlinear, is developed. Attention is also given to symbolic reasoning and manipulation.

The primary goal of the Geometry and Trigonometry strand is to develop visual thinking and ability to construct, reason with, interpret, and apply mathematical models of patterns in visual and physical contexts. The focus is on describing patterns with regard to shape, size, and location; representing patterns with drawings, coordinates, or vectors; predicting changes and invariants in shapes; and organizing geometric facts and relationships through deductive reasoning.

The primary role of the Statistics and Probability strand is to develop student ability to analyze data intelligently, to recognize and measure variation, and to understand the patterns that underlie probabilistic situations. The ultimate goal is for students to understand how inferences can be made about a population by looking at a sample from that population. Graphical methods of data analysis, simulations, sampling, and experience with the collection and interpretation of real data are featured.

The Discrete Mathematics strand develops student ability to model and solve problems involving enumeration, sequential change, decision-making in finite settings, and relationships among a finite number of elements. Topics include matrices, vertex-edge graphs, recursion, voting methods, and systematic counting methods (combinatorics). Key themes are discrete mathematical modeling, existence (Is there a solution?), optimization (What is the best solution?), and algorithmic problem-solving (Can you efficiently construct a solution?).

Each of these strands is developed within focused units connected by fundamental ideas such as symmetry, matrices, functions, and data analysis and curve-fitting. The strands also are connected across units by mathematical habits of mind such as visual thinking, recursive thinking, searching for and explaining patterns, making and checking conjectures, reasoning with multiple representations, inventing mathematics, and providing convincing arguments and proofs.

The strands are unified further by the fundamental themes of data, representation, shape, and change. Important mathematical ideas are frequently revisited through this attention to connections within and across strands, enabling students to develop a robust and connected understanding of mathematics.

Active Learning and Teaching

The manner in which students encounter mathematical ideas can contribute significantly to the quality of their learning and the depth of their understanding. *Contemporary Mathematics in Context* units are designed around multi-day lessons centered on big ideas. Lessons are organized around a four-phase cycle of classroom activities, described in the following paragraph—*Launch, Explore, Share and Summarize*, and *On Your Own*. This cycle is designed to engage students in investigating and making sense of problem situations, in constructing important mathematical concepts and methods, in generalizing and proving mathematical relationships, and in communicating both orally and in writing their thinking and the results of their efforts. Most classroom activities are designed to be completed by students working together collaboratively in groups of two to four students.

The launch phase promotes a teacher-led class discussion of a problem situation and of related questions to think about, setting the context for the student work to follow. In the second or explore phase, students investigate more focused problems and questions related to the launch situation. This investigative work is followed by a teacher-led class discussion in which students summarize mathematical ideas developed in their groups, providing an opportunity to construct a shared understanding of important concepts, methods, and approaches. Finally, students are given a task to complete on their own, assessing their initial understanding of the concepts and methods.

Each lesson also includes tasks to engage students in Modeling with, Organizing, Reflecting on, and Extending their mathematical understanding. These MORE tasks are central to the learning goals of each lesson and are intended primarily for individual work outside of class. Selection of tasks for use with a class should be based on student performance and the availability of time and technology. Students can exercise some choice of tasks to pursue, and at times they can be given the opportunity to pose their own problems and questions to investigate.

Multiple Approaches to Assessment

Assessing what students know and are able to do is an integral part of *Contemporary Mathematics in Context*, and there are opportunities for assessment in each phase of the instructional cycle. Initially, as students pursue the investigations that make up the curriculum, the teacher is able to informally assess student understanding of mathematical processes and content and their disposition toward mathematics. At the end of each investigation, the "Checkpoint" and accompanying class discussion provide an opportunity for the teacher to assess levels of understanding that various groups of students have reached as they share and summarize their findings. Finally, the "On Your Own" problems and the tasks in the MORE sets provide further opportunities to assess the level of understanding of each individual student. Quizzes, in-class exams, take-home assessment tasks, and extended projects are included in the teacher resource materials.

Acknowledgments

Development and evaluation of the student text materials, teacher materials, assessments, and calculator software for *Contemporary Mathematics in Context* was funded through a grant from the National Science Foundation to the Core-Plus Mathematics Project (CPMP). We are indebted to Midge Cozzens, Director of the NSF Division of Elementary, Secondary, and Informal Education, and our program officers James Sandefur, Eric Robinson, and John Bradley for their support, understanding, and input.

In addition to the NSF grant, a series of grants from the Dwight D. Eisenhower Higher Education Professional Development Program has helped to provide professional development support for Michigan teachers involved in the testing of each year of the curriculum.

Computing tools are fundamental to the use of *Contemporary Mathematics in Context*. Appreciation is expressed to Texas Instruments and, in particular, Dave Santucci for collaborating with us by providing classroom sets of graphing calculators to field-test schools.

As seen on page v, CPMP has been a collaborative effort that has drawn on the talents and energies of teams of mathematics educators at several institutions. This diversity of experiences and ideas has been a particular strength of the project. Special thanks is owed to the exceptionally capable support staff at these institutions, particularly at Western Michigan University.

From the outset, our work has been guided by the advice of an international advisory board consisting of Diane Briars (Pittsburgh Public Schools), Jeremy Kilpatrick (University of Georgia), Kenneth Ruthven (University of Cambridge), David A. Smith (Duke University), and Edna Vasquez (Detroit Renaissance High School). Preliminary versions of the curriculum materials also benefited from careful reviews by the following mathematicians and mathematics educators: Alverna Champion (Grand Valley State University), Cherie Cornick (Wayne County Alliance for Mathematics and Science), Edgar Edwards (formerly of the Virginia State Department of Education), Richard Scheaffer (University of Florida), Martha Siegel (Towson University), Edward Silver (University of Michigan), and Lee Stiff (North Carolina State University).

Our gratitude is expressed to the teachers and students in our 34 evaluation sites listed on pages vi and vii. Their experiences using pilot- and field-test versions of *Contemporary Mathematics in Context* provided constructive feedback and improvements. We learned a lot together about making mathematics meaningful and accessible to a wide range of students.

A very special thank you is extended to Barbara Janson for her interest and encouragement in publishing a core mathematical sciences curriculum that breaks new ground in terms of content, instructional practices, and student assessment. Finally, we want to acknowledge Eric Karnowski for his thoughtful and careful editorial work and express our appreciation to the editorial staff of Glencoe/McGraw-Hill who contributed to the publication of this program.

To the Student

Contemporary Mathematics in Context, Course 3 builds on the mathematical concepts, methods, and habits of mind developed in Courses 1 and 2. With this text, you will continue to learn mathematics by doing mathematics, not by memorizing "worked out" examples. You will investigate important mathematical ideas and ways of thinking as you try to understand and make sense of realistic situations. Because real-world situations and problems often involve data, shape, change, or chance, you will learn fundamental concepts and methods from several strands of mathematics. In particular, you will develop an understanding of broadly useful ideas from algebra and functions, from statistics and probability, from geometry and trigonometry, and from discrete mathematics. You also will see connections among these strands—how they weave together to form the fabric of mathematics.

Because real-world situations and problems are often open-ended, you will find that there may be more than one correct approach and more than one correct solution. Therefore, you will frequently be asked to explain your ideas. You also will increasingly be asked to provide more general arguments or proofs for mathematical statements. This text will provide you with help and practice in reasoning and communicating clearly about mathematics.

Because solving real-world problems often involves teamwork, you will continue to often work collaboratively with a partner or in small groups as you investigate realistic and interesting situations. As in Courses 1 and 2, you will find that two to four students working collaboratively on a problem can often accomplish more than any one of you would working individually. Because technology is commonly used in solving real-world problems, you will continue to use a graphing calculator or computer as a tool to help you understand and make sense of situations and problems you encounter.

As in Courses 1 and 2, you're going to learn a lot of useful mathematics—and it's going to make sense to you. You're going to strengthen your skills in working cooperatively and communicating with others as well. You're also going to strengthen your skills in using technological tools intelligently and effectively. Finally, you'll have plenty of opportunities to be creative and inventive. Enjoy.

Multiple-Variable Models

Linked Variables

Karate is a very impressive form of the martial arts. You may have seen live or video exhibitions of highly trained men and women breaking bricks and boards with chops from their hands, feet, or even heads. Some of you may have even attempted a karate chop and discovered that, without proper technique and training, it can hurt.

Think About This Situation

Karate chops break bricks and boards by applying carefully aimed bursts of energy. Different targets require different amounts of energy. Think about the four target boards pictured here:

1   **2**   **3**   **4**

a Which board do you think would require the greatest energy to break?

b The target boards differ in length and thickness. How would you expect those two variables to affect required breaking energy?

c Breaking energy E depends on board length L and thickness T. What sort of equation might be used to express E as a function of L and T?

d What other variables would you consider in judging the energy required to break a board? How would you expect those variables to be related to each other and to E, L, and T?

INVESTIGATION 1 ▶ Stressed to the Breaking Point

The key factor in those amazing karate exhibitions is actually the speed of the attacking fist or foot. In other situations, the important factor is how much weight a structure like a bridge, beam, or suspension cable can hold without breaking. The breaking weight of any structure certainly depends on the material used. But there are some common patterns relating breaking weight, length, and thickness in every case. You can discover the nature of those relations with a simple experiment!

Collect Data Get several long strands of dry pasta (such as spaghetti, vermicelli, linguine, or fettuccine), some paper clips, a paper cup, and a bunch of pennies or fishing weights. With two desktops or tables as supports and pasta as "bridges," use paper clips to hang the paper cup from the pasta. Add weight until the pasta breaks.

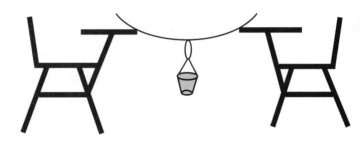

1. Find the breaking weight of one strand of pasta that spans gaps of different lengths. Use lengths from 2 to 6 inches in steps of 1 inch. Then try thicker bridges by using 2, 3, 4, and 5 strands of pasta. Record the (*gap length*, *number of strands*, *breaking weight*) data in a table like the one below.

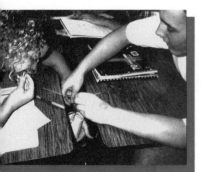

Breaking Weight

		Number of Strands				
		1	2	3	4	5
Gap Length (in.)	2	___	___	___	___	___
	3	___	___	___	___	___
	4	___	___	___	___	___
	5	___	___	___	___	___
	6	___	___	___	___	___

Look for Patterns Study the breaking-weight data from your experiment. Look for patterns that relate the three variables. Then complete the following activities about algebraic models of the relation among thickness, length, and breaking weight.

2. To discover how breaking weight W changes as the thickness T (in number of strands) of the pasta bridge increases, it might help to focus first on the data for bridges 5 inches in length and of several different thicknesses.

   a. Use your graphing calculator or computer software to make a scatterplot of the (T, W) data and to find an equation modeling the relation between those variables.

   b. How is the equation that seems to model the pattern in your (*thickness*, *breaking weight*) data for the 5-inch bridge similar to, and different from, other algebraic equations that you have studied?

   c. Now make scatterplots and find modeling equations relating T and W for bridges of other lengths. Share the workload among members of your group. Compare the results in each case.

   d. Based on your results from Parts a–c, write your conclusions about the way breaking weight seems to change as the thickness of the bridge increases.

3. Examine your experimental data and consider the way breaking weight W changes if only the length L of the pasta bridge increases.

   a. It might help to focus first on the data for a pasta bridge of one strand. Use your graphing calculator or computer software to make a scatterplot of the (L, W) data and to find an equation modeling the relation between those variables.

   b. Next have members of your group share the workload to make scatterplots and find modeling equations relating L and W for bridges of two, three, four, or five strands. Compare the results in each case.

   c. Based on your results from Parts a and b, write your conclusions about the way breaking weight seems to change as the length of the bridge increases.

4. Since breaking weight depends on both bridge length and thickness, it would be helpful to express that joint relation with a single equation. Here are four possibilities that were suggested by students in a class at Arbor High School:

$$W = 10T + L \qquad W = 10T - L \qquad W = 10T \times L \qquad W = \frac{10T}{L}$$

   a. Which of these equations gives patterns that are most similar to the data from your own experiments? How is that equation similar to, and different from, other algebraic rules that you have studied?

   b. How could you modify the rule in Part a to fit the specific numerical data from your own experiments better?

In Investigation 1, you conducted an experiment to explore possible relationships among three variables.

(a) When you try to model a relationship between two or more variables, what sorts of symbolic expressions would you try if

- one variable increases as another increases?
- one variable decreases as another increases?

(b) Given an equation relating three variables, how would you determine how changes in the variables relate to each other?

Be prepared to compare your group's ideas with those of other groups.

On Your Own

The likelihood of a fatal accident in a car, van, or small truck depends on many conditions. Two key variables are speed and mass of the vehicle.

a. What general relationship would you expect among the rate of fatal accidents, speed of the vehicle, and mass of the vehicle?

b. What data on highway accidents would help you find an equation to model the relationship in Part a?

c. If A represents the rate of fatal accidents, s represents vehicle speed, and m represents mass of the vehicle, which of the following equations would you expect to best express the relation among those variables?

  i. $A = 200(s + m)$

 ii. $A = 200(s - m)$

iii. $A = 200\frac{s}{m}$

 iv. $A = 200sm$

INVESTIGATION 2 ▶ Go with the Flow

White-water rafting and kayaking are two of the most exciting water sports. But, for most of us, the closest we get to white water is an amusement park ride! Parks all over the country offer a variety of water slides and rides. In almost every case, those slides and rides depend on a flow of water that is pumped through pipes to the top of the slide or ride.

1. Think about some of the water slides you've experienced or seen in pictures.

    a. If a park pump will lift water to the top of a slide at a rate of 250 gallons per minute, how much water will it provide in

      ■ 15 minutes?

      ■ 30 minutes?

      ■ 60 minutes?

    b. How much water will be pumped in 15 minutes if the pumping rate is increased to

      ■ 500 gallons per minute?

      ■ 750 gallons per minute?

      ■ 1,000 gallons per minute?

    c. Write an equation that expresses total water flow F as a function of pumping rate R and time of operation T.

2. Pumps also are used in a variety of other situations, such as city water systems, oil pipelines, tanker trucks, and farm irrigation systems. For example, jet fuel is pumped from a tanker truck into jet tanks between flights. The faster the task can be completed, the faster the airplane can get into the air again. So speed of refueling is important.

    a. If a tanker truck can pump 1,500 gallons of jet fuel per minute into a plane, how long will it take to load a total of 7,500 gallons into the plane?

    b. Write an equation that gives pumping time T as a function of fuel load F and pumping rate R.

    c. How will the pumping time change if the fuel load F increases? If the pumping rate R increases? How are those patterns of change predicted by the equation relating T, F, and R?

    d. If a tanker took 20 minutes to load 45,000 gallons of fuel in a plane, at what average rate was the tanker's pump operating?

    e. Write an equation that gives pumping rate R as a function of time T and fuel load F.

In much the same way that water is pumped through pipes of various sizes, electrons are pushed through wires to provide power for electrical appliances of all kinds. In a very simple circuit like the one sketched below, a current of electrons moves along a wire, from a battery to a light bulb. In this example, the light bulb converts some of the electrical energy into heat and light energy.

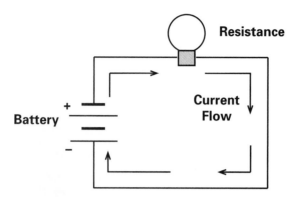

The key variables in such electrical systems are *voltage* (often labeled V and measured in volts), *current* (often labeled I and measured in amperes), and *resistance* (often labeled R and measured in ohms). Those variables are related by a scientific principle called **Ohm's law** that is often expressed as an equation: $I = \frac{V}{R}$.

3. Use Ohm's law to complete a table like the one below, showing the current that can be expected in circuits with several combinations of voltage and resistance.

Current *I* (in amperes)						
		Resistance *R* (in ohms)				
		1	2	3	4	5
Voltage *V* (in volts)	1					
	3					
	6					
	9					
	12					

  a. How does current in an electrical circuit change as voltage increases? As resistance increases?

  b. How could the patterns you noted in Part a be predicted from the form of the algebraic rule relating I to V and R?

4. Electrical instruments can be used to measure the voltage and current in any circuit. With that information, Ohm's law can be used to calculate the resistance of the circuit.

  a. If a kitchen toaster draws a current of 4 amperes on a 120-volt circuit, what is the resistance in the toaster?

b. If the starter of a car draws a current of 15 amperes from a 12-volt battery, what is the resistance of that starter?

c. What equation gives resistance R as a function of voltage V and current I?

d. What equation gives voltage V as a function of current I and resistance R?

Water, jet fuel, and electricity are not the only things that flow or are pumped from one place to another. In hot climates the heat seeps into air-conditioned buildings; in cold climates the heat flows out. Scientists and engineers have worked long and hard to find ways to block undesirable heat flow.

Think about what factors or variables will affect the heat flow out through the windows of an apartment or office building during a cold winter day.

5. One equation for estimating heat flow through a solid material such as glass, wood, or aluminum involves five variables:

$$R = kA\frac{\Delta T}{t}$$

The symbols and what they represent are as follows:

$R = $ Rate of heat flow, in Btu's (British thermal units) per hour

$k = $ Thermal conductivity for the specific material

$A = $ Area of the material, in square feet

$\Delta T = $ Difference in temperature between outside and inside, in degrees Fahrenheit

$t = $ Thickness of the material, in inches

a. Suppose sheets of glass, wood, and aluminum of the same area and thickness are exposed to the same difference in temperature. How would you expect the rate of heat flow to be different for these sheets of material?

b. The thermal conductivity of glass is 5.8. What is the heat-flow rate for a glass window that is 0.5 inches thick and has an area of 6 square feet, on a day when the outside temperature is 5°F and the inside temperature is 68°F?

c. Suppose that, instead of glass, the same window opening is covered with wood having thermal conductivity of 0.78. What is the heat flow for the same temperature condition, if the wood is 0.5 inches thick?

d. The thermal conductivity of aluminum is 1,400. What is the heat flow for the window under the same conditions if the opening is covered with aluminum 0.5 inches thick?

e. Review your response to Part a. Were you correct? If not, modify your response.

f. For this window opening, what thickness of glass would be required to achieve the same heat flow rate as the wood in Part c?

6. Consider the equation relating heat flow to several variables and your responses in Activity 5.

a. The symbol k stands for thermal conductivity of the material. Based on your study of the heat-flow relation, would you conclude that materials with low k are good *conductors* of heat (high flow rate) or good *insulators* (low flow rate)? What would you conclude for materials with high k values? What evidence would you use to support your answers?

b. What changes in the variables A, ΔT, and t would cause the rate of heat flow to increase? To decrease?

c. How are the patterns of change you expect reasonable, based on your thinking about the variables involved?

Checkpoint

The situations in Investigations 1 and 2 involved relations among several variables. In each case, those relations could be expressed well with a single equation showing one variable as a function of several others. Most examples were in the form $z = k \cdot \frac{x}{y}$, where z is a function of x and y, and k is some constant.

a In relations of that type, how will z change as x increases? As x decreases?

b How will z change as y increases? As y decreases?

c How do your answers to Parts a and b apply in the specific case of Ohm's law, which relates electrical current I, voltage V, and resistance R with the equation $I = \frac{V}{R}$?

d If you discover that a relation among z, k, x, and y has the form $z = k \cdot \frac{x}{y}$, what equation expresses the same relationship

■ with y as a function of k, x, and z?

■ with x as a function of k, y, and z?

Be prepared to explain your responses to the entire class.

In the "Power Models" unit of Course 2, you saw that situations in which two quantities vary *directly* with each other could be modeled by equations of the form $y = ax$. Situations in which two quantities vary *inversely* with each other were modeled by rules of the form $y = \frac{a}{x}$. Equations like $z = k \cdot \frac{x}{y}$ are called relations of **combined variation**. It is common to say that *z varies directly with x and inversely with y*.

On Your Own

One important concern of any business is productivity. For example, consider a soft drink factory that has several production lines.

a. If each filling machine in the plant fills 350 bottles per minute, how long will it take such a machine to fill the 70,000 bottles of the factory's soda drunk each day in Detroit, Michigan?

b. At what speed would the machine need to operate in order to fill 70,000 bottles in one 8-hour work shift?

c. How many bottles will be filled if the machine operates at a rate of 450 bottles per minute for an 8-hour shift?

d. Write equations showing the relation among filling rate R in bottles per minute, time T in minutes, and total number of bottles filled B. Express the relation in three different ways:

- B is a function of R and T.

- R is a function of B and T.

- T is a function of B and R.

e. For each equation in Part d, explain the changes in the output variable that will result from increases of each input variable. For example: In the case of the first equation, if R increases, how will B change? If T increases, how will B change?

INVESTIGATION ▶3 Combining Rates and Times

Equations relating several variables often can be combined to produce models of even more complex processes. For example, the Kalamazoo Bottling Company might have two production lines for bottling spring water: Machine 1 fills 300 bottles per minute and Machine 2 fills 200 bottles per minute. The total production of the plant is a function of the time that each machine operates.

1. The machines might be run for different amounts of time.

  a. How many bottles will Machine 1 fill in 30 minutes? In 400 minutes? In T_1 minutes?

  b. Copy and complete the table below to show the total production from different combinations of operating times (in minutes) of the two machines.

Combining Rates and Times 1

Machine 1 Time T_1 (in minutes)	Machine 1 Production	Machine 2 Time T_2 (in minutes)	Machine 2 Production	Total Production P
480		240		
480		180		
420		300		
360		360		

  c. Write a single equation relating total production of the plant P to time that the first machine is run T_1 and time that the second machine is run T_2.

2. Suppose that the second bottling machine is older and more expensive to operate, so the plant manager wants to use it as little as necessary to fill production quotas.

  a. Calculate the operating time needed for Machine 2 in each of the following cases.

Combining Rates and Times 2

Machine 1 Time T_1 (in minutes)	Machine 2 Time T_2 (in minutes)	Total Production P
420		144,000
480		156,000
480		168,000
600		234,000

b. Describe (in words) the calculations required to find the operating time of Machine 2 for various combinations of the other rate, time, and production figures. Then write an equation showing T_2 as a function of the other variables T_1 and P.

The rate-time-amount relations among variables in the spring water problem occur in many other, quite different situations. For example, most American students and workers spend a great deal of time commuting to and from school or work every day. When we have choices, we are always on the lookout for routes that reduce the distance or time and increase the average speed. The route home is often different in distance, average speed, and time from the route to school or work because of factors like one-way streets, errands, and so on.

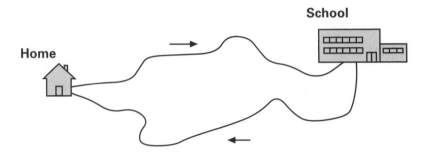

3. Study the data about the following commutes and then find the round-trip distance traveled in each case.

   a. Commute to work in 0.6 hour at an average speed of 25 miles per hour and home from work in 1.0 hour at an average speed of 20 miles per hour.

   b. Commute to school in $\frac{1}{3}$ hour at an average speed of 30 miles per hour and home from school in $\frac{1}{2}$ hour at an average speed of 24 miles per hour.

   c. Commute to work in 1.5 hours at an average speed of 40 miles per hour and home from work in 2.0 hours at an average speed of 30 miles per hour.

4. Write an equation expressing the relationship among the following five variables, using the given letter names.

   D = total commuting distance (in miles)

   S_1 = average speed to work or school (in miles per hour)

   S_2 = average speed home from work or school (in miles per hour)

   T_1 = time to work or school (in hours)

   T_2 = time home from work or school (in hours)

5. Use the relation in Activity 4 to answer each of the following questions.

   a. A commuter's round-trip was 45 miles. The trip to work took $\frac{1}{2}$ hour at an average speed of 40 miles per hour, and the trip home took $\frac{2}{3}$ hour. What was the average speed on the trip home?

   b. If a school bus takes 0.75 hour to cover its morning route at an average speed of 20 miles per hour and 0.5 hour in the afternoon at an average speed of 25 miles per hour, what total distance does the bus travel?

   c. If an airplane makes a 5,200-mile trip from New York to Los Angeles and back, averaging 450 miles per hour on the 6-hour outbound leg and 550 miles per hour on the return, how long does the return trip take?

6. Rewrite the equation you wrote in Activity 4 to do the following.

   a. Express time going to school or work T_1 as a function of the time returning home T_2, the total distance traveled D, and the average speeds of the two parts of the trip S_1 and S_2. (That is, **solve the equation** in Activity 4 **for T_1**.)

   b. Express average speed returning home S_2 as a function of the other four variables. (That is, solve the equation in Activity 4 for S_2.)

Checkpoint

The situations in Investigation 3 involved combinations of several variables in the general form $z = ax + by$.

   ⓐ What quantities were represented by z, a, x, b, and y in the problems about spring water bottling at Kalamazoo Bottling?

   ⓑ What quantities were represented by z, a, x, b, and y in the problems about distance, time, and average speed for commuters to school or work?

   ⓒ In what ways were the equations you derived to model spring water bottling and commuting similar?

   ⓓ How can the relation $P = 300T_1 + 200T_2$ be expressed in another equivalent form that shows T_1 as a function of P and T_2?

   Be prepared to share your group's responses and thinking with the class.

In planning entertainment events like concerts, plays, or sports games, one of the first problems is estimating the number of people who will attend and how the attendance will depend on ticket prices. Then you have to use that information to estimate income from ticket sales.

When Friends of Riverview Hospital decided to sponsor a benefit concert in their community's auditorium, they chose two ticket prices: $5 for students under 18 years of age and $8 for adults 18 or older. Children under 5 will be admitted free of charge.

a. What total ticket income will the concert generate for the following combinations of ticket sales?

- 200 students and 350 adults

- 150 students and 400 adults

b. Write an equation that gives income as a function of the numbers of tickets sold to students and to adults.

c. Suppose that the concert planners have a goal of $5,000 in ticket income and they expect to sell 500 tickets to students under 18. How many adult tickets must be sold to reach the income goal?

d. If the income goal is set at $7,000, what equation shows how the number of adult ticket sales needed to meet that goal depends on the number of tickets that will be sold to students?

e. If the planners want to consider the relation among a variety of ticket prices (*k* for students and *a* for adults), ticket sales (*x* for students and *y* for adults), and ticket income *I*, what equation expresses the connection among all five variables?

INVESTIGATION 4 ▶ Taking Algebraic X-Rays

Many times in mathematics you encounter two very different situations that turn out to have the same basic structure. If you take an "x-ray" that looks beneath the surface of the situations, you find the same mathematical "skeleton." For example, the relations among variables in Investigations 1, 2, and 3 all led to equations in three basic forms:

$$z = xy \qquad z = \frac{x}{y} \qquad z = ax + by$$

Because those forms occur so often, it helps to be good at predicting the patterns of change that each form implies. It also helps to be good at writing the given equations in other equivalent forms that might be useful for answering particular questions.

1. List the various relations among variables encountered in the previous three investigations and sort them in groups according to the three types at the bottom of page 14.

2. Consider the equation $z = xy$.

   a. How will z change as x increases and y is held constant?

   b. How will z change as x decreases and y is held constant?

   c. How will z change if x is held constant and y varies?

   d. Express or solve for x in terms of z and y.

   e. Express or solve for y in terms of z and x.

   f. Suppose $z = k(xy)$ for some constant k. How would your answers to Parts a–e change?

3. Consider the equation $z = \frac{x}{y}$.

   a. How will z change as x increases (or decreases) and y is held constant?

   b. How will z change as y changes and x is held constant?

   c. Express x in terms of z and y.

   d. Solve for y in terms of z and x.

   e. What reasoning supports your answers to Parts c and d?

   f. Suppose $z = k \cdot \frac{x}{y}$ for some constant k. How would your answers to Parts a–e change?

4. Consider the equation $z = ax + by$.

   a. Express or solve for x in terms of a, b, y, and z.

   b. Express a in terms of b, x, y, and z.

   c. Solve for y in terms of a, b, x, and z.

   d. Express b in terms of a, x, y, and z.

   e. What common reasoning pattern supports your answers to Parts a–d?

   f. If a and b are both positive numbers, how will z change as x or y increases?

5. When solving an equation for one variable in terms of the others, you used strategies involving basic *properties of equality* such as subtracting the same number from both sides of the equation or multiplying (or dividing) both sides of the equation by the same nonzero number. Properties of equality and the strategies for rewriting algebraic equations in equivalent forms often are used in solving problems involving proportions.

   a. Explain why the equation $\frac{a}{b} = \frac{c}{d}$ is equivalent to $ad = bc$.

   b. Explain why $\frac{a}{b} = \frac{c}{d}$ is equivalent to $\frac{b}{a} = \frac{d}{c}$.

Suppose you have modeled a situation involving three linked variables x, y, and z.

a How will the value of z change as values of x and y change when $z = xy$? When $z = \frac{x}{y}$? When $z = ax + by$, for various values of a and b?

b In what alternate forms can you express each of the equations in Part a? How do you know that the alternate forms are equivalent to the originals? In each case, how could you use properties of equality to convince someone else that your conclusions are correct?

Be prepared to share your thinking and methods with the class.

On Your Own

Solve each equation below and explain how you used properties of equality in the solution process.

a. Solve $z = 5xy$ for y in terms of x and z.

b. Solve $a = \frac{b}{c}$ for c in terms of a and b.

c. Solve $r = \frac{5s}{t}$ for s in terms of r and t.

d. Solve $p = 8m - 5n$ for m in terms of p and n.

e. Solve $\frac{a}{x} = \frac{b}{c}$ for x in terms of a, b, and c.

MORE
Modeling • Organizing • Reflecting • Extending

Modeling

These tasks provide opportunities for you to use the ideas you have learned in the investigations. Each task asks you to model and solve problems in other situations.

1. You may recall from past courses how compound interest causes a savings account to grow at an exponential rate. There is another type of interest called *simple interest*. That interest i depends on the principal invested p, the annual interest rate paid by the bank r, and the time in years for which the money is invested t.

a. How much simple interest will be earned by an account if $500 is invested at 4% annual interest for 1 year?

b. How much simple interest will be earned by an account of $500 at 8% annual interest for 1 year?

c. How much simple interest will be earned by an account if $1,000 is invested at 8% annual interest over 2 years? (With simple interest, any interest earned in the first year is *not* added to the principal when calculating interest for the second year.)

d. Write an equation that expresses simple interest earned as a function of principal invested, annual interest rate, and time in years.

e. What interest rate is required to earn $150 simple interest on $1,000 invested over 2 years?

f. Write an equation that expresses interest rate as a function of principal, time, and simple interest to be earned.

g. What savings deposit (principal) is required to earn simple interest of $75 in two years if the account pays 6% annual interest?

2. Recall that the perimeter P of any rectangle can be expressed as a function of the length L and width W of that rectangle in two equivalent ways: $P = 2L + 2W$ or $P = 2(L + W)$.

a. Find the perimeter of a rectangle that is 5 meters long and 3 meters wide.

b. Find the length of a rectangle that is to have perimeter 45 meters and width 5 meters.

c. Write an equation expressing length L as a function of perimeter and width of any rectangle. (Do this in two different ways, and check that the two ways produce the same results when specific values for P and W are given.)

d. Write an equation expressing width W as a function of perimeter and length of any rectangle. (Do this in two different ways, and check that the two ways produce the same results when specific values for P and L are given.)

e. Suppose you wished to determine the maximum area of a rectangular garden that could be enclosed with 50 meters of flexible fencing.

- Which of the equations in this task would be most useful in this regard?
- How would you use the equation to find the maximum area?
- What is your best estimate of the maximum area and of the dimensions of the enclosing rectangle?

3. Have you ever noticed that when you use a tire pump on a bicycle tire, the tire warms up as the air pressure inside increases? This illustrates a basic principle of science relating pressure P, volume V, and temperature T in a container: for any specific system, the value of the expression $\frac{PV}{T}$ remains the same even when the individual variables change.

a. For the expression $\frac{PV}{T}$ to remain constant, what changes in pressure or volume (or both) must result when the temperature increases?

b. What changes in volume or temperature must result when the pressure increases?

c. What changes in pressure or volume must result when the temperature decreases?

4. In many consumer businesses, packaging is an important factor in sales. Whether it's cosmetics, food, calculators, or toys, the manufacturer tries to design a package that is attractive but not too expensive to make. That often involves making choices among shapes and sizes of the package options.

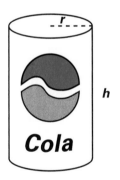

Many foods are packaged in cylindrical cans, and the volume each can holds is determined by its radius and height.

a. Express volume as a function of radius and height.

b. If the volume is fixed at 144 cubic inches, what equation would be helpful in showing how to calculate the height for various possible radii?

c. What is the height of a can that holds 144 cubic inches, if its radius is 2.5 in? If its radius is 3 in? Make sketches of the two cans.

d. Using the expression for height in Part b, write an equation for the surface area of the can in terms of the radius r.

e. Which of the two cans in Part c would take less material to make?

f. Which would be more appropriate as a beverage can? Why?

Organizing

These tasks will help you organize the mathematics you have learned in the investigations and connect it with other mathematics.

1. In Course 1, you may have discovered the formula $V + F = E + 2$, which relates the number of vertices V, the number of faces F, and the number of edges E of simple polyhedra. A proof of this formula was first provided by the Swiss mathematician, Leonhard Euler in 1752. The relation is often called **Euler's formula**.

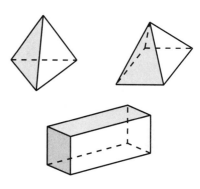

   a. What are V, E, and F for a triangular pyramid? Check Euler's formula.

   b. What are V, E, and F for a square pyramid? Check Euler's formula.

   c. What are V, E, and F for a rectangular box? Check Euler's formula.

   d. Write an equivalent form of Euler's formula that expresses E as a function of V and F. Check your answer for the polyhedra given in Parts a–c.

   e. Write an equivalent form of the Euler equation that expresses F as a function of V and E. Check your answer.

2. Recall that you can use two points on a line to determine an equation for the line. Suppose two points in a coordinate plane have coordinates (x_1, y_1) and (x_2, y_2).

   a. Write a formula that gives the slope b of the line containing the two points.

   b. Solve the equation in Part a for y_1 in terms of the other variables.

   c. In your equation from Part b, replace the point with coordinates (x_1, y_1) with a general point (x, y) on the line. Explain how this equation is now that of a line with slope b through the point (x_2, y_2).

   d. Use your equation from Part c to write the equation of the line that contains the points $(8, 12)$ and has slope -2. What is the y-intercept of this line?

3. Suppose two points in a coordinate plane have coordinates (x_1, y_1) and (x_2, y_2).

   a. Write a formula that gives the coordinates (x_m, y_m) of the midpoint of the segment joining those two points.

   b. Use the formula in Part a to find the midpoint of the segment joining $(2, 3)$ and $(7, 5)$.

   c. If $(12, 10)$ is the midpoint of the segment joining (x_2, y_2) and $(3, 5)$, what are the coordinates (x_2, y_2)?

   d. Write a formula that could be used to find one endpoint of a line segment when the other endpoint and the midpoint are given.

4. Formulas linking several variables are common in other school subjects and technical careers. Using mathematical ideas and methods of this lesson, you can make sense of many new situations. Test your skills in the following settings.

a. When providing intravenous fluids for patients needing additional body fluids, health care professionals use the relation $D = \frac{V}{4T}$, where D is the drip rate in drops per minute, V is the prescribed volume of fluid in ccs (cubic centimeters), and T is the prescribed amount of time in hours for the fluid to be given.

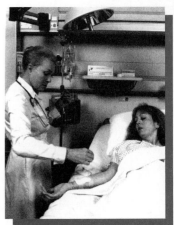

- Rewrite this equation, expressing T as a function of D and V.

- In what kinds of situations would this equivalent equation be useful?

b. During the winter, many people are interested not only in the temperature outside, but also in the *windchill*. The windchill tells how cold it seems when the wind is taken into account. One formula for quickly estimating windchill combines the actual temperature t in degrees Fahrenheit and the wind speed w in miles per hour to give windchill C: $C = t - 1.5w$.

- Solve this equation for w in terms of C and t.

- What information can you get readily from the equivalent equation?

c. Various formulas exist for determining medicinal dosages for children when adult dosages have been specified. One such formula, Clark's rule, is based on the weight w of the child. The formula is $C = \frac{wd}{150}$, where C is the child's dosage and d is the adult dosage.

- At what weight are the two dosages equal?

- Write a rule that expresses adult dosage as a function of weight and child dosage. Under what circumstances might such a rule be useful?

d. In building highways it is necessary to provide for expansion joints, or the highway will expand, buckle, and break on very hot days. Engineers are able to figure how much expansion must be allowed by using the formula $I = 0.000012L(T - t)$, where I is the amount of expansion at temperature T in degrees Fahrenheit; t is the temperature in degrees Fahrenheit at which the highway was built; and L is the length of the highway under construction. (Units for I are the same as for L.)

- Which form would be easier to use in calculating the amount of expansion $I = 0.000012L(T - t)$ or $I = 0.000012LT - 0.000012Lt$? Why?

- Under what conditions can no expansion be expected?

5. Based on the patterns you've discovered in working with multiple-variable models of many different situations, do the following:

a. Solve $d = rt$ for r in terms of d and t.

b. Solve $p = 4q + 12r$ for q in terms of p and r. Then solve for r in terms of p and q.

c. Solve $u = \frac{5v}{w}$ for w in terms of u and v. Then solve for v in terms of u and w.

d. Express the relation $6x + 4y = 24$ in an equivalent form where y is a function of x.

e. Express the relation $P = \frac{VT}{R}$ in an equivalent form where T is a function of P, V, and R.

f. For right $\triangle ABC$, $\tan B = \frac{b}{a}$. Solve this equation for b and then for a.

6. Solve the following proportions.

a. $\frac{2}{3} = \frac{x}{12}$

b. $\frac{t}{8} = \frac{3}{5}$

c. $\frac{9}{x} = \frac{3}{5}$

d. $\frac{23}{42} = \frac{10}{x}$

7. Rewrite each of the following equations for lines in the equivalent form $y = a + bx$ and determine the slope and y-intercept of each line.

a. $2x + 3y = 9$

b. $7 = 8x - 5y$

c. $12 = 8y - 5x$

d. $-4x + 3y = 15$

Reflecting

These tasks will help you think about what the mathematics you have learned means to you. These tasks also will help you think about what you do and do not understand.

1. Look back at the pasta-breaking experiment in Investigation 1. What are the independent and dependent variables in that experiment?

2. Think about your previous studies in mathematics and in other school subjects.

a. Give an example of an equation from a previous mathematics course (different from those in this lesson) that involves a relation among several variables. Identify the variables and explain the equation used.

b. Give an example of a formula from another school subject that involves a relation among several variables. Identify the variables and explain how the formula is used.

3. The principles that govern flow of electricity often are described in language that talks about flow, like water through a system of pipes, valves, and pumps.

    a. If you think about a water hose connected to an outdoor faucet, what elements of the situation correspond to the following:

- Current
- Resistance
- Voltage

    b. What would it mean to increase or decrease "voltage" in the water faucet model, and how does change in "voltage" affect flow of "current"?

    c. What would it mean to increase or decrease "resistance" in the water faucet model, and how does change in "resistance" affect flow of "current"?

4. The basic principle underlying the operation of air conditioners and heat pumps involves a relation between pressure, volume, and temperature in a container. Check with someone who knows about heating and cooling, and report how those variables change when the machinery is in operation.

Extending

Tasks in this section provide opportunities for you to explore further or more deeply the mathematics you are learning.

1. If a charter bus averages 30 miles per hour on the 90-mile trip from Baltimore to Philadelphia, how fast would it have to drive on the return trip in order to average 60 miles per hour for the entire round trip?

2. Rectangular boxes are probably the most common shapes used for packing. You know that any such box shape is determined by three measurements: length, width, and height.

    a. Write equations that express the following measurements in terms of the dimensions.

- Total surface area A of the box
- Volume V of the box

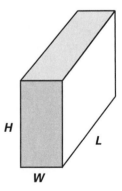

b. In designing packages, producers often decide first on the volume the box should hold. Then they have to see what combinations of dimensions would give that volume. Suppose a distributor of breakfast cereal wants the large economy-size container to hold 720 cubic inches of cereal.

- ◼ If the length and width of the box are to be 12 inches and 4 inches, respectively, what should the height of the box be?

- ◼ If the height of the box is to be 12 inches and the width 5 inches, what should the length of the box be?

- ◼ If the bottom of the box is to be a square and the height is to be 20 inches, what will the dimensions of the bottom be?

c. If a shipping box is to have fixed volume of 600 cubic inches, what equations would be convenient for calculating the following?

- ◼ Required height for many different combinations of length and width

- ◼ Required length for many different combinations of height and width

- ◼ Required width for many different combinations of height and length

d. Which box from Part b would take the least cardboard to produce?

3. When several electrical appliances are drawing power from the same supply circuit in your home, the current drawn by the total circuit is the sum of the currents drawn by the separate appliances. The voltage remains constant at the standard 120 volts for household use in the United States. So if two appliances with resistances R_1 and R_2 are operating at the same time, the current flow will be given by the following:

$$I = \frac{120}{R_1} + \frac{120}{R_2}$$

a. If a microwave with resistance 25 ohms and a refrigerator with resistance 15 ohms are operating at the same time on a kitchen circuit, what current is used?

b. Suppose a television and a hairdryer are both operating from the same bedroom circuit, drawing a total current of 6.5 amps. If the resistance of the hairdryer is 20 ohms, what is the resistance of the television set?

4. Refer to Modeling Task 4 on page 18. Suppose a container-manufacturing company is to design and manufacture cylindrical cans for 2-cycle lawn mower engine oil. The volume of each can is to be 0.236 liter. (Note that $1 \text{ cm}^3 = 1 \text{ mL}$.)

   a. In order to minimize the cost of materials, the company wishes to design a can that requires the smallest amount of metal possible. What should the dimensions of the can be?

   b. Compare your dimensions in Part a with those of a 0.236-liter can in a local hardware store. Write a brief report of your findings.

5. On many rivers the flow of water is determined by the rate at which water is released from behind power station dams. This is the case on the Savage River in western Maryland, a popular white-water river for kayaking. The speed of a river's current is also affected by the depth of water and the width of the river.

   Imagine yourself floating down the Savage River in a kayak or on a raft.

   a. How will your speed be related to the rate of water release, the width of the river at various spots, and the depth of the river at various spots?

   b. What sort of algebraic equation would show the way that speed is a function of water release rate, stream depth, and stream width?

Lesson 2

Algebra, Geometry, and Trigonometry

The highest point on the Earth's surface is the peak of Mount Everest in the Himalaya mountain range along the Tibet-Nepal border in Asia. The mountain is named after a geographer, Sir George Everest, who was the first English surveyor-general of colonial India. But the Tibetan name of *Chomo-Lungma* or Mother Goddess of the World seems a more appropriate title.

The most recent calculations indicate that *Chomo-Lungma* rises 8,872 meters (29,108 feet) above sea level. As early as 1850, surveyors had estimated the height of that peak with error of only 0.4%. The first climbers known to actually reach the summit were Tenzing Norgay and Edmund Hillary in 1953.

Think About This Situation

In previous courses, you learned several mathematical relationships and strategies for calculating heights, depths, and distances that could not be measured directly.

a How do you suppose early surveyors estimated the height of Mount Everest without reaching the peak themselves?

b What modern measuring tools might make that task easier?

c What strategies could you use to find the heights of other very tall objects such as skyscrapers, radio or television towers, smokestacks, or trees?

INVESTIGATION 1 ▶ Triangulation

One of the most effective strategies for calculating distances to points that cannot be reached is to model the situation with a triangle in which the segment of unknown length is one side and other parts can be measured. If you can make the model a right triangle, there are several ways to calculate the unknown length.

Study the diagram below of a radio transmission tower with two support wires attached to it and to the ground.

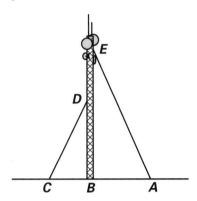

1. First focus on the triangle formed by the tower, the ground, and the shorter support wire.

   a. If $CB = 50$ feet and $BD = 100$ feet, how long is the support wire $\overline{CD}$?

   b. If you were asked to attach a support wire, 125 feet long, from point C to the tower, how high up the tower would you have to climb?

   c. What general relationship among sides of a right triangle have you used in answering Parts a and b?

   d. Refer to the diagram at the right. What calculations are required to find a missing length in a right triangle when the lengths of both legs (r and p) are known? What if the length of one leg and the hypotenuse (r and q, or p and q) are known?

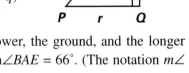

2. Next, focus on the triangle formed by the tower, the ground, and the longer support wire $\overline{AE}$. Length $AB = 75$ feet and m∠$BAE = 66°$. (The notation m∠ is read *the measure of angle... .*)

   a. How long is the support wire from A to E?

   b. How high up the tower is point E, where the support wire from A is attached?

   c. What is the degree measure of ∠AEB?

   d. How could you use the measure of ∠AEB and the length of $\overline{AB}$ to calculate the lengths of $\overline{EB}$ and $\overline{EA}$?

3. Refer to your work in Part a of Activity 1. Use the information to estimate the measures of ∠BCD and ∠BDC.

4. Think again about the problem of finding the height (above sea level) of Mount Everest or of other very tall structures. What measurements would allow you to calculate heights that cannot be measured directly? What mathematical principles and relationships would you need to make the calculations?

Checkpoint

The activities in Investigation 1 required combinations of facts about several parts of right triangles to find information about other parts.

ⓐ What general principle relates the lengths of the sides of a right triangle? How can that relationship be used to calculate the length of one side when the other two are known?

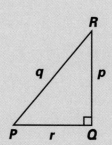

ⓑ What general relationships connect side and angle measurements in any right triangle? How can those relationships be used to calculate the unknown length of one side when another side length and angle measurement are given?

Be prepared to explain these right triangle relationships and their use to your classmates.

On Your Own

The following sketch shows the start of one surveyor's attempt to determine the height of a tall mountain without climbing to the top herself.

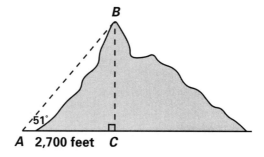

a. Use the given information to calculate the lengths of $\overline{AB}$ and $\overline{BC}$.

b. Suppose that a laser ranging device allowed you to find the length of $\overline{AB}$ and the angle of elevation $\angle BAC$, but you could not measure the length of $\overline{AC}$. How could you use this information (instead of the information from the diagram) to calculate the lengths of $\overline{AC}$ and $\overline{BC}$?

INVESTIGATION 2 The Law of Sines

As you worked on the activities in Investigation 1, you found several ways that the Pythagorean Theorem and the trigonometric ratios (sine, cosine, and tangent) could be used to calculate unknown side lengths of right triangles. If the triangle isn't (or might not be) a right triangle, it's not so easy to model the situation involving the unknown distance, but it can be done.

For example, suppose that two park rangers who are in towers 10 miles apart in a national forest spot a fire that is uphill and far away from both. Suppose that one ranger recognizes the fire location and knows that it is about 4.9 miles from that tower. With this information and the angles given in the diagram below, the rangers can calculate the distance of the fire from the other tower.

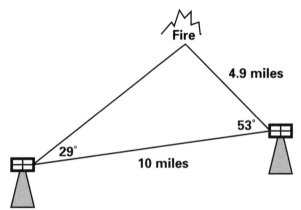

One way to start working on this problem is to divide the obtuse triangle into two right triangles as shown below:

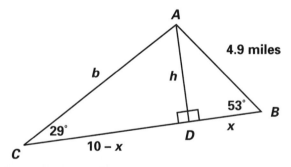

At first that does not seem to help much. Instead of two segments of unknown length, there are now four! On the other hand, there are now three triangles in which you can seek useful relationships among the known sides and angles.

1. Use trigonometry or the Pythagorean relationship for right triangles to find the length of $\overline{AC}$. When you have one sequence of calculations that gives the desired result, see if you can find a different approach.

2. In one Maryland class, a group presented their solution to Activity 1 and claimed that it was the slickest, quickest method possible. Check each step in their reasoning and explain why each step is or is not correct.

   (1) $\dfrac{h}{b} = \sin 29°$ (3) $\dfrac{h}{4.9} = \sin 53°$

   (2) $h = b \sin 29°$ (4) $h = 4.9 \sin 53°$

   (5) $b \sin 29° = 4.9 \sin 53°$

   (6) $b = \dfrac{4.9 \sin 53°}{\sin 29°}$

   (7) $b = 8.07$ miles

   Compare your solution with this reported solution.

3. The approach in Activity 2 to calculating the unknown side length of a triangle that is not itself a right triangle illustrates a very useful general relationship among sides and angles of *any* triangle. Explain why each step in the following derivation is correct.

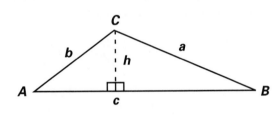

   (1) $\dfrac{h}{b} = \sin A$

   (2) $h = b \sin A$

   (3) $\dfrac{h}{a} = \sin B$

   (4) $h = a \sin B$

   (5) $b \sin A = a \sin B$

   (6) $\dfrac{\sin A}{a} = \dfrac{\sin B}{b}$

The relationship derived in Activity 3 holds in any triangle and for all three sides and angles as well. It is called the **Law of Sines** and can be written in two equivalent forms:

In any triangle ABC with sides of lengths a, b, and c opposite $\angle A$, $\angle B$, and $\angle C$, respectively:

$$\frac{\sin A}{a} = \frac{\sin B}{b} = \frac{\sin C}{c}$$

or equivalently,

$$\frac{a}{\sin A} = \frac{b}{\sin B} = \frac{c}{\sin C}.$$

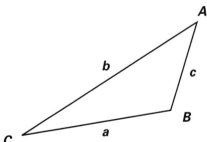

You can use this important relationship to calculate measures of angles and lengths of sides in triangles with even less given information than the fire-spotting problem at the beginning of this investigation. In practice, you only need to use the equality of two of the ratios at any one time.

4. Suppose that the two rangers spot another fire in a different spot, indicated on the next diagram. Use what you know about angles in a triangle and the Law of Sines to find the distances from each tower to the fire.

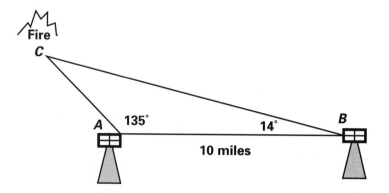

5. In parallelogram *ABCD* below, information is given about one side and two angles formed by the diagonals $\overline{AC}$ and $\overline{BD}$.

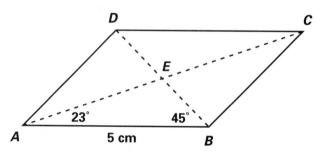

a. Recall from your previous study of mathematics that a parallelogram has 180° rotational symmetry about the point of intersection of its diagonals. Verify this fact by tracing parallelogram *ABCD* on a sheet of paper and rotating the paper about point *E*.

b. Use facts about triangles and the rotational symmetry property of parallelograms to find as much additional information as you can about the other 7 segments and 10 angles in the given figure. Do *not* use trigonometry.

c. Use the Law of Sines to find further information about the segments and angles in the figure.

The Law of Sines states a relation among sides and angles of any triangle. It can be used to find unknown side lengths or angle measures from given information. Suppose you have modeled a situation with $\triangle PQR$ as shown below.

a What combinations of information about the sides and angles of $\triangle PQR$ will allow you to find the length of $\overline{QR}$? How would you use that information to calculate QR?

b What combinations of information about the sides and angles of $\triangle PQR$ will allow you to find the measure of $\angle Q$? How would you use that information to calculate $m\angle Q$?

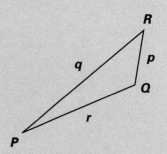

Be prepared to explain your thinking to the entire class.

On Your Own

A commuter airplane, off course over the Atlantic Ocean, reported experiencing mechanical problems around 9:15 P.M. The pilot sent two calls, one to Boston Logan International Airport and one to the regional airport in nearby Beverly. Air traffic controllers at the two airports reported the angles shown in the diagram below. How far was the plane from the closer airport?

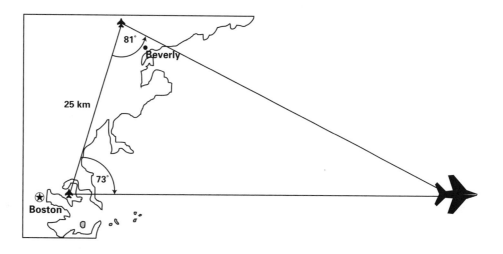

INVESTIGATION 3 The Law of Cosines

For all right triangles, the Pythagorean Theorem shows how the lengths of the two legs and the hypotenuse are related to each other. When that relationship is expressed as an equation, it is possible to solve for any one of the variables in terms of the others. It's natural to wonder what is so special about right triangles and how the relationship among the sides changes as the right angle changes to an acute or obtuse angle.

1. Consider a linkage with two sides of fixed length: 12 cm and 16 cm. Here $AC = 12$ cm and $BC = 16$ cm.

   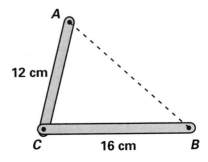

   a. What is the distance from A to B when the angle at C is a right angle?

   b. How does the distance from A to B change as $\overline{AC}$ is rotated to make smaller and smaller angles at C? How does that distance change if $\overline{AC}$ is rotated to make larger angles at C?

2. Using an actual physical linkage or careful drawings, test your answers to Activity 1 by carefully measuring the distance from point A to point B in these cases:

   a. $m\angle C = 30°$

   b. $m\angle C = 70°$

   c. $m\angle C = 130°$

   d. $m\angle C = 150°$

3. Why is it impossible to check the measured distances in Activity 2 by calculations using the Law of Sines, without getting more information?

There is a second trigonometric principle for finding relationships among side lengths and angle measures of any triangle. It is called the **Law of Cosines**.

In any triangle ABC with sides of lengths a, b, and c opposite ∠A, ∠B, and ∠C, respectively:

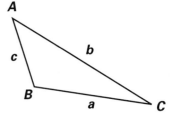

$$c^2 = a^2 + b^2 - 2ab \cos C$$

This is another of those very useful equations that link several geometric variables.

4. The Law of Cosines states a relation among the lengths of three sides of a triangle and the cosine of an angle of the triangle. If you know the lengths of two sides and the measure of the angle between the two sides, you can calculate the length of the third side.

a. State in words how you would calculate the length c in $\triangle ABC$ if you know a, b, and the measure of $\angle C$.

b. Write the Law of Cosines to calculate the length a in $\triangle ABC$ if you know b, c, and the measure of $\angle A$.

c. Write a third form of the Law of Cosines for $\triangle ABC$, for when you know the measure of $\angle B$.

d. Suppose in $\triangle PQR$ you needed to calculate the length of $\overline{QR}$. What information would you need in order to use the Law of Cosines? Write the equation you would use.

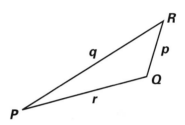

e. Suppose in $\triangle PQR$ you knew m$\angle P$, m$\angle R$, and the lengths p and r. Could you find the length q using the Law of Cosines? Explain your reasoning.

f. Using the information given in Part e, how could you find the length q using the Law of Sines? Which method would you prefer to use? Why?

5. Surveyors often are faced with irregular polygonal regions for which they are asked to locate and stake out boundaries, determine elevations, and estimate areas. Some of these tasks can be accomplished by using a site map and a transit as shown in the photo below. In one subdivision of property near a midsize city, a plot of land had the shape and dimensions shown.

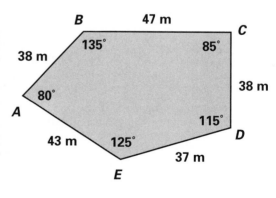

Examine the triangulation of the plot shown below.

a. How can the Law of Cosines be used to find AC?

b. Find AC to the nearest tenth of a meter.

c. How can the Law of Cosines be used to find AD?

d. Find AD to the nearest tenth of a meter.

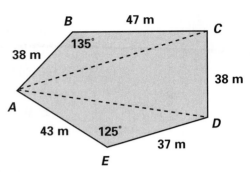

6. The Law of Cosines, $c^2 = a^2 + b^2 - 2ab\cos C$, states a relation among the lengths of three sides of a triangle ABC and the cosine of an angle of the triangle. If you know the lengths of all three sides of a triangle, you can calculate the cosine of an angle and then determine the measure of the angle itself.

a. Solve the equation $c^2 = a^2 + b^2 - 2ab\cos C$ for $\cos C$.

b. Using your results from Activity 5, find the measure of $\angle BAC$ to the nearest tenth of a degree. What is the measure of the third angle in $\triangle ABC$?

c. Now find the area of $\triangle ABC$.

d. Explain how you could determine the area of the entire pentagonal plot.

7. Now that you understand how to use the Law of Cosines, examine more closely its symbolic form and the information it conveys. Consider again the linkage with arms of lengths 12 cm and 16 cm positioned at various possible angles.

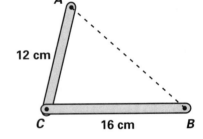

a. Record your data from Activity 2 in a copy of the table below. Then, using a physical linkage or careful drawings, complete the remainder of your table, showing how the distance from the end of one arm to the other changes as the angle at link point C changes.

m$\angle C$	30°	50°	70°	90°	110°	130°	150°
Length AB							

b. Now add a row to your table from Part a showing corresponding values of $2ab \cos C$.

m∠C	30°	50°	70°	90°	110°	130°	150°
Length *AB*							
$2ab \cos C$							

c. What is cos *C* when m∠*C* = 90°, and how does that simplify the equation for the Law of Cosines?

d. In what sense does the term "$2ab \cos C$" act as a *correction term*, adjusting the Pythagorean relationship for triangles in which ∠*C* is not a right angle?

8. As you have seen, the Law of Sines and the Law of Cosines can be used to find the measures of unknown angles as well as sides. You have to study given information about side and angle measurements to decide which law to apply. Then you have to work with the resulting equations to solve for the unknown angle or side measurements.

For example, suppose that two sides, $\overline{AB}$ and $\overline{BC}$, and a diagonal, $\overline{AC}$, of a parallelogram *ABCD* measure 7 cm, 9 cm, and 11 cm, respectively.

a. Draw and label a sketch of such a figure.

b. Which of the two trigonometric laws can be used to find the measure of an angle in that parallelogram?

c. Find the measure of an angle to the nearest tenth of a degree.

d. The diagonal *AC* splits the parallelogram *ABCD* into two triangles. Find the remaining measures of the angles in those triangles.

e. Find the length of diagonal *BD*.

Checkpoint

Consider △*ABC* shown at the right.

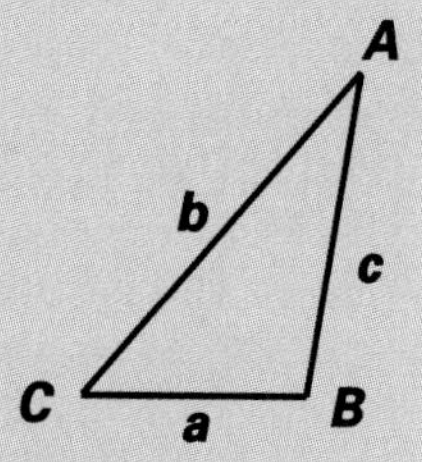

ⓐ What information would you need to know in order to use the Law of Cosines to find the length of $\overline{AC}$? What equation would you use to find that length?

ⓑ What information would you need to know in order to use the Law of Cosines to find the measure of ∠*A*? What equation would you use to find that angle measure?

ⓒ Suppose you know the lengths *a*, *b*, and *c*. What can you conclude about m∠*B* if $a^2 + c^2 > b^2$? If $a^2 + c^2 < b^2$? If $a^2 + c^2 = b^2$?

Be prepared to explain your thinking to the entire class.

A surveyor with transit at point *A* sights points *B* and *C* on either side of Asylum Pond. She finds the measure of the angle between the sightings to be 72°.

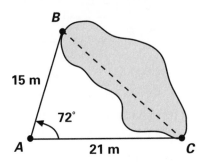

a. Find, to nearest tenth of a meter, the distance *BC* across the pond.

b. Find m∠*B* and m∠*C*.

INVESTIGATION 4 ▶ Solving for ...

The Pythagorean relationship, the trigonometric relationships in right triangles, the Law of Sines, and the Law of Cosines all express important connections between side and angle measurements in triangles. Those connections are given by equations involving several variables. The solutions of problems involving those connections often require rewriting the equations so that one of the variables is expressed in terms of the others.

"THIS IS THE PART I ALWAYS HATE."

As you have worked on other problems involving several variables, you have discovered and applied strategies that use several basic properties of numbers and equations. These properties can help you avoid the dilemma suggested in the above cartoon.

■ **Inverse Operations** make use of three arithmetic principles.

For any numbers p, q, and r:

$p + q = r$ *is equivalent to* $p = r - q$

$p \div q = r$ *is equivalent to* $p = r \cdot q$ *(if $q \neq 0$)*

If $p \geq 0$, then $\sqrt{p^2} = p$.

■ **Properties of Equality** justify the following operations on equations.

For any numbers p, q, and r, if $p = q$, then:

$p + r = q + r$

$p - r = q - r$

$p \cdot r = q \cdot r$

$p \div r = q \div r$ *(if $r \neq 0$)*

Also, if $p = q$ and $p, q \geq 0$, then $\sqrt{p} = \sqrt{q}$.

1. For each of the given principles of inverse operations and properties of equality shown above, do the following:

   a. Give several specific numerical examples illustrating the pattern.

   b. Describe the pattern in words, without the use of letter symbols or equations.

In the following activities, you are asked to show how these principles can be applied to answer the questions that arise in working with side and angle relationships of geometric figures.

2. Study the following strategies for solving $c^2 = a^2 + b^2$ for a in terms of b and c, assuming each variable is greater than or equal to zero. Explain how inverse operations and properties of equality justify each step in the solution procedures.

   a. Strategy 1

   Start with $c^2 = a^2 + b^2$.

   Step 1 $c^2 - b^2 = a^2$

   Step 2 $\sqrt{c^2 - b^2} = \sqrt{a^2}$

   Step 3 $\sqrt{c^2 - b^2} = a$

   b. Strategy 2

   Start with $c^2 = a^2 + b^2$.

   Step 1 $c^2 - b^2 = a^2 + b^2 - b^2$

   Step 2 $c^2 - b^2 = a^2$

   Step 3 $\sqrt{c^2 - b^2} = \sqrt{a^2}$

   Step 4 $\sqrt{c^2 - b^2} = a$

3. Study the following strategies for solving $\sin A = \frac{a}{c}$ for c in terms of a and $\sin A$. Explain how inverse operations and properties of equality justify each step in the solution procedures.

a. Strategy 1

Start with $\sin A = \frac{a}{c}$.

Step 1 $c \sin A = a$

Step 2 $c = \dfrac{a}{\sin A}$

b. Strategy 2

Start with $\sin A = \frac{a}{c}$.

Step 1 $c \cdot \sin A = c \cdot \dfrac{a}{c}$

Step 2 $c \cdot \sin A = a$

Step 3 $c \cdot \sin A \div \sin A = a \div \sin A$

Step 4 $c = a \div \sin A$

4. Show how to solve the equation $\dfrac{\sin A}{a} = \dfrac{\sin B}{b}$ for b in terms of a, $\sin A$, and $\sin B$. Justify each step of your reasoning.

5. Show how to solve the equation $c^2 = a^2 + b^2 - 2ab \cos C$ for $\cos C$ in terms of a, b, and c. Justify each step of your reasoning.

6. It is reported that when solving equations like $a^2 + b^2 = c^2$ for b in terms of a and c, beginning college students often reason as follows:

$$b^2 = c^2 - a^2$$
$$b = \sqrt{c^2 - a^2}$$
$$b = \sqrt{c^2} - \sqrt{a^2}$$
$$b = c - a$$

a. Assuming a, b, and c are positive numbers, what is the error in this reasoning?

b. What tips would you give to students to help them avoid this type of reasoning error?

The inverse operations and properties of equality strategies for manipulating trigonometric equations into equivalent and more useful forms also apply to equations modeling other relationships.

7. The perimeter P of any rectangle is related to its length L and width W by the formula $P = 2L + 2W$.

a. Solve the given equation for W in terms of P and L, and be prepared to justify each step in your solution process.

b. Explain how the new form of the equation could be helpful in exploring this problem: Find the dimensions of 20 rectangles that each have a perimeter of 500 meters.

8. Many practical problems come in the form of simple proportions. For example:

$$\frac{3 \text{ cans}}{\$0.89} = \frac{5 \text{ cans}}{c \text{ dollars}} \quad \text{or} \quad \frac{350 \text{ ft}}{4 \text{ sec}} = \frac{x \text{ ft}}{60 \text{ sec}}$$

   a. Solve each of these proportions and interpret your answers.

   b. Show how inverse operations can be used to solve the proportion $\frac{a}{x} = \frac{b}{c}$ for x. Assume $a, b, c \neq 0$.

   c. Show how properties of equality also can be used to solve the proportion in Part b.

Checkpoint

Consider $\triangle PQR$ shown at the right.

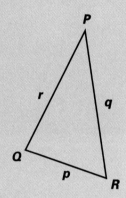

ⓐ Suppose you know the lengths of $\overline{PQ}$ and $\overline{QR}$ and the measures of $\angle Q$ and $\angle R$. Write two different equations that could be used to find the length q. Solve each equation for q.

ⓑ Describe three different ways you could find $m\angle P$ using the information given in Part a and your calculated value for q. For each method, write an equation of the form "$m\angle P = ...$" that gives the necessary calculations in terms of the known values of other variables.

Be prepared to share your methods and equations and to explain your reasoning.

▶ On Your Own

In rectangle $WXYZ$ shown here, information is given about a diagonal and an angle it forms with a side.

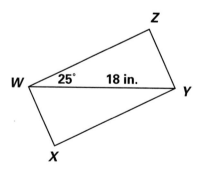

a. Write two different equations that could be used to find the length WZ. Solve each equation for WZ.

b. Using the given information and your answer to Part a, write three different equations that could be used to find the length ZY. Solve each equation for ZY.

Modeling • Organizing • Reflecting • Extending

Modeling

1. Two lighthouses *A* and *B* are 50 km apart. At 2 A.M., a freighter moving parallel to line *AB* is sighted at point *C* as shown in the diagram below.

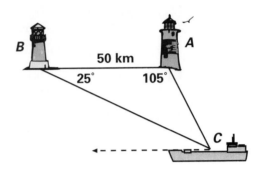

   a. How far is the freighter from lighthouse *B*? From lighthouse *A*?

   b. At 3 A.M., the angle at *A* is 86°. The angle at *B* is 29°. How far is the freighter from lighthouse *B*? From lighthouse *A*?

   c. How far has the freighter moved in the hour?

2. A pilot flying out of Chicago gets word that a major thunderstorm is directly in his plane's path. The pilot turns 35° to the right of his intended course and continues on this new flight path. After avoiding the worst of the storm, he turns 45° to the left of the new course and flies until returning to his original intended line of flight. The plane reaches its original intended course at a point 80 kilometers from the start of the detour.

   a. Draw a sketch of this situation.

   b. How much farther did the aircraft travel due to the detour?

3. In isosceles trapezoid *ABCD* shown below, $\overline{AB} \parallel \overline{CD}$ and $AD = BC$. Use the given information and what you know about line symmetry and angles of triangles to find the additional information requested below.

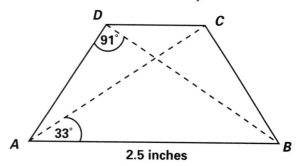

a. Find the measures of all angles shown in the figure.

b. Find the lengths of all segments shown in the figure.

4. A triangular region has sides measuring 121, 173, and 194 meters. Find the measure of the largest angle in the region.

5. A field is in the shape of a quadrilateral as shown.

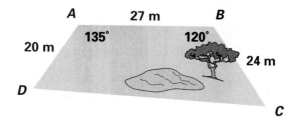

a. Find the measure of its fourth side.

b. Find the measures of the remaining angles of the quadrilateral.

c. Find its area.

Organizing

1. The label on a jar of creamy peanut butter claims that each serving (2 tablespoons) contains 16 grams of fat, 7 grams of carbohydrate, and 8 grams of protein. A recipe for peanut butter cookies calls for 5 tablespoons of peanut butter.

a. Write proportions whose solutions would tell the number of grams of fat *f*, carbohydrate *c*, and protein *p* from peanut butter in the cookie recipe.

b. Solve each of the equations in Part a.

c. Explain how the equations solved in Part b are similar to those involved in using trigonometric relations to find side lengths in right triangles.

2. The triangles sketched below are *similar* with vertex A corresponding to vertex P, B to Q, and C to R.

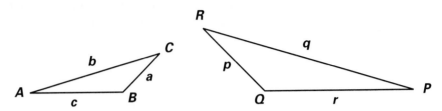
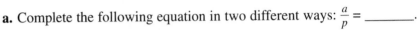
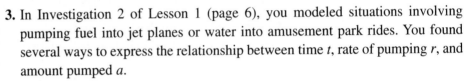
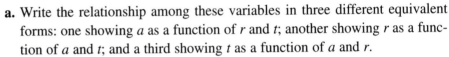

a. Complete the following equation in two different ways: $\frac{a}{p} = $ _____.

b. In each equation of Part a, solve for p in terms of the other side lengths.

c. Explain how your work in Part b is like that used in applications of the Law of Sines.

3. In Investigation 2 of Lesson 1 (page 6), you modeled situations involving pumping fuel into jet planes or water into amusement park rides. You found several ways to express the relationship between time t, rate of pumping r, and amount pumped a.

a. Write the relationship among these variables in three different equivalent forms: one showing a as a function of r and t; another showing r as a function of a and t; and a third showing t as a function of a and r.

b. Explain the principles that guarantee equivalence of the equations in Part a.

4. Many simple situations can be modeled by writing and solving linear equations of the form $a + bx = c$.

a. Show the general form of solutions for all such equations by solving for x in terms of a, b, and c.

b. Explain the principles that guarantee your answer in Part a is correct.

c. Produce a similar solution formula for equations of the following form:

$$a + bx = c + dx$$

That is, solve for x in terms of a, b, c, and d, and explain the principles that guarantee your formula is correct.

Reflecting

1. In using the Law of Cosines to evaluate the length of one side in a triangle, you need to combine values of a, b, and $\cos C$ with the rule

$$c^2 = a^2 + b^2 - 2ab \cos C.$$

Write two different sequences of operations that will give the correct value for c.

2. Both the Law of Sines and the Law of Cosines give equations relating four geometric variables.

   a. In each case, how many of those variables must be known in order to find the values of the other variables?

   b. The linear equation $a + bx = c$ also has four variables. How many of those variables must be known in order to find the values of the other variables?

3. The Law of Sines comes in two similar forms:

   $$\frac{\sin A}{a} = \frac{\sin B}{b} \text{ and } \frac{a}{\sin A} = \frac{b}{\sin B}.$$

   a. Why are these two forms equivalent?

   b. When is each form better to use than the other? Why?

4. For a right triangle labeled as shown below, $\sin A = \frac{a}{c}$. In any triangle with vertices and sides labeled in the same pattern as shown here, the Law of Sines gives $\frac{\sin A}{a} = \frac{\sin C}{c}$.

   a. Rewrite the given Law of Sines to express $\sin A$ as a function of a, c, and $\sin C$.

   b. In what sense does the equation you wrote in Part a show how to adjust the right triangle definition for $\sin A$ to give correct values of $\sin A$ when the angle at C is not a right angle?

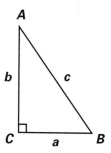

Extending

1. Conduct the following experiment using a linkage with arms of lengths 16 cm and 12 cm joined at point C.

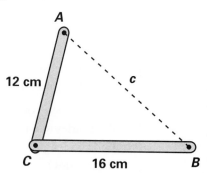

   a. Make a table of values for the length $c = AB$ as the angle at C varies from $0°$ to $360°$ in steps of $10°$. Then sketch a graph of c as a function of the measure of $\angle C$.

   b. What relations have you studied that have graphs similar to the graph of this relation between the measure of $\angle C$ and the opposite side length c?

   c. How would you expect the table and graph to continue for measures of $\angle C$ from $360°$ to $720°$?

2. A lighthouse 30 meters high stands at the top of a high cliff. The line of sight from a point X on the bow of a ship to point A at the top of the lighthouse is at an angle of 18° to the horizontal. The line of sight from point X to point B at the bottom of the lighthouse makes an angle of 14° with a horizontal line. Draw a sketch of the situation and then determine the approximate height of the cliff.

3. In this lesson, you have investigated and used connections among algebra, geometry, and trigonometry. Examine the algebraic reasoning below, which connects the Pythagorean Theorem to a striking result in trigonometry.

Step 1 $a^2 + b^2 = c^2$

Step 2 $\frac{a^2 + b^2}{c^2} = \frac{c^2}{c^2}$

Step 3 $\frac{a^2}{c^2} + \frac{b^2}{c^2} = 1$

Step 4 $\left(\frac{a}{c}\right)^2 + \left(\frac{b}{c}\right)^2 = 1$

Step 5 $(\sin A)^2 + (\cos A)^2 = 1$

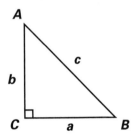

a. Provide an explanation for each step in the above reasoning.

b. Predict the value of $(\sin 43.2°)^2 + (\cos 43.2°)^2$. Check your prediction.

c. For what range of degree measures of $\angle A$ do you think $(\sin A)^2 + (\cos A)^2 = 1$? Explain your reasoning.

4. In general, to find the area of a triangle you need to know the length of one side and the altitude to that base.

a. How could you find the area of any triangle ABC if you were given b and c and the measure of $\angle A$? If given a and c and the measure of $\angle B$?

b. If you knew only the lengths of the three sides of a triangle, how could you find the length of an altitude to one of those sides?

c. Use your strategy to find the area of a triangle ABC in which $a = 12.5$ cm, $b = 20$ cm, and $c = 25$ cm.

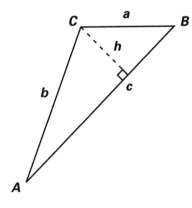

5. Modern satellite communication systems make it possible for us to determine our exact (within a meter or so accuracy) location on the Earth's surface by sending a signal from a handheld Global Positioning System (GPS) device. The GPS sends signals to satellites, which relate the signal angle and distance to known reference sites. This technology makes it possible to have a system built into an automobile that shows a dashboard map giving both car and selected destination locations and how to reach the destination.

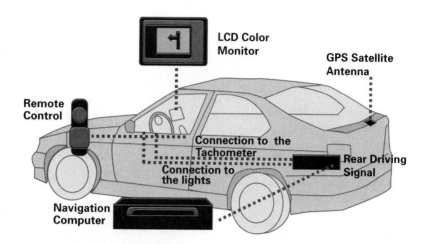

An actual GPS uses *spherical trigonometry* because of the spherical shape of the Earth. But consider a simpler problem of locating objects on a large flat surface, using sensors atop very tall towers. Devise a system that you think would allow the sorts of calculations required to locate a GPS transmitter on a map grid.

Lesson 3

Linked Equations

Modern American businesses use millions of cars and trucks of various sizes to make pickups, deliveries, and service calls. Whether they are hauling dirt, delivering packages or pizzas, or making house calls for mowing lawns or repairing appliances, many businesses need transportation. Unfortunately, start-up businesses often don't have enough cash on hand to buy new cars or trucks or to pay the full price all at once. Other businesses may want to use their cash resources for other things. In any case, renting or leasing a vehicle is an option to consider.

Think About This Situation

The owners of A-1 Auto Parts need a second delivery truck to fill orders from repair shops in their service area. They have to lease the truck, because they don't have enough cash to buy one.

ⓐ What do you know about how typical automotive-lease plans work?

ⓑ What business conditions will the store owners need to consider as they choose a lease plan?

ⓒ How are those conditions related to each other?

ⓓ How could you model the relations among variables to help find the best choice among available options?

INVESTIGATION 1 ▸ Comparison Shopping

When the owners of A-1 Auto Parts looked for a delivery truck, they found a small pickup they liked and got the following offers of lease payment plans from the dealer:

Plan A They could make a down payment of $2,500 and then monthly payments of $150.

Plan B They could make a down payment of only $500 and then monthly payments of $230.

They had to make a choice between higher down payment with lower monthly payments, or lower down payment with higher monthly payments.

1. In your group, think about the situation and the factors that are involved in each offer.

   a. What might explain the differences in down payment and monthly payment rates for the two offers?

   b. What other costs might there be for a person or business leasing a truck?

   c. What factors would you consider in making the choice between the two lease payment plans?

2. In each payment plan, the money you pay to the car dealer adds up as time passes. Write an equation giving total payment as a function of the number of months in the lease for each lease plan. Use M for number of months, P_A for total amount paid under lease Plan A, and P_B for total amount paid under lease Plan B.

3. Study the relations between months and total dollars paid under the two lease plans.

   a. Which plan involves the greater total payment after 60 months?

   b. For what periods of time will the total payment be greater under Plan A than under Plan B?

   c. For what periods of time will the total payment be greater under Plan B than under Plan A?

   d. For what periods of time will the total payment under the two plans be equal?

4. On a single coordinate system like the one to the right, sketch graphs showing the two payment plans, with total payments under each plan as a function of the number of months for which payments have been made. Explain how the graphs illustrate your answers to Activity 3.

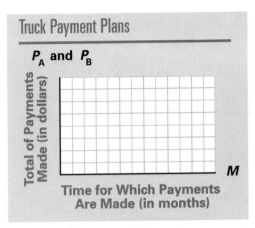

Truck Payment Plans

P_A and P_B

Total of Payments Made (in dollars)

M

Time for Which Payments Are Made (in months)

5. Suppose that as a third option you consider buying the truck at the start, with a cash payment of $12,500.

   a. Add another graph to the coordinate system of Activity 4 so it shows the third option too.

   b. For what periods of time will the total payment under Plan A be less than the full purchase price? Explain how this is shown on the graph.

   c. For what periods of time will the total payment under Plan B be less than the full purchase price? Explain how this is shown on the graph.

   d. What advantages and disadvantages are there for buying the truck rather than leasing?

Checkpoint

Comparing various lease or payment plans often involves examining systems of equations. Think about the costs to the consumer for the general situation shown here.

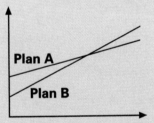

Plan A

Plan B

$$\text{Plan A: } y = a + bx$$
$$\text{Plan B: } y = c + dx$$

a Typically, on what factors would both equations depend? How are these factors shown in the graph?

b Write an equation or inequality that expresses the conditions under which the following are true:

   ■ Plan A costs less than Plan B.

   ■ Plan B costs less than Plan A.

   ■ Plan A and Plan B cost the same.

c How would you go about solving each equation or inequality?

Be prepared to explain your algebraic relations and solution methods.

On Your Own

Cellular Plus telephone company offers three monthly service plans.

- Plan A costs $70 per month with unlimited air time.
- Plan B costs $35 per month plus $0.30 per minute of air time.
- Plan C costs $25 per month plus $0.50 per minute of air time.

a. Write equations showing how the monthly cost for each type of telephone service depends on the number of minutes M of air time. Use C_A, C_B, and C_C to stand for the costs of the three types of service.

b. Compare the three service plans to find the number of minutes of air time for which each is cheapest.

c. Sketch a graph that illustrates your answer to Part b.

INVESTIGATION 2 ▶ Supply and Demand

Buying and selling, earning and spending—money and the things it buys play an important part in the lives of most Americans. Well over 100 million of us go to work on a regular basis and use the money we earn to buy things we want and need: food, shelter, clothes, cars, entertainment, and education. When summer approaches, most high school and college students start thinking about finding summer jobs.

Want Ads – Help Wanted

Fast Food– Restaurant seeks summer help; cashiers, cooks, cleanup; 20 hours per week all shifts available. Call 555-5678.

Camp Staff– Summer playground and camp counselors age 15 or older. Good pay and lots of fresh air. Call 555-6543.

Natural Lawns– Summer help needed. $6.40 per hour. No prior experience required. Call 24 hours 1-800-555-1589.

Child Care– Tiny Tots Day Care Center seeks summer help for child care positions. Hours 7–5 four days per week. Send references to Box Q.

In some cities and towns there is work in shops, restaurants, and seasonal service jobs like lawn mowing, farmwork, or life-guarding. But there often aren't enough jobs to ensure that everyone who wants one will be employed.

To help students find summer work, both to earn money and to get work experience, many city and county governments have special summer jobs programs. Students are hired to do cleanup and construction jobs in parks or other community facilities. As with all other government projects, these programs have a set budget.

1. In Kent County, the government budget sets aside $100,000 each summer for student salaries in a youth-jobs program. Together as a class, consider some of the decisions the officials who run the program may have to make before announcing their plans and inviting applicants for the jobs.

   a. What decisions can you imagine the jobs-program planners have to make in setting up the program each year?

   b. What limitations would they have to consider in making those decisions?

   c. How are the decisions related to each other; that is, how does one decision affect the other options?

One plan for the Kent County summer jobs program focused on connections among pay for each student worker, hours worked, and number of students who would be interested in jobs at various levels of pay. The jobs-program staff were unsure how much they should offer as pay.

2. Recall that the county has $100,000 to spend on student salaries.

   a. How many student workers can be hired if the county pays $2,000 per worker for a summer contract covering eight weeks? How many can be hired if the county pays only $1,500 per worker?

   b. If the number of students who could be hired is represented by H and the offered summer pay rate is represented by P, what equation gives H as a function of P?

   c. Recall your previous work with algebraic models in Courses 1 and 2. What type of model is your equation in Part b?

   d. Describe the shape of the graph expected for this equation. Describe the pattern in a table of values for this equation.

3. The jobs-program staff figured that if they offered pay that was too low, then few students would be willing to take the jobs. After doing a survey in one high school, they arrived at the following estimates of the relation between summer pay P and number of students A they can expect to apply for the jobs.

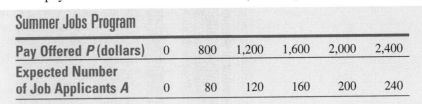

Summer Jobs Program						
Pay Offered P (dollars)	0	800	1,200	1,600	2,000	2,400
Expected Number of Job Applicants A	0	80	120	160	200	240

   a. Does the pattern in the table seem reasonable? Why or why not?

   b. If the staff wanted to display their options relating offered pay P to expected number of student applicants A in a graph, what type of graph should they use?

   c. What equation is a good model for the relation showing A as a function of P?

   d. What type of model is your equation in Part c?

4. The decision to be made by officials in the Kent County jobs program is how much pay to offer for the eight-week summer contracts. Use the supply and demand equations from Activities 2 and 3 to do the following.

   a. Begin by finding all possible summer-pay offers for which the expected number of job applicants would

   ■ equal the number of jobs that could be provided.

   ■ exceed the number of jobs that could be provided.

   ■ fall short of the number of jobs that could be provided.

   b. Use the information from Part a and other considerations to write a brief report stating your recommendation on summer-pay rate and explaining your reasoning with supporting tables, graphs, and equations.

5. To make their recommendation more convincing, the program officers told the County Board that they found the optimal pay rate P by writing an equation or inequality for each condition given in Activity 4 Part a and then finding solutions for those conditions. Explain how the equation and inequalities given below correspond to problem conditions. Then, explain how the solutions could be found in tables and graphs of the relations among pay, job applications, and students hired. Finally, explain how the solutions could be found by reasoning with the symbols themselves.

   a. $\frac{100,000}{P} = 0.1P$

   b. $\frac{100,000}{P} > 0.1P$

   c. $\frac{100,000}{P} < 0.1P$

Checkpoint

The situation for the Kent County jobs program involved two output variables related to the same input variable.

ⓐ What were the input and output variables in this case?

ⓑ What system of equations modeled the program planning?

ⓒ How are the two modeling equations linked, and how is this shown on a graph of the two equations?

ⓓ How was your method for solving this system of equations similar to methods you used previously for solving systems of linear equations?

Be prepared to share your group's descriptions with the entire class.

On Your Own

Revise your supply and demand models, your graphs, and your recommendations about pay offers for the following changes in the Kent County budget for student workers' salaries.

a. The budget decreased to a total of $80,000.

b. The budget increased to a total of $120,000.

INVESTIGATION 3 ▸ Peak Profit

People running businesses that sell products must make many decisions that affect their profits. Those decisions include deciding what prices to charge for their products.

Consider the case of stage producers who have a contract to bring a musical production to a summer theater. They have to estimate *costs* of putting on the show, *income* from ticket sales and concessions, and the *profit* that can be made. When all these factors are considered, they have to decide what prices to charge for tickets.

The following activities ask you to analyze one possible method of making business plans for such a production. Study each step in the process and see if the proposal seems to use sensible and accurate reasoning.

1. The first step in deciding how to set ticket prices for the musical production was to do market research on what prices people would probably pay. A market research survey produced predictions of ticket sales S that could be expected for various possible ticket prices P. After plotting the data and estimating the best-fitting linear model for the relation between P and S, the equation $S = 2,500 - 50P$ was proposed as the probable relation between price and number of tickets that would be sold.

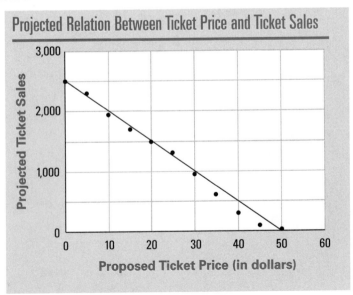

Projected Relation Between Ticket Price and Ticket Sales

y-axis: Projected Ticket Sales (0 to 3,000)
x-axis: Proposed Ticket Price (in dollars) (0 to 60)

a. How do you think the producers or their market-research staff gathered the (*ticket price*, *ticket sales*) data that are plotted on the graph?

b. What does the pattern in the graph say about the probable relation between ticket price and number of tickets that would be sold for the musical?

c. Is the pattern in the graph reasonable? Does it match the relation you would expect? Why or why not?

d. In the equation $S = 2,500 - 50P$, what do the values 2,500 and –50 tell about the way ticket price and ticket sales are related?

e. How would you find the equation to model the market-research data points?

2. After estimating the connection between ticket prices and probable ticket sales, the producers wanted to see the probable connection between ticket prices P and dollar income I from ticket sales. They created the following table of projections.

Projected Income from Ticket Sales

Ticket Price (dollars)	0	5	10	20	30	40	50
Number of Tickets	2,500	2,250	2,000	1,500	1,000	500	0
Ticket Income (dollars)	0	11,250	20,000	30,000	30,000	20,000	0

a. According to this table, how will ticket income be affected by choice of ticket price? Does the pattern in the table seem reasonable? Why or why not?

b. How could the entries in the "Ticket Income" row be calculated from the other information in the table?

c. Anna proposed the equation $I = P(2,500 - 50P)$ for the relation between ticket price and ticket income; James proposed $I = 2,500P - 50P^2$. Which of these two rules is correct? Why?

d. What price is likely to give the maximum ticket income? What would that income be?

3. The next step in making the business plan was to estimate operating costs for the production. The planners knew that some costs were fixed (for example, pay for the cast and rent of the theater), but others would vary depending on the number of tickets sold (for example, number of ushers and ticket takers). After estimating all the possible operating costs, they decided on the equation $C = 17,500 + 2S$ for operating costs as a function of number of tickets sold.

a. According to that rule, what are the projected fixed operating costs, and what is the projected operating cost for each person who buys a ticket for the musical?

b. How will operating costs change as the number of tickets sold increases?

c. Since ticket sales seem to depend on price charged $S = 2,500 - 50P$, it is possible to express operating cost C as a function of price. What equation would express that relation?

d. How will operating costs change as the ticket price increases?

4. With equations relating projected ticket income to ticket price and operating cost to ticket price, the entertainment promoters tried to put everything together in a picture of the relations among price, costs, and income.

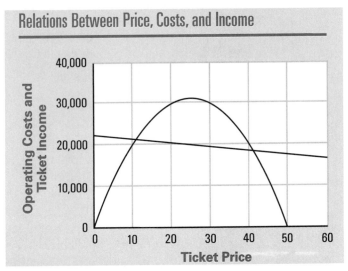

a. These graphs show the relations between ticket price, operating cost, and ticket income. How do they show each of the following?

- Ticket prices for which operating costs exceed income
- Ticket prices for which income exceeds operating costs
- Ticket prices for which costs equal income

b. If you use the rules for income and operating costs as functions of ticket price, what specific numerical answers do you get for the questions in Part a?

c. What questions are answered by solving the following equation and inequalities?

- $2,500P - 50P^2 = 22,500 - 100P$
- $2,500P - 50P^2 < 22,500 - 100P$
- $2,500P - 50P^2 > 22,500 - 100P$

d. Obtain or make a copy of the graphs above relating income, operating costs, and ticket price. On the x-axis, mark those points corresponding to solutions of the equation and inequalities in Part c. If possible, use different colors as suggested below.

- In blue: $2,500P - 50P^2 = 22,500 - 100P$
- In red: $2,500P - 50P^2 < 22,500 - 100P$
- In green: $2,500P - 50P^2 > 22,500 - 100P$

5. Of course, the producers would probably like to make as large a profit as possible.

    a. Use the equations relating income and expenses to ticket price to produce a table of projected profits for various possible ticket prices.

    b. Use the table and a graph to find the ticket price giving maximum profit for the musical production. What is the maximum profit to be expected?

    c. Use your answer from Part b to estimate the number of tickets that will be sold, the operating cost, and the ticket sales income at the ticket price which gives maximum profit.

Checkpoint

This investigation involved a situation with four different output variables (*ticket sales*, *income*, *cost*, and *profit*) depending on a single input variable (*ticket price*).

a What are the four equations showing how the dependent variables are related to *ticket price*? Which of those relations are linear models? Quadratic models? Some other sort of nonlinear model?

b The following graphs show *operating costs*, *ticket sales income*, and *profit* all as functions of *ticket price*. Explain what each labeled point tells about the business situation and how you would find the coordinates of those points.

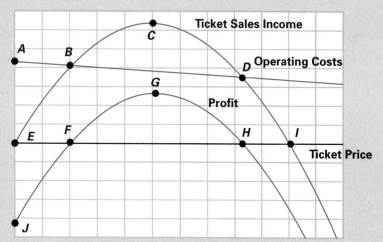

c In what ways is this system similar to, and different from, those modeling the planning of the A-1 Auto Parts truck leasing and the Kent County summer-jobs program in previous investigations?

Be prepared to share and explain your responses.

When Alicia and Jamal went to apply for restaurant jobs, they each found several different opportunities.

Offer 1, Server:

> Pay is $7.50 per hour, with work uniforms provided free of charge.

Offer 2, Server:

> Pay is $5.25 per hour and includes a $100 hiring bonus with the first week's check. Again, work uniforms are provided.

Offer 3, Host/Hostess:

> Pay is $8.75 per hour, but new clothes for this job cost about $250.

The question for both of them was which offer to take. Money that would be earned seemed the only factor, since all three places were close to their homes and all of the jobs were jobs they would enjoy. The parents of both had agreed to loan them the money for new clothes, but the loans had to be repaid as soon as possible.

a. Write equations that will give the possible earnings under each plan as functions of the number of hours worked.

b. Sketch or use a graphing calculator or computer software to display graphs of all three relations in Part a for time worked from 0 to 250 hours. Explain how the graphs can be used to find the best offer for various amounts of time worked.

c. Produce a table showing sample (*hours worked*, *earnings*) data for the three job offers from 0 to 250 hours, in steps of 10 hours. Then explain how the entries help determine the best offer.

d. Using methods of your choice, solve the following equation and inequalities. Then explain what questions about the three offers can be answered by the various solutions.

- $7.50x = 8.75x - 250$
- $5.25x + 100 > 8.75x - 250$
- $7.50x < 5.25x + 100$

Modeling • Organizing • Reflecting • Extending

Modeling

1. St. Michael School received two bids for charter buses to transport their senior class on a one-week field trip to Washington, D.C. in April.

   ■ East Coast Tour Bus company proposed a flat rate of $1,350 per bus.

   ■ Delmarva Charters offered a price per bus of $525 for a driver and $2.25 per mile for use of the bus.

   a. Sketch graphs that could be used to illustrate the situation, and describe your plan for making a choice between the two companies.

   b. Under what conditions would East Coast Tour Bus offer the better price per bus? When would Delmarva Charters offer the better price per bus?

   c. Write equations or inequalities whose solutions would help make a choice.

2. When Undercut Transit heard about St. Michael School's field trip plan (see Modeling Task 1), they submitted a different bid: $4.95 per mile for each bus, with driver included.

   a. Sketch graphs that illustrate the options, and describe your plan for making a choice among the three competing companies.

   b. Under what conditions will Undercut Transit offer the best price?

   c. Write equations or inequalities whose solutions would help make a choice.

3. At Martin Luther King High School, the athletic booster club sponsors an annual basketball game between teachers and the school's intramural league all-stars. As a research project, the economics class investigated possible ticket prices, attendance, and expenses. They found the following information:

   ■ The operating costs C (in dollars) would depend on the number of tickets sold T with rule $C = 250 + 0.50T$.

   ■ The number of tickets sold T would probably depend on price charged P (in dollars) with rule $T = 800 - 100P$.

a. Examine the equations relating cost, ticket sales, and ticket price. What do the numbers 250, 0.50, 800, and –100 tell about the situation?

b. What single equation would show how operating costs depend on ticket price charged?

Based on their work with ticket prices, ticket sales, and operating costs, the economics class members reached these further conclusions:

- Income from ticket sales I would be related to ticket price P by the equation $I = 800P - 100P^2$.

- Cost of operating the game would be related to ticket price by the equation $C = 650 - 50P$.

c. Sketch graphs that show both income and operating costs as functions of ticket price. Label the points whose coordinates would help answer the following questions:

- For what ticket prices would the game break even; that is, when would operating costs equal income from ticket sales?

- For what ticket prices would ticket revenue be as large as possible?

d. How could the price giving maximum profit be found from the graphs in Part c?

e. Write an equation expressing profit PR as a function of ticket price.

f. Find the maximum profit possible and the ticket price that will give that maximum profit. Explain how to find your answer using an appropriate graph, a table of (*ticket price*, *profit*) values, or some other reasoning method.

4. When John and Carla were 14 years old, they had summer jobs. John saved $600 from his earnings, and Carla saved $550 from her earnings. They both decided to put their money into savings accounts.

- John found an account that would pay interest at an annual rate of 8%, but at the end of each year he took out the interest. Each year his original deposit stayed in the account.

- Carla's account only paid 7% interest, but she decided not to withdraw any money. The interest was added to her account at the end of each year, and she began earning interest on the interest added.

a. How much total money would each person receive from the banks if they closed their accounts at the end of only 1 year? How much would they receive if they closed their accounts after 2 years?

b. Write equations showing the total amounts of money that John and Carla would have withdrawn if they closed their accounts after n years.

c. Sketch graphs of the money total models, showing patterns under each plan for 15 years.

d. In how many years, if ever, will Carla's total be more than John's?

Organizing

1. Refer to Modeling Task 3, pages 57 and 58. Explain how the modeling equations $I = 800P - 100P^2$ and $C = 650 - 50P$ can be derived from the planning information about the basketball game.

2. The graphs below show the way two different variables depend on the same input variable x. One equation is $y_1 = 20 + 0.5x$. The other is $y_2 = 3 + 1.5x$.

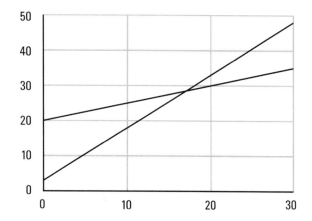

a. Make a copy of these graphs. On the x-axis, mark the points corresponding to solutions of the following equation and inequalities. If possible, use the colors suggested when you mark the points.

   ■ In blue: $20 + 0.5x = 3 + 1.5x$

   ■ In red: $20 + 0.5x > 3 + 1.5x$

   ■ In green: $20 + 0.5x < 3 + 1.5x$

b. Explain how you could solve the equation and inequalities in Part a by reasoning with the symbolic forms and by using a graphing calculator or computer software.

3. The graphs below show the way two different variables depend on the same input variable x. One equation is $y_1 = \frac{50}{x^2}$. The other is $y_2 = x^2 - 5x$.

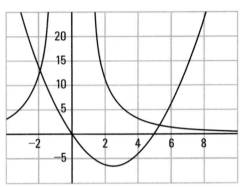

a. Make a copy of these graphs. If possible, color the graph of $y_1 = \frac{50}{x^2}$ in yellow.

b. What connections between equations and graphs for different model types allow you to match $y_1 = \frac{50}{x^2}$ and $y_2 = x^2 - 5x$ to their graphs in this case?

c. On the x-axis, mark the points corresponding to solutions of the following equation and inequalities. If possible, use the colors suggested.

- In blue: $\frac{50}{x^2} = x^2 - 5x$
- In red: $\frac{50}{x^2} > x^2 - 5x$
- In green: $\frac{50}{x^2} < x^2 - 5x$

d. Use the graph and trace or use the table commands of a graphing calculator or computer software to locate accurate estimates of the solutions to the equation and inequalities in Part c.

4. Even if you use technology-produced graphs or tables to solve equations and inequalities, it helps to know the number of solutions expected. That helps you catch mistakes that might be made in entering algebraic expressions or commands into the calculator or computer and provides a check on your selected viewing window. Suppose you are given a system of two equations relating two different variables to the same input variable.

a. Describe the possible number of solutions to the system if both equations are linear. Draw sketches to illustrate each possibility.

b. Describe the possible number of solutions to the system if one equation is linear and one equation is quadratic. Draw sketches to illustrate each possibility.

c. Describe the possible number of solutions to the system if one equation is linear and one equation is exponential. Draw sketches to illustrate each possibility.

d. Describe the possible number of solutions to the system if one equation is linear and one equation is inverse variation. Draw sketches to illustrate each possibility.

Reflecting

1. In this lesson and in the "Power Models" unit of Course 2, you saw that modeling business profit prospects often required consideration of several variables along with the relations among those variables. Key variables include number of units U produced and sold, operating costs C, price P per unit, income I, and profit PR. Using the language "is a function of," describe at least four different relations among U, C, P, I, and PR. (For example, "Income I is a function of units sold U and price P per unit.")

2. Refer to Modeling Task 3, pages 57 and 58. Explain how the economics class at Martin Luther King High School might have determined the modeling rules:

$$C = 250 + 0.50T$$

$$T = 800 - 100P$$

3. The situations of this lesson involved making choices. In each case, there were some mathematical variables to think about when making the choices. However, choices among options usually are not based solely on mathematics.

   a. What nonnumerical factors would you consider in planning a summer job program for teenagers?

   b. What nonnumerical factors would you consider in choosing a charter bus line for a school field trip?

   c. What factors other than ticket price would affect the profits of a musical production?

4. If you were going to use mathematical evidence to convince someone to follow your advice in one of the decision problems of this lesson, which presentation do you think would be most effective: a graph of the relations involved, a table of sample data on the relations involved, or some equations and their solutions concerning the relations involved? Give reasons for your choice.

5. Suppose after graduation you planned to buy a new car or truck.

   a. Research the advantages of leasing a vehicle. What are the disadvantages?

   b. How might you use the mathematics you have studied to help choose a lease or loan plan?

Extending

1. Look again at your answers to Organizing Task 4, page 60, and construct specific equations illustrating each possible pattern.

2. Think about various ways that you could solve each of the following types of equations.

- $ax + b = cx + d$
- $ax + b = cx^2 + dx + e$
- $ax + b = c(d^x)$
- $ax + b = \dfrac{c}{x^2}$

a. Describe two different graphical ways in which you could solve each of these equations using a graphing calculator or computer software.

b. In Investigation 4 of Lesson 2, several *properties of equality* were identified. (See page 37.) Two of those properties also relate to inverse operations. They are restated in a slightly different form below.

(1) If $a + b = c$, then $a = c - b$.

(2) If $ab = c$, then $a = c \div b$ $\left(\text{or } a = \dfrac{c}{b}\right)$, provided $b \neq 0$.

To what properties of equality do these two properties correspond?

c. Use these properties of equality to explain why both graphical methods you proposed in Part a give the same solutions.

d. Are there also two different methods for solving these equations using calculator- or computer-produced tables of values? Explain your thinking.

3. The properties of equality restated in Part b of Extending Task 2 are useful for rewriting equations in equivalent forms in which solutions are seen readily. There are two useful, corresponding *properties of inequality*:

(1) If $a + b > c$, then $a > c - b$.

(2) If $ab > c$ and $b > 0$, then $a > \dfrac{c}{b}$.

If $ab > c$ and $b < 0$, then $a < \dfrac{c}{b}$.

a. Test these properties of inequality using different choices of values for a, b, and c.

b. Write and test corresponding properties for the relation $<$.

c. Explain how the properties of equality in Extending Task 2 and these properties of inequality support the reasoning with symbolic forms you used to solve the equation and inequalities in Organizing Task 2, Part b (page 59).

d. What do you see as the advantages and disadvantages of solving equations and inequalities using symbolic reasoning rather than graphical and tabular methods?

Lesson 4

Linear Programming

In previous lessons, you've seen that important decisions in business often involve many variables and relations among those variables. The key to making good decisions is finding a way to organize and compare options.

For example, the plant manager of the Integrated Technologies factory must plan for and supervise production of two video game models, the basic IT-95 and the more advanced IT-2000. Demand for both games is high, so IT can sell whatever is produced.

To plan the work schedule, the manager has to think about these conditions:

- Assembly of each IT-95 takes 0.6 hour, and each IT-2000 takes 0.3 hour of technician time. The plant can apply at most 240 hours of technician time to assembly work each day.

- Testing of each IT-95 takes 0.2 hour, and each IT-2000 takes 0.4 hour. The plant can apply at most 160 hours of technician time each day for testing.

- Packaging time is the same for each model. The packaging department of the plant can handle at most 500 games per day.

- The company makes a profit of $50 on each IT-95 and $75 on each IT-2000.

Think About This Situation

Suppose you were the manager of the Integrated Technologies plant and had to make production plans.

a How would you come up with the time estimates for assembly, testing, and packaging?

b How would you come up with the expected profit for each game?

c How might you use all the above data to decide how many IT-95 and IT-2000 models should be produced to give maximum profit for the factory?

INVESTIGATION 1 Picture Your Options

Many problems like those in the Integrated Technologies factory are solved by a mathematical strategy called **linear programming**. The following investigations will help you understand and learn how to use this important problem-solving strategy, as well as some of the mathematical ideas and skills on which it depends.

The production scheduling problem at Integrated Technologies requires choice among many options. The manager must decide what combination of IT-95 and IT-2000 models will give greatest profit. But there are **constraints** or limits on the choice: there can be *at most* 240 hours of assembly labor required, *at most* 160 hours of testing labor required, and a total of *at most* 500 video games to be packaged for shipping.

1. One way to search for the production plan that will maximize profit is to make some guesses and test the profit prospects for those guesses. For each of the following possible combinations of IT-95 and IT-2000 models, check to see if the three constraints are satisfied. If the constraints are satisfied, find the profit that could be earned.

   a. Suppose the manager schedules production of 100 IT-95 and 200 IT-2000 models.

   - Will the assembly time for these games be within the limit of 240 hours per day?
   - Will the testing time for these games be within the limit of 160 hours per day?
   - Will the total number of units produced fall within the packaging limit of 500 per day?
   - If the constraints are satisfied, what profit would be earned?

   b. Suppose the manager schedules production of 200 IT-95 and 100 IT-2000 models. Investigate the four questions in Part a for this case.

   c. Answer the questions in Part a, assuming the manager schedules production of 400 IT-95 and 100 IT-2000 models.

   d. Which of these production combinations is the best choice?

As you checked the possible production plans in Activity 1, you tested many options for each phase of production. It would be nice to have a systematic way of organizing the search for a maximum profit decision. One part of the linear programming strategy for solving such problems is to look at a graph of the options.

If x represents the number of IT-95 models and y represents the number of IT-2000 models, then the scheduling goal is to find a pair (x, y) that meets the constraints and gives maximum profit. Using a grid like the one below, you can search for the combination of video game models that will give maximum profit. The point (100, 200) represents 100 IT-95 and 200 IT-2000 video games. These numbers satisfy the constraints and give a profit of $50(100) + $75(200) or $20,000.

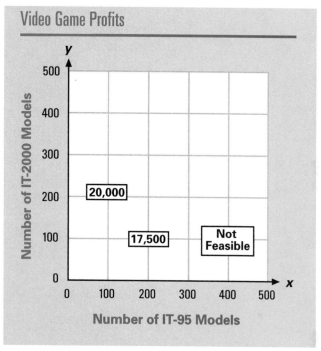

2. Each **lattice point** on the grid (where horizontal and vertical grid lines intersect) represents a possible combination of video game models. Points whose coordinates satisfy all the constraints are called **feasible points**.

   a. Based on your work in Activity 1, explain the labels on the points with coordinates (200, 100) and (400, 100).

   b. Think about how you checked if the three constraints were satisfied. Name another point that you suspect will not be a feasible (possible) point. Check your conjecture.

   c. For the remaining lattice points on this graph, check to see if the constraints are satisfied by the coordinates. Look for patterns that may simplify your work.

   d. If the coordinates of a point satisfy all constraints, calculate and record on a copy of the grid the profit that would be earned by that combination of IT-95 and IT-2000 models. If the point is not feasible, write "NF" on the lattice point to indicate that it is not feasible.

3. Based on the completed grid:

a. Describe the region where all three constraints are satisfied.

b. Pick the number of model IT-95 and IT-2000 video games that you think the factory should produce in order to make maximum profit. Be prepared to explain why you believe that your answer is correct.

Problems like this production scheduling problem—with several *variables*, several *constraints*, and an *objective* like maximizing profit—occur in many different situations. For example, think about the variables and constraints in choosing the foods you eat. Usually you choose things that taste good, but it is important to consider also the cost of that food and the way it satisfies your body's dietary needs.

4. For some people, like athletes or astronauts, selection of a good diet is a carefully planned scientific process. Each person wants a high performance diet at minimal cost or (in the case of astronauts) minimal total weight. Consider the following, simplified version of the problem facing NASA space flight planners who must provide food for astronauts.

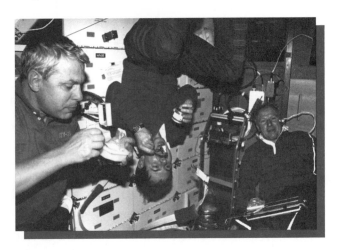

- Suppose there are two kinds of food to be carried on a space shuttle trip: special food bars and cartons of a special drink.
- Each food bar provides 5 grams of fat, 40 grams of carbohydrate, and 8 grams of protein.
- Each carton of drink provides 6 grams of fat, 25 grams of carbohydrate, and 15 grams of protein.
- Minimum daily requirements for each astronaut are *at least* 61 grams of fat, *at least* 350 grams of carbohydrate, and *at least* 103 grams of protein.
- Each food bar weighs 65 grams and each drink weighs 118 grams.

Determining what combination of food bars and drinks will give minimum daily requirements of fat, carbohydrate, and protein with least total weight seems complicated. But you can get a good start toward a solution by doing some systematic testing.

a. For each of the following numbers of food bars and drink cartons, check to see if they will provide at least the daily minimums of fat, carbohydrate, and protein. Then find the total weights of the feasible combinations.

- 4 food bars and 10 cartons of drink
- 10 food bars and 4 cartons of drink
- 10 food bars and 10 cartons of drink
- 4 food bars and 4 cartons of drink

b. Record your findings on a copy of the grid below. The case of 4 food bars and 10 drink cartons already has been plotted. Fill in data for the other combinations you tested in Part a.

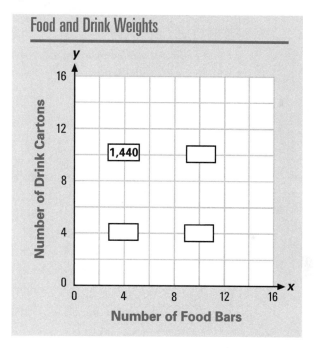

c. Now test the remaining lattice points on this grid to get a picture of the *feasible* combinations of food bars and drink cartons that meet the *constraints*. For each feasible combination, find the total weight and plot it on your copy of the grid.

5. Now analyze the completed grid showing the predicted weight for each feasible lattice point.

a. Describe the region where constraints are met.

b. Use your work to decide how many food bars and drink cartons should be used per astronaut in order to provide minimum daily food requirements while making total weight as small as possible. Be prepared to explain how you can be sure that your answer is correct.

Checkpoint

Problems that can be analyzed by linear programming have several common features: variables, constraints, and an objective.

a What are the variables, constraints, and objective in the video-game-production problem?

b What are the variables, constraints, and objective in the astronaut-diet problem?

c What is a feasible point in a linear programming problem? What would feasible points and "not feasible" points tell you in the video-game-production and astronaut-diet problems?

Be prepared to compare your reponses to those of other groups.

On Your Own

A new store has an option to lease selling space of up to 10,000 square feet. The leased space would be divided into two sections, one for books and the other for music and videos. Furnishings for the two kinds of selling space cost $5 per square foot for books and $7 per square foot for music and videos. The store has a budget of at most $60,000 for furnishings. Each square foot of book-selling space generates an average of $75 per month in sales; each square foot of music-and-video-selling space generates an average of $95 per month in sales.

a. Identify the variables, constraints, and objective.

b. Find two feasible points and one not feasible point, and evaluate the objective at the two feasible points.

c. What mix of book-and-music/video-selling space will maximize sales?

INVESTIGATION 2 Using an Algebraic Model

As you worked on the production-planning problem for Integrated Technologies and on the astronaut-diet problem, you probably thought, "There's *got* to be an easier way than testing all these possible combinations!" It often helps to use a computer or calculator in exploring the many possible options. To use these technology tools, it is essential to express the problem in algebraic form.

Think again about the situation at Integrated Technologies. Recall that assembly time required for each IT-95 was 0.6 hour and for each IT-2000 was 0.3 hour. Using x to represent the number of IT-95 models and y to represent the number of IT-2000 models, the constraint "at most 240 hours of assembly time per day" can be written $0.6x + 0.3y \leq 240$.

1. Build an algebraic model for the video-game-production problem.

   a. First analyze the inequality $0.6x + 0.3y \leq 240$. What is represented by $0.6x$? By $0.3y$? By $0.6x + 0.3y$?

   b. Now write inequalities and expressions to represent the following in symbolic form.

   ■ Testing of each IT-95 takes 0.2 hours and each IT-2000 takes 0.4 hours. The plant can apply at most 160 hours of technician time each day for testing.

   ■ Packaging time is the same for each video game model. The packaging department of the plant can handle at most 500 games per day.

   ■ The company makes a profit of $50 on each IT-95 and $75 on each IT-2000.

In the language of linear programming, the last expression you wrote is called an **objective function** because it shows how the goal of the problem is a function of, or depends on, the input variables.

Translating a problem into algebraic form is one step toward a solution. But you still have to figure out how to use the *constraint inequalities* and the objective function to solve the given problem. By writing constraints in symbolic form, you can use a graphing calculator or computer software to help produce a graph of the *feasible points*.

2. Look again at the Integrated Technologies scheduling problem and the assembly time constraint. The graph below shows points meeting the assembly time constraint $0.6x + 0.3y \leq 240$. *Points that are **not** feasible have been shaded out of the picture.*

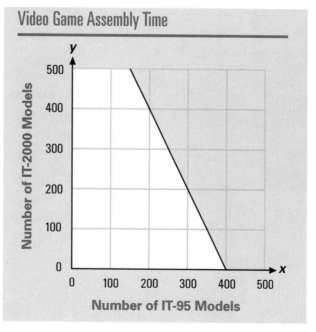

Video Game Assembly Time

   a. Have each member of your group select a different point from the shaded region and verify that it is not a feasible point.

b. Now, have each group member select a different feasible point and verify that its coordinates satisfy the assembly time constraint inequality.

c. Next, focus on points that lie along the boundary line of the feasible set.

- What do you notice about assembly time required for those combinations of IT-95 and IT-2000 models?

- What is the equation of this boundary line?

d. Share ideas with other students for graphing the boundary of this constraint on feasible points quickly, by hand or using your graphing calculator.

e. Does it seem reasonable that all the feasible points are on one side of the line and all points that are not feasible are on the opposite side of the line? Explain your thinking.

3. Now, consider the packaging time and testing time constraints at Integrated Technologies.

a. On two separate grids, locate points that meet the constraints $x + y \leq 500$ and $0.2x + 0.4y \leq 160$ by shading out the points that are not feasible.

b. Using your results from Part a and a copy of the graph in Activity 2, shade all the points that are not feasible. Describe the region where points have coordinates that meet all three constraints. Describe the boundary of the feasible set you've found.

c. Describe at least three different ways you could find the point of intersection of a pair of boundary conditions. Choose one of those methods and find the coordinates of the point of intersection of a pair of lines on your graph.

d. If you have entered the equation of the boundary line for each constraint in the functions list, another quick way to find the point of intersection of a pair of boundary equations is to use the "intersect" option, if available, on your graphing calculator or computer software. Using the calculator option typically involves selecting the two "curves" whose intersection you wish to find. Consult your manual to learn how to use this option. Find the coordinates of the point of intersection for each remaining pair of boundary lines.

e. Finally, evaluate the objective function, $P = 50x + 75y$, at various points in the feasible region. Try to find the point that gives the largest possible profit. Think about ways to do this without checking every possible (x, y) pair: are there reasonable places to look for the values of x and y that will maximize profit?

f. What would be your recommendation on the numbers of IT–95 and IT–2000 video games that Integrated Technologies should plan to produce each day?

As you located the feasible set and the maximum profit point for the video-game-production problem, you probably discovered ways to use what you know about linear equations and inequalities to speed the location process. Test your ideas on the astronaut-diet problem described in Activity 4 of Investigation 1 (page 66).

4. Recall that there are two kinds of food to be carried on a space shuttle trip: special food bars and cartons of a special drink.

   ■ Each food bar provides 5 grams of fat, 40 grams of carbohydrate, and 8 grams of protein.

   ■ Each carton of drink provides 6 grams of fat, 25 grams of carbohydrate, and 15 grams of protein.

   ■ Each food bar weighs 65 grams and each drink weighs 118 grams.

   a. Translate the *constraints* and *objective* into algebraic form:

      ■ Include *at least* 61 grams of fat.

      ■ Include *at least* 350 grams of carbohydrate.

      ■ Include *at least* 103 grams of protein.

      ■ Keep total weight of food bars and drink cartons as low as possible.

   b. On a copy of a grid like the one below, graph each constraint to show the feasible set of (*food bars*, *drink cartons*) combinations.

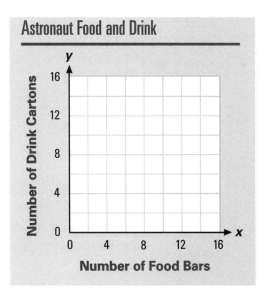

Astronaut Food and Drink

(Graph with vertical axis labeled "Number of Drink Cartons" marked 0, 4, 8, 12, 16 and horizontal axis labeled "Number of Food Bars" marked 0, 4, 8, 12, 16)

   c. Evaluate the objective function at various points in the feasible region to find the point that gives the smallest possible weight. Think about ways to do this without checking every possible (*x*, *y*) pair: are there reasonable places to look for the values of *x* and *y* that will minimize weight?

   d. What would be your recommendation for the combination of food bars and drink cartons that will provide the daily minimums of fat, carbohydrate, and protein with least total weight?

Checkpoint

The video-game-production and astronaut-diet problems are examples of *linear programming* problems. Each involved several *variables*, several *constraints* or limits on those variables, a *feasible set* of values for the variables that meet the constraints, and an *objective function*.

a Review your work on the video-game-production problem.
  - What are the variables, constraints, and objective function?
  - How can the conditions be expressed in symbolic form?
  - What is the feasible set in the problem, and how can the boundaries of that region be located with the help of a graphing calculator or computer software?
  - Where in the feasible set does the objective function seem to take its maximum value?

b Review your work on the astronaut-diet problem.
  - What are the variables, constraints, and objective function?
  - How can the conditions be expressed in symbolic form?
  - What is the feasible set in the problem, and how can the boundaries of that region be located with the help of a graphing calculator or computer software?
  - Where in the feasible set does the objective function seem to take its minimum value?

c Now consider both linear programming problems.
  - What patterns do you see that make it reasonable to use the word *linear* to describe them all? How about the word *programming*?
  - If you were faced with another linear programming problem, how would you go about locating the feasible set and finding the points in the set that maximize or minimize the objective function?

Be prepared to share your thinking, methods, and findings with the entire class.

Paisan's Pizza makes gourmet frozen pizzas for sale to supermarket chains. They make only deluxe pizzas, one vegetarian and the other with meat. Their business planning has these constraints and objective:

- Each vegetarian pizza takes 12 minutes of labor and each meat pizza takes 6 minutes of labor. The plant has *at most* 3,600 minutes of labor available each day.

- The plant freezer can handle a total of *at most* 500 pizzas per day.

- Vegetarian pizza is not quite as popular as meat pizza, so the plant makes *at most* 200 of this type each day.

- The sale of each vegetarian pizza earns Paisan's $3 profit and each meat pizza earns $2 profit. The company would like to maximize its profit.

a. Translate the constraints and objective in this situation into algebraic form.

b. On a copy of a grid like the one below, graph each constraint to determine the feasible set for this situation.

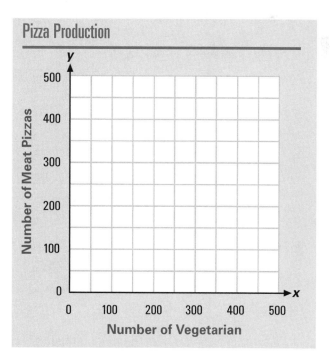

c. Evaluate the objective function at various points in the feasible region to find the point that gives maximum profit.

INVESTIGATION 3 ▸ Finding the Best Feasible Points

This lesson began with two situations with several *variables*, several *constraint inequalities*, and an *objective function* to be maximized or minimized. You found that to work effectively in such settings it helped to be skillful in writing, graphing, and interpreting linear equations and linear inequalities. In this investigation, you can put that knowledge of linearity to work and discover the key to finding the best among all *feasible* points.

1. To find the feasible region for the Integrated Technologies production planning problem, you graphed the constraint inequalities below.

$$0.6x + 0.3y \leq 240 \qquad 0.2x + 0.4y \leq 160 \qquad x + y \leq 500$$

Given these constraints, the objective was to find the combination (*number of IT-95 models, number of IT-2000 models*) that gave maximum profit. The objective function was $P = 50x + 75y$ because the company makes \$50 profit on each IT-95 and \$75 profit on each IT-2000.

a. The feasible set for this situation is shown as the unshaded region in the diagram below. On a copy of this graph, write the linear equations that correspond to each segment of the boundary.

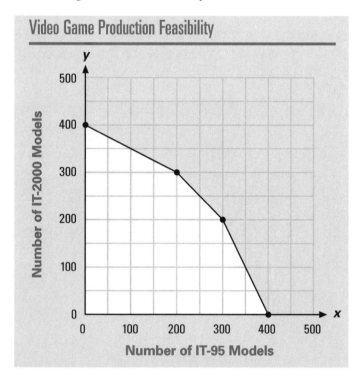

Video Game Production Feasibility

Number of IT-2000 Models (y-axis)
Number of IT-95 Models (x-axis)

b. Looking at the graph, what do the coordinates of the points at the corners of the feasible region appear to be? Do these coordinates agree with those you found in Activity 3 of Investigation 2 (page 70)? Resolve any differences and then record the correct coordinates on your copy of the graph.

c. Now think about the objective function $P = 50x + 75y$.

- How does the value of P change as the numbers x and y of video-game models increase within the feasible region?

- Imagine a "production" point (x, y) moving outward across the feasible region in search of maximum profit. Where would you expect the combination (x, y) giving maximum profit to occur? List likely candidates and reasons for your choices.

d. By dividing the work among your group, calculate the profit for each of the points you listed in Part c. Record your tests in a table like the one below.

Video Game Profit

IT-95 Models	IT-2000 Models	Profit (in dollars)

- Of these points, which gives the maximum profit?

- Compare your combination of models to be produced for maximum profit with that found by other groups.

2. The next graph shows the feasible region for the astronaut-diet problem that you also worked on earlier. Remember, the objective was to find a combination of food bars and drink cartons that would give needed fat, carbohydrate, and protein with minimum total weight of the food. The objective function was $W = 65x + 118y$, because each food bar weighed 65 grams and each drink carton weighed 118 grams.

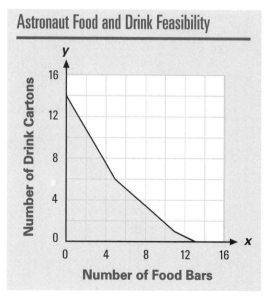

Astronaut Food and Drink Feasibility

a. Where would you expect the minimum weight combination to occur? List several likely candidates.

b. Calculate the total weight for each combination using a table like the one below. Decide which combination gives minimum weight.

Astronaut Food and Drink

Food Bars	Drink Cartons	Weight (in grams)

c. Explain why it is reasonable that the minimum weight combination occurred where it did in the feasible region.

3. Based on your work in Activities 1 and 2, where do you think the maximum or minimum value of the objective function for a linear programming problem will occur? Why does this make sense?

Checkpoint

You've now worked out solutions to several typical linear programming problems and learned some of the basic mathematical ideas and skills needed. Suppose you were going to describe linear programming to someone who knew some algebra.

a How would you describe the kinds of problems to which linear programming can be applied?

b What steps would you list in the procedure for solving linear programming problems?

c What key idea simplifies the search for "best" feasible points in linear programming problems?

Be prepared to share your group's descriptions with the entire class.

On Your Own

Recall that Paisan's Pizza had to decide how many of its gourmet pizzas to make for sale to supermarket chains. (See the "On Your Own" on page 73.) They had labor constraints, freezer capacity constraints, and a limited market for the vegetarian style pizza.

In symbolic form, the constraints and objective function could be written:

- $12x + 6y \leq 3{,}600$ (Labor to make pizzas)
- $x + y \leq 500$ (Freezer capacity)
- $x \leq 200$ (Market for vegetarian pizza)
- $P = 3x + 2y$ (Profit function)

The graph below shows the feasible set for this problem.

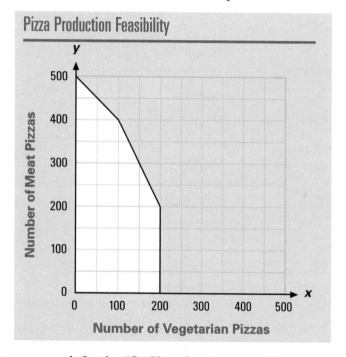

Pizza Production Feasibility

a. Refer to your work for the "On Your Own" on page 73.

- Compare the symbolic forms you developed for the constraints and objective function with those given above. Resolve any differences.
- Compare the feasible set you found for this situation with the graph shown above. Resolve any differences.

b. At what points should you check the profit to see if it is the maximum?

c. Describe at least three ways in which you can determine the coordinates of these points.

d. What combination of vegetarian and meat pizzas will yield the maximum profit for Paisan's Pizza?

INVESTIGATION 4 Linear Equations and Inequalities

In each of the linear programming problems you've worked so far, the constraints have been in two forms: $ax + by \leq c$ or $ax + by \geq c$. To find the feasible sets you had to locate all points with coordinates (x, y) that satisfied those inequalities. So it seems wise to develop some skill in working with inequalities of that type and in anticipating the kinds of graphs to expect.

In the video-game-production and astronaut-diet problems, only positive values of x and y made sense, so graphs were in the first quadrant. Other problems involve negative numbers, so the following activities ask you to investigate inequalities and their graphs considering both positive and negative values of the variables involved. Look for patterns in the results that will help you with other similar problems in the future.

1. Given below are inequalities and graphs that show the coordinate plane split by lines into *half-plane regions*. Match each inequality listed in Parts a through j with the region I through X that represents it, and be prepared to explain the reasons for your choice. The scales on the coordinate axes are 1.

   a. $x \geq 2$ **b.** $x \leq 2$

   c. $2x + 3y \leq 3$ **d.** $2x + 3y \geq 3$

   e. $y \geq x$ **f.** $y \leq x$

   g. $y \leq 0.5x - 2$ **h.** $y \geq 0.5x - 2$

   i. $3x + 2y \geq 4$ **j.** $3x + 2y \leq 4$

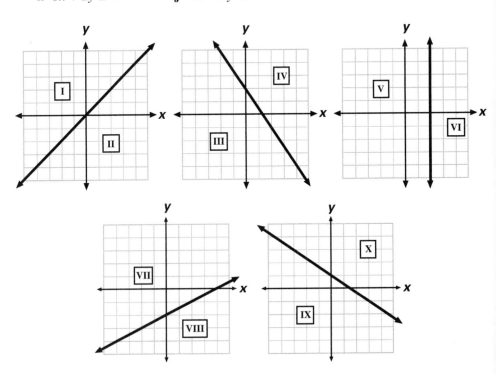

2. On separate coordinate axes, sketch graphs for each of the following inequalities. In each case, outline and label as *feasible* the region that meets the given condition. Be prepared to explain your strategy in each case.

   a. $y \geq -x$ **b.** $y \leq 2x + 3$

   c. $y \geq -4$ **d.** $2x + 6y \leq 12$

3. On a single coordinate system, outline and label as *feasible* the region whose points satisfy the constraints $y \leq 2x + 3$ and $y \geq -x$.

4. On a single coordinate system, outline and label as *feasible* the region whose points satisfy the constraints $-3x + y \geq -2$ and $x + y \leq 6$.

5. On a single coordinate system, outline and label as *feasible* the region whose points satisfy the constraints $x + y \leq 4$ and $x - 2y \geq 6$.

Checkpoint

This investigation explored the general question of graphing linear inequalities in several familiar forms.

a   What steps would you follow to graph an inequality in the form $ax + by \leq c$ or the form $ax + by \geq c$?

b   What steps would you follow to graph an inequality in the form $y \leq a + bx$ or $y \geq a + bx$?

Be prepared to describe and explain your steps to the whole class.

On Your Own

The sketch at the right shows a graph of the equation $5x + 2y = 6$.

a. Sketch a copy of this graph. Shade and label as feasible the regions where points have coordinates satisfying the inequalities:

- $5x + 2y \geq 6$
- $5x + 2y \leq 6$

b. Describe two methods for graphing the linear equation $5x + 2y = 6$.

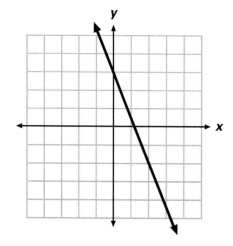

Modeling • Organizing • Reflecting • Extending

Modeling

1. The Backstage Dance Studio director must plan for and operate many different classes, 7 days a week, at all hours of the day. Saturday is a very important day for younger students, and each Saturday class fills up quickly.

   To plan the Saturday schedule, the director has to consider these facts:

   ▪ It's not easy to find enough good teachers, so the studio can offer at most 8 tap classes and at most 5 jazz classes.

   ▪ The studio has limited classroom space, so it can offer a total of at most 10 classes for the day.

   ▪ The studio makes profit of $150 from each tap class and $250 from each jazz class.

   a. What are the variables in this situation?

   b. Write algebraic inequalities giving the constraints on the variables.

   c. The director wants to make as much profit as possible. Write the objective function for this situation.

   d. Graph the constraints and outline the feasible set for the situation.

   e. Find the schedule of classes that gives maximum profit.

   f. The director of Backstage Dance Studio really wants to promote interest in dance, so she also wants to maximize the number of children who can take classes. Each tap class can accommodate 10 students, and each jazz class can accommodate 15 students.

   Write an objective function that reflects the maximum number of students, rather than maximum profit. Find the schedule that gives maximum student participation.

2. A sporting goods manufacturer produces skateboards and in-line skates. Its dealers demand at least 30 skateboards per day and 20 pairs of in-line skates per day. The factory can make at most 60 skateboards and 40 pairs of in-line skates per day.

   a. Write and graph inequalities expressing the given constraints on skateboard and in-line skate manufacturing.

   b. How many combinations of in-line skates and skateboards are possible?

   c. Suppose the total number of skateboards and pairs of in-line skates cannot exceed 90. What inequality expresses this constraint? Graph this new constraint.

   d. Find coordinates of corners for the new feasible region.

   e. Suppose the profit on each skateboard is $12 and on each pair of in-line skates is $18. Write the profit function.

   f. How many of each product should the company manufacture to get maximum profit?

3. The manufacturing facility that supplies a chain of Packaging Plus stores received a rush order for 290 boxes. It had to fill the order in eight hours or less.

   ■ The factory has a machine that can produce 30 boxes per hour and costs $15 per hour to operate.

   ■ The factory can also use two student workers from other, less-urgent tasks; together those students can make 25 boxes per hour at a cost of $10 per hour.

   What combination of machine and student work times will meet the order deadline for least total cost?

4. The Dutch Flower Bulb Company bags a variety of mixtures of bulbs. There are two customer favorites: The Moonbeam mixture contains 30 daffodils and 50 jonquils, and the Sunshine mixture contains 60 daffodils and 20 jonquils.

   The company imports 300,000 daffodils and 260,000 jonquils for sale each year. The profit for each bag of the Moonbeam mixture is $2.30. The profit for each bag of the Sunshine mixture is $2.50. The problem is deciding how many bags of each mixture the company should make in order to maximize profit without exceeding available supplies.

   a. Write and graph the constraint inequalities.

   b. Write the objective function.

   c. Find the combination of Moonbeam and Sunshine bags that will maximize profit.

Organizing

1. Give sets of inequalities that define each of the *shaded* regions below. The scales on the coordinate axes are 1.

   a.   **b.**

   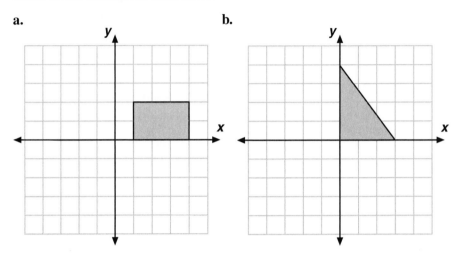

2. Suppose each shaded region in Organizing Task 1 represents the feasible set for a linear programming problem. List the points that you would test in a profit equation. Explain why you picked those points.

3. Sketch the feasible regions defined by the following inequalities. Use the given equations for profit P and cost C to find (x, y) combinations yielding maximum profit or minimum cost within the feasible regions.

   a. $3y - 2x \geq 6$

   $0 \leq x \leq 4$

   $y \leq 5$

   $P = 5x + 3y$

   b. $x \leq 10$

   $2x + y \geq 20$

   $y \leq 14$

   $C = 20x + 5y$

   c. $x + 2y \geq 8$

   $0 \leq x \leq 16$

   $0 \leq y \leq 12$

   $P = 4x + 12y$

4. Describe a situation that could be modeled by the constraint inequalities and the objective function from Part a, b, or c of Organizing Task 3 above.

5. You often can discover creative ways of carrying out mathematical tasks. For example, Angelyn proposed the following procedure to solve a system of linear equations. To solve the system $0.2x + 0.4y = 160$ and $x + y = 500$, she reasoned as follows:

Angelyn

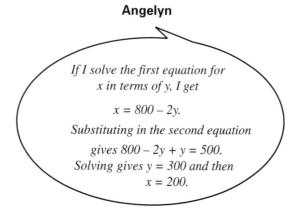

If I solve the first equation for x in terms of y, I get

$x = 800 - 2y.$

Substituting in the second equation gives $800 - 2y + y = 500$. Solving gives $y = 300$ and then $x = 200$.

a. Try to figure out the reasoning used by Angelyn. Check her answer by using a different method to solve the system of equations.

b. Do you think Angelyn's procedure will always work? Try it with the system $x + y = 500$ and $0.6x + 0.3y = 240$.

Reflecting

1. Solving linear programming problems includes finding the boundary of the feasible region. Describe at least three different ways to find the points where the boundary lines defining the region intersect.

2. How would the graphs of the following two inequalities differ?

$2x + y \leq 6$ $\qquad\qquad$ $2x + y < 6$

How could you show their differences in sketches of their graphs?

3. When solving a linear programming problem, how do you identify the variables, constraint inequalities, and objective function?

4. Realistic linear programming problems in business and engineering usually involve many variables and constraints. Why do you think that linear programming was not used much until fairly recently?

Extending

1. A city recreation department offers Saturday gymnastics classes for beginning and advanced students. Each beginner class enrolls 15, and each advanced class enrolls only 10. Available teachers, space, and time lead to these constraints:

   ■ There can be at most 9 beginner classes and at most 6 advanced classes.

   ■ The total number of classes can be at most 7.

   ■ The number of beginner classes should be at most twice the number of advanced classes.

   a. What mix of beginner and advanced classes will give the most children a chance to participate?

   b. Suppose the recreation department director sets new constraints for the schedule of gymnastics classes:

   ■ The same limits exist for teachers, so there can be at most 9 beginner and 6 advanced classes.

   ■ The program should serve at least 150 students, with 15 in each beginner class and 10 in each advanced class.

   The new goal is to minimize the cost of the program. Each beginner class costs $500 to operate, and each advanced class costs $300. What combination of beginner and advanced classes should be offered?

2. Explain why the minimum or maximum value of the objective function for a linear programming problem seems always to occur near the boundary of the feasible region.

3. The Bestform Ring Company makes class rings for high schools and colleges all over the country. Production of each ring is a three-step process involving molding, engraving, and polishing. The following chart gives information concerning the time (in hours) that it takes to produce 100 high school rings or 100 college rings and the time that machines and operators are available during one day.

Class Ring Production

Stage in Ring Making	Time to Make 100 High School Rings (in hours)	Time to Make 100 College Rings (in hours)	Machine and Operator Time Available Each Day (in hours)
Molding	1.2	2	14
Engraving	0.6	3	15
Polishing	2	2	20

If the company makes $500 profit on each 100 high school rings and $525 on each 100 college rings, how many of each should be produced to maximize profit, assuming all rings of either type can be sold?

4. The Junior Class of Oakland Mills High School sells juice at the Columbia Fair to raise funds for the Junior-Senior Prom. The students have 50 gallons of lemonade and 30 gallons of orange juice. The juniors mix and sell two drinks: Carnival Juice, which is two quarts orange juice to two quarts lemonade, and Lemon Punch, which is three quarts lemonade to one quart orange juice. If the profit is $1.60 per gallon on the Carnival Juice and $1.92 per gallon on the Lemon Punch, how many gallons of each mixture should the juniors make to maximize their profit?

The lessons in this unit have involved many different situations in which more than two variables were related to each other in important ways. In Lesson 1, you investigated situations that could be modeled by functions with several input variables. Lesson 2 focused specifically on geometric contexts that could be modeled by multiple-variable relations involving trigonometry: the Law of Sines and the Law of Cosines. Situations in Lesson 3 were modeled by systems of equations in which two output variables were linked by a single input variable. In Lesson 4, you examined situations in which there were multiple constraints, modeled by inequalities using two input variables, and an objective function to be maximized or minimized, which involved the same two input variables. The problem contexts that follow will help you organize your thinking on multiple-variable relations, how they can be modeled, and how those models can help in making decisions.

1. The sounds you hear, from musical instruments and human voices to whispering wind and crackling lightning, all are carried by vibrating waves of air. The pitch of a sound is determined by the frequency of vibration; a higher frequency gives a higher pitch. That frequency depends on certain properties of the sound source.

   For example, when the drummer in a band hits one of the cymbals, the frequency F of its sound varies directly with the density k of the material and inversely with the square of the cymbal's diameter D.

   a. What changes in the variables k and D would lead to higher-pitched sound, and what changes would lead to lower-pitched sound?

b. Why are the patterns of change you described in Part a reasonable, based on your experience with cymbals, drums, or other similar musical instruments?

c. Write equations showing the relation between F, k, and D. Express the relation in three different ways:

- F is a function of k and D.
- k is a function of F and D.
- D^2 is a function of F and k.

2. When architects design buildings, they have to balance many factors. Construction and operating costs, strength, ease of use, and style of design are only a few.

For example, when architects designing a large city office building began their design work, they had to deal with the following conditions:

- The front of the building had to use windows of traditional style to fit in with the surrounding historic buildings. There had to be at least 80 traditional windows on the front of the building. Those windows each had an area of 20 square feet and glass that was 0.25 inches thick.

- The back of the building was to use modern style windows that had an area of 35 square feet and glass that was 0.5 inches thick. There had to be at least 60 of those windows.

- In order to provide as much natural lighting for the building as possible, the design had to use at least 150 windows.

a. Write the constraint inequalities that match conditions of this situation. Then sketch the region of feasible points.

b. One way to rate the possible designs is by how well they insulate the building from loss of heat in the winter and loss of air-conditioning in the summer. The heat loss R in Btu's per hour through a glass window can be estimated by the equation $R = \frac{5.8A}{t}$, where A stands for the area of the window in square feet and t stands for the thickness of the glass in inches.

- What are the heat flow rates of the traditional and modern windows?

- Use the results from above to write an objective function if the goal is to choose a combination of traditional and modern windows that minimizes heat flow from the building.

- Find the combination of window types that meets the constraints and minimizes the objective function.

c. Minimizing construction cost is another consideration. The traditional windows cost $200 apiece. The modern windows cost $250 apiece.

- Write an objective function if the goal is to minimize total cost.

- Find the combination of traditional and modern windows that will meet the constraints and minimize total cost of the windows.

d. If you were the architect, what combination of traditional and modern windows would you recommend and why?

3. En route to sea, a freighter travels 50 km due west of home port. It then turns, making an angle of 132° with its former path. It travels 80 km before radioing home port.

a. Draw a diagram showing the path of the freighter.

b. How far is the freighter from its home port?

c. If sea conditions permitted, through what angle could the freighter have turned from its original course to go directly from home port to the position at which it radioed the port?

d. Describe a second way in which you could find an answer for Part c.

4. On any long trip along American interstate highways, you are sure to meet hundreds of large trucks. They carry cargo of all kinds between nearby cities and across the country from coast to coast. One problem faced by trucking companies is finding the most efficient operating speed. Consider the case of a company that hauls radioactive waste materials

from a nuclear power plant to a special storage facility that is 800 miles away.

  a. List as many advantages as you can for planning a fairly high speed for the trucks on this job. List advantages for a slower speed.

  b. One factor to consider is that pay for the truck driver is related to the time it takes to make the 800-mile trip. How is time T for the 800-mile trip related to speed S in miles per hour?

  c. If the truck driver earns $25 per hour, what equation gives the driver cost C_D (in dollars) as a function of speed in miles per hour for the trip? Describe the pattern of change in driver cost as speed increases.

  d. Another factor to consider is the cost of fuel for the trip. For trucks owned by the hauling company, the fuel cost C_F (in dollars) for the 800-mile trip is related to the speed of the truck by the equation $C_F = \frac{6S^2 + 7{,}200}{S}$. Describe the pattern of change in fuel cost as truck speed increases.

  e. At what speed is the cost of fuel equal to the cost of paying the driver?

  f. What equation shows how total operating cost for the trip (fuel and driver pay) changes as driving speed changes? How can that equation be used to find the driving speed that minimizes cost for each trip? What is the minimum cost? At what speed?

5. In your work with multiple-variable models, it often was helpful (1) to rewrite algebraic expressions and (2) to sketch graphs of linear equations and inequalities, and to do both quickly and accurately. Check your level of skill in these areas by completing the following tasks.

  a. Solve the equation $z = \frac{5x}{y}$ for y in terms of x and z.

  b. Solve the equation $z = \frac{5x}{y}$ for x in terms of y and z.

  c. Solve the equation $z = 5x + 11y$ for x in terms of y and z.

  d. Solve the equation $\frac{d}{\sin 100°} = \frac{88}{\sin 27°}$.

  e. Rewrite the equation $3.5x + 1.8y = 2.7$ so that it can be graphed using a graphing calculator or computer software.

  f. Sketch the graph of $2x - 6y \geq 13$.

Checkpoint

You have investigated several different multiple-variable situations in this unit. In some cases, a single equation can express the relation among several variables. In other cases, more than one equation is needed to show how several output variables depend on a single input variable. And in still other cases, several variables are related by constraint inequalities, and the goal is to find values of the variables that maximize or minimize an objective function.

ⓐ Consider the equation $z = \frac{3x}{y}$.

- How does z change as x increases or decreases?
- How does z change as y increases or decreases?
- What equivalent equation shows y as a function of x and z?
- What equivalent equation shows x as a function of y and z?

ⓑ Consider the equation $z = 3x + 5y$.

- How does z change as x or y increases? As x or y decreases?
- What equivalent equation shows x as a function of y and z?

ⓒ What clues do you use to decide if modeling a problem situation requires the Law of Cosines? If it requires the Law of Sines?

ⓓ If two variables y_1 and y_2 are both functions of x, describe how you can use graphs and tables to find values of x for which each of the following is true:

- $y_1 > y_2$
- $y_1 < y_2$
- $y_1 = y_2$

ⓔ Describe the roles played by the following elements of linear programming problems:

- Constraints
- Feasible points
- Objective function

ⓕ What steps are involved in graphing an inequality like $3x + 5y \leq 10$?

ⓖ For each of the following cases, describe what clues you use to decide if a problem situation requires that type of modeling.

- Several variables related by a single equation
- Several equations with the same input variable
- Analysis by linear programming

Be prepared to share your responses and explain your thinking.

Modeling Public Opinion

Voting Models

Have you ever been asked the question, "What's your opinion?" It seems that on any given issue, there are many different opinions. It is easy enough to discover individual opinions: just listen to talk radio, read the op/ed page of a newspaper, or simply ask people. It's not so easy to determine **public opinion**—the opinion of a group of people. But assessing public opinion is important because it influences many decisions, such as which TV shows should be canceled or which educational programs should be used in your school.

There are two essential steps to determining public opinion: getting individual opinions, and then somehow consolidating the individual opinions into public opinion. In this unit, you will investigate mathematical tools for measuring and analyzing public opinion.

Think About This Situation

An entrepreneur wants to open a new fast-food restaurant franchise. First, she needs to decide which restaurant would be best. The opinions of the community are obviously very important to her planning. Suppose she tries to determine the collective opinion of all students in your school about different fast-food restaurants.

a What are some methods that the entrepreneur could use to determine student opinion?

b Suppose someone suggests taking a survey of some, but not all, students. Do you think this is a good way to measure student opinion? What are some advantages and disadvantages of using a survey like this to determine public opinion?

c Suppose someone else decides to get every student's opinion by having every student vote. What are some advantages and disadvantages of using this method to determine public opinion?

d Describe some situations in which voting is used to determine public opinion. Is there any difference in the way the voting is carried out and analyzed in those situations?

INVESTIGATION 1 ▸ Ranking Choices

To assess public opinion, you might try to get the opinion of every individual in the group, or you might try to get opinions from just a sample of people in the group. If you ask only a sample, then you have to determine carefully what you can say about the whole group's opinion. Selecting and interpreting data from a sample will be your task in future lessons of this unit. But even if you ask everyone in a group, you still have to combine all the individual opinions to yield a group opinion.

1. Suppose your class is going on a field trip to a nearby math and science museum. One of the most important decisions the class will have to make is where to eat lunch! Everyone will be on the same bus, so you all will have to go to the same restaurant. The choices are McDonald's, KFC, and Taco Bell.

   a. How can you fairly make the decision about where to eat lunch? Working together as a class, list as many decision-making methods as you can.

   b. Did you think about any methods in Part a other than voting? If not, go back and list some nonvoting methods.

   c. Now consider voting. Suppose you decide to choose a restaurant by voting. Everyone could vote for his or her favorite restaurant, or everyone could vote by ranking the restaurants in order of preference. Which voting method do you think will give you the most information and help you make the best decision? Explain.

2. Think about the method of voting by ranking the choices.

   a. What are some situations in which voting is done by ranking the choices?

   b. If voting is done by ranking the choices, how can the winner be chosen? List as many methods for choosing a winner as you can.

3. Now it is time for your class to vote on the three restaurants.

   a. Use a ballot like the one at the right. Vote by ranking the restaurants. Rank them according to your preference by writing "1" next to your favorite restaurant and "2" and "3" next to your second and third preferences.

   b. Based on your ballots, summarize the preferences of everyone in your class.

   > **BALLOT**
   >
   > Enter your preference for each restaurant.
   >
   > ☐ KFC
   >
   > ☐ McDonald's
   >
   > ☐ Taco Bell

4. Now, analyze the preferences expressed by your class.

    a. Did your class use all possible rankings? How many possible rankings are there for three restaurants?

    b. How many students in your class chose McDonald's as their first preference?

    c. How many voters in your class chose Taco Bell as their first preference?

    d. Which restaurant received the most third-preference votes?

5. Think about how to use the class preferences to decide where to eat lunch.

    a. Working in small groups, and using all the information on class preferences, decide which restaurant should be the winner. Explain the reasoning you used to choose the winner.

    b. Compare your winner, and the method you used, with those of other groups.

6. A class in Iowa organized their individual rankings of restaurants in a **preference table** like the one below:

Restaurant Preference Table

	Rankings					
KFC	1	1	2	2	3	3
McDonald's	2	3	1	3	1	2
Taco Bell	3	2	3	1	2	1
Number of Voters	**6 voters**	**4 voters**	**6 voters**	**7 voters**	**5 voters**	**5 voters**

    a. What do the entries in the first "rankings" column mean?

    b. How many different rankings were made by this class? Do you think the same number of rankings will appear in all preference tables involving three choices?

c. Examine the opinions below about which restaurant is the winner. With which of these students do you agree? Why?

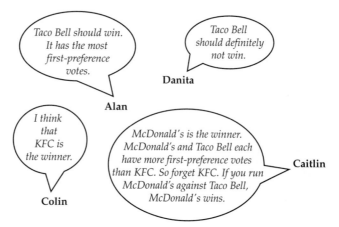

d. How could Danita explain to Alan that Taco Bell should not win?

e. Verify Caitlin's claim that McDonald's and Taco Bell each have more first-preference votes than KFC. Explain why McDonald's is the winner using Caitlin's method.

f. Give a reasonable explanation for Colin's thinking.

7. As a class, use a preference table to reanalyze your preference data from Activity 3. Which restaurant is the winner?

Checkpoint

When you vote by ranking the candidates, you can use a variety of different methods to analyze the results.

a Describe each of the different vote-analysis methods you have considered so far.

b Which vote-analysis method do you think should be used to choose the restaurant at which the class will eat lunch?

Be prepared to defend your recommended analysis method and critique those proposed by others.

Voting based on ranking the candidates, as you have been doing, is sometimes called **preferential voting**. Preferential voting is used for political elections in Australia, Ireland, and South Africa, and it is used in many sports competitions. However, preferential voting is not used in U.S. political elections. By the end of this lesson, you will be able to make some recommendations about whether or not preferential voting should be used more widely.

On Your Own

Consider the following ballots from an election to determine public opinion about favorite nighttime activities.

Concert	2
Ball game	3
Dance	1

Concert	1
Ball game	2
Dance	3

Concert	3
Ball game	2
Dance	1

Concert	3
Ball game	2
Dance	1

Concert	2
Ball game	1
Dance	3

Concert	2
Ball game	1
Dance	3

Concert	2
Ball game	3
Dance	1

Concert	2
Ball game	1
Dance	3

Concert	2
Ball game	1
Dance	3

Concert	2
Ball game	1
Dance	3

Concert	3
Ball game	2
Dance	1

Concert	1
Ball game	2
Dance	3

Concert	2
Ball game	3
Dance	1

Concert	3
Ball game	2
Dance	1

Concert	2
Ball game	1
Dance	3

Concert	2
Ball game	1
Dance	3

Concert	2
Ball game	1
Dance	3

Concert	1
Ball game	2
Dance	3

Concert	2
Ball game	3
Dance	1

Concert	2
Ball game	3
Dance	1

Concert	1
Ball game	2
Dance	3

Concert	3
Ball game	2
Dance	1

Concert	2
Ball game	1
Dance	3

Concert	1
Ball game	2
Dance	3

Concert	2
Ball game	3
Dance	1

a. Construct a preference table summarizing the results of the balloting.

b. Use the preference table you constructed in Part a to find a winner using two different methods. Describe, in writing, the methods you used.

INVESTIGATION 2 ▶ Different Methods, Different Winners

You have seen that there are many ways to analyze the results of preferential voting. In this investigation, you will explore some of the most commonly used vote-analysis methods. Some of these methods may be ones that you have considered already.

For Activities 1 through 5, consider the preference table at the top of the next page, which summarizes voting on preferred athletic shoe brands in one class. The "Number of Voters" row indicates how many voters chose the same ranking. In this case, we have four voter blocks of different sizes.

Athletic Shoe Preference Table

	Rankings			
Fila	1	1	3	3
Nike	3	2	1	2
Reebok	2	3	2	1
Number of Voters	4	6	7	8

1. A **majority** winner is the candidate that gets more than half of the first-preference votes. Find the majority winner, if there is one.

2. A **plurality** winner is the candidate that receives the most first-preference votes. Find the plurality winner, if there is one.

3. Another common analysis method is the **runoff method**. Using this method, you count the first-preference votes to choose the top two candidates, and then you run off the top two against each other.

   a. Which of the athletic shoe brands received the most first-preference votes? Which brand received the next highest number of first-preference votes? These are the top two candidates. On a copy of the athletic shoe preference table, cross out the row for the brand that is not one of the top two.

   b. Now run off the top two brands against each other. Which brand will be chosen by the block of 7 voters? Why? Which brand is the winner?

   c. What are some other situations in which the runoff method is used to choose a winner?

   d. Look back at the vote-analysis strategies used by Colin, Caitlin, and Alan on page 95. Which student used the runoff method? Who used the plurality method?

4. The **pairwise-comparison method** is based on the runoff method. Developed by the philosopher and social scientist Marie Jean Antoine Nicolas Caritat, the Marquis de Condorcet (1743–1794), this method is sometimes called the *Condorcet method*. (Condorcet is pronounced *con-door-say*.) Using this method, all pairs of candidates are run off against each other. The pairwise-comparison winner, if there is one, is the candidate that beats every other candidate.

The Marquis de Condorcet

   a. In the pairwise-comparison method, each possible pair of candidates will have a runoff. List all possible pairings of athletic shoe brands using Fila, Nike, and Reebok.

   b. Consider the pair Fila and Nike. Run off Fila against Nike. Use a copy of the athletic shoe preference table to help you carry out this runoff. Which candidate wins the runoff?

c. Run off all the other pairs of brands. Write down the winner from each runoff.

d. Find the pairwise-comparison winner, if there is one.

5. Another common vote-analysis method is the **points-for-preferences method**. This method was first proposed by an amateur mathematician, Jean-Charles de Borda, who was a French cavalry officer and naval captain in the eighteenth century. It is sometimes called the *Borda count method*. In this method, points are assigned to each preference, and the winner is the candidate that gets the most total points. For example, 3 points could be assigned to first preference, 2 points to second preference, and 1 point for third preference. There can be many other point assignments.

a. Using the point assignments above, how many total points does Reebok get?

b. Find the points-for-preferences winner using the point assignments above.

c. What are some situations in life in which the points-for-preferences method is used to choose a winner?

Checkpoint

Compare the results of using the five vote-analysis methods in Activities 1 through 5. Which brand do you think should be considered the overall winner? Why?

Be prepared to defend your recommended winner and critique the recommendations of others.

On Your Own

Reproduced below is the restaurant preference table from Activity 6 of Investigation 1. Determine the winner under each of the five vote-analysis methods you have studied.

Restaurant Preference Table

	Rankings					
KFC	1	1	2	2	3	3
McDonald's	2	3	1	3	1	2
Taco Bell	3	2	3	1	2	1
Number of Voters	6	4	6	7	5	5

You now know how to analyze a preference table in many ways to help you determine a winner. However, carrying out the various methods can be quite time-consuming. Use of specially designed computer or calculator software considerably reduces the time and effort required and allows you to do a deeper analysis. Use the *Preferential*

```
PREFERENTIAL VOTING
VERSION 2.0

VOTE AND
ANALYZE RESULTS

PRESS ENTER
TO CONTINUE
```

Voting calculator software, or similar software, to complete Activities 6 through 9. These activities use the preference table below, which shows the results of student voting in an election for junior class president.

Junior Class President Preference Table

	Rankings					
Charnell	1	5	5	5	5	5
Marie	5	1	2	4	2	4
Lamar	4	4	1	2	4	2
Rodene	2	3	4	1	3	3
Richard	3	2	3	3	1	1
Number of Voters	36	24	20	18	8	4

6. Find the winner using the plurality method.

    a. Give one reason why the plurality winner is a good choice for the next junior class president.

    b. Give one reason why the plurality winner is *not* a good choice for the next junior class president.

7. Next use the points-for-preferences method to determine the winner. Use a point assignment similar to the one described in Activity 5, but for five candidates (5 points for first preference).

    a. As a group, decide on another set of point assignments, and then find the points-for-preferences winner using those points.

    b. Assign points in such a way that the winner is the choice that gets the *least* total points.

    c. Assign points in such a way that Rodene is *not* the winner.

    d. Give one reason why a points-for-preferences winner should be declared the winner of this election. Give one reason why a points-for-preferences winner should *not* be declared the winner of this election.

8. Find the pairwise-comparison winner. Do you think the pairwise-comparison winner is a fair choice for the next junior class president? Why or why not?

9. Find the runoff winner. Did you get the same winner with this method as with any of the other methods? Do you think the runoff winner is a fair choice for the junior class president?

10. Examine the winners you found in Activities 6 through 9. Are there any surprises? Who do you think should be declared the new junior class president?

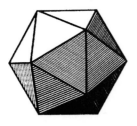

MAA logo

11. Another common voting method is **approval voting**. Since 1987, the Mathematical Association of America (MAA) has elected its officers using approval voting. (The actual 2001 ballot is reproduced below.) The United Nations Security Council also uses approval voting. For this method, every voter selects *all* the candidates he or she approves of. You still can cast only one vote per candidate, but you can vote for as many candidates as you like. For example, if there are five candidates and you approve of three of them, then you can cast a vote for each of the three. The winner in such an election is the candidate that receives the most votes.

> **The Mathematical Association of America**
> **2001 Ballot**
> Balloting is by approval voting. For each office,
> you are advised to vote for one or two candidates.
> One will be elected.
>
> **President Elect (2002)**   **First Vice-President (2002–03)**
> ☐ Ronald L. Graham   ☐ Carl C. Cowen
> ☐ John W. Kenelly   ☐ Genevieve M. Knight
> ☐ Hugh L. Montgomery   ☐ William Y. Velez
> ☐ _____   ☐ _____

a. In the ballot above, why do you think the MAA advises that members vote for one or two candidates?

b. When using approval voting, you don't rank the candidates; you simply cast a vote for all candidates you approve of. Thus, a preference table is not needed. However, to get an idea of how approval voting works, consider again the preference table of votes for a junior class president reproduced below.

Junior Class President Preference Table

	Rankings					
Charnell	1	5	5	5	5	5
Marie	5	1	2	4	2	4
Lamar	4	4	1	2	4	2
Rodene	2	3	4	1	3	3
Richard	3	2	3	3	1	1
Number of Voters	36	24	20	18	8	4

- Assume that voters will approve of their top three choices. For each group of voters in the table, place a check mark next to the candidates the voters will approve of.

- Compute the approval winner and explain your method.

- Compare the approval winner to the winners you found using the other vote-analysis methods in Activities 6 through 9.

Checkpoint

In Investigation 2, you used six vote-analysis methods: majority, plurality, points-for-preferences, runoff, pairwise-comparison, and approval.

a Summarize each of these vote-analysis methods.

b For each of these methods, give one argument supporting it as a good way to accurately measure public opinion. Then give one reason why it is not such a good way to accurately measure public opinion.

c Which method do you think is the most fair? Why?

Be prepared to share your reasons for and against each vote-analysis method with the class.

On Your Own

Historically, a third-party candidate has had little impact in United States Presidential elections. The 1992 election was a notable exception. The three major candidates were George Bush, Bill Clinton, and Ross Perot. Although Clinton won, both of the other two candidates received a significant share of the popular vote. Of course, the president is elected through the *electoral* college, but think about what the election results might have been if a different voting model were used instead. The final popular vote tallies from the election were as follows:

Clinton 44,908,254

Bush 39,102,343

Perot 19,741,065

Since voters did not vote by ranking the candidates, there is no exact preference table for this election. However, opinion polls can be used to construct an approximate preference table. (In the next lessons of this unit, you will learn how to analyze opinion polls carefully.) Suppose the opinion polls at the time suggest these three assumptions:

- If a person voted for Clinton, then Perot would have been the second choice.
- If a person voted for Bush, then Perot would have been the second choice.
- For the people who voted for Perot, half would have chosen Clinton as their second choice and half would have chosen Bush.

a. These assumptions, though broad and open to some debate, provide a basis for constructing a reasonable preference table. Complete the preference table below for the 1992 presidential election.

1992 Presidential Election Approximate Preference Table

	Rankings			
Clinton	1			
Bush	3			
Perot	2			
Number of Voters	44,908,254	39,102,343	9,870,532	9,870,532

b. Is there a majority winner?

c. What percent of the total votes does the plurality winner get?

d. Determine the winner using runoff, points-for-preferences, and pairwise-comparison. Are there any surprises?

INVESTIGATION 3 Fair Is Fair, Isn't It?

Looking over all the voting methods you have investigated so far, you'll notice that each one has some drawback. You might be wondering if any voting method is fair. Or, even more fundamental, you might be wondering just what "fair" means. These are very important and difficult questions.

The mathematical approach to answering these questions is first to formulate a mathematical definition of fairness and then to see if any voting method satisfies the definition. In 1949, the Nobel Prize-winning economist Kenneth Arrow did just this. He reached a conclusion about fair voting methods called **Arrow's Theorem**, which is one of the most surprising and famous theorems of this century. In the following activities, you will explore this theorem.

1. Consider the following preference table for three candidates.

Preference Table				
	Rankings			
A	1	2	3	2
B	2	3	1	1
C	3	1	2	3
Number of Voters	**12**	**10**	**8**	**4**

    a. Determine the runoff winner.

    b. Suppose the four voters represented in the last column change their ranking to 1-2-3, so that they now give more support to candidate *A*. Modify the preference table and determine the new runoff winner.

    c. What seems unfair about this situation?

2. Arrow proposed six fairness conditions, listed below, that should be satisfied by any fair voting method. Then he *proved* that no voting method can satisfy all six conditions whenever there are more than two candidates! Which of the fairness conditions is violated in the situation from Activity 1?

Fairness Conditions

■ **Unanimous**   The decision reached using a fair voting method should agree with the unanimous will of the voters. That is, if all voters prefer choice *X* over choice *Y*, then the voting method should pick *X* as the winner over *Y*.

■ **Decisive**   A fair voting method should be decisive. That is, it should decide for any two choices *X* and *Y* whether *X* beats *Y*, *Y* beats *X*, or there is a tie.

■ **Ordered**   A fair voting method should establish an order among the candidates, so that if *X* is preferred over *Y*, and *Y* is preferred over *Z*, then *X* is preferred over *Z*.

■ **Consistent**   Preference trends among the individual voters should be reflected by the results of a fair election. For example, suppose voter preferences change so that *X* is raised in some or all of the voters' rankings. Then if *X* beat *Y* before the change, *X* should still beat *Y* after the change.

■ **Relevant**   A fair voting method should ignore irrelevant alternatives. That is, for any two candidates *X* and *Y*, the final decision about whether *X* beats *Y* should depend only on how the voters rank *X* versus *Y*, and not on how they rank other candidates.

■ **Non-Dictatorship**   The decision should not always be based solely on the preference of one voter.

3. This preference table summarizes voter preferences in an election for class president.

Class President Preference Table

	Rankings			
Jill	1	1	4	4
Sammi	4	3	1	3
Amir	3	4	2	1
Orlando	2	2	3	2
Number of Voters	45	27	45	36

a. Who is the runoff winner?

b. Suppose Jill's family moves just after the election. The winner in Part a claims this should have no effect on who wins the election. However, the other candidates demand that Jill be removed from the preference table, and the results recomputed.

- Study the ranking of the 27 voters in the second column who had Jill as their first preference. If Jill is removed, who is their new first preference? Their new second preference? Their new third preference? Update the preference table with your answers.

- Similarly, modify the table to reassign the votes of the block of 45 voters who had Jill as their first preference.

c. According to your new preference table in Part b, who is the runoff winner after Jill drops out? Compare winners before and after Jill drops out.

d. In your opinion, is it fair that a person can win an election when all candidates are on the ballot but loses when a losing candidate drops out?

e. Which of Arrow's fairness conditions is violated in this situation? Explain.

Checkpoint

Fairness and fair voting are important issues in any society.

a How is fairness of voting methods analyzed mathematically?

b Discuss why each of Arrow's conditions should be satisfied by any fair voting method.

Be prepared to share your thinking with the entire class.

You have seen that there are drawbacks to all the voting methods you have considered. Arrow's Theorem proves that when there are more than two candidates, *every* possible voting method violates at least one of his fairness conditions. (Arrow's conditions are widely accepted as a good definition of a fair voting method, but mathematicians continue to look for definitions that may be even better.)

In any case, decisions must be made, and they should be as fair as possible. Although no voting method satisfies all of Arrow's conditions, most experts recommend points-for-preferences, using a point assignment in which there is a common difference between point values, such as 4-3-2-1. But there is no magic formula. You must apply your knowledge of the different voting methods to each particular decision-making situation and then decide on the best voting method to use.

▶On Your Own

Think about which voting method you would recommend in each of the situations below.

a. There are two choices for a new school mascot. All students will vote to decide which mascot to adopt. Which voting method would you recommend? Why?

b. There are three candidates for president of the junior class. Two candidates have some differences, but their views are generally similar and they are both popular. The remaining candidate has views that are very different from the other two, and those views are shared by a significant group of students. Which voting methods would you *not* recommend for this situation? Which method would you recommend? Justify your recommendations.

c. There are six finalists in the school talent show. All students will vote to choose the overall winner. Choose one voting method that you would recommend. Choose one method other than majority that you would not recommend. In each case, defend your answer.

Modeling

1. The preference table below summarizes the results of asking all students at a rural high school to rank the importance of four environmental protection policies.

Environmental Protection Preference Table

	Rankings				
Recycle	1	4	4	4	2
Plant Trees	2	3	1	2	3
Conserve Electricity	3	1	3	3	4
Decrease Litter	4	2	2	1	1
Number of Voters	**56**	**48**	**41**	**35**	**29**

a. Using the points-for-preferences method, assigning 3 points to all first-preference votes, 2 points to second-preference, 1 point to third-preference, and 0 points to fourth-preference, which policy should be considered most important to the students?

b. Do you think the point scheme in Part a is reasonable? Why or why not?

c. Does the winner change if you double all the point allocations in Part a? How about if you square all the point allocations in Part a?

d. Hester suggested a modified runoff method. The two policies that get the most first- or second-preference votes undergo a runoff. Find the winner using this method.

2. Some friends and their families are planning a weekend picnic. As part of the day's activities, they want to play a group ball game. Which ball game should they play? They decide to have everyone rank the five different games. The results are shown in the following preference table.

Game Preference Table

	Rankings		
Softball	1	5	5
Soccer	2	1	2
Basketball	3	4	1
Football	4	3	4
Volleyball	5	2	3
Number of Voters	**18**	**16**	**3**

a. Which game is the plurality winner? Do you think the group should choose this game to play? Why or why not?

b. Which game is the pairwise-comparison winner?

c. Find the winners under some other vote-analysis methods.

d. A decision must be made! Which voting method would you recommend to the group? Defend your answer.

3. In Investigation 1, you carried out an election to find your class's favorite restaurant from among McDonald's, KFC, and Taco Bell. Now you will carry out an election in another context of your choice.

a. Choose something about which you can conduct a small election. You might decide to find out about the favorite TV show of some of your friends and family, their favorite soft drink, or their preferred candidate in an upcoming political election.

b. Next, choose three or four "candidates" for the election, make at least 15 ballots like the ballot you completed in Investigation 1, and have friends and family members complete the ballots. (The "candidates" could be different TV shows, different political candidates, different soft drinks, or whatever you are voting on.)

c. Make a preference table summarizing the results of your balloting.

d. Analyze your preference table using each of the six methods from this lesson. Record the winner under each method and discuss which candidate you think should be declared the overall winner.

4. The New Hampshire Primary is the first primary in every U.S. presidential election year. It is an important part of every candidate's campaign. Public opinion throughout the nation can be greatly influenced by how a candidate performs in the New Hampshire Primary. The 1996 New Hampshire Primary provides an interesting case study of the difficulties that can arise in elections involving more than two candidates. In 1996, the major Republican candidates competing in the New Hampshire Primary included Pat Buchanan, Bob Dole, and Lamar Alexander. Pat Buchanan won. This victory contributed to the following events: Dole's campaign faltered, Alexander soon dropped out of the race, and Buchanan gained influence in the Republican party. As in all presidential primaries, the plurality method was used. The final counts are shown below.

Actual Vote Counts for the 1996
New Hampshire Republican Primary

Pat Buchanan	56,923 votes
Bob Dole	54,814 votes
Lamar Alexander	47,214 votes

By examining exit polls, it is possible to make reasonable assumptions about how voters would have ranked the three candidates. Suppose such a poll resulted in the following preference table.

Primary Election, Estimated Preference Table

	Rankings			
Buchanan	1	3	2	3
Dole	2	1	1	2
Alexander	3	2	3	1
Number of Voters	56,923	27,407	27,407	47,214

a. Do you agree that Buchanan was the plurality winner?

b. Compare the actual vote counts to the estimated results shown in the preference table. What assumptions were made to get the estimated results?

c. Determine the winner using runoff, points-for-preferences, and pairwise-comparison.

d. Based on this estimated preference table and your understanding of voting and fairness, who do you think should have been declared the winner of the 1996 New Hampshire Republican Primary? Justify your answer.

e. Do you think the plurality method is the vote-analysis method that should be used in presidential primaries? Why or why not?

5. Sometimes voters vote insincerely to try to change the outcome of an election. Such voting is called **insincere** or **strategic voting**. For example, consider the election for junior class president that you analyzed in Investigation 2 (page 99). Suppose the 20 voters in the third column of the preference table decide to vote strategically (and insincerely) and switch their first and second preferences. The modified preference table is shown below.

Modified Junior Class President Preference Table

	Rankings					
Charnell	1	5	5	5	5	5
Marie	5	1	1	4	2	4
Lamar	4	4	2	2	4	2
Rodene	2	3	4	1	3	3
Richard	3	2	3	3	1	1
Number of Voters	36	24	20	18	8	4

a. Determine the majority, plurality, points-for-preferences, runoff, and pairwise-comparison winners based on this modified preference table.

b. Did this strategic switch in preference produce different winners than those in Investigation 2 for the comparable methods?

c. Give a reason why the 20 voters who switched preferences might have gotten together to plan the switch.

d. Suppose the voters know the election will be analyzed using the runoff method. Find an instance of strategic voting that will benefit one of the groups of voters (using the original, sincere preferences given on page 99).

Organizing

1. You now have experience finding winners with several voting methods. Think about whether those methods always produce winners.

   a. Is there a majority winner for all possible preference tables? If not, construct a simple preference table for which there is no majority winner.

   b. Is there a plurality winner for all possible preference tables? If not, construct a simple preference table for which there is no plurality winner.

   c. Complete the preference table below with a ranking for the group of 4 voters so that there is no pairwise-comparison winner.

Preference Table

	Rankings		
Choice *A*	1	2	
Choice *B*	3	1	
Choice *C*	2	3	
Number of Voters	8	6	4

2. Suppose that a group of 12 students decides to vote to play volleyball, softball, or soccer at their picnic. Each student votes for her or his choice. If the results of the voting are represented in a bar graph, describe the possible shape of the graph in each of the following cases.

   a. There is a majority winner.

   b. There is a plurality winner but no majority winner.

   c. There is no plurality winner.

3. In this task, you will count the total number of rankings possible (without ties) in a preference table.

   a. With three choices, *A*, *B*, and *C*, there are six possible rankings:

   $$ABC, ACB, BAC, BCA, CAB, CBA.$$

   List all possible rankings if there are four choices. Explain how you know that you have listed all possible rankings.

   b. There are 720 different rankings possible with six choices. Explain how to use this fact to find the number of possible rankings of seven choices.

   c. If *NOW* is the number of rankings possible for a certain number of choices and *NEXT* is the number of rankings possible with one more choice, write an equation showing the relationship between *NOW* and *NEXT*.

   d. **Factorial** notation is an economical way of writing certain products of consecutive integers. For example, $5 \cdot 4 \cdot 3 \cdot 2 \cdot 1 = 5!$ which is read as "5 factorial." Similarly, $8!$ equals $8 \cdot 7 \cdot 6 \cdot 5 \cdot 4 \cdot 3 \cdot 2 \cdot 1$ and is read as "8 factorial." Use factorial notation to write an expression for the number of possible rankings with three choices, four choices, and ten choices.

   e. Use the factorial function on your calculator to compute the number of possible rankings for 5 choices, 10 choices, and 50 choices.

4. When using the pairwise-comparison method, you have to run off all possible pairs of choices. Think about how many possible pairs there could be.

   a. List all the pairs that need to be run off if there are three choices: *A*, *B*, and *C*. How many pairs are there?

   b. List all the pairs that need to be run off if there are four choices: *A*, *B*, *C*, and *D*. How many pairs are there?

   c. Make a table with the number of choices in one column and the number of possible pairs in another column. Record your results from Parts a and b. Continue the table for the cases of five and six choices.

   d. Describe any patterns you see in your table from Part c. Use your pattern to predict how many possible pairs there are with 10 choices. Predict the number of pairs with *n* choices.

5. The pairwise-comparison method can be modeled with a digraph, as follows. The vertices represent the candidates, and two vertices are connected by an arrow from one to the other if the one candidate beats the other in their pairwise runoff. For example, if *A* and *B* are two of the candidates and *A* beats *B* in the *A-B* runoff, then there is a directed edge from *A* to *B*. Draw a digraph representing a pairwise-comparison analysis of each of the preference tables at the top of the next page.

a.

Preference Table 1

	Rankings			
Candidate A	1	3	3	2
Candidate B	3	1	2	3
Candidate C	2	2	1	1
Number of Voters	**8**	**6**	**4**	**4**

b.

Preference Table 2

	Rankings		
Candidate A	1	2	3
Candidate B	3	1	2
Candidate C	2	3	1
Number of Voters	**8**	**6**	**4**

c. Can you tell just by looking at a digraph model whether or not there is a pairwise-comparison winner? Explain and illustrate your answer.

Reflecting

1. Which voting model was most difficult for you to understand? Why?

2. Plurality is the most commonly used voting method for political elections in the United States. Do you think this is the best method to use? Write a brief paper explaining the advantages and disadvantages of the plurality method.

3. Does Arrow's Theorem mean that voting is useless and fairness is impossible? Explain.

4. Sometimes in an election there are several candidates, but only two seem to have much chance of winning. The others are called "long shots." This is often the case when there are "third-party" candidates in a presidential election. In such situations, you sometimes hear voters complain that they would like to vote for the long-shot candidate, but they feel that doing so would be throwing their vote away. One advantage of approval voting is that you can vote for a long-shot candidate and yet still vote for one of the front-runners as well. Ask some adults you know who have voted in presidential elections if they ever felt that there was a candidate they wanted to vote for, but didn't because it seemed like they would just be throwing their vote away. Tell these adults how approval voting would solve this problem. Write a paragraph describing whom you talked to, what they said, and how they reacted to your explanation of approval voting.

5. Discuss what you have learned about voting methods for making fair decisions with some adults. Then interview them by asking the following questions. Write a summary of the interview.

- Before our conversation, did you know about different voting methods and their advantages and disadvantages?

- Are you surprised by what I have told you?

- What are examples in your life in which a group needed to make fair decisions?

- What methods were used to make those decisions?

- What do you think is the fairest method to use for electing the President of the United States?

Extending

1. Voting and social decision-making are topics that have intrigued philosophers as well as mathematicians. For example, read the three quotations below. Choose the one that you find most interesting, explain what you think the author meant, and briefly discuss whether you agree or not.

a. "The principle of majority rule must be taken ethically as a means of ascertaining a real 'general will,' not as a mechanism by which one set of interests is made subservient to another set. Political discussion must be assumed to represent a quest for an objectively ideal or 'best' policy, not a contest between interests." (Jean-Jacques Rousseau, *The Social Contract*, 2nd edition, revised, translated. New York: G.P. Putnam's Sons, 1906.)

b. "The idealist doctrine then may be summed up by saying that each individual has two orderings, one which governs him in his everyday actions and one which would be relevant under some ideal conditions and which is in some sense truer than the first ordering. It is the latter which is considered relevant to social choice, and it is assumed that there is complete unanimity with regard to the truer individual ordering." (Kenneth Arrow, *Social Choice and Individual Values*, 2nd edition. New Haven: Yale University Press, 1963.)

c. "[As a basis of political or free society] it is not necessary that everyone subject to the laws should take part in voting them, still less that he should consent to their application to himself, but that it should represent an idea of common good, which each member of the society can make his own so far as he is rational, i.e., capable of the conception of a common good, however much particular passions may lead him to ignore it." (T. H. Green, *Lectures on the Principles of Political Obligation*. New York: Longmans, Green and Co., 1895.)

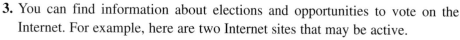

2. Describe the voting method used in your school for the election of class officers. Discuss the method with your group, and prepare a report for the student government proposing the fairest voting strategy to use in the next election. You might promote one of the methods you studied in this lesson, some combination or modification of those methods, or a method of your own. Point out both advantages and disadvantages of your suggestion and indicate benefits of your strategy over the system currently in use.

3. You can find information about elections and opportunities to vote on the Internet. For example, here are two Internet sites that may be active.

- *http://www.vote-smart.org/*

   This site has information about current national and state elections in the United States.

- *http://www.casting-vote.com*

   This site allows you to cast votes on a wide variety of topics including politics, humor, and lifestyles.

   a. Try to visit these sites. Find two other Internet sites that have elections or election information.

   b. Find an Internet site that is conducting an election. Vote in the election. Do people vote for their favorite candidate or do they rank the candidates? What recommendation, if any, would you make to the site manager about the fairest vote-analysis method for the type of election being conducted?

4. Consider the preference table on the next page, showing the results of ranking different types of energy sources. Copy the preference table onto your own paper. You need to do this so that you will have plenty of room to cross things out and make changes.

Energy Source Preference Table

	Rankings				
Oil	1	4	4	4	2
Solar	2	3	1	2	3
Coal	3	1	3	3	4
Nuclear	4	2	2	1	1
Number of Voters	37	32	30	21	7

a. Which energy source received the fewest first-preference votes? Eliminate this choice by crossing out its row.

b. Which groups of voters had the energy source you eliminated as their first preference?

c. For each group of voters in Part b, assign a new first preference. Change their most-preferred remaining choice into their new first preference.

d. Repeat Parts a–c for the modified schedule.

e. Continue in this way until there is only one choice left. This remaining choice is the **sequential-elimination** winner. Using this sequential-elimination method, which energy source is the voters' preferred energy source?

f. The sequential-elimination method is included in some voting software. For example, it is included in the *Preferential Voting* software that runs on your calculator. Use voting software to verify the sequential-elimination winner and compare it to the winners under the other methods included in the software.

g. Explain the connection between the sequential-elimination method and the runoff method when there are only three choices.

```
ANALYZE ELECTION
 1:PLURALITY
 2:RUNOFF
 3:PAIRWISE
 4:POINTS
 5:ELIMINATION
 6:MAIN MENU
```

5. In this task, you will compare the plurality and sequential-elimination methods (see Extending Task 4).

a. Construct a preference table for which the plurality winner is different from the winner using the sequential-elimination method.

b. Construct a preference table for which the plurality winner is the *same* as the winner using the sequential-elimination method.

c. Can you find conditions under which the plurality winner will always be the same as the sequential-elimination winner?

Lesson 2

Surveys and Samples

In Lesson 1, you learned how to measure and analyze public opinion in situations where every person has the opportunity to vote. However, it is possible to measure public opinion without getting everyone's opinion. This can be done using *surveys*, which gather opinions from a *sample* of the population.

Surveys are used often by government agencies, the media, and consumer-oriented businesses. With access to computers that easily compile information, more and more data are gathered from surveys to analyze public opinion about issues, products, and people. If surveys are to be efficient and provide accurate information, they must be based on probabilistic concepts and they must be carried out according to standard rules. In this lesson, you will learn some of the mathematics behind surveys, and you will apply what you learn as you analyze surveys reported in the media.

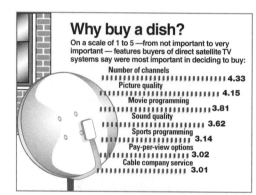

Why buy a dish?

On a scale of 1 to 5 —from not important to very important — features buyers of direct satellite TV systems say were most important in deciding to buy:

Number of channels IIIIIIIIIIIIIIIIIIIIIIIIIIIIIIIII**4.33**
Picture quality IIIIIIIIIIIIIIIIIIIIIIIIIIIIIII**4.15**
Movie programming IIIIIIIIIIIIIIIIIIIIIIIIII**3.81**
Sound quality IIIIIIIIIIIIIIIIIIIIIIIII**3.62**
Sports programming IIIIIIIIIIIIIIIIIIIII**3.14**
Pay-per-view options IIIIIIIIIIIIIIIIIIII**3.02**
Cable company service IIIIIIIIIIIIIIIIIIII**3.01**

Source: *USA Today*, May 29, 1996.

Think About This Situation

The Nielsen Media Research company uses surveys to measure public opinion related to television viewing. The company gets information from only some of America's television viewers, from which it draws conclusions about all viewers. For example, here is one of its survey questions:

On which night do you prefer to watch TV?

a According to the Nielsen findings, the night most viewers prefer to watch television is Sunday; the least preferred night is Saturday. (Source: Nielsen Media Research, 1997.) Why do you think TV networks and advertisers are interested in results like these?

b Describe some surveys with which you are familiar. Have you ever been part of a survey?

c Why do you think surveys are given to a sample of people instead of asking an entire population to vote?

d What background information about a survey do you think is important to know when you read and analyze that survey?

People take surveys about many different things. Sometimes surveys are taken to investigate a trend, such as Internet use or jobless rates, for different segments of the population. One of the most common types of surveys is an *opinion poll*, which is used to describe public opinion on some topic.

1. The Scripps Howard News Service and Ohio University conducted a survey to determine Americans' opinions about heroes. The pollsters defined a *hero* to be "anyone with admirable courage other than family members or biblical figures."

   a. Using this definition of "hero," list at least two people whom you consider to be heroes. Compare your list to those of others in your group.

   b. Describe how you could use voting methods to report the most popular hero for your class.

   c. Suppose you wanted to report the most popular hero according to everyone in your school. Describe how you could do this.

   d. Suppose you are given a report of a survey that says Americans' top three heroes are John F. Kennedy, Martin Luther King, and Abraham Lincoln. Describe any doubts you might have about the survey or any questions you would like to ask the people who prepared the report.

2. Read the following excerpt from an article entitled, "The Endangered U.S. Hero."

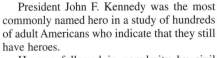

The Endangered U.S. Hero
By Thomas Hargrove and Guido H. Stempel III
Scripps Howard News Service

President John F. Kennedy was the most commonly named hero in a study of hundreds of adult Americans who indicate that they still have heroes.

He was followed in popularity by civil rights leader Martin Luther King, Abraham Lincoln, Persian Gulf War leader Norman Schwarzkopf and former first lady Jacqueline Kennedy.

But perhaps the real winner was "none-of-the-above."

A survey of 1,000 adults conducted by Scripps Howard News Service and Ohio University found that most Americans said they do not have personal heroes.

And three of the top five—Kennedy, King and Schwarzkopf—have faced intense revi-

sionist criticism in recent years.

The survey asked adults to name up to four heroes whom they admire. The group identified 206, ranging from Socrates to Ralph Nader.

Among the most popular were religious figures like Mother Teresa and political figures such as President Clinton.

The telephone survey was conducted from July 17 to Aug. 1 among 1,000 randomly selected Americans at least 18 years old. Interviews were conducted at the E.W. Scripps School of Journalism at Ohio University.

The survey has a margin of error of 4%.
Source: *Milwaukee Journal*, August 14, 1994.

Mother Teresa

a. How did your list of heroes compare to the heroes identified in this article?

b. Were any of your questions or doubts from Part d of Activity 1 resolved? Which ones?

c. It is important to know some details about the survey so that you can judge its validity. For example, who was surveyed and how was the survey conducted? List all the information contained in the article that you think is important for understanding the survey and deciding if it is valid. Is there some important information missing?

3. Individual opinions can be collected by using a census or by using a sample survey. A **census** collects information from every individual in a **population**, which is the entire set of people or objects you would like to describe in some way. A **survey** usually is given to a **sample**, that is, a subset of a population. A survey can be used to form a picture of the entire population without contacting every individual.

a. Did the article which you read in Activity 2 describe a census or a sample survey?

b. Describe the population that was being studied.

c. Describe the sample that was used.

4. Work with a partner to decide whether you would conduct a census or sample survey to answer each of the questions below. Also, describe the population in each case. Compare your answers to those of others in your group.

a. How do people who go to movies feel about a new movie?

b. How do people in your class feel about a particular new movie?

c. Is a manufacturer producing very many defective lightbulbs?

d. How many people are going to eat a hot lunch at school this week?

e. Does the soup you are making have enough seasoning?

f. Who are people going to vote for in the next presidential election?

5. The results of a survey may be interesting, but before the results are accepted, it is important to consider carefully how the survey was constructed and carried out. Some questions you should consider are the following:

- What is the issue of interest or the variable being studied?
- Who sponsored the survey?
- What is the population?
- How was the sample selected?
- How large is the sample?
- What was the *response rate* (percentage of sample responding)?
- How were the responses obtained?
- What were the exact questions asked?

a. Why do you think the answers to the questions above are important to know when you read about a survey?

b. List other information you think would be important to include in an article describing the results of a survey. For each, indicate why the information might be important.

6. Read the following article, "Textbooks too few, too old, say teachers."

   a. Answer the questions given in Activity 5 as they pertain to this article. If the information you listed in Activity 5 Part b is given, record that information as well.

   b. Do you think that, based on the information given, you can confidently accept the results in this article?

Textbooks too few, too old, say teachers
By Tamara Henry

Textbook shortages are so severe in some schools that teachers "scrounge, beg, borrow or buy" them, or use books so old that Nelson Mandela is still in jail in South Africa.

A survey of 1,000 elementary and secondary teachers, to be released today at a Miami school by the Association of American Publishers, found:

- 39% say students don't have enough textbooks.

- 42% didn't assign homework because books had to be left at school.

- 52% say kids get wrong information from outdated material; 25% use 10-year-old books.

- 71% use their own money to buy reading materials.

The survey didn't indicate where the problem is most severe, but Michael Casserly, executive director of Council of the Great City Schools, believes it is in urban schools.

"Maybe it's a case of mistaken priorities," says Rick Blake of the AAP. He points to the 1994 Census report that the USA spent $2 billion for textbooks, $16 billion for pet food and $81 billion for alcohol.

Florida Gov. Lawton Chiles, who will be on hand for the survey release, calls for "the most basic kinds of education reform—providing textbooks and resource materials."

Chiles has asked for a $20 million increase in his state textbook budget; education officials estimate $136.4 million is needed to end the shortage.

Source: *USA Today,* February 29, 1996.

---

7. Examine these results of an Iowa poll on speed limits as reported in the *Des Moines Register.*

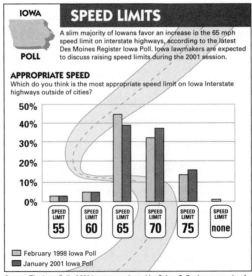

IOWA POLL

SPEED LIMITS

A slim majority of Iowans favor an increase in the 65 mph speed limit on interstate highways, according to the latest Des Moines Register Iowa Poll. Iowa lawmakers are expected to discuss raising speed limits during the 2001 session.

APPROPRIATE SPEED
Which do you think is the most appropriate speed limit on Iowa Interstate highways outside of cities?

SPEED LIMIT 55 | SPEED LIMIT 60 | SPEED LIMIT 65 | SPEED LIMIT 70 | SPEED LIMIT 75 | SPEED LIMIT none

☐ February 1998 Iowa Poll
■ January 2001 Iowa Poll

Source: The Iowa Poll of 800 Iowans conducted by Selzer & Co. has a margin of error +/– 3.5 percentage points.

The Iowa Poll, conducted January 15–21, 2001 asked the following:

The Iowa Legislature sets speed limits for Iowa highways. It is currently 65 miles per hour. Which of the following would be the most appropriate speed limit on Iowa interstate highways outside of cities—55 miles per hour; 60 mph; 65 mph; 70 mph; 75 mph?

The Iowa Poll, conducted for the Des Moines Register by Selzer & Co. of Des Moines, is based on interviews with 800 Iowans age 18 or older. Interviewers contacted households with randomly selected telephone numbers. Percentages based on the full sample may have a maximum margin of error of plus or minus 3.5 percentage points. Republishing the copyrighted Iowa Poll without credit to the Des Moines Register is prohibited.

Source: *Des Moines Register,* January 31, 2001. Copyright 2001 The Des Moines Register and Tribune Company.

a. Answer the questions given in Activity 5 as they pertain to this poll. If the information you listed in Activity 5 Part b is given, record that information as well.

b. Do you think that, based on the information given, you can confidently accept the results in this poll?

Information from a sample is often gathered and summarized using methods similar to some of the voting methods you studied in Lesson 1. However, the full potential of voting methods is not always used in surveys. You learned that there are many sensible voting methods and that the method used can greatly influence the results. The results of some of the surveys you have been studying in this lesson may have been improved if the pollsters had used what you know about voting methods.

8. Examine the news item below. To see how different voting methods might be used to gather and summarize the sample data, suppose that the sample consisted of 1,000 working women.

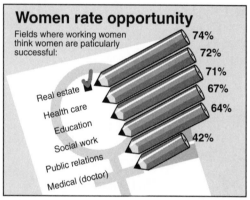

Source: *USA Today*, January 8, 1996.

a. The article states that the respondents could name more than one field. Suppose that, in fact, the 1,000 women in the sample used approval voting to give their opinions on the fields in which women are particularly successful. How many of the 1,000 women approved of (voted for) real estate? How many voted for social work?

b. Suppose that the 1,000 women in the sample ranked the fields. For example, suppose that the rankings for the first three fields are shown in the preference table at the right.

Find the plurality, runoff, and pairwise-comparison winners. Which field do you think should be reported as the top-rated field in this sample of 1,000 working women?

Field Preference Table

	Rankings		
Real Estate	1	2	3
Health Care	2	1	2
Education	3	3	1
Number of Voters	450	300	250

Checkpoint

Voting, surveys, and censuses can be used to measure and analyze public opinion.

a Describe the difference between taking a sample survey of the students in your school and taking a census of the students.

b What is meant by the "population" when you take a survey?

c List some information you need to know about a survey before you can completely understand and accept the results.

d How can voting methods be used to gather and summarize the individual opinions of people in a sample? Give an example using one survey in this investigation (other than the "Women rate opportunity" survey).

Be prepared to share your responses and thinking with the entire class.

On Your Own

Examine the following article from the October 22, 2001 edition of *USA Today*.

Nike has a ball with hip-hop ads

Ad Track

USA TODAY HARRIS POLL

A weekly look at how much consumers like a major advertising campaign compared with other ads rated by this poll – and how effective they think the ads are in helping to sell the product.

Today's ad

Nike

Ads for Nike appear to be hip-hop music videos, rather than traditional ads. The first spot opens slowly with basketball players dribbling on a shadowy court. The pace quickly picks up to the sound of dribbling basketballs and a pulsing musical beat, with NBA players Vince Carter and Jason Williams dribbling and passing balls behind their backs. The spot ends with a bouncing basketball and the words: nikebasketball.com.

Feel the beat: Ads for Nike feature NBA players moving a basketball to pulsating music.

Like the ads a lot

All respondents	31%
Ad Track survey avg.	22%

Dislike the ads

All respondents	12%
Ad Track survey avg.	13%

Among key target groups

Male	27%
Female	37%

Think the ads are very effective

All respondents	28%
Ad Track survey avg.	23%

To subscribe to Harris Ad Track Research Service, contact David Krane of Harris Interactive at 212-539-9648. Based on a nationwide poll of 611 adults who had seen the Nike ads. Poll was conducted Aug. 24-28; margin of error is ± 4.0 percentage points. Overall average based on 269 ads.

Source: USA TODAY research by Darryl Haralson

USA TODAY

a. What population is the survey on page 120 trying to describe?

b. Does the article give you all the necessary background information about the survey? What additional information would you like to know?

c. Why do you think *USA Today* sponsored the survey? Who else might find the survey useful and how might they use the results of the survey?

d. Describe how advertisers might use vote analysis methods to track public opinion about ads.

INVESTIGATION 2 Bias in Surveys

When interpreting survey results, it is important to consider how the survey was constructed and carried out. In this investigation, you will examine how *bias* may occur in a survey.

1. Study the survey on fast-food restaurants shown below.

a. Responses to some items provide factual information rather than information about someone's opinion. Identify the "fact" items in the survey. Why do you think it is important to include such items in surveys?

b. Several of the items in the survey relate to some of the voting methods you have studied in this unit. Identify these items and the voting method each suggests.

c. Identify items in this survey for which the wording may cause bias and unfairly slant the results. Describe what kind of inaccurate results may be produced.

Survey on Fast-Food Restaurants

Please check the appropriate response.

Age: 14 ____ 15 ____ 16 ____ 17 ____ 18 ____

Male ____ Female ____

Grade _____

a. Name your favorite fast-food place.

b. How many times during a typical week do you eat at a fast-food restaurant?

c. Rank in order the factors that are important to you in choosing a fast-food restaurant.

_____ Location

_____ Food and price

_____ Cleanliness

_____ Service

_____ Atmosphere

d. Do you think someone old and not in touch with students' preferences should be in charge of fast-food restaurants?

e. Do you agree or disagree with each statement:

  i. The menus in fast-food restaurants should not be changed to deny accommodation for senior citizens.

  ii. Due to the inveterate nature and intransigent behavior of a segment of the school population, students should not be allowed on the premises of eating establishments after 7:00 P.M.

f. What, in your opinion, are key factors that enable a fast-food restaurant to succeed?

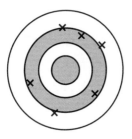

Errors due to chance

Errors due to bias

Surveys are often used to estimate information about a population. For example, the percentage of "successes" in a sample can be used as an estimate of the percentage of successes in the population. Of course, the sample result probably will not be equal to the true population result. Two possible sources of error are chance and bias. Chance errors are random and tend to cancel each other. **Bias**, on the other hand, tends to push every measurement in the same direction, resulting in systematic deviation from the true population value that you are trying to estimate. Consider possible errors when shooting at a target. The target diagrams to the left illustrate errors in shots due to chance and errors due to bias.

2. The design of a survey is said to be **biased** if it results in systematic deviation from the population value that you want to estimate. Roughly speaking, bias is systematic deviation from the truth. Poor wording is just one of many possible causes of bias. Examine the following situations for ways bias might occur in a survey.

    a. Read the article below and briefly summarize it. List at least two possible sources of bias identified in the article. In each case, describe how inaccurate results could have been produced.

Police poll found to be full of flaws
By Diana Griego Erwin

Last April's police union survey blasting the Sacramento Police Department's top brass for poor leadership was "amateurish ... designedly incomplete, misleading and, ultimately, biased."

This is according to a review of the survey by two scholars known for their work in survey research. Their analysis of the Sacramento Police Officers Association survey and its finding found the results of "minimal validity" and "deeply flawed."

SPOA's survey gave Police Chief Arturo Venegas Jr. 1.4 points out of 10.

Commissioned by the Coalition for Community Oriented Policing (CCOP), a community group that embraces Venegas' policing policies, the newest report raises questions about the lengths SPOA leaders will go to undermine public confidence in the chief. It will be distributed Monday to Sacramento Mayor Joe Serna Jr., the City Council and the SPOA.

Information sent out with the original survey questioned the competence of the chief and his top managers and stated the survey would be used for political purposes to improve working conditions for union members.

Other flaws included lack of confidentiality and arithmetic mistakes.

Confidentiality was sacrificed by having officers return the surveys to the union or any SPOA board member. To be valid and confidential, they should have been returned to Trenton West, the firm hired to analyze the survey, the report said.

SPOA President Gene Burchett agreed. He said the SPOA distributed the surveys before hiring the firm, and Trenton West officials had these same criticisms.

"We made it clear that because of the problems there was no scientific validity attached to the survey," Trenton West CEO Dora Kingsley said Saturday. Trenton West's president is Dave Swim, a retired Stockton police captain.

"We still think it's an accurate reflection of those who responded, but—those who responded—maybe that's a problem, too," Burchett said.

The report found that few officers with less than five years of service (or those hired under Venegas' command) responded. Of the 171 union members in that group, only six returned the surveys, the report said.

Source: *The Sacramento Bee*, September 21, 1997.

---

b. Suppose students in your school are interviewed in groups about whether they have ever cried during a movie. Explain why this survey could be biased.

c. Suppose an employer personally asks employees how they like working for the company. Do you think this survey design is biased? Explain.

3. In Activity 2, the manner in which the information was obtained may have caused bias. Bias can also be introduced by the method of selecting the sample. For each sampling plan described below, explain how bias may occur.

a. In a survey to find out about how people feel about pets, a response form is placed in a newspaper with a request that people cut it out and return it.

b. In a survey about who should be the National Basketball Association (NBA) Player of the Year, television viewers are asked to call in their vote at the end of the final game in the NBA Playoffs.

c. In a survey about how often people go out to eat, interviewers called people at home during the hours 5:00–7:00 P.M.

4. Unfortunately, it often happens that not everyone asked to respond to a survey will do so. This "nonresponse" is another source of bias. For each of the situations below, explain how the nonresponse could cause bias.

a. A university sent out a survey to find out how alumni felt about the usefulness of their education. The results were overwhelmingly positive. Unknown to the university, many alumni were not employed in the profession they chose as a university major, yet few of those alumni returned the survey.

b. A school board sent out a survey to determine public opinion about raising taxes for the public school system. The results indicated strong support for raising taxes to improve public schools. Further analysis showed that there was a significant population of senior citizens in the community, and few of those people responded.

c. Consider again the police poll from Activity 2 Part a. Identify the nonresponse and explain how it could cause bias.

d. Consider again the survey about eating out in Activity 3 Part c. Describe possible nonresponses and explain how this could cause bias.

Identify four possible sources of bias in a survey and give an example of each.

Be prepared to explain possible sources of bias and your examples to the class.

On Your Own

Pei and Hugh would like to organize a two-day regional music festival at which members of local high school bands would form ensembles of various sizes and then perform. They decided to survey members of high school bands in the region to determine if they would participate in the festival. They selected 15 band members from each of the 10 schools in their region by getting the names of 15 people from each school band director. On their survey they asked, "Would you be interested in a two-day music festival for our region?"

a. Key elements of a survey that you examined in the last investigation include the following:

- the variable or issue that is being studied
- the population under investigation
- the exact questions asked
- the sample and how it is selected

Identify these key elements in the music festival survey.

b. Identify any possible sources of bias in this survey.

INVESTIGATION 3 ▶ Selecting a Sample

An essential part of conducting any survey is selecting a sample. Many different methods can be used to select a sample from a population. But no matter what method is used, the sample must be selected carefully if the survey is to be unbiased. Explore possible ways of selecting a sample and their consequences in the following activities.

1. Begin by looking carefully at the set of circles shown below.

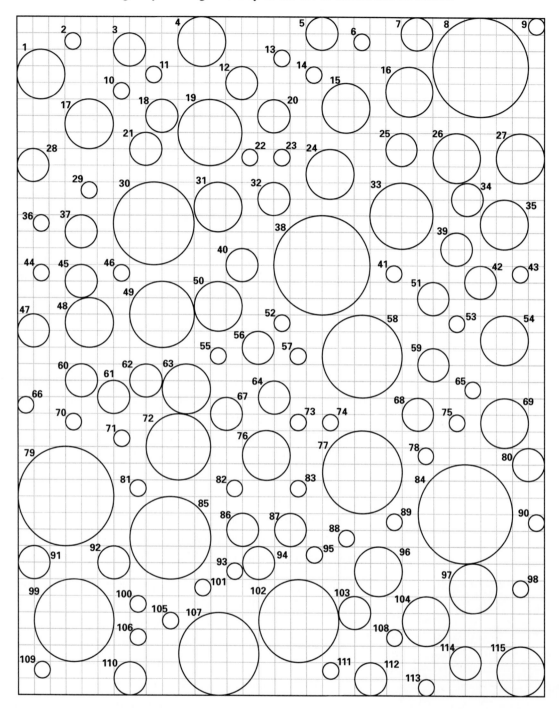

    a. Without consulting other group members, quickly make an educated guess for the average area of the circles. Record your guess.

    b. How could you find the average area of all the circles? How could you estimate the average area without measuring all the circles?

c. Each member of your group should select five circles he or she thinks are fairly typical and find the average of the areas of the five circles.

d. Next, each member of your group should generate five random numbers between 1 and 115 inclusive and select the corresponding circles. Find the average area of the five randomly selected circles.

e. Now, pool your data to make three class lists and three number line plots for the averages generated in Parts a, c, and d.

■ How do the three plots compare?

■ Compute and compare the means for the three lists.

f. Your teacher will tell you the actual average area of the circles on the previous page. Compare that area to the means computed in Part e. Was anything surprising in this comparison? Can you make any conjectures from this experiment?

g. Mark the actual average circle area on the number line plots prepared in Part e. Describe any patterns you see in how the data in each plot are distributed about the actual average.

h. Do you think any of the methods of sample selection in this activity cause bias? Which sampling method do you think is the best? Explain your reasoning.

One of the best methods for sample selection is *random sampling*. Selecting a *simple random sample* is like putting everyone's name in a hat, mixing them up, and then pulling a handful of names out of the hat. More precisely, a **simple random sample** of size *n* is a collection of *n* individuals from the population chosen in such a way that every collection of *n* individuals has an equal chance of being the one selected.

2. You have been examining a population of circles. Now consider the population of students in your school. Suppose you are interested in student opinion about a proposed new school mascot. Describe how you would select a sample of students that you could use to get an estimate of public opinion.

3. Which of the following methods produces a simple random sample of 50 teenaged drivers in a town?

■ Go to the high school, ask for a list of students, and select 50 at random using a table of random digits. If any of the 50 students aren't drivers, replace them with different randomly selected students.

■ Contact the Department of Motor Vehicles, get a list of all drivers under age 20, and select 50 at random using a table of random digits.

■ Contact the Department of Motor Vehicles, get a list of all drivers under age 20, choose a person at random using a random digit table, and then select that person and the next 49 whose names appear on the list.

4. When reading reports of surveys in publications, it is important to consider the sampling process that was used in the survey.

a. Read the article below on Internet use and describe how the sample was selected.

Who Are Internet Users?
By Michael J. Martinez

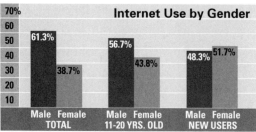

Internet Use by Gender

TOTAL: Male 61.3%, Female 38.7%
11-20 YRS. OLD: Male 56.7%, Female 43.8%
NEW USERS: Male 48.3%, Female 51.7%

The Web remains a male domain, these figures show. But look at the graph on the right: New Web users are slightly more likely to be women.

For the first time, women outnumber men among new Internet users, according to a new survey from Georgia Tech.

Among those Internet users who have been online for less than a year, nearly 52 percent were female, found the poll by the college's Graphics, Visualization, & Usability Center. Survey administrator Colleen Kehoe said it's the first time that women have taken a statistical lead over men in the nine years the survey has been done.

"Lots of people have predicted that women will catch up to men as far as Internet use goes, and we're seeing that come true here," Kehoe says.

And there are more younger women getting online. The survey, conducted among 12,591 Internet users in April, shows that females accounted for nearly 44 percent of users between the ages of 11 and 20.

Among the survey's findings are:

■ 38.7% of the respondents were female which is up from the previous two surveys.

■ Users' average age was 35.1, about the same as past surveys.

■ The largest category of users (45%) has used the Internet for 1 to 3 years.

■ 62.6% of respondents access the Web from home.

■ 67.2% of respondents pay for their own Internet access.

GVU's survey is conducted over the Web: participants respond to a questionnaire posted on the Web. Announcments about the survey appeared in Internet-related newsgroups, as banners in search engines (e.g. Yahoo, Excite) and advertising networks, and as announcements in newspapers and magazines.

Source: www.abcnews.com/;
www.gvu.gatech.edu/user_surveys/

b. Now look back at the other articles you read in this lesson. Which articles describe surveys that use random sampling?

Checkpoint

Sample selection is an important part of conducting a survey.

ⓐ Explain why random sampling is a good method for sample selection.

ⓑ Explain why choosing a sample according to what you think is "representative" or "typical" is not a good method for sample selection.

ⓒ Explain why each of the following is *not* an example of simple random sampling:

■ The sample consists of those who call in on a toll-free number to state their opinion after a news show.

■ The sample consists of those returning a survey in a magazine.

■ In a survey of a college's alumni, the sample consists of 50 names randomly selected from the active membership list of the college's alumni association.

Be prepared to share your explanations and thinking with the entire class.

Suppose you plan to use a survey to find out how students in your school feel about permitting seniors to leave campus for lunch.

a. How could you get a random sample? Explain why your method will give you a random sample.

b. Describe a good way to administer the survey, and explain why your method will not result in any bias.

MORE
Modeling • Organizing • Reflecting • Extending

Modeling

1. Critique the survey reported in the article below, based on the issues identified on page 117. Also, identify any possible sources of bias in the survey.

Nicolet High School
Alumni suggest emphasis on job-seeking skills
By David Thome of The Journal Staff

Glendale—Five years after leaving Nicolet High School, most graduates say they were well-prepared for college and work, but would have liked more information on conducting job interviews and on which jobs had the best prospects.

The school's second five-year survey of graduates also indicates that while former students felt they have developed good work habits at Nicolet, more than half changed their career plans since graduation.

Associate Principal Mike Salkowski said some courses and activities will be refined to address deficiencies identified by the grads. Guidance counselors, for example, will be asked to provide more information on which careers are likely to have more or fewer opportunities in the future.

About a fourth of all grads from the classes of 1986 and '87 responded to surveys the school sent out in 1991 and '92.

More than 80% of respondents from both classes said at Nicolet they learned to work well with others, solve problems, accept responsibility and meet deadlines.

"I'm glad they gave high marks to 'problem solving' and 'working with others,'" Salkowski said. "People who do hiring tell us that those things are very much on their minds. The days of working in your own cubicle on your own, narrow things are gone."

He said that he was surprised that three-fourths of the responding grads said they hadn't received enough information on job interviewing and resumes.

Since 1987, however, Nicolet had added classes and other activities that emphasize job-seeking skills, including a simulated job interview for all sophomores.

Salkowski said he also was intrigued that only 42% of the '87 grads were working in or studying toward the same career they planned on in high school. While there's no way to determine whether 42%

is high or low compared with other high schools, Salkowski said he would be concerned if the figure dropped in subsequent years.

Half of the '86 grads said in their five-year study that they had the same career plans as they had during high school. Salkowski noted that the state of the economy may have caused part of the difference.

According to the five-year surveys:

- 38% of '87 and 43% of the '86 grads still were in school after five years.
- 62% of '87 grads had full-time jobs after five years, compared with 52% of '86 grads.
- 19% of the Class of '87 and 18% of the Class of '86 have gone to graduate school.
- 63% of '87 grads and 60% of '86 grads felt Nicolet offered adequate instruction in using computers

Source: *Milwaukee Journal*, December 15, 1993.

---

2. Carefully read the article below.

Federal job survey revised
By Mark Memmott

Washington—The nation's unemployment rate could jump next year, when the Bureau of Labor Statistics changes the way it collects information on unemployment.

Tests indicate BLS' estimate of the jobless rate might rise half a percentage point in January, compared with December, because of revisions in its monthly survey of 60,000 households. The unemployment rate now is 6.8%. BLS will report the January rate Feb. 4.

There's also a chance the rate might not rise at all. Despite the test results, "we want to make it very clear we really have no idea what will happen" to the January estimate, says Jack Bregger, assistant BLS commissioner.

No matter what happens, investors and the public must realize "it's not a big change, it's not a small change," says BLS Commissioner Katharine Abraham. "It's a different measurement based on a redefined survey. You can't compare it to the old numbers."

BLS has been working since 1986—and has spent $40 million—on its first major change in the unemployment survey since 1967.

The goal is a more accurate estimate of unemployment. BLS says it has improved definitions of what it means to be laid off, working part time and too discouraged to look for work.

The revisions won't affect BLS' monthly survey of businesses, from which it estimates the number of jobs on payrolls.

Abraham and other top BLS officials said Tuesday that a September '92 through August '93 test of the new survey showed the average jobless rate those 12 months was 7.6%. Average based on the current survey: 7.1%. A major reason for the difference, BLS says, is that the new survey more accurately counts women as part of the labor force.

BLS says the current survey leads some women to classify themselves as home-

Katharine Abraham
(Photo by Tom Horan, GPN)

makers even though they may also be working outside the home or looking for work. By including those women as part of the would-be workforce, the new survey raised the average jobless rate for women over the 12-month test to 6.8%, from the current survey's 6%.

Source: *USA Today*, November 17, 1993.

Change ends homemaker bias

A key question will be reworded to avoid steering women toward saying they are "keeping house":

Current question
What were you doing most of last week?
- ■ Working or something else?
- ■ Keeping house or something else?
- ■ Going to school or something else?

New question
Last week, did you do any work for either pay or profit?

---

a. How was the federal job survey revised? Why was the revision considered necessary?

b. The article does not fully describe the federal job survey. What additional information do you think is needed in order to completely understand the survey?

3. Examine each of the following survey situations. Do you think the survey design is biased? Explain your reasoning in each case.

    a. The following question was asked on an opinion poll about taxes: "Do you agree that the current high tax structure is excessive?"

    b. The following instructions were given for an opinion poll about movies: "Rate the movies 1 to 10, where 1 is best."

    c. The survey results were obtained from those who called the network office after hearing the debate on television.

    d. To determine the number of people looking for jobs, an interviewer asked survey respondents, "Are you unemployed?"

4. The following is an excerpt from an article in the *Pittsburgh Tribune-Review*.

Teen survey: Freedom—with limits
By Gerard DeFlitch
Tribune-Review

They feel that adults—especially their parents—have been a bit slow in granting the freedom they deserve. They understand the need for some restraints, but plan to be less strict when it comes time to raise their own families. They are the teen-agers of western Pennsylvania, and a survey shows them to be in general agreement with but slightly more conservative than the average American youth.

More than 250,000 of their peers in grades six through 12 participated in the survey, whose central question was: "Do you have enough freedom?" The poll was conducted by USA Weekend magazine and the Sunday newspapers—including this one—that carry it each week. Results of the national survey, detailed in today's issue of the magazine, provide a fascinating look at a subject of extreme importance to these almost-adults.

Just as fascinating are the responses from teens who read the Tribune-Review. Nationally, 47 percent say they don't have enough freedom, 37 percent say they have the right amount, and 16 percent say they have too much. Among 107 Tribune-Review respondents 45 (42 percent) say they have the right amount, 34 (32 percent) say they don't have enough, and 28 (26 percent) say they have too much.

Source: Gerard DeFlitch, *Pittsburgh Tribune-Review*, May 4, 1997.

---

    a. What is the population for the survey?

    b. Does the excerpt indicate how the sample was selected?

    c. How could the surveyors have selected a simple random sample?

Organizing

1. Below is a group of rectangles.

   a. Show this page to 40 people and ask them: "Which rectangle do you prefer?" Write a brief summary of your survey results.

   I

   II

   III

   IV

   V

   VI

   VII

   b. Explain how you would modify the survey so that people could respond by preferential voting.

   c. A **golden rectangle** is a rectangle where the ratio of the length to the width is $\frac{1 + \sqrt{5}}{2}$ or approximately 1.618. Such a rectangle is believed to be one of the most visually pleasing rectangular shapes.

   ■ Which rectangle on the survey is closest to being a golden rectangle?

   ■ Is there a relation between the rectangle most preferred in your survey and a golden rectangle?

2. In Activity 1 of Investigation 3 (page 125), you considered the average area of a collection of circles. Think about some characteristics of "average circles."

   a. Does a circle of average radius have average circumference? Justify your answer.

   b. Does a circle of average radius have average area? If so, explain why. If not, give an example of a small collection of circles such that a circle of average radius does not have average area.

3. Examine the news item below entitled, "Small-business help wanted."

Source: *USA Today*, February 20, 1996.

   a. According to the news item, small-business owners were asked what they wanted most in a new employee. What method of voting is indicated by this question and the way the results are reported?

   b. As you discovered in Lesson 1, you can get more information about public opinion if you ask people to rank their choices, rather than just vote for their favorite. Design a questionnaire that you could use to get each person's ranking of the four given employee characteristics: dependability, honesty, good attitude, and competence.

   c. Suppose that the sample consisted of 200 small-business owners and their rankings are summarized in the following preference table.

Employee Characteristics Preference Table					
	Rankings				
Dependability	1	1	3	4	4
Honesty	4	3	1	3	3
Good Attitude	3	4	4	1	2
Competence	2	2	2	2	1
Number of Voters	27	43	54	38	38

■ How many first-preference votes does each characteristic get? Does this match with the data reported in the news item on the previous page?

■ Find the winner using the plurality, runoff, and points-for-preferences methods.

■ Which characteristic would you report as the one most valued by the 200 small-business owners in this sample? Give an argument justifying your choice. If you feel it would strengthen your argument, determine the winner using other vote-analysis methods.

Reflecting

1. Think of two examples at school in which it would be useful to give a survey to determine public opinion. In each case, briefly describe the issue of interest and why the survey would be useful.

2. Find an example of a survey on TV, in the newspaper, or on radio. Write a brief summary of the survey which includes a discussion of the key issues you have studied in this lesson.

3. In Lesson 1, you studied voting and methods of vote analysis. In this lesson, you studied surveys and investigated some examples in which vote-analysis methods were used to gather and summarize sample data. Do you think that the use of vote-analysis methods in surveys can improve surveys? Explain your reasoning.

4. The age in which we live has been called the Information Age. We are bombarded with information every day—on TV and the radio, in newspapers, magazines, and books, and on the Internet. Surveys are one common source of information. After having completed this lesson, do you feel that you are a better "consumer" of the information given in surveys? Explain.

Extending

1. Suppose you want to survey your class for some very personal information. If you ask students directly, they might not tell the truth. This would create bias in your survey. Getting honest answers to sensitive questions is a common problem for pollsters. One way to solve this problem is to use a *randomized response technique*.

Using this technique, the survey designer pairs a sensitive question (to be answered "yes" or "no") with a harmless question, to which the interviewer could not possibly know the answer and which has a known proportion of "yes" responses. For example, the harmless question might be "Is the coin you just (secretly) tossed a head?" When the respondent comes to the sensitive question, he or she secretly rolls a standard die and flips a coin. If the result of the die roll is 1 or 2, then the respondent answers the harmless question about the coin flip. If the result of tossing the die is 3, 4, 5, or 6, then the respondent answers the sensitive question. The interviewer records the number of "yes" answers.

a. Explain why only the respondent knows which question is being answered.

b. Explain why the interviewer does not know the correct answer to either question.

c. Write an equation showing how the proportion of all "yes" responses is related to the proportion of "yes" responses to the sensitive question and to the proportion of "yes" responses to the harmless question.

d. Suppose in a sample of 40 people there were 31 "yes" responses. Estimate the proportion of "yes" responses to the sensitive question.

2. Write a brief report on the United States Census. You may find a source in a library, call the Bureau of the Census in Washington, D.C., or find the information on the Internet. Your report should include answers to the following questions as well as any other interesting facts you find.

a. How often is the Census given?

b. When did the Census start and why?

c. What is done with the information collected by the Census?

d. What questions does the Census ask?

e. Explain why a census may be biased because of nonresponse.

3. Select a topic that is of interest to students at your school. Write a question about the topic in a way that you think will cause bias. Then rephrase the question in a way that you think will cause bias in a different direction. Give each question to at least 30 different people. Collect responses and compare the results. Did the difference in wording have the effects you thought it would? Explain.

Lesson **3**

Sampling Distributions: From Population to Sample

Perhaps you've wondered about the "margin of error" that is reported in many of the surveys you have read about. Or maybe you're wondering how a pollster can make such precise claims about an entire population based on just a sample from that population, even if the sample is random, the sample size is large, the questions are worded well, and the survey design is unbiased, in general. These are important things to wonder about! In the next two lessons, you will develop the mathematics needed to relate samples to populations. This mathematics will allow you to model public opinion more effectively.

The first step is to understand both how likely a sample outcome is and how much variability there is among samples. You may have noted this type of variability in your exploration of distributions in "Simulation Models" from Course 1 and "Patterns in Chance" from Course 2. In this lesson, you will investigate proportions and totals obtained from samples and study the likelihood and variability of those sample outcomes. You will begin by considering experiments involving tossing a coin.

Think About This Situation

Suppose you toss a coin 100 times.

a About how many heads would you expect to occur?

b If a friend also tossed a coin 100 times, do you think your friend would get the same number of heads as you did?

c Is it likely that 90 heads will occur? Is it possible?

d Would you think the coin toss was fair if heads occurred 55 times? 65 times? 95 times? For what number of heads would you begin to suspect that the coin toss might not be fair?

INVESTIGATION 1 ▸ Is It Likely or Unlikely?

One way to understand the likelihood and variability of sample outcomes is to examine the *sampling distribution*. A **sampling distribution** is the distribution of the outcomes from all possible samples of the same size taken from a given population.

1. Consider an experiment in which you toss a coin 50 times and record the number of heads. Tossing the coin 50 times is like taking a sample of size 50 from the population of all possible coin tosses. For this experiment, the number of heads in 50 tosses is the sample outcome of interest.

   a. In general, how many heads would you expect to get in 50 tosses?

   b. Work together in your group to toss a coin 50 times and record the number of heads.

   c. Describe how you could simulate this experiment using random numbers. Each member of your group should simulate the experiment two times using a random number generator or a table of random digits. Remember that one experiment consists of tossing a coin 50 times and counting the number of heads. Record your results.

   d. Pool the results of this simulation from all groups, and make a number line plot of the number of heads in 50 tosses. Describe this simulated sampling distribution.

   e. Which outcomes are most likely? Where do these outcomes appear in the number line plot? Which outcomes are very unlikely? Where do the unlikely outcomes appear in the number line plot?

2. Another class performed this experiment of tossing a coin 50 times and recording the number of heads. They repeated the experiment 60 times. The plot at the right shows the observed distribution of the number of heads in the 60 samples.

   a. Describe how this simulated sampling distribution is similar to and different from the distribution your class constructed in Activity 1. Explain why your class did not get exactly the same sample outcomes as this class.

   b. What numbers of heads are unlikely? Where do the unlikely outcomes appear in the distribution? Where do the likely outcomes appear?

Number of Heads	Number of Samples
18	♦ ♦
19	♦
20	♦ ♦ ♦
21	♦ ♦ ♦ ♦ ♦
22	♦ ♦ ♦ ♦
23	♦ ♦ ♦
24	♦ ♦ ♦ ♦ ♦ ♦
25	♦ ♦ ♦ ♦ ♦ ♦ ♦ ♦ ♦
26	♦ ♦ ♦ ♦ ♦ ♦ ♦
27	♦ ♦ ♦ ♦ ♦ ♦ ♦ ♦ ♦ ♦
28	♦ ♦ ♦ ♦
29	♦ ♦
30	♦ ♦ ♦ ♦
31	♦ ♦

c. If someone else tossed a coin 50 times, do you think 35 heads would be a likely outcome, based on this sampling distribution? Would 27 heads be likely? Would 30 heads?

While working through the previous two activities, you and your classmates probably had some debates about which outcomes should be considered "likely." In fact, there are many reasonable criteria you might use for deciding if an outcome is likely or not. We will adopt a common and useful criterion: from now on, a **likely outcome** is one that occurs in the middle 90% of the sampling distribution. **Unlikely outcomes** are those in the upper or lower 5% of the distribution. Using these definitions, you will be able to analyze surveys and samples systematically, and everyone will get consistent results.

3. Now look back at the distribution in Activity 2.

a. Which outcomes are in the lowest 5% of the distribution? Which outcomes are in the highest 5%? (If there is no clean cutoff point, you should choose a cutoff point that leaves *fewer* than 5% of the outcomes in the unlikely range.)

b. What is the interval of likely outcomes?

4. A useful representation of a sampling distribution that highlights the likely and unlikely outcomes is a modified box plot. Again, refer back to the distribution in Activity 2.

a. Draw a box around the likely outcomes in the distribution. A plot like this is called a **90% box plot**. The likely outcomes are in the box (including the edges of the box), and the unlikely outcomes are those outside the box.

b. Based upon your 90% box plot, is the outcome of 19 heads classified as likely or unlikely? How about an outcome of 28 heads?

c. Suppose the coin-tossing experiment is conducted one more time and 30 heads occur. Based upon your 90% box plot, is this considered a likely or unlikely outcome?

5. Consider the 90% box plot shown below.

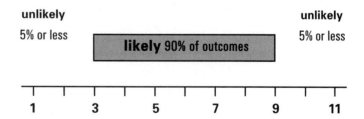

Explain this sentence: "The probability of getting an outcome outside of the interval from 3 to 9 is about 0.1."

6. According to the United States Bureau of the Census, in 1998 approximately 40% of those who purchased sneakers were under 14 years old. (Source: United States Bureau of the Census, *Statistical Abstract of the United States: 2000* (120th edition.) Washington, D.C., 2000.)

a. What is the population in this situation?

b. Carry out a simulation of selecting a random sample of 30 people from this population and recording how many are under 14 years old.

c. Another class simulated 60 samples of size 30 from the population. Each sample represented 30 sneakers buyers.
For each of these samples, they recorded the number of buyers under 14 years old. The results are shown in the histogram below. Make a 90% box plot summarizing this simulated sampling distribution.

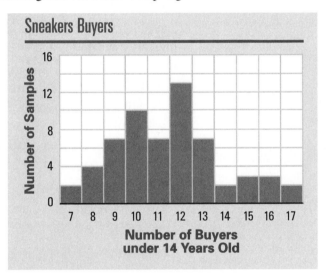

d. Which sample outcomes are considered likely?

e. According to this sampling distribution, what percentage of the samples have more than 16 buyers under 14 years old?

f. Suppose a friend reports that he sampled 30 sneakers buyers and found that only 7 were under 14 years old. According to your 90% box plot, is this a likely outcome? Suppose you suspect that this outcome did not occur simply due to chance. List several reasons that might account for this unusually low sample outcome.

Checkpoint

A sampling distribution can be used to provide a criterion for whether or not a sample outcome is likely.

a What is a sampling distribution? In general, what kind of information does a sampling distribution give you? How can a sampling distribution be represented?

b Describe a simulation that could be used to generate a simulated sampling distribution from a population in which 20% have the characteristic in question.

c What is a 90% box plot?

d Describe how to use a 90% box plot to determine whether a sample outcome is likely or unlikely.

Be prepared to share your explanations and descriptions with the class.

On Your Own

In 1999, 68% of United States households had cable television. The following 90% box plot shows the results of simulating a large number of random samples of 30 U.S. households and recording the number in each sample with cable television. (Source: *The World Almanac and Book of Facts 2001*. Mahwah, NJ: World Almanac, 2001.)

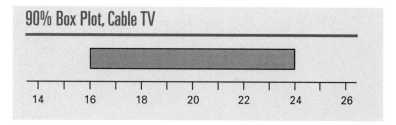

90% Box Plot, Cable TV

14 16 18 20 22 24 26

a. About what percentage of samples had more than 24 households with cable television?

b. Suppose you simulated a new random sample of 30 households in this situation and found that 23 have cable television. Are your results likely or unlikely according to the box plot? Explain.

c. Simulate a random sample of 30 households and find the number that have cable television. Describe how you simulated your sample outcome. Based on the 90% box plot, is your sample outcome likely or unlikely?

INVESTIGATION 2 Box Plot Charts for a Fixed Sample Size

In Investigation 1, you learned how to classify sample outcomes as likely or unlikely. You found that a 90% box plot is a convenient way to summarize a sampling distribution in terms of the likely and unlikely sample outcomes. You investigated situations involving a variety of sample sizes and populations. In this investigation, you will systematically study 90% box plots of likely sample outcomes for samples of size 30, taken from different populations.

1. Divide Parts a, b, and c below among groups in your class. For your assigned part, do the following.

    - Design a simulation to model the given situation, conduct the simulation 60 times, and construct a 90% box plot. It may be helpful to use special functions on a graphing calculator or software like the SIMBOX option of the *Sampling* calculator software.

    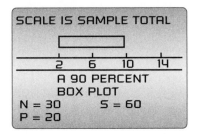

    - Use the box plot to answer the given question.

    - If you use software or a special function on a calculator, explain what the software or special function does.

    a. About 20% of the 1999 U.S. adult population did not have a high school diploma. (Source: U.S. Census Bureau, *Statistical Abstract of the United States*, Washington, D.C., 2000.) In a random sample of 30 U.S. adults taken in 1999, how many people would you be likely to find who do not have a high school diploma?

    b. About 20% of the students at a particular school are absent at least 10 days a semester. If you took a random sample of 30 students from this school, about how many would be likely to have been absent at least 10 days last semester?

    c. In 1997, about 20% of Americans aged 55 years and older lived in households that had a computer. (Source: U.S. Census Bureau, *Population Profile of the United States: 1999*, Washington, D.C., March 2001.) In a random sample taken in 1997 of 30 Americans aged 55 or older, how many would you be likely to find who lived in a household that had a computer?

2. Compare your answers and box plots from Activity 1 to those of groups that worked on different parts of that activity. Describe and explain the similarities and differences.

3. In Activity 1, your class generated 90% box plots for different situations in which the characteristic in question occurred in 20% of the population. Although there was some variability among the box plots, they were all reasonably similar. It will be useful to generate box plots for other population percents. For example, consider the population percents below, showing the portion of students enrolled in each academic area for the 2001–2002 school year at Libertyville High School.

Current Enrollment, Libertyville High	
Subject	**Percentage**
English	90%
Mathematics	80%
Social Studies	70%
Science	60%
Foreign Language	50%
Physical Education	40%
Technical Education	30%
Music	20%
Art	10%

Each group should choose at least one of the subject areas, but make sure that each subject area is covered by at least one group. You can omit Music since you have already worked with situations involving 20% populations. (Your teacher may wish to assign subject areas.)

a. Suppose you take a random sample of 30 Libertyville students and find the number who are enrolled in your chosen subject area. Construct and explain how to use a simulated 90% box plot to find the likely sample outcomes in this situation. Run at least 60 trials of your simulation.

b. Display a copy of your 90% box plot in your classroom.

4. Based on your class's box plots from Activity 3, answer the following questions.

a. Forty percent of all car owners own a midsize car. If you randomly sample 30 car owners, is it likely that 15 of these people own a midsize car?

b. According to the United States Bureau of the Census, about 70% of U.S. households in 2000 had cable TV. (Source: Television Bureau of Advertising, Inc., *Trends in Television*, 2000.) Suppose a random sample of 30 households was taken that year, and only 10 had cable service. Is this surprising?

c. About 50% of the population in 1999 was 36 years or older. (Source: U.S. Census Bureau, *Profile of the United States: 1999*, Washington, D.C., March 2001.) Suppose that in 1999, a random sample of 30 people included only 10 who were 36 years or older. Is this likely?

5. It will be easier to use the box plots that your class has constructed if you organize them all into one chart.

    a. On a copy of the chart below, carefully draw in the box plots that your class constructed so that there is a box plot opposite each population percent indicated on the vertical axis.

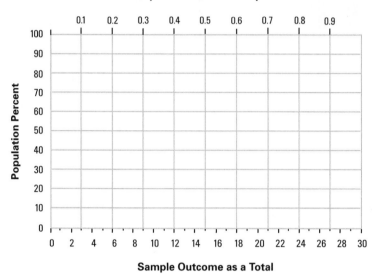

Sample Outcome as a Proportion

Sample Outcome as a Total

    b. For what size samples can the chart be used?

    c. Describe any patterns you see in the chart.

6. Use the chart from Activity 5 to help answer each of the following questions.

    a. Approximately 10% of the population is left-handed. If 18 of 30 injured people in a hospital ward are left-handed, what conclusions might you draw?

    b. Approximately 50% of all children born are girls. In some communities, newborns are listed in the newspaper. If you took a random sample of 30 newborn children listed in the paper, what would be likely results for the number of girls you would find?

    c. Is 17 a likely sample outcome for a population percent of 40% and a sample size of 30? Explain why or why not.

    d. Eighty percent of all students in a school participate in an extracurricular activity. In a random sample of 30 students from the sophomore class, only 18 students participated in an extracurricular activity. Do you think the sophomores are very different from the rest of the school? Explain why or why not.

On Your Own

In 2001, about 85% of households in the United States had a VCR. (Source: Television Bureau of Advertising, Inc., http://www.tvb.org/tvfacts/index.html.) Suppose you have a random sample of 30 U.S. households taken in 2001, and you find the number of households that have a VCR. Use simulation to find the likely sample outcomes in this situation.

INVESTIGATION 3 Standard Charts for Different Sample Sizes

In the previous investigation, you studied 90% box plots for a variety of population percents, but always with a sample size of 30. Of course, sample sizes will not always be 30! In this investigation, you will explore situations involving different sample sizes.

1. Examine the 90% box plot chart for a sample size of 30 that you constructed in Activity 5 of the last investigation. That chart shows 90% box plots for different population percents, but always with a sample size of 30. How do you think that chart would change if you used a sample size of 20?

2. Standard box plot charts have been made for many different sample sizes. The box plots in the standard charts are constructed using a very large number of simulated samples or using theoretical methods from probability. Below are standard charts for random samples of sizes 20, 40, 80, and 100.

90% Box Plots from Samples of Size 20

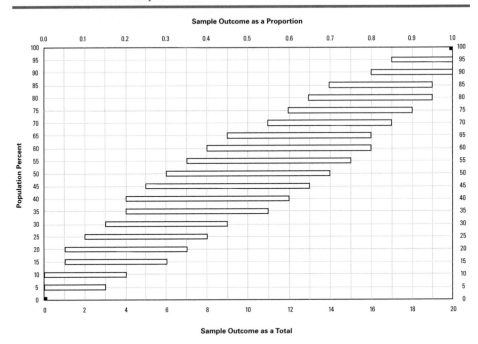

90% Box Plots from Samples of Size 40

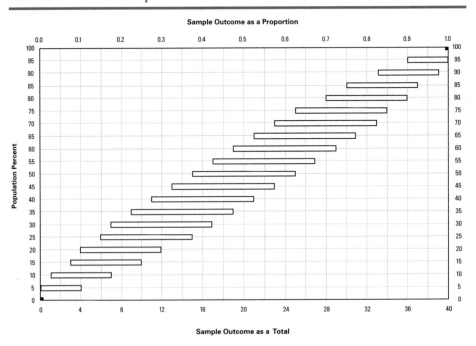

Compare these charts to each other and to the chart you constructed for sample size 30. Describe at least two patterns you see in individual charts or between charts.

90% Box Plots from Samples of Size 80

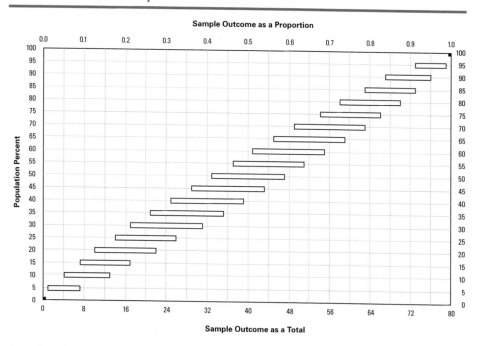

90% Box Plots from Samples of Size 100

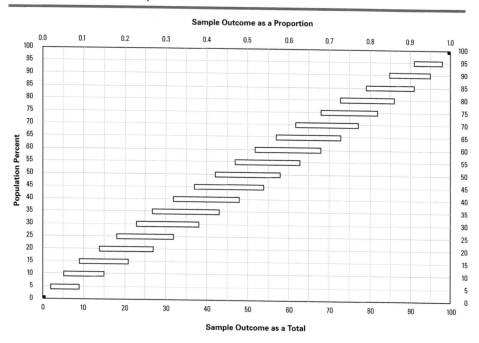

3. Notice that the standard charts have a scale showing sample outcomes as proportions along the top and a scale showing sample outcomes as totals along the bottom.

a. Suppose 80% of students in a school ride the bus to school. Find the interval of likely values for the number of bus-riding students in a random sample of 40 students from that school. Find the interval of likely values for the *proportion* of bus-riding students in a random sample of 40 students.

b. Assume that approximately 10% of the population is left-handed. Suppose you take a random sample of 80 people and find the proportion who are left-handed. What are the likely values for this proportion?

c. Compare the top and bottom scales on the charts for different sample sizes. Explain why, as you go from chart to chart, one of these scales changes while the other does not.

4. In 1999, approximately 20% of all U.S. residents lived in the nine Northeastern states. (Source: U.S. Census Bureau, *Population Profile of the United States: 1999*, Washington, D.C., March 2001.) Assign one person in your group to consider samples of size 20, another to consider samples of size 40, one to consider samples of size 80, and one to consider samples of size 100. Based on your assigned sample size, answer each question below, using the standard 90% box plot charts.

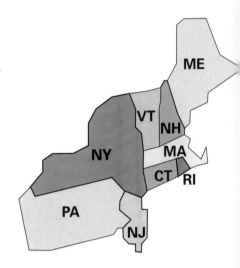

a. In a random sample of U.S. residents in 1999, where the sample size is equal to your assigned sample size, about what *proportion* of people in the sample would be likely to have been living in the northeastern states? Record your sample size and the interval of likely values for the sample proportion.

b. Suppose that 14 people lived in the Northeast in your sample. Is this a likely sample outcome?

c. Compare your answer to Part b to the answers of others in your group. Explain why it makes sense that 14 northeastern residents could be likely for some sample sizes but not for others.

d. Compare your interval in Part a to the intervals of others in your group.

■ Describe any patterns you see.

■ As the sample sizes get larger, what happens to the width of the 90% box plots? Explain why this relationship makes sense. (To investigate the precise relationship, see Extending Task 3 on page 152.)

5. By using 90% box plots, you can decide whether sample outcomes from a known population are likely. However, there can be many explanations for an unlikely sample outcome. Consider the three following situations.

   a. According to the *AP National Summary Reports* from the College Board, about 70% of the students who took an Advanced Placement Calculus test in March 2000 scored 3 or better on a scale of 1 to 5, where 5 is best. (Source: http:/www.collegeboard.org/ap/library/state_nat_rpts_00.html) Sam chose a random sample of 100 students in a nearby district who took an AP Calculus test and found that only 60 of them scored 3 or better. He reported to his class that "the results of my survey clearly indicate that students in this district do not score as well as students nationwide." Do you agree with Sam's statement? Why or why not?

   b. Suppose a study is done on the effects of a drug used to treat people with Lou Gehrig's disease. In a sample of 100 people with Lou Gehrig's disease, 20 of them had a remission when they used the drug. Without the drug, only 10% of the population had a remission. What do you think about the effectiveness of the drug?

   c. There is concern in a small Texas town about the rate of cancer among those who live there. According to health records, only 1 person in 5 people in the state will have cancer. In a random sample of the records of 100 residents in the town, 30% had cancer. Do you think the town residents have grounds for concern?

Checkpoint

Each 90% box plot chart shows 90% boxes for a range of population percents, based on a particular sample size.

a For a fixed population, describe how a 90% box plot of a sampling distribution changes as the sample size increases.

b Suppose you suspect that an unusually large number of people have a disease that might be caused by something in their environment. Describe how you could use a 90% box plot to help determine whether the number of people with the disease is truly unusual.

c Throughout this lesson you have used 90% box plots.

   ■ What does the "90%" in the phrase "90% box plot" mean?

   ■ Describe how a 95% box plot would differ from a 90% box plot. How might you redefine which outcomes are *likely*? In which case would you get a greater number of likely sample outcomes?

Be prepared to share your descriptions and thinking with the entire class.

On Your Own

In 2000, about 70% of the flights run by USAir arrived on time, according to the Air Travel Consumer Report from the Office of Aviation Enforcement and Proceedings (February, 2001).

a. In a random sample of 40 USAir flights, give an interval that indicates how many would be likely to arrive on time.

b. A consumer group selected a random sample of 40 USAir flights at one airport and found that 32 were on time. Does this mean that arrivals at that airport were better than usual in terms of being on time? Explain why or why not.

c. Describe how the interval of likely sample outcomes would change if the sample size is increased. Check your answer by finding the interval for a random sample of 80 flights and comparing it to the interval you found in Part a.

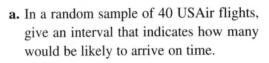

Modeling

1. A number of students each surveyed a random sample of 30 people from the same population to determine how many families had pets. Their results are represented in the distribution on the right.

   a. Explain what the 6 tallies after 7 represent.

   b. How many students were involved in collecting the data?

   c. Make a 90% box plot from the distribution.

Number of Families With Pets	Number of Samples
3	
4	♦ ♦
5	
6	♦ ♦ ♦
7	♦ ♦ ♦ ♦ ♦ ♦
8	♦ ♦ ♦ ♦ ♦ ♦ ♦
9	♦ ♦ ♦ ♦ ♦ ♦ ♦ ♦ ♦ ♦ ♦ ♦
10	♦ ♦ ♦ ♦ ♦ ♦
11	♦ ♦ ♦ ♦ ♦ ♦ ♦ ♦
12	♦ ♦
13	♦ ♦ ♦
14	♦

d. Sallee was absent the day the students brought in and analyzed their results. She added hers to the table the next day, claiming that in her random sample of 30 people she found only 3 people that have pets in their family. Do you think she really took a random survey of 30 people?

e. In approximately how many random samples would you expect to get an outcome that is unlikely?

2. Past records show that 30% of all automobile accidents in a certain community are caused by drivers under the age of 19. A local school district decided to conduct a large campaign on driving safely. Several months after the campaign was underway, a random sample of 40 police accident reports was selected. Only 11 of the 40 accidents were caused by someone under the age of 19. Does this seem to be a substantial reduction or not? Explain.

3. In 1995, approximately 35% of high school students in the United States had jobs. (Source: U.S. Census Bureau, *Statistical Abstract of the United States: 1996* (116th edition). Washington D.C., 1996.) Suppose that, at that time, a research team was investigating three schools in your area to determine whether the number of stu-

dents employed was typical. In the first school, they found that 10 students from a random sample of 40 held jobs. They randomly sampled 100 students in the second school and found that 41% had jobs. In the third school, they randomly sampled 80 students and found that 36 had jobs. How do these schools compare? Did any of them have an unusual number of employed students? Explain.

4. Women comprised about 45% of the U.S. workforce in 2000. (Source: *The World Almanac and Book of Facts, 2001*. Mahwah, NJ: World Almanac 2001.) Suppose you took a random sample of 100 working people in the United States in 2000, and you counted the number of women in the sample.

a. Use one of the standard 90% box plot charts to find the likely sample outcomes in this situation.

b. If you found that in a sample of 100 employees at a given company, only 40 of them were women, would you consider you had possible grounds for discrimination in hiring practices? Explain why or why not.

5. In 1993, approximately 10% of women in the age group 45 to 64 had heart disease, and 30% of women aged 65 and over had heart disease. (Source: United States Bureau of the Census, 1994.)

a. For each age category, describe how you could simulate the process of selecting a random sample of 20 women from 1993 and finding the number of women in the sample who had heart disease.

b. Use simulation to create a 90% box plot for each age category. Compare them to the standard box plots. Explain any differences.

c. Suppose you found that 5 of the women in a random sample of 20 women aged 45 to 64 had heart disease. Is this unusual? Would your answer change if the sample was selected from women over the age of 64? Explain how you made your decisions.

Organizing

1. In Activity 4 of Investigation 3, you examined the effect of different sample sizes on the width of 90% box plots, when the width was measured on the sample *proportion* scale of box plot charts. Now consider the sample *total* scale.

   a. Find the width of the 90% box plot for a population percent of 30% for sample sizes 20, 40, 80, and 100, as measured on the sample total scale.

   b. Compute the ratio of the width of each interval to the sample size. That is, compute $\frac{\text{width of interval}}{\text{sample size}}$. This is called the *relative width* of the interval.

   c. As the sample sizes get larger, what happens to the relative width of the intervals? Explain why this pattern makes sense. Compare this pattern to what you found about how width changes when it is measured on the sample proportion scale.

2. Discuss whether the following statements are true. In each case, give a justification for your claim.

   a. The interval of likely outcomes for samples from an 80% population is closely related to the interval of likely outcomes for samples of the same size from a 20% population.

   b. As the sample size increases, the size of the interval of likely values for the sample *total* decreases.

   c. As the sample size increases, the size of the interval of likely values for the sample *proportion* decreases.

   d. It is reasonable that an unlikely outcome will occur in about 1 out of every 10 random samples.

3. The manufacturer of a multicolored hard candy announced that 20% of the candy it makes is cherry flavored. Eighty students were each given a sample of 20 of the hard candies. Of the 80 samples, 20 had over 8 cherry-flavored candies. Set up a simulation or use your box plot charts to determine what conclusions you might make based on this sample evidence.

4. Obtain the number of male and female students in your school from the attendance office. Use this to establish the percentage of each for your school. (You may have to estimate a percentage to use with your box plot charts.)

   a. Based on this percentage, how many females are likely to be in a random sample of 20 students in your school?

   b. Take a random sample of 20 students enrolled in advanced mathematics courses. How many females were in your sample? Is this number unusual? What might explain your results?

   c. Choose another course and take a random sample to determine whether the number of males in the course is unlikely.

Reflecting

1. Think of a situation in your community or at school for which you know the population percent. Describe the situation and explain how you could find an interval of likely outcomes for samples from the population.

2. Kodjo simulated 40 random samples of size 30 from a population in which 60% of the individuals have a certain characteristic. Toni simulated 40 random samples of size 30 from a different population in which 60% of the population have a different characteristic. Henrique simulated 200 random samples of size 30 from the same population as Toni. Each of the three students made a 90% box plot based on their results.

   a. Will any of the box plots be the same? Will any be similar?

   b. There are two different populations referred to in this situation. Suppose a new sample of size 30 is generated from each population. Would it be reasonable to use any one of the box plots to judge the likelihood of these two new sample outcomes? Explain.

3. Percents are involved in different parts of the activities and tasks in this lesson. Explain the differences in the following uses of percent:

   - 90% box plots
   - 90% of the population has a given characteristic
   - 90% of a random sample has a certain characteristic

Extending

1. Discuss whether the following statements are true. In each case, give a justification for your claim.

   a. The interval of likely sample outcomes for samples of size 80 is half as big as that for samples of size 40.

   b. For all purchases of running shoes in 1998, about 30% were for consumers who were 17 years old or younger. (Source: U.S. Census Bureau, *Statistical Abstract of the United States: 2000* (120th edition). Washington, D.C., 2000.) Suppose you select a sample of 40 running-shoe purchases in 1998 and find that only 5 of them were for consumers aged 17 years or less. You can definitely conclude that your sample came from an environment in which a disproportionate number of purchases was for youths.

2. In Investigation 3, when you first started using standard box plot charts, it was stated that the box plots in the standard charts were constructed using a very large number of simulated samples or using theoretical methods from probability.

   a. Consider a 90% box plot for samples of size 20 from a population with a percent of 30%. Construct such a box plot using at least 1,000 samples. Compare it to the box plot on your standard chart. Explain any differences.

   b. *Challenge*: Construct the box plot in Part a using theoretical methods from probability. To do this you might want to consult a reference book or someone familiar with theoretical probability methods. Write a complete description of how to construct the box plot. Compare your box plot to the box plot on the standard chart.

3. In Activity 4 Part d of Investigation 3 (page 146), you found a relationship between sample size and the width of 90% box plots. Now you will use software to examine that relationship more closely. Using software like the STDBOX option of the *Sampling* calculator software, carry out the following experiment. Consider 90% box plots and 95% box plots for sample proportions.

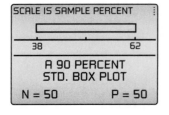

   a. Using the software to construct standard box plots, compare widths of box plots when a sample size is increased by factors of 2 and 4. Use a population percent of 50%, and use the largest sample sizes accepted by the software.

   b. Look for patterns and state the relationship between box plot width and sample size as precisely as you can.

   c. Use the relationship in Part b to predict what happens to the width of box plots when the sample size is increased by a factor of 5 and by some other factors. Check your predictions by using the software to construct the box plots.

Confidence Intervals: From Sample to Population

In this lesson, you will investigate two important related questions:

■ How can you make inferences about an entire population based on information from just a sample?

■ How confident can you be about such inferences?

For example, how can a pollster confidently report public opinion on such issues as crime or genetic engineering when only a few people are polled? In situations like these, the pollster uses a sample to estimate an unknown population characteristic, such as the percent of all people who favor a tougher stance on crime. In this lesson, you will learn how to estimate an unknown population percent using a *confidence interval*.

Interestingly enough, in order to develop this method for estimating an *unknown* population characteristic, you first need to investigate sampling from populations with a *known* characteristic, as you did in Lesson 3. In that lesson, you started with a known population characteristic, such as the percent of women workers in the population or the percent of all students who scored well on the Advanced Placement Calculus examination. Knowing the population percent, you used a 90% box plot to decide whether a particular sample outcome was likely.

Now you are going to reverse the process. You will learn how to use information about samples and sampling distributions to estimate the unknown population percent. For example, information about how a few voters feel about a political candidate can be used to describe how all voters feel, as seen in the following newspaper article about the 2000 United States presidential campaign.

Gore leading Bush by 10%, new poll shows

By Richard Benedetto

Democratic presidential candidate Al Gore moved into a clear lead over Republican George W. Bush in the latest USA TODAY/CNN/Gallup Tracking Poll. The poll, released Thursday, showed the vice president ahead by 10 percentage points, 51%–41%.

It marks the first time that the vice president has gone over 50% support and the first time he has had a double-digit advantage over the Texas governor. The lead is also outside the poll's

+/−4 percentage-point margin of error. That suggests that the Gore lead is more than just a statistical tossup.

The Gore lead is driven by independent voters. While 88% of Republicans support Bush and 88% of Democrats support Gore, the vice president leads among independents 46%–33%.

The numbers have to be disappointing to Bush strategists, who had hoped that an appearance on the *Oprah Winfrey Show* and a shift back

to an emphasis on issues would help stem the vice president's momentum.

The USA TODAY/CNN/Gallup Tracking Poll interviews 250 likely voters each night. The last three nights of polling are combined to produce the latest results.

Source: *USA Today*, September 22, 2000.

The USA TODAY/CNN/Gallup Tracking Poll reported in the article "Gore leading Bush by 10%, new poll shows" measured public opinion about the two candidates for President of the United States in September 2000.

a Based on the information given in the article, what is your estimate for the percentage of likely voters who supported Al Gore at the time the poll was taken?

b Do you think that with another sample of the same size, the pollsters would have gotten the same results?

c Do you think it is probable that exactly 51% of all likely voters in the country supported Vice President Gore at that time? Is it possible?

d The article reports a margin of error of plus or minus 4 points. What do you think that means?

e Do you think it is possible that only 45% of all likely voters in the country supported Vice President Gore at the time of the poll?

INVESTIGATION 1 Likely Populations

Politicians want to know how the public feels about certain political issues. Manufacturers want to know how the public feels about their products. It is important in many contexts to determine public opinion. But in most cases, you have to measure public opinion about an issue using only a sample. In this investigation, you will learn how to use your knowledge of likely sample outcomes and 90% box plots to do this.

1. Suppose a poll taken by a candidate in a primary election for President of the United States asks voters to identify their greatest concern. In a random sample of 80 voters, 16 of them identify crime as their greatest concern.

   a. Based on the sample outcome of 16 out of 80, what is your estimate for the percent of all voters in the entire population who identify crime as their greatest concern? Describe the reasoning you used to get your estimate.

   b. If you haven't already done so, think about how you could state your estimate as an interval of likely population percents. Try to describe a method for determining such an interval.

In Activity 1, you estimated an unknown population percent based on the outcome from a particular sample selected from that population. In Part b of that activity, you worked on constructing an interval of likely population percents. This is the basic idea behind what is called a *confidence interval*. In the following activities, you will investigate confidence intervals in a more precise and systematic manner.

2. Consider again the poll from Activity 1, in which 16 voters out of a random sample of 80 identify crime as the issue that concerns them the most. Think about how to use this sample information to estimate the percent of all voters in the population who identify crime as their greatest concern.

   a. Suppose the population percent is 25%. Is the sample outcome of 16 a likely outcome for that population percent? How can you tell?

   b. Suppose the population percent is 30%. Is the sample outcome of 16 a likely outcome for that population percent?

   c. Describe how you could use a box plot chart to find all the population percents for which 16 is a likely sample outcome.

   - Express this range of population percents as an interval.

   - If you wished to report a single value as an estimate of the population percent, which value from the interval would you report? Why is that percent a reasonable estimate?

   - State the interval of population percents for which 16 is a likely sample outcome as one value plus or minus a number of percentage points.

   d. Consider all three ways of reporting the population percents for which 16 is a likely sample outcome from Part c. Do any of these match your estimate for the population percent from Activity 1? What are some advantages and disadvantages of each way of reporting?

3. In a random sample of size 40 from the same population, 22 people identified the economy as their greatest concern. A 90% box plot chart for sample size 40 follows.

   a. Determine an interval of population percents for which this sample outcome of 22 is a likely outcome. Explain why this interval provides a reasonable estimate for the unknown population percent of all voters who identify the economy as their greatest concern.

90% Box Plots from Samples of Size 40

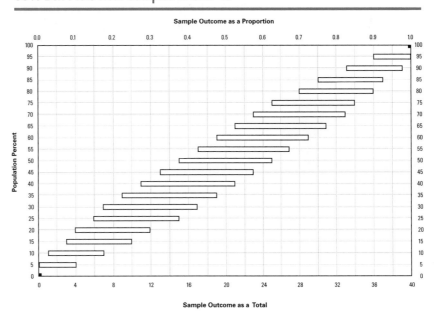

b. Marita drew a vertical line from the sample outcome of 22 up through the boxes. Make a sketch of the box plot chart and show the vertical line Marita drew. Describe how this vertical line can be used to find the interval of population percents for which 22 is a likely sample outcome. How does Marita's method compare to the method you described in Part b of Activity 1?

c. State an estimate for the unknown population percent as one value plus or minus another value.

The intervals that you found in Activities 1 through 3 are called *90% confidence intervals* for the actual unknown population percent. *Roughly, a confidence interval for the actual population percent is an interval of likely population percents.* More precisely, a **90% confidence interval** for the actual population percent is the interval of all population percents for which the given sample outcome is a likely outcome, where "likely outcome" is defined in terms of 90% box plots. For a confidence interval such as 15% to 25%, expressed in the form 20% ± 5%, the 5% is called the **margin of error**.

4. For each of the situations below, use confidence intervals to help answer the question posed.

a. In 1995, there was a federal proposal to replace paper dollars with coins, because coins last longer and are cheaper to circulate. Before implementing the proposal, the federal government wanted to know what percentage of Americans opposed this policy. To help find out, the Gallup organization questioned a random sample of Americans. Almost 75% of the people in the Gallup Poll opposed the proposal. (Source: *USA Today*, June 14, 1995.) The Gallup Poll used a large sample. To make the computations simpler, suppose 75% of the people in a random sample of 80 adults in Greenback County oppose the proposal. What percentage of all adults in Greenback County is likely to oppose the proposal?

b. A school board wants to find out how the people in their district feel about discipline in the schools. In a random sample of 40 people in the school district, 18 of them say they think the schools are not tough enough. About what percentage of all people in the district think the schools are not tough enough?

c. A candidate for a local election took a random survey of 100 people in her district and found that 52% of them intended to vote for her. Should she assume she has a majority and will win the election? Why or why not?

5. In a random sample of 100 people in a certain community, 73% of the people said they always wear seat belts.

a. What percentage of people in the entire community from which the sample was selected do you think always wear seat belts?

b. Do you think a 90% confidence interval for the population percent is guaranteed to contain the actual population percentage of people who always wear seat belts? Explain why or why not. Assume that the survey was properly conducted.

6. Now that you know how to construct a confidence interval, explore some of the properties of confidence intervals by completing the following activity. To begin, each student in your class should have a small bag of "M&M's"® Chocolate Candies.

   a. Select a random sample of 20 candies from your bag. Use the sample to find a 90% confidence interval for the actual population percent of red candies.

   b. Compare your confidence interval to those of other members of your group. Are they all the same? Should they be the same? Explain.

   c. For M&M's® Chocolate Candies in June 2002, the population percent for red candies was 20%. Check the M&M's Web site to get the current percent. Does the confidence interval you produced from your sample contain the actual population percent?

   d. Your class should produce at least 30 confidence intervals. (If there are fewer than 30 students in your class, your teacher may ask you to use another sample of 20 candies from a new bag to construct another confidence interval.) How many confidence intervals produced by students in your class contain the actual population percent? Explain the results.

7. Now consider the following three statements as you look back at your work in the previous activities. For each statement, discuss and give an example that illustrates the statement.

   a. Two different samples of the same size from the same population can generate two different confidence intervals for the population percent.

   b. Not all confidence intervals contain the actual population percent.

   c. Suppose you draw many samples from a given population, and for each sample you generate a 90% confidence interval for the population percent. You would expect that about 90% of these confidence intervals will contain the actual population percent.

8. Suppose someone surveyed a random sample of students in your school. The person reported a 90% confidence interval of 50% to 70% for the percent of all students for whom basketball is their favorite sport.

   a. Based on the box plot charts you have, about what sample size do you think was used in the survey? Explain how you made your choice.

   b. The athletic director at the school decided, based on the results of the survey, to show videos of the school's basketball games during lunch and study halls for a small fee to each viewer. Do you think this will be a successful endeavor?

9. Most major polls use a 95% confidence level to report results.

   a. In Activity 2, you found a 90% confidence interval based on a poll in which 16 voters in a random sample of 80 identified crime as their greatest concern. How would a 95% confidence interval differ from the 90% confidence interval? Use software such as *Sampling* to determine a 95% confidence interval for this poll to check your conjecture.

   b. Refer to the article about the 2000 U.S. presidential campaign, page 153. How would you interpret the USA TODAY/CNN/Gallup Tracking Poll results for registered voters now?

Checkpoint

In this investigation, you explored the use of confidence intervals to interpret sample statistics.

ⓐ Describe the connection between the two topics in each item below:
- Confidence interval and the informal idea of likely populations
- Confidence interval and margin of error

ⓑ Describe how to construct a 90% confidence interval.

ⓒ Explain what happens to the width of a 90% confidence interval as sample size increases.

ⓓ In Lessons 3 and 4, you studied two related but very different problems. In one type of problem, you use a known population percent to find the likely sample outcomes. In the other type, you use a particular sample outcome to estimate the unknown population percent. Which of these two problems can be solved using confidence intervals? Explain how to solve the other type of problem.

ⓔ Suppose 32 people in a randomly selected sample of 80 people answer "yes" to a question. Then the 90% confidence interval for the actual percent of people in the population who would answer "yes" is 35% to 45%. For each statement below, do you think it is a good explanation of what "90% confidence" means in this situation? Why or why not?

- There is a 90% chance that the actual population percent is between 35% and 45%.

- The given interval was determined using a method that gives a correct result 90% of the time.

- The sample outcome of 32 out of 80 is a likely sample outcome from populations with percents from 35% to 45%.

- If we draw many random samples of size 80 from this population and generate a 90% confidence interval for each, then about 90% of these confidence intervals will contain the actual population percent.

Be prepared to share your descriptions and thinking with the entire class.

▶ **On Your Own**

According to a survey conducted by the National Pasta Association, about 35% of people surveyed indicated that spaghetti was their favorite pasta. (Source: National Pasta Association, *Pasta Home Page*, http://www.ilovepasta.org/press_room.html)

a. Assuming the survey was given to a random sample of 40 people, determine an interval of population percents that you think are likely. (Use 90% box plots as your criterion for likely.)

b. Assuming the survey was given to 100 randomly selected people, find a 90% confidence interval for the percent of people in the whole population who indicate spaghetti is their favorite pasta.

c. How confident are you that the intervals you determined in Parts a and b will contain the actual percent of people who indicate spaghetti is their favorite pasta? Give a careful explanation of your answer.

d. Express your answers to Parts a and b in terms of margin of error.

MORE
Modeling • Organizing • Reflecting • Extending

Modeling

1. According to the International Mass Retail Association, 60% of consumers age 8 to 17 surveyed think it is important to consider brands when they buy sneakers. (Source: *USA Today*, July 21, 1995.)

   a. Brand name recognition and purchases are very important in some segments of the retail industry.

   ■ If there were 40 people in the sample, what is your estimate of the percentage of all consumers aged 8 to 17 who think brands are important in buying sneakers?

   ■ How would this estimate change if there were 100 people in the sample?

   b. About 40% of those polled think brand names are important in buying toys and games. Find a 90% confidence interval for the actual percentage of the population who think brand names are important in buying toys and games. Use samples of size 20 and size 40.

   c. Describe and explain any patterns shown in this task between sample size and width of the confidence interval.

2. A poll taken before the presidential election of 2000 reported the following: "The poll had Gore ahead of Republican George W. Bush, 48%–43%. …So the race remains statistically deadlocked." (margin of error: 4 points). Why did the newspaper choose not to say one of the candidates was ahead? (Source: *USA Today*, September 19, 2000.)

3. Find a poll or survey that is reported in a newspaper. Identify the margin of error. Explain what it means in terms of the survey results.

4. Cellular phones were once a novelty. Now they are becoming more and more commonplace.

   a. Twenty percent of people who owned a cellular phone in 1999 did not own one in 1998 (Source: *The World Almanac and Book of Facts 2001*. Mahwah, NJ: World Almanac 2001.) Suppose you took a random sample of 40 teachers in your school who owned a cellular phone in 1999 and found that only 4 of them did not own one in 1998. Does this mean that teachers in your school are not typical?

   b. Suppose you took a random sample of 40 people in your town who owned a cellular phone in 1999 and found that 13 of them did not own one in 1998. What conclusion could you draw about the percentage of people in your town who owned a cellular phone in 1999 but not in 1998? Defend your conclusion by using confidence intervals.

Organizing

1. What relationship, if any, is there between margin of error and sample size? How is this relationship connected with box plots for various sample sizes?

2. The line plot on the next page shows a month-by-month pattern of change in one region's public opinion about the baseball strike in 1994–1995, much as it would have looked in a newspaper article. The plot shows the estimated percentage of people in the population supporting the strike. The opinion poll each month had a margin of error of 4%.

   a. On a copy of the graph, for each month, plot points illustrating the margin of error and sketch a vertical line segment showing the confidence interval.

   b. Shade a band through the graph that illustrates the changing confidence intervals for the actual percentage of people in the population supporting the strike.

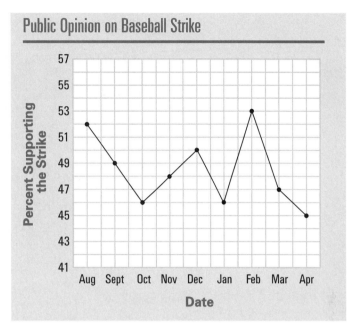

Public Opinion on Baseball Strike

c. Suppose you represented the owners of a striking team and you wanted to use this information to claim that public support for the strike fluctuated widely over the given time span. Give an argument supporting that claim.

d. Suppose you represented the players and you wanted to claim that public support never wavered. Give an argument supporting that claim.

3. The following formula can be used to estimate the margin of error for a 90% confidence level:

$$margin\ of\ error = 1.645 \sqrt{\frac{\hat{p}\hat{q}}{n}}$$

where $\hat{p}$ (read "p hat") is the sample proportion, $\hat{q}$ is $1 - \hat{p}$, and n is the sample size. (This formula should be used only if $n\hat{p} \geq 10$ and $n\hat{q} \geq 10$.)

a. Describe how the margin of error changes in the following cases:

- The sample size increases.
- The sample proportion increases.

b. Find the margin of error for samples of sizes 20 and 80 when $\hat{p} = 0.5$ using the following three methods.

- The above formula
- Your standard box plot charts
- Software, such as the BOXCHART feature of the *Sampling* calculator software, with population percent intervals of 2%

c. Describe and explain any differences among the answers you get using the three different methods.

d. Describe the pattern in the margin of error results for sample size 20 and sample size 80.

4. Read the article below, which appeared in a college campus newspaper.

Cut administration salaries, poll says

Students want top UI (University of Iowa) administrators to reduce their salaries by 6 percent to aid the university in potential budget cuts, the UI Student Government president said Thursday.

That was the most frequent suggestion students voiced to the UISG in response to a mass e-mail last week soliciting input on how to cut the university budget, UISG President Nick Klenske announced Thursday.

From the 20 responses, the most reported recommendation was for the administration to take a 6 percent salary reduction, a gesture in response to the proposed 6 percent (budget) cut. Some students also called on coaches and other workers in the Athletics Department to take similar cuts from the portions of their salaries that are state-funded.

Administrations, who don't interact face-to-face with the students, should take the cut instead of teaching assistants and professors, Klenske said

"Those who directly teach the students shouldn't suffer," he said. "When we need to make cuts we should target non-educational aspects of the UI first."

Source: *The Daily Iowan*, April 27, 2001.

---

    a. Critique this poll and the conclusion stated in the headline. Use at least two big ideas that you have learned about surveys, samples, and confidence intervals.

    b. Would any of the voting models you learned about in Lesson 1 be useful for measuring and analyzing public opinion on the issues in this article? Explain.

5. In Lessons 3 and 4, you considered two basic questions: "Which sample outcomes are likely?" and "What is the population percent?" Explain how to answer each question.

Reflecting

1. Suppose you selected a random sample of 90 registered voters from your town or city, and 90% of the sample preferred candidate A in the local school board election. A 90% confidence interval for the percentage of all registered voters in town who prefer candidate A can be expressed as 90% ± 5%. There are a lot of 90s in this problem! Explain the meaning of each "90."

2. Suppose you read about a survey in the newspaper, but no margin of error nor sample size is given. What conclusions can you draw?

3. Describe two situations in which the margin of error would make you question the conclusions drawn from a survey.

4. Jeri said that confidence intervals were difficult for her to understand at first. She said it took her a while to realize that what you are confident in is not really a particular interval, but rather a method of generating intervals. Explain what you think she means by this statement.

5. Refer to Activity 7 Part c, page 157. Draw a diagram that you think illustrates that statement.

Extending

1. In an article entitled "White House assertions on FBI files are widely rejected, survey shows" from the *Wall Street Journal* (June 6, 1996), the following statement is made:

   "Chances are 19 of 20 that if all adults with telephones in the U.S. had been surveyed [instead of surveying just a sample of adults with telephones], the finding would differ from these poll results by no more than 2.2 percentage points in either direction among all adults... ."

   Explain the meaning of this statement. Do you think that this is an accurate way to state the "confidence level" of the survey? Your answer and explanation should include a discussion of how the statement relates to the ideas of confidence interval and margin of error.

2. Organizing Task 3, page 161, introduces the margin-of-error formula for a 90% confidence level. If you use a 95% confidence level instead of a 90% level, the margin of error can be estimated using the following formula:

$$\text{margin of error} = 1.96\sqrt{\frac{\hat{p}\hat{q}}{n}}$$

   where $\hat{p}$ is the sample proportion, $\hat{q}$ is $1 - \hat{p}$, and n is the sample size. (This formula should be used only if $n\hat{p} \geq 10$ and $n\hat{q} \geq 10$.)

   a. Use this formula to compute the margin of error for the survey reported in the article on the 2000 U.S. presidential campaign at the beginning of the lesson, page 153. Explain any differences between the margin of error stated in the article and the margin of error computed using the above formula.

   b. In 1997, the Odyssey company conducted a survey about online services. 18% of 2,500 adults who had computers at home and were at least aware of the online services America Online® and Microsoft Network® rated these services as good or very good. (Source: *New York Times on the Web*, http://www.nytimes.com, September 8, 1997.) Are the criteria of $n\hat{p} \geq 10$ and $n\hat{q} \geq 10$ satisfied in this situation? What is the margin of error at a 95% confidence level?

   c. A Gallup Poll immediately following the 2000 Democratic National Convention found that 50% of 1,043 adults say that the Democratic Party better represents their values. (Source: The Gallup Organization, August 22, 2000. Available: www.gallup.com/poll/releases) What is a 95% confidence interval for the percentage of all adults at that time who said the Democratic Party better represents their values?

   d. In June 2001, the Gallup organization conducted a survey of 1,004 adults about job equity. The organization reported that 32% of the women in the survey believe that men and women enjoy equal job opportunities in the United States. The survey had a margin of error of 3 percentage points. Is this stated margin of error consistent with the formula for margin of error given above? Explain. (Source: The Gallup Organization, June 29, 2001. Available: www.gallup.com/poll/releases)

3. Refer to the formula for the margin of error for a 95% confidence level in Extending Task 2.

   a. Use a sample proportion of 0.5. Describe what happens to the margin of error as the sample size increases. Compare your results here to those you got for a 90% confidence interval in Organizing Task 3 on page 161.

   b. Use a sample proportion of 0.8. How does this affect the change in the margin of error as the sample size increases?

   c. If the sample size increases by factors of 4, 5, and 9, what happens to the margin of error?

4. In an article in *USA Today* about the height of today's athletes, the following statements appeared: "Average heights have leveled, but that doesn't show what's happening in the very tall segment … 'Though the group has not, on average, increased you may see shifts at the extreme percentile. More people get a chance to reach their maximum,' says [Robert] Malina, [professor of anthropology and kinesiology at the University of Texas]." (Source: *USA Today*, June 6, 1995.) Does this make sense? Can you explain what is meant by the quoted statements?

5. Examine the following chart and read the summary of the poll.

Politicians

■ **Iowa's highest-ranking** elected officials are winning strong approval, the Iowa Poll shows.

▶ *Do you approve of the job being done by. . .*

	U.S. Sen. Charles Grassley	U.S. Sen. Tom Harkin	Gov. Terry Branstad
Yes	75%	71%	70%
No	10%	16%	23%
Unsure	15%	13%	7%

Based on interviews with 800 Iowa adults.

MARY ELLEN KELLEY / THE REGISTER

Source: *Des Moines Register*, February 24, 1998. Copyright 1998 the Des Moines Register and Tribune Company. Reprinted with permission.

The Iowa Poll, conducted Jan. 31–Feb. 4, asked the following:

   I'd like to begin by mentioning the names of some current public figures who hold office. For each, please tell me if you approve or disapprove of the job they are doing. Bill Clinton as president. Al Gore as vice president. Charles Grassley as U.S. senator. Tom Harkin as U.S. senator. Terry Branstad as governor.

   The Iowa Poll, conducted for The Des Moines Register by Selzer and Co. Inc. of Des Moines, is based on interviews with 800 Iowans age 18 or older. Interviewers contacted households with randomly selected telephone numbers. Percentages based on the full sample may have a maximum margin of error of plus or minus 3.5 percentage points. Republishing the copyrighted Iowa Poll without credit to The Des Moines Register is prohibited.

   a. Does the summary of the poll provide enough information for you to accept the results with confidence? Explain, based on the analysis of background information you carried out in Lesson 2.

   b. Based on this poll and the information given, estimate the confidence interval for the percentage of all adults in Iowa who approve of Senator Grassley. Explain how you determined the confidence interval.

   c. A major poll like this typically uses a large sample size and a 95% confidence level. However, consider a simpler situation. Suppose that, in a random sample of 100 Iowa adults, 75% approved of Senator Grassley. Based on such a poll, what is a 90% confidence interval for the percentage of all adults in Iowa who approve of Senator Grassley?

   d. Compare the confidence intervals in Parts b and c. Explain any similarities and differences.

Lesson 5   *Looking Back*

In this unit, you have studied two mathematical methods for measuring and analyzing public opinion: voting and surveys. You learned about different methods of voting, such as preferential voting and approval voting. Using preferential voting, you found that different vote-analysis methods, such as plurality and points-for-preferences, can yield different winners. These methods also can be applied to help gather and summarize survey data. While voting is used in situations in which every person has the opportunity to vote, sample surveys are used to estimate public opinion based on the opinions of just a few individuals in the population. You used confidence intervals and margin of error to make such estimates and to describe the level of confidence in the estimate. In this lesson, you will review and pull together all these key ideas related to voting and surveys.

1. Conduct and interpret the results of a survey as described below.

   a. Working with a partner, prepare a two-question survey.

   - For the first question, think of a school-related question about which you would like to gather information. Design your question so that it has a "yes" or "no" answer. (For example: *Should the winter dance be formal? Should the school change its mascot? Are you in favor of the new library policy?*)

   Student Survey

   Yes No

   1. _____   ☐ ☐
      _____
      _____

   2. Are you left-handed? ☐ ☐

   - For the second question, assume that approximately 10% of the population is left-handed. Your question is: *Are you left-handed?*

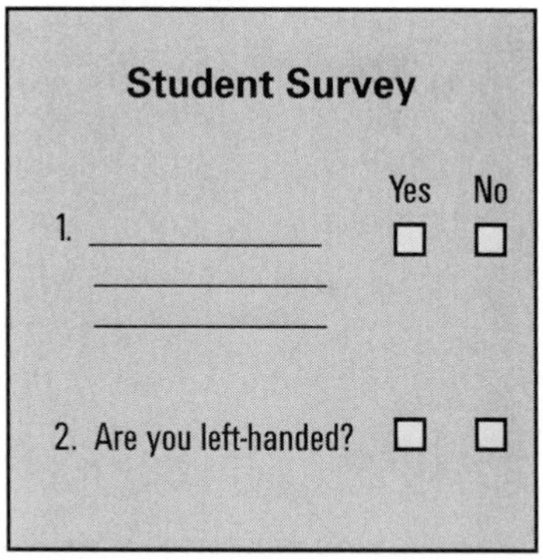

   b. Randomly select 20 students and ask them your two questions.

   c. Summarize the results of your survey for each question. Draw any conclusions that you think are reasonable. Explain your conclusions.

   d. Describe the differences in the conclusions you drew, the reasoning you used, and your methods of analysis for the two different questions.

2. Examine this *Fan Favorites* clipping from *USA Today*.

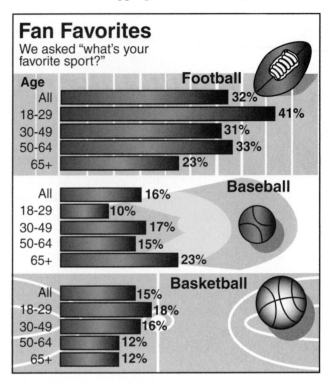

Fan Favorites
We asked "what's your favorite sport?"

Football

Age	
All	32%
18-29	41%
30-49	31%
50-64	33%
65+	23%

Baseball

All	16%
18-29	10%
30-49	17%
50-64	15%
65+	23%

Basketball

All	15%
18-29	18%
30-49	16%
50-64	12%
65+	12%

Source: *USA Today*, May 26, 1995.

a. Describe two trends in the data that are interesting or surprising to you.

b. In Lesson 2, you analyzed surveys based on several basic questions and criteria. Referring to those questions, do you think you have been given enough information to understand and accept the results of the *Fan Favorites* survey? Explain.

c. Suppose the results shown for 18- to 29-year-olds are based on a random sample of 100 people aged 18 to 29 in Akron, Ohio. About what percent of all 18- to 29-year-olds in Akron would indicate football as their favorite sport? Express your answer as a confidence interval.

d. The question asked in the poll was "What's your favorite sport?" What kind of voting method does this suggest? Reword the question so that preferential voting methods could be used to gather and summarize the sample data.

3. Approximately 15% of all people in the United States were not covered by health insurance in 1998. (Source: U.S. Census Bureau, *Statistical Abstract of the United States: 2000*. Washington, D.C., 2000.) Assume that figure is still valid today.

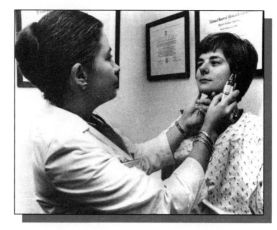

   a. Suppose you randomly select 40 people in the United States and 10 of them are not covered by health insurance. Is this a likely sample outcome? Explain.

   b. Simulate a random sample of 20 people from this population and find the number of people in the sample who are not covered by health insurance. Is your simulated sample outcome likely?

   c. Imagine simulating 500 random samples of size 80. (Don't actually do it!) How many of the simulated sample outcomes will be likely outcomes?

4. A new sanitary landfill is to be located in one of four neighboring counties: Calaveras, Montclair, Jefferson, or King. All residents voted on where they thought it should be located, with the results shown in the following preference table.

Landfill Preference Table

	Rankings				
Calaveras	1	1	3	4	4
Montclair	3	4	4	1	3
Jefferson	2	3	1	2	1
King	4	2	2	3	2
Number of Voters	3,658	3,034	2,518	2,421	1,755

If the location of the landfill is to be decided based on these data, in which county should the landfill be built? Justify your answer. Your analysis should include finding the "winner" using at least two different vote-analysis methods.

Checkpoint

In this unit, you have studied a variety of concepts and techniques for measuring and analyzing public opinion.

ⓐ List and explain two or three important points you have learned about voting. Give an example illustrating each point.

ⓑ When public opinion is estimated by sample surveys, issues of bias, sample selection, and interpretation need to be carefully considered.

- What does it mean for the design of a survey to be biased? Give an example of a source of bias in a survey.

- Describe and give an example of a simple random sample. Why is random sampling a good method of sample selection?

- List and discuss at least four key questions that you should ask when analyzing any survey.

ⓒ Describe connections and differences between 90% box plots and 90% confidence intervals. Give an example of a question that can be answered using a single 90% box plot. Give an example of a question that can be answered using a 90% confidence interval.

ⓓ In this unit, you learned how to draw conclusions about samples based on information about the population. You also learned how to reason in the opposite direction, that is, how to make inferences about a population based on information about a sample.

- Lesson 3 is entitled, "Sampling Distributions: From Population to Sample." Explain how finding sampling distributions and 90% box plots involves reasoning "from population to sample."

- Lesson 4 is entitled, "Confidence Intervals: From Sample to Population." Explain how finding confidence intervals involves reasoning "from sample to population."

Be prepared to share your descriptions and thinking with the entire class.

On Your Own

Write, in outline form, a summary of the important mathematical concepts and methods developed in this unit. Organize your summary so that it can be used as a quick reference in future units and courses.

Symbol Sense and Algebraic Reasoning

Unit 3

169

Lesson 1

Algebra and Functions

Are you a bicyclist, a skater, a skateboarder, a skier, or a snowboarder? Do you enjoy high and fast roller coasters at amusement parks? Many popular sports and recreations like these involve rolling or sliding down and up hills.

For example, when you ride a roller coaster, there is a motor that pulls you to the top of the first hill. But then gravity pulls you down, momentum carries you up to the top of the next hill, and so on. The big question is how far the energy gained on a downhill ride or slide will carry you uphill on the other side.

Think About This Situation

Suppose that you were asked to design an exciting, but safe, roller coaster for an amusement park.

a What variables would you have to consider in designing the first hill so that downhill momentum would carry the cars up and over the second hill without a pull?

b What changes in the design would be needed if you wanted to put a loop in the track so that the cars and riders turn upside down in a 360° turn?

If possible, test your ideas with simulations of roller coaster designs using flexible, grooved track and small cars like those that come with HOT WHEELS® setups.

INVESTIGATION 1 ▶ Defining Functions

When students at a Colorado high school considered the "down and up" questions about roller coasters, they thought about ski and dirt bike jumping. They wondered about the relationship between length and steepness of the run leading to a jump ramp and length of the jumps from the end of that ramp. Using HOT WHEELS® track set pieces, they collected data relating *length of run* to *length of jump* by various HOT WHEELS® cars.

For one of their setups and cars, they collected the following data and produced the accompanying graph. You might get different results with a different track and jump-ramp setup.

Jump Ramp Experimental Data	
Run Length (cm)	Jump Length (cm)
15	0
30	0
60	20
90	45
120	70
150	90
180	105
210	115
240	120

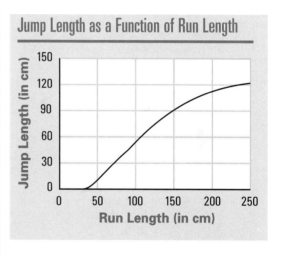

Jump Length as a Function of Run Length

The graph shows the relationship between run length *x* and jump length *y*. *For each x value, there is exactly one corresponding value of y.* When this happens, we say that the variable *y is a function of x* or that *the relation between run length x and jump length y is a function.*

This sort of functional relationship between variables is often written using symbolic shorthand. To show that *y* is a function of *x*, mathematicians and other professional users of mathematics commonly write "$y = f(x)$." Then facts and questions about the function can also be written in symbolic shorthand form.

For example, to express the fact that a run of 90 centimeters will give a jump of 45 centimeters, you could write "$f(90) = 45$." Similarly, you could write "$f(180) = 105$" to show that a run of 180 centimeters leads to a jump of 105 centimeters. These function equations are usually read "f of 90 equals 45" and "f of 180 equals 105." Written in this form, the "$f(90)$" does *not* mean "f times 90."

1. Refer to the function graph relating run length to jump length.

   a. What is meant by $f(75) = 30$? How is that fact shown on the graph?

   b. What value of y satisfies the equation $y = f(120)$, and what does that information tell about jump length?

   c. What values of x satisfy the equation $100 = f(x)$, and what does that information tell about jump lengths?

   d. What value of y satisfies the equation $y = f(210)$, and what does that information tell about jump length?

   e. What values of x satisfy the equation $0 = f(x)$, and what does that information tell about jump lengths?

In previous units and courses, you've studied a variety of other functions relating variables. For example, you might recall this graph showing how the height of a bungee jumper varies during the ups and downs of a jump.

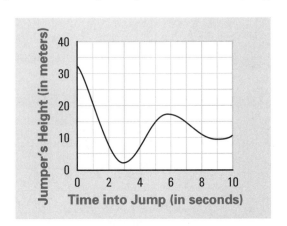

In this situation, the jumper's height is a function of time. It is common to choose letter names for functions that remind us of the quantities involved. In this case, it would be helpful to use the letter h, for height, to name the function. Then we would write $y = h(x)$.

2. Use the graph above to answer these questions about the function relating jump time and height.

   a. What information is expressed by $h(8) = 12$?

   b. What value of y satisfies $y = h(4)$, and what does the answer tell you about the jump?

   c. What values of x satisfy $15 = h(x)$, and what do they tell you about the jump?

In a relation between two variables x and y, y is a **function of** x when there is exactly one y value corresponding to each given x value. The notation "$y = f(x)$" indicates a clear prediction of y from x. You might have noticed in the bungee example that the correspondence doesn't always have the same property when viewed in the opposite direction, from y to x. For instance, the jumper is 15 meters above the ground at several times in the jump.

3. The graphs below illustrate three different relations between variables. Match each graph with the following relation that it seems most likely to represent. Be prepared to explain your reasoning.

   a. Age and height (in centimeters) for a group of 20 young people of various ages

   b. Age and IQ for the same group of 20 young people

   c. Average height (in centimeters) for young people at various ages

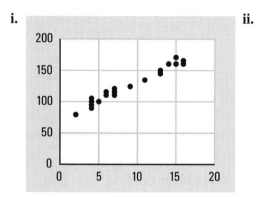

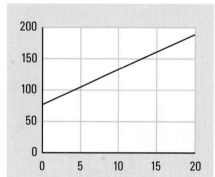

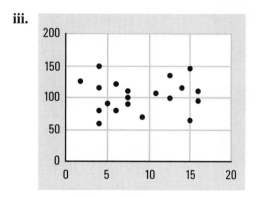

4. Determine whether or not each of the graphs in Activity 3 represents a function relating two variables. Explain your reasoning in each case.

Investigation 1 focused attention on relations between variables that are called *functions*.

ⓐ What examples would you use to illustrate situations in which one variable is a function of another?

ⓑ What are some examples of relations between variables that are not functions?

ⓒ Suppose x and y are labels for two related variables.

- When is it proper to say that a relation between variables y and x is a function, with y a function of x?

- How can you tell from a graph of (x, y) data whether y is a function of x?

- What does an equation like $f(5) = 12$ tell about the relation between variables x and y when $y = f(x)$?

Be prepared to share your ideas with the entire class.

On Your Own

The graph below shows the *height* of a baseball in flight as *time* passes.

a. Why is it correct to say that *height* of a baseball is a function of *time* in flight?

b. Use the symbols $y = h(x)$ to represent this function.

- What does the equation $h(1.5) = 18$ tell about the flight of the ball?

- What is the value of $h(3)$, and what does it tell about the flight of the ball?

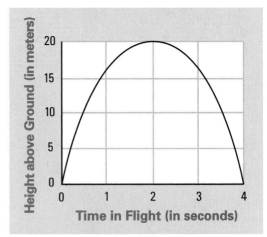

- What values of x satisfy the equation $10 = h(x)$, and what do those values tell about the flight of the ball?

c. Why do you think the notation $h(x)$ was used instead of $f(x)$?

INVESTIGATION 2 Functions with Symbolic Rules

In previous work, you've investigated tables, graphs, and symbolic rules for several of the most common patterns of change: linear, exponential, power (direct and inverse), quadratic, and trigonometric models. You've written the symbolic rules for those patterns as equations. Those rules can also be written using "$f(x)$" notation.

For example, in stores that sell athletic shoes of various kinds, the cost of doing business includes fixed expenses (like rent and pay for employees) and variable expenses (like the number of pairs of shoes bought from manufacturers). Operating costs of any store will be a function of those two main factors.

T*he typical American now owns two or three pairs of athletic shoes, which range in price from a $20 pair of old-fashioned sneakers at a discount store to $135 for top-of-the-line basketball shoes. One big seller has been Nike's Air Pegasus, which, like nearly all athletic shoes, is manufactured by suppliers in Asia. This accounting is based on a sale at an outlet of a large national retailer.*

—By Steven Pearlstein

Production labor	$2.75
Materials	9.00
Rent, equipment	3.00
Supplier's operating profit	1.75
Duties	3.00
Shipping	.50
Cost to Nike	**$20.00**
Research/development	$.25
Promotion/advertising	4.00
Sales, distribution, administration	5.00
Nike's operating profit	6.25
Cost to retailer	**$35.50**
Rent	$9.00
Personnel	9.50
Other	7.00
Retailer's operating profit	9.00
COST TO CONSUMER	**$70.00**

SOURCES: Nike Inc., Reebok International Inc., The Finish Line Inc., Just for Feet Inc., Melville Corp., U.S. Customs Service, Athletic Footwear Assn., industry consultants and executives, *The Washington Post*

1. At All Sport Shoes, the manager estimates the monthly operating cost for the store (in dollars) using a function of the number of pairs of shoes that the store purchases from its suppliers. The rule for that function is $C(x) = 17,500 + 35x$.

   a. Evaluate and explain the meaning of each of the following:

   - $C(100)$ - $C(250)$ - $C(0)$

   b. What do the numbers 17,500 and 35 tell about the relation between the number of pairs of shoes purchased from the manufacturer and the total cost of doing business at the store for one month?

   c. What values of x satisfy $C(x) = 24,500$, and what do those values tell about the store's monthly business costs?

   d. What table and graph patterns do you expect for this cost function?

   e. What numbers make sense as input values for the variable x? What numbers are realistic as output values for the function $C(x)$?

2. The population of the United States over several years can be estimated by the function model $P(x) = 276(1.009)^x$, where x is the number of years after 2000 (so 2000 is represented by $x = 0$) and $P(x)$ is U.S. population in millions.

a. Evaluate and explain the meaning of each of the following:

- $P(0)$
- $P(5)$
- $P(15)$
- $P(100)$

b. What table and graph patterns do you expect for this population function?

c. What do the numbers 276 and 1.009 tell about the estimated relation between time and population? How do these two numbers affect tables and graphs of the function?

d. What values of x satisfy the equation $P(x) = 400$, and what does your answer tell about U.S. population growth?

e. What numbers make sense as input values for the variable x? What numbers are realistic as output values for the function $P(x)$?

3. If you bounce up from a trampoline, your height above the trampoline surface varies over time on each bounce. The pattern for a single bounce might be given by a function model $h(t) = -16t^2 + 24t$. (Here, time t is in seconds, and height $h(t)$ is in feet.)

a. Evaluate and explain the meaning of each of the following:

- $h(0)$
- $h(0.5)$
- $h(1.2)$

b. What table and graph patterns do you expect for this function rule?

c. What do the numbers -16 and 24 tell about the relation between height above the trampoline and time? How do these two numbers affect tables and graphs of the function?

d. According to this model, when would you reach your maximum height above the trampoline? What height would that be?

e. After how much time would you return to the surface of the trampoline?

f. What numbers make sense as input values for the variable t? What numbers make sense as output values for the function $h(t)$?

4. If you ride on a Ferris wheel, your height above the ground will vary as the wheel turns. Suppose the wheel starts spinning for a ride when you are in the same position as the seat marked with an asterisk (*) in the diagram at the right.

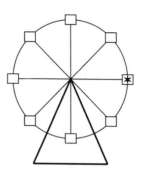

   If the wheel has a radius of 30 feet and spins so that you first move up from the indicated position, making a full turn every 6.28 seconds, your height (in feet) at any time during the ride (in seconds) could be estimated by the function model $h(t) = 30 \sin t + 35$. (Since t is not a degree measure, this equation assumes that the input variable is measured in radians.)

   a. Evaluate and explain the meaning of each of the following:

   - $h(0)$
   - $h(1.6)$
   - $h(3)$
   - $h(4.7)$
   - $h(6.28)$
   - $h(7.85)$

   b. For what values of the input variable t is $h(t)$ equal to 35?

   c. What do the numbers 30 and 35 in the function rule tell about the situation being modeled?

   d. What patterns will you find in tables and graphs of this function rule, and how do they relate to the motion of the Ferris wheel?

   e. What numbers make sense as input values for the variable t? What numbers would you expect as output values for the function $h(t)$?

For any function $f(x)$ relating two (or more) variables, it is customary to refer to the variable x as the *input* and the second variable as the *output*. In many situations and for many function rules, only some numbers make sense as inputs. Those numbers make up what is called the **domain** of the function. In a similar way, only some numbers will occur as outputs of the function. Those numbers make up what is called the **range** of the function.

   There are two ways to think about domain and range for a function that models a real-world problem situation. On one hand, you might ask what numbers are realistic or *practical* as inputs and outputs. On the other hand, you might ask what numbers *theoretically* can be used as inputs for the given algebraic rule (regardless of whether they make sense in the problem situation).

5. The function predicting monthly business costs for All Sport Shoes had the rule $C(x) = 17{,}500 + 35x$, where x was the number of pairs of shoes ordered from the manufacturer and $C(x)$ was the monthly operating cost in dollars.

   a. A table of (*number of pairs of shoes*, *cost*) data might begin like this:

x	0	1	2	3	4
$C(x)$	17,500	17,535	17,570	17,605	17,640

   What does this pattern suggest about the *practical domain* and *range* of the cost function?

b. For what input values of x can you use the rule $C(x) = 17,500 + 35x$ to calculate an output value (regardless of whether the input or output makes sense in the shoe business)? What is the range of output values that will occur as all possible values of x are used? What do your answers say about the *theoretical domain* and *range* of this function?

6. Look back at your work with the other function models in this investigation.

    a. Describe the *theoretical* domains and ranges for the functions below.

       ■ $P(x) = 276(1.009)^x$

       ■ $h(t) = -16t^2 + 24t$

       ■ $h(t) = 30 \sin t + 35$

    b. Describe the *practical* domains and ranges for the functions in Part a when they are used as models to predict their respective relations:

       ■ Estimated U.S. population as a function of time in years after 1995

       ■ Height of a trampoline bouncer as a function of time into a bounce

       ■ Height of a Ferris wheel rider as a function of time into the ride

Checkpoint

In Investigation 2, you explored the use of function notation to express symbolic rules for several types of algebraic models.

a Which of those situations (if any) involved the following function types?

    ■ Linear models

    ■ Exponential models (growth or decay)

    ■ Power models (direct or inverse)

    ■ Quadratic models

    ■ Trigonometric models

b For each of the five function types listed in Part a, what general patterns do you expect in the following?

    ■ Graphs

    ■ Tables of (x, y) values

    ■ Symbolic rules

c What are the theoretical domains and ranges of the various models listed in Part a? How are the domains of those models sometimes limited by practical considerations?

Be prepared to share your ideas with the class.

On Your Own

In Course 2, the relation between sound *intensity* and *distance* from the source of that sound (like a stereo system) was explored using the function with rule $I(d) = \frac{20}{d^2}$. This symbolic rule gives intensity in watts per square meter as a function of distance (in meters) from the source.

a. Evaluate and explain the meaning of each of the following:

- $I(1)$
- $I(2)$
- $I(3)$
- $I(0.5)$
- $I(10)$

b. What patterns of change occur in tables and graphs of this function? How can those patterns be predicted from the function rule without any calculations?

c. What are the practical domain and range of this function? Explain your reasoning.

d. What are the theoretical domain and range of this function? Explain your reasoning.

MORE

Modeling • Organizing • Reflecting • Extending

Modeling

1. In a wildlife experiment, all fish were removed from a lake and the lake was restocked with 1,000 new fish. The population of fish then increased over the years. Fish population in a newly stocked lake is a function of time t since the first fish were deposited in the lake. Let $y = P(t)$ represent that function, and use information from the graph below to complete the following tasks.

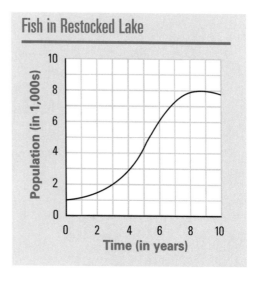

Fish in Restocked Lake

a. Estimate and explain the meaning of $P(6)$.

b. Estimate and explain the meaning of $P(4)$.

c. Estimate and explain the meaning of the t value for which $P(t) = 7$.

d. Use function notation to express the following statement: "The fish population after five years will be 4,500."

e. Estimate and explain the meaning of $P(5) - P(4)$.

2. The depth of water at an ocean pier changes over time as tides go in and out. Let $y = D(t)$ represent the function giving water depth as a function of time t during one 24-hour day, and use information from the graph below to complete the following tasks.

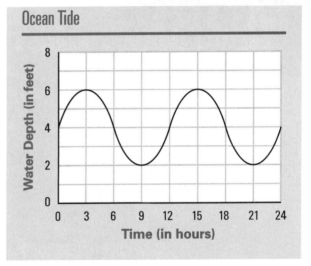

Ocean Tide

a. Use function notation to express the following statement: "Water depth after three hours is six feet."

b. Estimate and explain the meaning of $D(9)$.

c. Estimate and explain the meaning of $D(15)$.

d. Estimate and explain the meaning of $D(22)$.

e. Estimate and explain the meaning of the t values for which $D(t) = 4$.

3. Planners of an amusement park estimate that the number of daily customers will be related to the chosen admission price x (in dollars) by the function $c(x) = 10,000 - 250x$.

a. Calculate and explain the meaning of $c(15)$ and $c(30)$.

b. Find the value of x satisfying the equation $c(x) = 4,000$, and explain what it tells about the relation between admission price and number of customers.

c. Describe the practical domain and range of the function $c(x)$.

d. Describe the theoretical domain and range of the function $c(x)$.

4. Insulin is an important hormone produced by the body. In 5% to 10% of all diagnosed cases of diabetes, the disease is due to the body's inability to produce insulin; the people with this form of diabetes must take medicine containing insulin. Once the insulin gets to the bloodstream, it begins to break down quickly. When 10 units of insulin are delivered to a person's bloodstream, the amount remaining after t minutes might be modeled by an equation like $i(t) = 10(0.95)^t$.

a. Calculate and explain the meaning of $i(5)$ and $i(20)$.

b. Find a value of t satisfying the equation $i(t) = 1$, and explain what it tells about the relation between time and amount of insulin in the person's bloodstream.

c. Describe the practical domain and range of the function $i(t)$.

d. Describe the theoretical domain and range of the function $i(t)$.

5. The following sketch shows a 100-foot bridge suspended from cables between two towers, each 30 feet high. The height of the suspension cable above the bridge surface is a function of distance x from the left end of the bridge with rule $h(x) = 0.01x^2 - x + 30$. All distances are measured in feet.

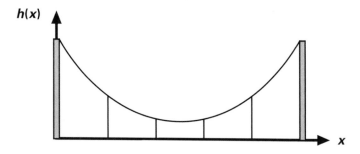

a. Calculate and explain the meaning of $h(25)$ and $h(65)$.

b. Find the value of x satisfying $h(x) = 13$, and explain what it tells about the relation between distance along the bridge and height of the suspension cable.

c. Describe the practical domain and range of the function $h(x)$.

d. Describe the theoretical domain and range of the function $h(x)$.

6. When a shoe company launches a new model, it has certain startup costs for design and advertising. Then it has production costs for each pair of shoes that is made. When the planning department of Start Line Shoes estimated costs of a proposed new model bearing a popular athlete's name, it reported that the average cost per pair of shoes (in dollars) would depend on the number made, with the equation $C(x) = 29 + \frac{25,000,000}{x}$.

   a. Calculate and explain the meaning of each of the following:

   ▪ $C(1)$

   ▪ $C(1,000,000)$

   ▪ $C(2,500,000)$

   b. For what value of x is $C(x) = 40$, and what does this value tell about the business prospects of the new shoe line?

   c. Sketch a graph of $C(x)$ using $0 \leq x \leq 10,000,000$ and $0 \leq y \leq 100$. Then explain what the shape of that graph shows about change in average production cost for the shoes as numbers produced increase. Try graphing over a larger interval of x values. What do you think is the lowest production cost per pair possible for Start Line Shoes?

   d. What connection is there between the graph of $C(x)$ and one of the basic function types you've studied in earlier units?

Organizing

1. Examine the tables below, each of which describes a relation between y and x. In which of these tables is y a function of x? If the relation described by a table is not a function, explain why not.

   a.

x	1	2	3	4	5	6	7	8	9
y	3	5	7	9	11	13	15	17	19

   b.

x	1	2	3	4	5	6	7	8	9
y	3	5	7	9	11	9	7	5	3

   c.

x	1	2	3	4	5	4	3	2	1
y	3	5	7	9	11	9	7	5	3

   d.

x	9	4	1	0	1	4	9	16	25
y	-3	-2	-1	0	1	2	3	4	3

2. Examine each of the graphs below describing a relation between *y* and *x*. In which of these graphs is *y* a function of *x*? If the relation described by a graph is not a function, explain why not.

a.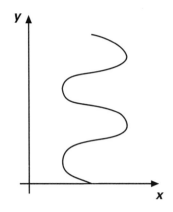

b.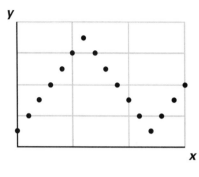

c.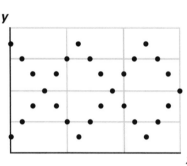

d.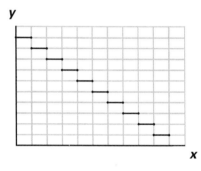

3. The diagram below shows three right triangles with a common right angle at *C*. Think back to your work with the trigonometric ratios: sine, cosine, and tangent.

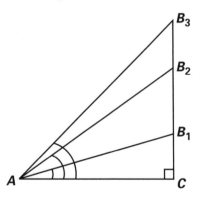

a. As the acute angle at *A* changes, what happens to each of these ratios?

b. Is each ratio a function of the measure of $\angle A$? Explain your reasoning.

c. What does sin *A* = 0.5 mean? How is this notation similar to the function notation introduced in this lesson?

4. In previous units, you calculated absolute values and may have calculated square roots to measure variation in sets of numerical data.

   a. Is the relation between each real number and its absolute value a function? Explain your reasoning.

   b. Is the relation between each nonnegative real number and its square root a function? Explain.

   c. What symbolic notation indicates that a variable y is the absolute value of x?

   d. What symbolic notation indicates that a variable y is the square root of x?

Reflecting

1. In previous courses, you've studied a variety of patterns relating variables. Give some examples of *linear models*, *exponential models*, or *power models* to illustrate the importance of being able to predict values of one variable y from another variable x in the way that functions do.

2. Scatterplots often show the trend of a relation between variables, but they don't allow you to predict y exactly from x. For example, both the scatterplot and linear model on the diagram below show how *weight* of a bungee jumper is related to *stretch* of the bungee cord.

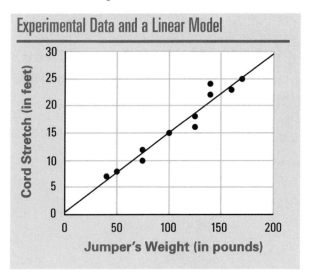

Experimental Data and a Linear Model

   a. In what ways is the linear model more useful than the scatterplot?

   b. In what ways does the scatterplot give more useful information about the relation?

3. Suppose the relation between Judy's height in centimeters and age in years is given by a function $y = h(x)$, where x is her age and y is her height.

   a. What does $h(16)$ represent?

   b. What does $h(14) - h(13)$ represent?

   c. Look back at the notation in Parts a and b and consider what each expression represents in words. What advantage is there to using function notation? Are there disadvantages? Explain.

4. It often is said that calculators have "built-in" functions. Explain what this means in terms of particular functions on your calculator.

5. What strategies have you used to find the practical domain and range of a function rule that is used to model some real-world situation? What strategies have you used to find the theoretical domain and range?

Extending

1. Many services that we use on a daily basis are priced with rules that ignore fractions. For example, a long-distance telephone call might cost $1.25 per minute or any fraction of a minute. This means that calls lasting any part of one minute will cost $1.25, calls of any length between one and two minutes will cost $2.50, and so on.

   There are two functions that are particularly helpful in modeling situations in which that kind of rounding is involved. One is the **floor function**, $f(x)$, and the other is the **ceiling function**, $c(x)$. The floor function always gives the greatest integer less than or equal to x. The ceiling function always gives the smallest integer greater than or equal to x.

   a. Use these definitions to complete a table like the one below.

x	0	1.3	2.9	−4.5	−3.88	4.78	5	100	−0.02
$f(x)$									
$c(x)$									

   b. The cost of shipping a package from one city to another is often a function of the weight of that package. Suppose one company charges $1.50 for each pound or fraction of a pound. What rule, involving the ceiling or floor function, gives the cost for shipping a package of exact weight x (in pounds)?

c. The cost of a cellular telephone call is $1 for the first minute and $0.25 for each minute or part of a minute beyond the first. What rule, involving the ceiling or floor function, gives the cost for a call that lasts x minutes? (Again, x might be a fractional number.)

d. The managers at Computer World decided to reward each salesperson based upon the dollar value of the merchandise sold during the month. At the end of each month, the managers will award $10 of store credit for every $5,000 worth of sales. What rule involving the ceiling or floor function will give the amount of store credit C for monthly sales of m dollars?

2. Suppose $g(x)$ is defined *piecewise* as follows:

$$g(x) = \begin{cases} 4 - x^2 & \text{if } x < 2, \\ x - 3 & \text{if } x \geq 2 \end{cases}$$

a. Give numerical values for $g(-2)$, $g(0)$, $g(2)$, and $g(10)$.

b. Sketch the graph of $y = g(x)$.

c. Explain why $y = g(x)$ is or is not a function.

d. Investigate how you might use your calculator or computer software to graph piecewise-defined rules. Write a report of your findings.

3. The function $F(x) = \frac{1}{12}x$ converts measurements from inches to feet, and the function $Y(x) = \frac{1}{3}x$ converts from feet to yards.

a. How can you use these functions to find the number of yards in 48 inches?

b. Explain the meaning of $Y(F(x)) = \frac{1}{36}x$.

c. If we define $f(x) = 2x$ and $g(x) = x^2$, then what are $f(g(x))$ and $g(f(x))$?

d. If we define $f(x) = 3x + 5$ and $g(x) = \frac{x-5}{3}$, then what are $f(g(x))$ and $g(f(x))$?

Lesson 2 ▶ *Algebraic Operations: Part 1*

Music is a major form of entertainment in our society. Production and sale of music are also big businesses. All across the country, there are thousands of individuals and groups practicing hard and hoping to make it big with a best-selling single or album. Unfortunately, as the following information shows, even a big hit might not bring much profit to the musicians.

What an Unknown Band Might Expect for Its First Album on a Major Label

ADVANCES and RECOUPABLE COSTS

The label advances money to the band, and it also deducts some of its own expenses from initial royalties:

■ Recording advance	$200,000
■ One video	$75,000
■ Touring	$40,000
■ Independent promotion	$50,000
Total advances and recoupable costs	**$365,000**

EARNINGS (based on 200,000 CDs sold)

A CD might cost $15, but the label makes deductions before calculating band royalties.

Original CD price	$15.00
■ 25 percent off for packaging and pressing cost	−$3.75
■ 10 percent off for discounts to retailers	−$1.50
■ Other discounts (11 percent)	−$1.65
Base CD price	**$8.10**

The typical band earns 10 percent per CD.

$8.10 × 0.1 = $0.81 per CD

$0.81 per CD × 200,000 CDs sold =	**$162,000**

If the band writes all of its own songs, it can expect another $0.52 per CD for publishing rights	**$104,000**

THE BOTTOM LINE (for 200,000 CDs sold)

Total band income from CD sales	$266,000
Minus label's advances and costs	−$365,000
Amount needed before band sees profit	**$99,000**

Source: Maggie Lange, Esquire; Perkins, Smith and Cohen, LLP. Boston, Massachusetts.

The table on the previous page shows how a band can sell 200,000 compact discs and make no profit at all.

a How much money is taken in from the sale of the CDs?

b Who makes profit from these sales?

c How would the band's profit or loss change if sales were more or less than 200,000 copies?

d Why would a band enter a business deal like this?

INVESTIGATION 1 ▶ How to Succeed in Business

The table on the previous page showed profit (actually, loss!) prospects for a band whose compact disc sold 200,000 copies. It's interesting to see what the story would be for a band if only 50,000 or 100,000 copies of a CD were sold, or if the CD became a hit and at least 500,000 copies were sold.

1. Suppose that when a new band recorded its first album with a major label, it had to deal with these business conditions:

- Expenses of $365,000 for the recording advance, video production, touring, and promotion (to be repaid out of royalties)
- Income of $0.81 per CD from royalties
- Income of $0.52 per CD for publishing rights

The band's profit on the CDs would depend on sales. The group's business manager could express the profit function in several different ways. Here are two possibilities:

$$P_1(x) = (0.81x + 0.52x) - 365,000$$

$$P_2(x) = 1.33x - 365,000$$

a. Do both function rules express the correct relation between sales and profits? How could you convince someone of your answer?

b. Which of the two rules do you believe expresses the band's profit function in the most useful way? Why?

c. What would the band's profit be if only 50,000 copies were sold? If 500,000 copies were sold?

d. How many CD copies must be sold for the band to break even?

2. Profit for the record company is also a function of sales. For the band in Activity 1, the label had the following production and distribution conditions to consider.

   ■ Studio, video, touring, and promotion expenses of $365,000

   ■ Pressing and packaging costs of $3.75 per CD

   ■ Discounts to music stores of $1.50 per CD

   ■ Other discounts of $1.65 per CD

   Until the band's share of income repays the $365,000 for studio, video, touring, and promotion expenses, the band gets no share of the $15 per CD of sales income.

   a. Use the information given above to write two equivalent expressions for the function that shows how the record company's profit depends on the number of CDs sold while the band is still repaying its advance. (The company would have other expenses, such as staff salaries and office expenses like electricity and rent. For this activity, though, you should ignore those expenses.)

      ■ Write one rule that shows how each income and cost item enters the overall calculation of profit.

      ■ Write another rule that will give profit for any number of CDs sold with the simplest possible calculation.

   b. Explain how the two rules you wrote in Part a can be checked for equivalence using tables and graphs and by reasoning with the symbolic forms themselves.

   c. What profit would the company make on sales of 50,000 CDs? On 100,000 copies?

   d. How many copies of this CD must be sold for the record company to break even?

   e. The company's profit function changes when the band has repaid its advance. Write two different expressions for profit as a function of CD sales beyond that point: one that shows each income and expense item, and another that is the simplest to use for actual calculation. Then explain in several ways how you know the two rules are equivalent.

As you have seen, bands don't often make much money on sales of their recordings. However, they do make money from concert tours and sales of T-shirts and other merchandise.

3. Suppose a band with a moderate following is preparing to go on a four-week tour. A market research survey gives the following information about prospects for a single show on the tour:

- Ticket sales x and ticket price p are related by $p = -0.04x + 30$. The venue pays the band 10% of the income from ticket sales. Income from ticket sales is $I(x) = (-0.04x + 30)x$.

- About 15% of ticket buyers will also buy a T-shirt, giving the band $5 profit for each sale.

- About 5% of ticket buyers will buy a poster, giving the band $3.50 profit for each sale.

- All the band's other expenses for each show will average about $300.

Because one of the band's main goals is to make a profit, the band manager might combine all the given information in a single relation showing profit as a function of the number of tickets sold at a show.

a. One possibility is the following equation:

$$P(x) = 0.10(-0.04x + 30)x + 5(0.15x) + 3.50(0.05x) - 300$$

How does each part of this function rule relate to the given information?

b. In what ways could you rewrite this rule for the profit function in a simpler yet equivalent form?

c. How can you check to see that the simpler function rules you wrote in Part b are equivalent to the original?

d. What is the maximum profit that the band could make from the show? How many ticket buyers will produce that maximum profit? What ticket price will produce that maximum profit?

As you explored profit and loss possibilities in the music business, you found several cases in which quite different symbolic rules expressed the same relation between variables.

ⓐ What does it mean if someone says two function rules are *equivalent*?

ⓑ Describe at least three different ways that can help you check the equivalence of different function rules.

ⓒ Write equivalent algebraic rules for the following functions.

- $P_1(x) = 3x + 7x$
- $P_2(x) = (3x + 5)x$
- $P_3(x) = 5x - 7x + 2x$

ⓓ Which of the following pairs of function rules are equivalent?

- $C_1(x) = (1.05x + 10x) - 27{,}000$
  $C_2(x) = 11.05x - 27{,}000$
- $I_1(x) = (-0.7x + 12)x + 5(0.25x) + 4(0.80x) - 1{,}600$
  $I_2(x) = 15.75x - 1{,}600$
- $P_1(x) = (-0.005x + 50)x + 6(0.12x) + 2.8(0.10x) - 130{,}000$
  $P_2(x) = -0.005x^2 + 51x - 130{,}000$

Be prepared to explain your answers and reasoning to the entire class.

▶On Your Own

When a pair of athletic shoes costs $70 in a retail store, that price is based on several factors.

- Average manufacturer's income is about $20 per pair of shoes.

- Average wholesaler's income is about $15.50 per pair of shoes.

- Average retailer's operating costs are about $25.50 per pair of shoes sold.

Source: "Why It Costs $70 for a Pair of Athletic Shoes," *Washington Post*, May 3, 1995.

a. One way to express retailer's profit as a function of the number of pairs of shoes sold is $P(x) = 70x - (20x + 15.50x + 25.50x)$. Write this function rule in several other equivalent forms, including one that you think is the simplest possible.

b. How much profit does the retail store make on each pair of shoes sold, and how is that shown in your simplest-form answer in Part a?

c. Suppose the athletic shoe store estimates that price p and monthly sales x of its most popular shoe model are related by $x = 500 - 4p$. Write a symbolic rule that will give income I from sales of that shoe model as a function of the price charged: $I(p) =$ _____.

d. Write the income function rule in Part c in other equivalent forms. Which form do you think is the simplest form? Why?

e. If that most popular shoe has cost factors that are the same as the averages described above, what function rule will give store profit on the most popular model alone?

f. Write the profit function from Part e in several equivalent forms, including one that you think is simplest for calculations.

INVESTIGATION 2 Equivalent Expressions

As you worked on the activities of Investigation 1, you found several cases in which different symbolic rules could be used for the same function. You might have found, for example, that for any input value of x the following is true:

$$0.81x + 0.52x = 1.33x$$

You were told that the band in Activity 1 of Investigation 1 received $0.81 in royalties on each CD sold and another $0.52 per CD for publishing rights, so it makes sense that the total income was $1.33 per CD. For any values of x, it seems quite reasonable that $0.81x + 0.52x = 1.33x$. The two profit function rules

$$P_1(x) = (0.81x + 0.52x) - 365,000$$

and

$$P_2(x) = 1.33x - 365,000$$

really are equivalent.

Sometimes you may have symbolic expressions without any details about a real-world situation being modeled. Still, it may be that simplifications and rearrangements can be made without changing the meaning of the functions involved. Look at the example above, and then consider the following question:

Does $ax + bx = (a + b)x$ for any value of x, regardless of the specific values of a and b?

In the following activities, you will explore this question and others that are similar. You will look for other ways that algebraic expressions can be rewritten without changing their meaning and for basic, general principles for rewriting algebraic expressions in equivalent forms.

1. Below are 21 equations. In some of those equations, the related expressions give identical outputs for all input values of x. In other equations, the related expressions give equal outputs for only a few specially chosen x values. In a few of the equations, the related expressions never give the same output from a given input.

   Working with a partner, examine the equations and separate them as best you can into three groups:

   a. Equations that are true for all values of x

   b. Equations that are true for only some values of x

   c. Equations that are true for no values of x

   Share your ideas with the other members of your group. Resolve any differences, and then prepare convincing arguments in support of each agreed-upon conclusion.

   ## Which Expressions Are Equivalent?

$4x^2 + 5 = 5 + 4x^2$	$(6x^2 + 3x) + 5x = 6x^2 + (3x + 5x)$
$7(2x) = 14x$	$2(x^2 + 3x + 1) = 2x^2 + 6x + 2$
$\frac{1}{3}(18x + 15) = 6x + 15$	$7x^2 = (7x)^2$
$3(5x + 2) = 15x + 2$	$5\left(\frac{2}{5} + 2x\right) = 2 + 2x$
$x(9 + x) = (9 + x)x$	$(6 \div 3x) \div x = 6 \div (3x \div x)$
$(12x + 2) + 17 = 12x + (2 + 17)$	$7 \div 14 = 14 \div 7x$
$-(4x^3 - 5x^2 + x) = -4x^3 + 5x^2 - x$	$6 + (x^2 + x) = (6 + x^2) + x$
$5(2x^2 + x) = 10x^2 + 5x$	$x - 7 = 7 - x$
$4x + 3x = 3x + 4x$	$7(x + 5) = 7x + 35$
$(3 + 2x) + x = 3 + (2x + x)$	$8 - (5 - x) = (8 - 5) - x$
$2(3x^2) = 6x^2$	

2. Now, working together as a group, sort the equations that are true for all values of the variable x into types that seem to involve similar patterns.

   a. Write, in your own words, descriptions of the various patterns you found. For example, you might notice that several equations are similar in form to $4x + 3x = 3x + 4x$ and summarize this pattern by saying "You can switch the order of the terms being added."

b. For each pattern you agree on, make up another algebraic equation that shows its application. For example, the equation "$7 + 12x = 12x + 7$" illustrates the same pattern as "$4x + 3x = 3x + 4x$."

3. Compare your types of equations and pattern descriptions to those of other groups in class.

Mathematicians have spent a great deal of time studying arithmetic and algebraic operations to find basic principles that can guide work with symbolic expressions. They have generally agreed on the following basic properties of numbers and operations. You have already encountered most of these properties in your previous work with algebraic expressions.

Algebraic Properties

Commutative Property

Of Addition:	For any numbers a and b, $a + b = b + a$
Of Multiplication:	For any numbers a and b, $a \times b = b \times a$

Associative Property

Of Addition:	For any numbers a, b, and c, $a + (b + c) = (a + b) + c$
Of Multiplication:	For any numbers a, b, and c, $a \times (b \times c) = (a \times b) \times c$

Distributive Property

Of Multiplication Over Addition:	For any numbers a, b, and c, $a \times (b + c) = a \times b + a \times c$
Of Multiplication Over Subtraction:	For any numbers a, b, and c, $a \times (b - c) = a \times b - a \times c$

4. Compare the patterns and descriptions that you identified in Activity 2 to the list of properties and names that are standard in mathematical usage. Then brainstorm with your group members about helpful ways to think about and remember the names of these properties.

5. Study each of the following arguments and identify the algebraic properties that justify each step. Then, try to reach the same conclusion using a different sequence of steps.

a. $5x + (3 + 7x)$ is equivalent to $5x + (7x + 3)$

is equivalent to $(5x + 7x) + 3$

is equivalent to $(5 + 7)x + 3$

is equivalent to $12x + 3$

b. $-5(x + 6) + 4x$ is equivalent to $(-5x + -30) + 4x$

is equivalent to $(-30 + -5x) + 4x$

is equivalent to $-30 + (-5x + 4x)$

is equivalent to $-30 + (-5 + 4)x$

is equivalent to $-30 + (-1x)$

6. Write each of the following symbolic expressions in at least three different but equivalent forms. In each case, explain which algebraic properties guarantee the equivalence.

    a. $3 + (5x + 9)$

    b. $5(7x + 13x)$

    c. $-5x^2 + (5x^2 + 35x)$

    d. $2x^2 + (5x + 10x^2)$

    e. $7x^2 + 14x$

The basic properties of numbers and operations seem to apply to expressions that involve at most three terms. But they can be applied to prove more general commutative, associative, and distributive properties that are quite useful.

7. For each of these function rules, find the shortest possible symbolic expression that is equivalent to the original. Be prepared to explain how you are using generalized forms of the basic algebraic properties in your reasoning. Use your graphing calculator to provide evidence that the original and final forms are equivalent. Divide the workload among members of your group.

    a. $f(x) = 7 + 12x + (-4) + 7x + (-4x) + 5$

    b. $g(x) = 5[x + 4 + 3x + (-9)]$

    c. $h(t) = t(-5t + 40t + 11) + 30t^2 + (-8t)$

    d. $j(r) = (7r^2 + 9r + 12) + [24 + (-7r) + 4r^2]$

    e. $k(x) = (4x^3 + 5x^2 + 1.5x + 12) + x(4x^2 + 3x + 2)$

When you analyze functions by operating with only their symbolic rules, it's easy to make mistakes. If you carefully apply the commutative, associative, or distributive properties, you'll always transform a given rule into an equivalent symbolic form. But there are some very tempting "shortcuts" that lead to trouble.

8. Check the following attempts to write algebraic expressions in equivalent forms. In some of these attempts, a common mistake has been made.

    ■ For those that *are* correct, identify the algebraic properties that guarantee equivalence.

    ■ For those that are *not* correct, see if you can explain the probable errors in thinking that led to the incorrect results. Then write a second expression that *is equivalent* to the first and identify the algebraic properties that guarantee equivalence.

    a. Is $3x + 7x$ equivalent to $10x^2$?

    b. Is $7(5x + 3)$ equivalent to $35x + 3$?

    c. Is $-9x^2 + 4x^2$ equivalent to $-5x^2$?

    d. Is $(-5t)(-8t)$ equivalent to $40t$?

    e. Is $9x^3 + 5x^2$ equivalent to $14x^5$?

    f. Is $9n^2 + 12n + 15$ equivalent to $3(n^2 + 4n + 15)$?

The basic properties of numbers and operations can be used to write equivalent forms that simplify calculations.

a Which properties are used to write equivalent expressions in the following ways?

- By changing the grouping of terms
- By changing the order of terms to be added or multiplied
- By changing the order in which a combination of addition and multiplication operations is performed

b Which algebraic properties justify each step in the argument below? For any numbers a, b, and c and a variable x:

$a(x + b) + cx$ is equivalent to $(ax + ab) + cx$

is equivalent to $(ab + ax) + cx$

is equivalent to $ab + (ax + cx)$

is equivalent to $ab + (a + c)x$

c What basic algebraic properties guarantee the equivalence of each pair of expressions below?

$$(0.81x + 0.52x) - 365{,}000 = 1.33x - 365{,}000$$

$$(-0.04x + 30)x = -0.04x^2 + 30x$$

d Write your own examples to illustrate common mistakes in attempts to write equivalent algebraic expressions, and explain the error in each example.

Be prepared to share your use of and thinking about algebraic properties with the entire class.

The algebraic expressions and function rules that you've worked with in this investigation all involve symbolic forms that are called *polynomials*. A **polynomial** is a symbolic expression of the form $a_nx^n + \cdots + a_2x^2 + a_1x + a_0$. The **degree** of a polynomial is the largest integer n for which $a_n \neq 0$. A polynomial in which terms are written in order of decreasing (or increasing) powers is said to be **in standard form**.

Associated with any polynomial is a function $p(x) = a_nx^n + \cdots + a_1x + a_0$. You'll find that the algebraic rules for many functions can be written in equivalent standard polynomial form. For example, the standard form of the rule for $j(r) = (7r^2 + 9r + 12) + [24 + (-7r) + 4r^2]$ is $j(r) = 11r^2 + 2r + 36$.

On Your Own

Use algebraic properties to reason about equivalent forms of the following algebraic expressions.

a. For each algebraic expression below, write at least three equivalent forms. Write one in standard polynomial form and one that has more terms than the given form.

- $5x + (7 + 9x)$
- $(7x^2 + 3x + 4) + 4x(3x + 2)$

b. Which properties justify the statements below?

- $3 + [5 + (-8)] = 3 + (-8 + 5)$
- $5(28) = 5(20) + 5(8)$

c. What is the error in the reasoning below?

$$3(16) = 3(10 + 6)$$
$$= 3(10) + 6$$
$$= 30 + 6$$
$$= 36$$

d. Write these polynomials in standard form.

- $3 + 5x + 7x^4 - 3x^2$
- $x - 2x^2 + 8 + 9x$

INVESTIGATION 3 What a Difference Subtraction Makes

As you studied and applied the basic algebraic properties to write equivalent expressions for function rules, you might have wondered why those properties seem to involve only addition and multiplication. In the music business problems, you had to deal with subtraction in predicting profit. For example, the record company profit function could be derived by subtracting expenses from income to give the following rules.

Before the band advance is repaid:

$$P_1(x) = 15x - (1.65x + 1.50x + 3.75x + 365,000)$$

After the band advance is repaid:

$$P_2(x) = 15x - (1.65x + 1.50x + 3.75x + 0.81x + 0.52x)$$

Of course, there is a much simpler way to write this profit function. In this investigation, you will find some guidelines for writing simpler equivalent forms in cases like this, when subtraction or division appears in an expression.

1. Given below is another group of equations, this time involving subtraction in various ways. Working with a partner, examine the equations to find those that you think relate equivalent expressions. Share your ideas with your group and resolve any differences. Then prepare convincing arguments in support of each agreed-upon conclusion.

Which Expressions Are Equivalent?

$4x^2 - 5 = 5 - 4x^2$	$(6x^2 - 3x) - 5x = 6x^2 - (3x - 5x)$
$2(x^2 - 3x - 1) = 2x^2 - 6x - 2$	$3(5x - 2) = 15x - 6$
$\frac{1}{3}(18x - 15) = 6x - 5$	$10 - (7 + 2x) = (10 - 7) + 2x$
$6 - (x - 2) = (6 - x) - 2$	$3 - (9 - x) = (9 - x) - 3$
$7x - 14 = 14 - 7x$	$(x - 1) - 6 = 6 - (x - 1)$
$-(5x^3 - 6x^2 - x) = -5x^3 + 6x^2 + x$	$2 - (3 - x^2) = (2 - 3) - x^2$

2. Based on your analysis of these equations, summarize your conclusions about rewriting expressions involving subtraction.

   a. Is subtraction a commutative operation? That is, does $a - b = b - a$ for all numbers a and b? Explain your reasoning.

   b. Is subtraction an associative operation? That is, does $a - (b - c) = (a - b) - c$ for all numbers a, b, and c? Why or why not?

   c. Does $a(b - c) = ab - ac$ for all numbers a, b, and c? Explain your reasoning.

Your results from work on Activities 1 and 2 should make you cautious about rewriting algebraic expressions involving subtraction. One of the best ways to avoid the pitfalls of subtraction is to use the basic connection between subtraction and addition. For any numbers a and b: $a - b = a + (-b)$.

In words, the above definition of subtraction says that the difference "a minus b" is equal to the sum "a plus the opposite of b."

3. Test this definition of subtraction on these specific cases:

   a. Compare $15 - 8$ and $15 + (-8)$.

   b. Compare $15.8 - 23.5$ and $15.8 + (-23.5)$.

   c. Compare $\frac{2}{3} - \frac{1}{6}$ and $\frac{2}{3} + \left(-\frac{1}{6}\right)$.

   d. Compare $24 - (-6)$ and $24 + 6$.

   e. Compare $-18 - (-10)$ and $-18 + 10$.

There is one other important caution about dealing with arithmetic and algebraic expressions that involve subtraction. It applies to expressions that include parentheses, such as the following:

$$(4 + 2x) - (7 + 5x)$$

Using the connection between subtraction and the opposite of a number, you can rewrite this expression:

$$(4 + 2x) + [-(7 + 5x)]$$

4. To discover a way to find the opposite of the sum (or difference) of two terms, experiment with some specific arithmetic and algebraic cases. Determine which of the following expressions are equivalent.

   a. Compare $-(5 + 12)$, $(-5 + 12)$, and $[-5 + (-12)]$.

   b. Compare -5, $-(-5)$, and 5.

   c. Compare $-(23 - 11)$, $(-23 - 11)$, and $(-23 + 11)$.

   d. Compare $-(4 + 2x)$, $(-4 + 2x)$, and $[-4 + (-2x)]$.

   e. Compare $-(10 + 7)$, $(-1)(10 + 7)$, and $(-1)(10) + (-1)(7)$.

   f. Compare $-(3x - 5)$, $(-3x + 5)$, and $(-3x - 5)$.

   g. What general pattern do you see for dealing with expressions like $-(a + b)$? Like $-(a - b)$?

5. Using variables, write a summary of your findings in Activity 4. Compare your summary to those of other groups. Reach agreement on a property involving the "opposite of a sum." Write a similar property involving the "opposite of a difference."

6. Write each of the following symbolic expressions in at least three different but equivalent forms. In each case, explain which algebraic properties guarantee the equivalence.

   a. $5x - 7x$

   b. $-(5x + 9) + 3$

   c. $-2x^2 - (5x - 10x^2)$

   d. $-5x^2 - (5x^2 + 35x)$

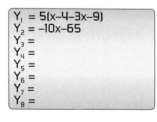

7. For each of the following function rules, find the shortest possible symbolic expression that is equivalent to the original. Be prepared to explain how you are using generalized forms of the basic algebraic properties in your reasoning. Use a graphing calculator or computer software to check that the original and final forms are equivalent.

   a. $f(x) = 7 + 12x - 4 - 7x - 4x + 5$

   b. $g(x) = 5(x - 4 - 3x - 9)$

   c. $h(t) = t(-5t - 40t - 11) - 30t^2 - 8t$

   d. $j(r) = (7r^2 - 9r - 12) + (24 - 7r - 4r^2)$

   e. $k(x) = (4x^3 - 5x^2 - 1.5x + 12) - x(4x^2 + 3x - 2)$

8. Just as there are tempting but incorrect ways to rewrite algebraic expressions involving addition of terms, there are some common mistakes in working with expressions involving subtraction. Study the following pairs of expressions. In writing some of these pairs, common mistakes were made. For those that are not equivalent, see if you can explain the mistake that was made in trying to write an equivalent form of the first given expression. For those that are equivalent, explain which property was used correctly.

CAUTION

a. Is $-5(x + 2)$ equivalent to $-5x + 2$?

b. Is $(-3x - 12)$ equivalent to $-3(x - 4)$?

c. Is $-3x - 9$ equivalent to $9 - 3x$?

d. Is $(-5n)(-8n^2)$ equivalent to $-40n^2$?

e. Is $(24t^3 - 18t^2 - 3t)$ equivalent to $3t(8t^2 - 6t - 1)$?

Checkpoint

When subtraction appears in arithmetic or algebraic expressions, there are some cautions about evaluating and rewriting those expressions in equivalent forms.

a What properties are true for addition but not for subtraction?

b What properties are true for both addition and subtraction?

c How would you proceed in simplifying each of the following algebraic expressions?

- $5x - 7x + 8$
- $-(5x + 7)$
- $-5(7x + 12)$
- $-4x(6x - 7)$

d What seem to be the common mistakes in attempts to rewrite algebraic expressions involving subtraction and negative numbers in equivalent forms?

Be prepared to share your ideas with the rest of the class.

> **On Your Own**

Use properties of subtraction to help you reason about equivalent forms of the following algebraic expressions.

a. For each algebraic expression below, write at least three equivalent forms. Make one as simple as possible, and write one that is actually longer than the given form.

- $7x - 12x + 8 - 3x - 7$
- $5x + (7 - 9x)$
- $(7x^2 - 3x - 4) - 4x(3x + 2)$

b. Without doing the indicated calculations, explain why properties of addition, subtraction, and multiplication guarantee that these statements are true.

- $3 - (5 - 8) = 3 + [8 + (-5)]$
- $5(18) = 5(20) - 5(2)$

c. Where are the errors in this reasoning?

$$-48 = -3(16)$$
$$= -3(20 - 4)$$
$$= -3(20) - 3(4)$$
$$= -60 - 12$$
$$= -48$$

MORE
Modeling • Organizing • Reflecting • Extending

Modeling

1. The operators of a high school all-star football game did some market research to help in setting prices to maximize operating profit. The following estimated relationships were found.

- Ticket price p and ticket sales x will be related by $p = -0.002x + 40$.
- Income from sales of food and drinks will average $1.50 per ticket sold.
- About 25% of the ticket buyers will park at the stadium, giving income of $5 per car.
- Expenses for the game will include operating expenses of about $100,000 and average food and drink costs of $0.50 per ticket sold.
- Past experience suggests that between 8,000 and 12,000 tickets will be sold.

a. Write algebraic rules for functions that give game *income* (i) from ticket sales, (ii) from food and drink concessions, and (iii) from parking. Write each rule as a function of the number of tickets sold.

b. Write an algebraic rule for the function giving game *profit* as a function of number of tickets sold. Write this profit function in two ways:

■ One showing the separate contributions to profit from ticket sales, food and drink sales, and parking.

■ One showing the shortest possible rule for calculating profit.

c. According to the information collected, what is the maximum profit possible? What ticket price will give the maximum profit?

d. Do the results of your work in Part c seem reasonable, or would you ask the market researchers to justify their conclusions? Explain your reasoning.

2. Temperature is measured on two common scales, Fahrenheit and Celsius. Those scales are related by the equation $F = 1.8C + 32$. Some people like to use the following rule, which they find easier to remember:

To convert Celsius to Fahrenheit, double and add 30.

a. Write this alternate rule as an equation: $F = $ _____.

b. Is the rule in Part a equivalent to the original rule? Explain your reasoning.

c. Solve $F = 1.8C + 32$ for C in terms of F.

d. Similarly, there is another approximate rule for converting Fahrenheit to Celsius:

To convert Fahrenheit to Celsius, subtract 30 and divide by 2.

Write this rule as an equation: $C = $ _____. Explain whether the rule is equivalent to the one you derived in Part c.

e. Use tables or graphs to compare the two rules for converting from Celsius to Fahrenheit. Under what conditions do you think it's reasonable to use the easy-to-remember alternate?

3. One standard formula for calculating the area of a trapezoid is given by the equation $A = \frac{1}{2}(b_1 + b_2)h$, where the variables b_1, b_2, and h represent the lengths of the two bases and the height of the trapezoid, respectively.

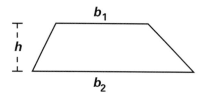

a. The sketch below shows a way of thinking about the area of a trapezoid that leads to a different formula: $A = \frac{1}{2}hb_1 + \frac{1}{2}hb_2$.

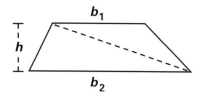

- Explain with a geometric argument why this other formula works.

- Use algebraic reasoning to show that this formula is equivalent to the standard form.

b. The sketch below shows yet another way of thinking about the area of some trapezoids, which leads to the formula $A = \frac{1}{2}h(b_2 - b_1) + b_1h$.

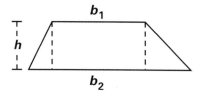

- Explain with a geometric argument why this formula gives the correct area.

- Use algebraic reasoning to show that this formula is equivalent to the standard formula.

4. The expense of dining out at a restaurant, other than fast-food restaurants, usually involves not only the price of the meal, but also tax and a tip. The standard tip for acceptable service is at least 15% of the price of the meal.

a. If p is the price of a meal, write a rule giving the cost C of the meal plus tip (*but not including tax*).

```
        ─    ●    ─
        Guest Check
TABLE NO.  NO. PERSONS  SERVER NO.  CHECK NO.
                                   2651
2  pasta w/ marinara  16.00
2  salad                6.00
2  ice cream            3.00
2  coffee               3.00




                            28.00
TAX                          1.68

  Thank You - Call Again   29.68
GUEST RECEIPT
NO. PERSONS    DATE    CHECK NO.      AMOUNT
                        2651
Tops 45740
```

b. Rewrite your rule in Part a in an equivalent form that is easier to calculate using a calculator.

c. Frequent diners often find it easier to calculate the tip mentally.

   To calculate a 15% tip, find 10% of the meal price, and add $\frac{1}{2}$ of that result to it.

   Try this mental method on a meal bill that totals $28.00. Explain why this method works.

d. Now rewrite the rule in Part a to show this mental shortcut.

e. Suppose you are traveling through a state in which there is a 6% tax on restaurant meals. Modify your rule in Part a to show the total expense of the meal. Then rewrite this rule in the shortest form possible.

Organizing

1. Identify the algebraic properties that justify equivalence of these pairs of algebraic expressions. Some examples might involve a chain of operations in which several different properties are applied.

   a. $-4(2x + 7) = -8x - 28$

   b. $21 + 14x = 7(2x + 3)$

   c. $5s + (9 + 12s) = 17s + 9$

   d. $-36x^2 = (9x)(-4x)$

   e. $5m + 12m + 3 = 3 + 17m$

   f. $16t^2 - 160t = 16t(t - 10)$

2. Sketch graphs showing why the following pairs of algebraic expressions are *not* equivalent.

   a. $x - 2$ is not equivalent to $2 - x$.

   b. $-3x^2 + 5$ is not equivalent to $-5 + 3x^2$.

   c. $5(2x + 3)$ is not equivalent to $10x + 3$.

   d. $(2x)(3x)$ is not equivalent to $6x$.

   e. $-3(x + 4)$ is not equivalent to $-3x + 12$.

3. Rewrite each of the following function rules in standard polynomial form, and record the number system properties that justify each step in the simplification process.

   a. $f(x) = 5(9 + x)$

   b. $g(x) = (2x - 11)(7x)$

   c. $h(x) = 6(x - 3) - 5(x - 2)$

   d. $i(x) = 12 - 5x^2 + 21x$

e. $j(x) = 8(x^2 + 4x - 5) - 6(-2 - 7x^2 + 4x)$

f. $k(x) = -(x^2 + 4x) - (-3x - 5) - (2x^2 + 5x - 7)$

g. $m(x) = (x^4 + 4x^2 - 11) - (7x^3 + 5x + 12)$

h. $n(x) = -\frac{2}{3}(9x - 12x^2 + 6)$

4. In many situations in everyday life, it makes sense to find the *average* or *arithmetic mean* of two given numbers. In the following questions, the notation "$a \barwedge b$" will be used to represent the operation "find the average of numbers a and b."

   a. Evaluate:

   - $23 \barwedge -9$
   - $5.4 \barwedge 3.2$
   - $(500 \barwedge 1{,}500) \barwedge 2{,}500$

   b. Give a rule for evaluating "$a \barwedge b$" for any two numbers a and b.

   c. Is the operation $\barwedge$ commutative?

   d. Is the operation $\barwedge$ associative?

   e. Does the operation of multiplication distribute over the operation of finding the average?

5. In your previous work with matrices, you saw that they too have properties for addition like those summarized on page 194.

   a. Give an example showing the commutativity of addition of 2×2 matrices.

   b. Thinking about how you add matrices, explain why it is reasonable to expect that addition of matrices is commutative.

   c. Thinking again about how you add matrices, explain why it is reasonable to expect that addition of matrices is associative.

   d. Give an example of a property of multiplication of numbers that does *not* hold for multiplication of matrices.

Reflecting

1. In many of the tasks in this lesson, you performed an algebraic operation commonly referred to as *combining like terms*. You replaced algebraic expressions of several terms (like "$3x^2 - 7x^2$") with equivalent expressions of only one term ("$-4x^2$"). What do you think the phrase "like terms" means, and what examples would you give to show someone what you mean?

2. You've found that there are some common errors that occur when people operate on symbolic expressions in an effort to produce equivalent but more useful forms. What advice would you give to help someone understand why each of the following pairs of expressions is not equivalent?

   a. $a(x + b)$ is not equivalent to $ax + b$.

   b. $x - b$ is not equivalent to $b - x$.

   c. $(ax)(bx)$ is not equivalent to abx.

   d. $-(x - b)$ is not equivalent to $-x - b$.

3. What algebraic properties can be illustrated by the following sketches if you compare areas of the large rectangles to the areas of the smaller components?

a.

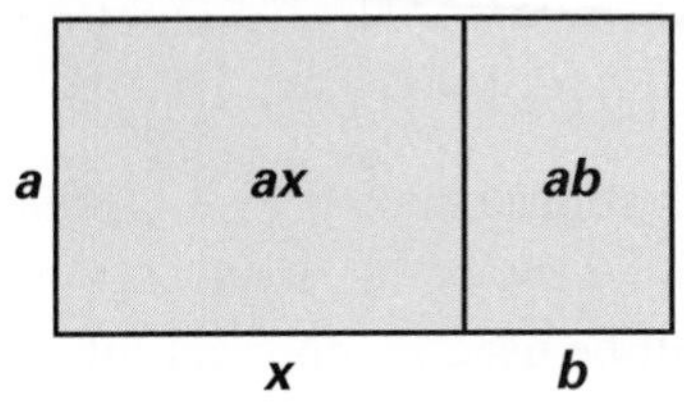

b.

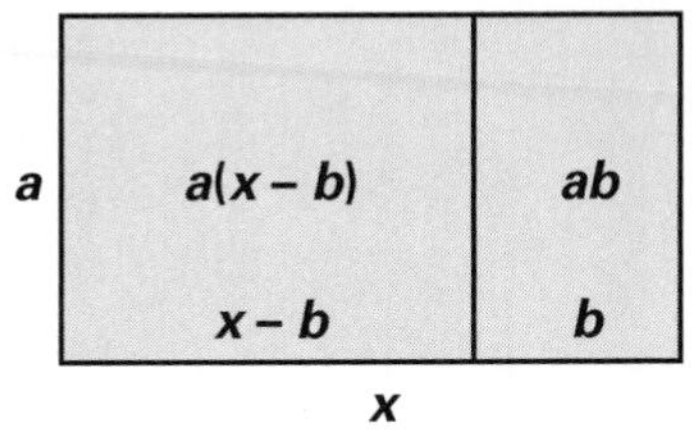

4. G. H. Hardy (1877–1947), a well-known mathematician who taught for many years at Cambridge University in England, wrote:

"A mathematician, like a painter or a poet, is a maker of patterns. If his [or her] patterns are more permanent than theirs, it is because they are made with ideas."

What do you think about Hardy's statement? To what extent have you been a "maker of patterns" in your work in this unit?

Extending

1. Examine the step-by-step algebraic reasoning in simplifying the following expressions. State the property that justifies each step.

a. $(-x \cdot 9)\frac{1}{9} + 5x = -x\left(9 \cdot \frac{1}{9}\right) + 5x$
$$= -x \cdot 1 + 5x$$
$$= -x + 5x$$
$$= x(-1 + 5)$$
$$= 4x$$

b. $3(a + x) + (-3a) = 3a + 3x + (-3a)$
$$= 3x + 3a + (-3a)$$
$$= 3x + 0$$
$$= 3x$$

c. $-5(a - 4) + 7(a - 4) = (-5 + 7)(a - 4)$
$$= 2(a - 4)$$
$$= 2a - 8$$

2. Graph the following functions, and see if you can discover anything about the relationship between the degree of a polynomial function and the graph of the function. Explore other functions and their graphs to test your hypothesis.

   a. $g(x) = x^2 + 7x + 12$

   b. $h(x) = x^3 - 5x^2 - 4x + 20$

   c. $f(x) = x^4 - 13x^2 + 36$

3. Suppose that a problem you are working on involves the following polynomial functions.

   $$f(x) = 4x^3 + x^2 + 7x - 17$$
   $$g(x) = 3x^2 + 4x - 7$$
   $$h(x) = 5x + 2$$
   $$j(x) = 5x^4 + 3x^2$$

   With partners to share the workload, find all possible sums and differences of the four given polynomial functions. Study the results in search of a pattern describing how the degree of a sum or difference of polynomials is related to the degrees of the polynomials being added or subtracted.

4. Consider the following operation on geometric points of a plane: For any two given points A and B, A **tri** $B = C$ is the point located at the third vertex of an equilateral triangle. The triangle is formed so that one moves counterclockwise in going from A to B to C. For any single point A, A **tri** $A = A$.

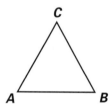

   a. Is "tri" a commutative operation?

   b. Is "tri" an associative operation?

   c. Think back to the averaging operation "⊼" in Organizing Task 4, page 205. What numbers could be generated with this operation, starting from 0 and 1 and applying "⊼" repeatedly?

   d. Suppose you start from two given points and apply the "tri" operation repeatedly to pairs chosen from the original points and points generated from those starting points. For example, after finding $C = A$ tri B, you can generate $D = A$ tri C and $J = D$ tri B, among others. What points of the plane can be generated in this way?

Lesson 3 Algebraic Operations: Part 2

In several earlier problem situations in this unit, you worked with quadratic functions that had rules of the form

$$f(x) = ax^2 + bx + c.$$

For example, if a gymnast bounces up off a trampoline, her height in feet above the trampoline at any time t seconds might be given by a quadratic function with rule

$$h(t) = -16t^2 + 24t.$$

Think About This Situation

Examine the graph below of the function $h(t) = -16t^2 + 24t$ giving a gymnast's height in feet above a trampoline at time t seconds. Following are three key questions that can be asked about this situation:

■ When will the gymnast reach maximum height?

■ What will that height be?

■ When will she return to the trampoline surface?

a How does the graph show estimates for answers to all three key questions above?

b How could information from the graph be used to derive the function rule itself?

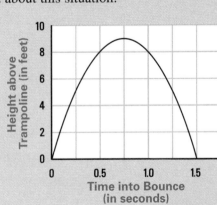

INVESTIGATION 1 ▸ Products and Factoring

The function rule $h(t) = -16t^2 + 24t$ can be used to produce a graph or a table of data describing the gymnast's bounce. But you can calculate values for the maximum height and landing time by using only algebraic reasoning with the rule.

1. Analyze the following way of answering the three key questions in the "Think About This Situation" on the previous page. Explain how properties of the function $h(t)$ and algebraic operations justify each step.

   (1) The function rule $h(t) = -16t^2 + 24t$ can be rewritten as $h(t) = -8t(2t - 3)$.

   (2) The gymnast returns to the trampoline surface when $h(t) = 0$.

   (3) $h(t) = 0$ when $-8t(2t - 3) = 0$.

   (4) $-8t(2t - 3) = 0$ when $-8t = 0$ or when $(2t - 3) = 0$.

   (5) $-8t = 0$ when $t = 0$, and $(2t - 3) = 0$ when $t = 1.5$.

   (6) The maximum value of $h(t)$ is $h(0.75)$ or 9.

   (7) Therefore, the maximum height of 9 feet occurs 0.75 seconds after the gymnast bounces off the trampoline. She returns to the trampoline surface 1.5 seconds after she bounces upward.

The reasoning used in Activity 1 involved rewriting the given quadratic expression in an equivalent form from which it was easy to see when $h(t) = 0$. The idea was to write the given quadratic rule as a product of two *linear factors*. That technique is often called **factoring the quadratic**. The same idea can be used with a variety of other similar functions.

2. Below is a list of quadratic functions. For each function $f(x)$, do the following:

   ■ Use symbolic reasoning to find all x for which $f(x) = 0$. These values are called the **zeroes** of the function.

   ■ Use the zeroes of $f(x)$ and other things you know about quadratic functions to sketch a graph of the function.

   ■ Check the results of your reasoning by producing appropriate calculator tables and graphs.

   a. $f(x) = x(x - 5)$ **b.** $f(x) = -x(x + 3)$

   c. $f(x) = (x + 3)(x - 5)$ **d.** $f(x) = (x - 6)(x - 1)$

   e. $f(x) = -(x + 7)(x + 2)$ **f.** $f(x) = (x - 3)(x - 3)$

   g. $f(x) = (5x + 12)(x - 3)$ **h.** $f(x) = (2x + 5)(3x + 1)$

   i. $f(x) = -6(-7x + 11)(2 - x)$

3. Find all x for which $f(x) = 0$ in each of the following cases. Then use your calculator to produce graphs of the given functions and look for patterns relating the zeroes of the functions and the properties of their graphs.

a. $f(x) = x(x - 5)(x + 3)$ **b.** $f(x) = -x(x - 3)(x + 5)$

c. $f(x) = (x + 6)(2x - 1)(x - 4)$ **d.** $f(x) = x(3x - 3)(x - 1)(x + 2)$

e. $f(x) = (x^2 - 4)(3x + 5)$

4. Study your results from Activities 2 and 3 to find patterns relating rules, zeroes, and graphs of functions. Use your observations to write rules for functions that satisfy the following conditions.

a. $f(4) = 0$ and $f(1) = 0$

b. $g(5) = 0$ and $g(-3) = 0$

c. $h(7) = 0$, $h(0) = 0$, and $h(2) = 0$

d. $j(-1) = 0$ and $j(-5) = 0$

Look back over your work on Activities 2 through 4. You probably have some ideas about the way that a function rule, if written in *factored form*, can be quite useful in finding the zeroes and sketching graphs of polynomial functions, especially quadratics. If a function rule is expressed in the form of a product of linear factors, you can find the x-intercepts quickly. The next two activities will suggest some strategies you can use for functions that are not written in factored form, such as $f(x) = x^2 + 5x + 6$ or $g(x) = 4x^2 + 20x$.

5. Justify each step in the following reasoning sequences, which show connections between factored form and the more familiar forms of quadratic rules.

a. $f(x) = (x + 3)(x + 2)$ **b.** $g(x) = (x - 3)(x + 5)$

$\quad = (x + 3)(x) + (x + 3)(2)$ $= (x - 3)(x) + (x - 3)(5)$

$\quad = (x^2 + 3x) + (2x + 6)$ $= (x^2 - 3x) + (5x - 15)$

$\quad = x^2 + 5x + 6$ $= x^2 + 2x - 15$

c. $h(t) = (5t + 2)(t - 4)$ **d.** $j(x) = 7x(2x + 5)$

$\quad = (5t + 2)(t) - (5t + 2)(4)$ $= (7x)(2x) + (7x)(5)$

$\quad = (5t^2 + 2t) - (20t + 8)$ $= 14x^2 + 35x$

$\quad = 5t^2 - 18t - 8$

The examples in Activity 5 show how the factored form of a quadratic function rule can be transformed into a more familiar form. To reason in the other direction, that is, to find the factored form that matches a given standard form quadratic rule, it helps to find the common thread in all such problems.

6. Consider the variety of functions with rules in the form $f(x) = (x + a)(x + b)$. Rules like these can always be rewritten in standard quadratic form. Complete this equation:

$$(x + a)(x + b) = x^2 + \underline{\hspace{1cm}}x + \underline{\hspace{1cm}}$$

Study how the results in each part of this standard quadratic form are related to the numbers a and b in the factored form of the function rule. How can these relations help you factor quadratic expressions like $x^2 + 5x + 6$?

7. Now see if you can use the patterns relating factored and standard form for quadratic function rules to write factored forms for each of the following rules. Compare your factorizations to those of other groups.

a. $f(x) = x^2 + 6x + 8$ **b.** $g(x) = x^2 + 7x + 12$

c. $h(x) = x^2 - 7x + 12$ **d.** $i(x) = x^2 - x - 12$

e. $j(x) = x^2 - 5x - 14$ **f.** $k(x) = x^2 - 6x + 8$

g. $m(x) = -x^2 + 6x - 8$ **h.** $n(x) = x^2 - 9$

i. $p(x) = x^2 + 6x + 9$ **j.** $q(x) = x^2 + 9$

k. $r(x) = x^2 + 6x - 7$ **l.** $s(x) = 2x^2 + 7x + 3$

8. Use symbolic reasoning to find the vertex of each parabola described by the rules given in Activity 7. Divide the workload among members of your group, and then share and explain your findings.

Checkpoint

Quadratic functions can be written with symbolic rules in the form $f(x) = ax^2 + bx + c$. Sometimes these rules can be rewritten in an equivalent factored form $f(x) = (mx + r)(nx + s)$.

ⓐ Which form do you find more helpful in finding zeroes of the function without producing tables or graphs? Why?

ⓑ Which form do you find more helpful in predicting whether the function has a maximum or minimum value? Why?

ⓒ Which form do you find more helpful in finding the maximum or minimum value? Why?

ⓓ How could you use information from both forms of the rule to make an accurate sketch of the graph of the function?

ⓔ In the simpler cases, in which $x^2 + bx + c = (x + m)(x + n)$, how are the numbers b and c in the general form of the quadratic related to the m and n in the factored form?

Be prepared to share your ideas with the entire class.

> **On Your Own**

Use what you have learned about factoring to help you complete the following tasks.

a. Rewrite each of the following function rules in an equivalent factored form (if possible).

- $f(x) = x^2 - 5x + 6$
- $g(x) = x^2 + 10x + 16$
- $h(x) = x^2 - 36$
- $j(x) = x^2 + 10$
- $k(t) = 7t^2 + 14t$

b. For each of the following functions, reason with the symbolic forms to find all x for which $f(x) = 0$. Then sketch a graph and find the minimum or maximum value of the function.

- $d(x) = (2x - 5)(x + 4)$
- $f(x) = x^2 + 5x - 6$
- $g(x) = x^2 - 12x$
- $h(x) = -x^2 + 7x + 18$

c. Write function rules (in factored and standard form) with these properties:

- $f(3) = 0$ and $f(5) = 0$
- $g(-2) = 0$ and $g(8) = 0$
- $h(-4) = 0$ and $h(0) = 0$
- $r(-5) = 0$, $r(2) = 0$, and $r(7) = 0$

d. For each function in Parts a through c, explain how you could use a graphing calculator to check your answer.

INVESTIGATION 2 ▶ Special Products and Factoring

Quadratic and higher-degree polynomials occur in many situations in both standard and factored forms. There are two special cases that have especially interesting and useful patterns.

1. Write each of the following indicated products in standard polynomial form. Then compare the factors and product in each case to look for a shortcut method for finding similar types of indicated products.

  a. $(x + 4)(x - 4)$ **b.** $(t - 3)(t + 3)$ **c.** $(s + 1)(s - 1)$

2. Write each of these quadratic expressions in factored form. Compare your result in each case to the pattern observed in Activity 1 to look for a shortcut method of factoring this special type of quadratic polynomial.

  a. $x^2 - 25$ **b.** $x^2 - 81$ **c.** $x^2 - 36$

3. Sketch graphs of each of the following quadratic functions. Use your understanding of symmetry and the connection between zeroes and factors to explain why the factored forms you found in Activity 2 make sense.

  a. $f(x) = x^2 - 25$ **b.** $g(x) = x^2 - 81$ **c.** $h(x) = x^2 - 36$

4. The expressions you have been investigating in Activities 1 through 3 involve the *difference of two squares*. Here is another way of thinking about factoring expressions like $x^2 - a^2$.

   a. What is the area of the shaded square below on the left?

   b. Refer to the figure on the right. What is the area of the white square? Of the shaded region?

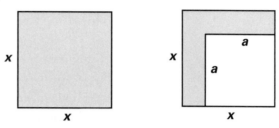

   c. Suppose the shaded region above on the right is cut and reassembled as shown below. Write two expressions giving the area of the new shape.

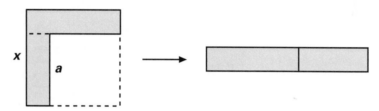

   d. How does the sequence of sketches and algebraic expressions for areas in Parts a through c confirm the general pattern observed in factoring the difference of two squares in Activity 2?

The product and factoring pattern that you explored in Activities 1 through 4 involves the difference of squares of numbers. There is another simple pattern for expanding and factoring another special type of quadratic called a *perfect square*.

5. Use algebraic properties to expand each of the following expressions to standard polynomial form. Then look back over the results to see if you can find a general shortcut for expanding expressions in the form $(x + a)^2$ and $(x - a)^2$.

   a. $(x + 3)^2$ **b.** $(x + 7)^2$

   c. $(x + 1)^2$ **d.** $(x - 5)^2$

   e. $(x - 6)^2$

6. Write expressions for areas of the regions in the diagram at the right. Then explain how the diagram illustrates a general pattern for expanding expressions in the form $(x + a)^2$ to standard polynomial form.

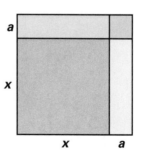

7. Use your discoveries in Activities 5 and 6 to write, if possible, each of these polynomials in factored form.

    a. $x^2 + 8x + 16$ **b.** $x^2 + 10x + 25$

    c. $x^2 - 6x + 9$ **d.** $x^2 - 2x + 1$

8. When beginning students are asked to expand expressions like $(x + a)^2$, one very common error is often made. What do you think that error is, and how could you help someone avoid making the error?

Checkpoint

Some quadratic functions have special connections between their standard polynomial and factored forms that allow some shortcuts in symbolic manipulation.

  ⓐ What standard polynomial form is always equivalent to a product in the form $(x - a)(x + a)$?

  ⓑ What standard polynomial form is always equivalent to an expression in the form $(x + a)^2$? In the form $(x - a)^2$?

  ⓒ How could you use a sketch like the one in Activity 6 to convince someone that the expression $(x + 3)^2$ is *not* equivalent to $x^2 + 9$?

  Be prepared to share your responses and thinking with the entire class.

▶ On Your Own

Use what you have learned about special products and factoring to help you complete the following tasks.

a. Write each of these expressions in expanded standard polynomial form.

    ■ $(x + 4)(x - 4)$ ■ $(x + 7)(x - 7)$

    ■ $(x + 8)^2$ ■ $(x - 9)^2$

    ■ $(x + 5)(x - 4)$

b. Write each of these polynomials in factored form (where possible).

    ■ $r^2 - 36$ ■ $m^2 + 9$

    ■ $m^2 + 6m + 9$ ■ $m^2 - 12m + 36$

INVESTIGATION 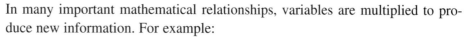 Division and Fractions

In many important mathematical relationships, variables are multiplied to produce new information. For example:

- Distance, rate, and time are related by the formula $d = rt$.
- Savings account interest, principal, rate, and time are related by $i = prt$.
- Volume of a cylinder is related to radius and height by $V = \pi r^2 h$.

In solving problems that involve relationships like those, it is often helpful to express the relationships using division and fractions. For example:

- Time of a trip is related to distance and rate by $t = \dfrac{d}{r}$.
- Height of a cylinder is related to volume and radius by $h = \dfrac{V}{\pi r^2}$.

To work effectively with such relationships, it helps to be skillful in working with some basic types of algebraic fractions. Use what you already know about numerical fractions and division to investigate the following situations. As you complete the activities, try to formulate some general guidelines for operating with algebraic fractions.

1. When the Student Government Association (SGA) at River Hill High School planned an all-school formal dance, SGA members set ticket prices at $10. They hired a disc jockey for $300 and had to plan on a custodial fee of $100.

   a. What algebraic expression gives the rule for calculating *total profit* from the dance as a function of the number of tickets sold?

   b. There were various proposals for sharing profits from the dance. What function rule would describe the share for the senior class if profits were shared in the following way?

   - Equally among the four classes in the school
   - In a ratio 4:3:2:1 among the four classes in the school, with higher classes getting the greater shares

   c. Write an equation giving average *profit per ticket* as a function of the number of tickets sold. Sketch a graph of that function (for 0 to 500 tickets), and explain what its shape tells about the relation between number of tickets sold and profit per ticket.

You now know that linear and quadratic function rules can be expressed in a variety of equivalent ways. Rules that involve fractions and inverse variation can also be written in different forms. Your choice among equivalent forms will often be influenced by the information you want from the function rules.

2. Consider the following questions about the profit and profit-per-ticket functions from planning for the River Hill High School dance.

   a. Under the plan to divide profits equally among the four classes in the school, the following three rules were proposed for senior class profit as a function of number of tickets sold.

   $$s_1(t) = \frac{10t - 400}{4} \qquad s_2(t) = \frac{1}{4}(10t - 400) \qquad s_3(t) = 2.5t - 100$$

   ■ Are these equivalent rules? If not, how do you know? If so, what reasoning about fractions supports your conclusion?

   ■ Which of the three rules seems to model the given situation in the most informative way? Why?

   ■ Which of the rules is probably most convenient for calculations? Why?

   b. Under the plan to split dance profits among classes in the ratio 4:3:2:1, the senior class share can be predicted by the function $s(t) = \frac{4}{10}(10t - 400)$.

   ■ Write at least two other equivalent rules for this function and explain how you know they are equivalent.

   ■ Identify the rule that you believe seems to model the situation in the most informative way. Which rule is most convenient for calculations?

   c. In studying the relation between ticket sales and profit per ticket for the dance, SGA members came up with two different rules:

   $$f_1(t) = \frac{10t - 400}{t} \qquad f_2(t) = 10 - \frac{400}{t}$$

   ■ Assuming $t \neq 0$, do you believe the two rules are equivalent? If not, how can you demonstrate the differences? If they are, what reasoning might have led to each form?

   ■ Which of the two given rules seems to model the situation in a more informative way? Which is more convenient for calculations?

   ■ Find yet another equivalent rule for profit per ticket.

   ■ Examine tables and graphs of the various profit-per-ticket functions as the number of tickets sold gets very large. Describe the way that average profit changes as number of tickets increases, and describe how that pattern of change could be predicted by analyzing the function rule itself.

In your analysis of the function rules for the River Hill High School dance profits, you probably used a variety of strategies for studying equivalence of different fractional forms. You probably also found that rearranging a given rule in a different equivalent form often reveals new information about the relationship among variables or makes calculations easier. There are two basic kinds of rearrangement that occur often: combining two fractions by multiplication or addition, and rewriting a given fraction as a product or sum of terms. The number system properties that you've used in studying polynomials and rules for operation with fractions can be used to guide those symbolic manipulations.

3. Study each of the following procedures to write algebraic fractions in equivalent forms. In Parts b, c, and f, assume $x \neq 0$. Identify the algebraic properties and properties of fractions that justify each step.

a. $\dfrac{2}{3} + \dfrac{5x}{3} = 2\left(\dfrac{1}{3}\right) + 5x\left(\dfrac{1}{3}\right)$

$= (2 + 5x)\left(\dfrac{1}{3}\right)$

$= \dfrac{2 + 5x}{3}$

b. $\left(\dfrac{4x^2}{15}\right)\left(\dfrac{25}{x}\right) = \dfrac{100x^2}{15x}$

$= \dfrac{20x^2}{3x}$

$= \dfrac{20x}{3}$

c. $\dfrac{2}{3} - \dfrac{5}{x} = \dfrac{2x}{3x} - \dfrac{15}{3x}$

$= \dfrac{2x - 15}{3x}$

d. $\dfrac{3}{5}(7x^2 + 8x) = \dfrac{3(7x^2 + 8x)}{5}$

$= \dfrac{21x^2 + 24x}{5}$

e. $\dfrac{3}{5}(7x^2 + 8x) = \dfrac{3}{5}(7x^2) + \dfrac{3}{5}(8x)$

$= \dfrac{21x^2}{5} + \dfrac{24x}{5}$

f. $\dfrac{8x^2 + 32x}{4x} = \dfrac{8x^2}{4x} + \dfrac{32x}{4x}$

$= 2x + 8$

4. Just as there are some common errors in manipulation of linear and quadratic algebraic expressions, there are some common and tempting errors in work with algebraic fractions. Study the following examples and explain why each pair of expressions is not equivalent. In Parts a and b, assume $x \neq 0$. In Parts c and d, assume $x \neq -\dfrac{3}{2}$.

a. Why is $\dfrac{15x^2 + 7}{3x}$ *not* equivalent to $5x + 7$?

b. Why is $\dfrac{4x^2 + 32x}{4x}$ *not* equivalent to $x^2 + 32$?

c. Why is $\dfrac{6x^2 + 12}{2x + 3}$ *not* equivalent to $3x + 4$?

d. Why is $\dfrac{6x^2}{2x + 3}$ *not* equivalent to $3x + 2x^2$?

Checkpoint

Operations with algebraic fractions are based on principles for working with numerical fractions and properties of the number system. Suppose that a, b, c, and d stand for any numbers (b, $c \neq 0$) or algebraic expressions.

ⓐ What fractional expressions will be equivalent to the following:

- $a \cdot \dfrac{1}{b}$
- $\dfrac{a}{b}(c + d)$
- $a + \dfrac{b}{c}$
- $\dfrac{a}{b} + \dfrac{d}{c}$
- $\dfrac{ab}{bc}$
- $\dfrac{ad}{bc}$

ⓑ How can the fraction $\dfrac{a + b}{c}$ be written as a sum of two fractions?

ⓒ What properties of numbers, fractions in particular, justify each of your responses in Parts a and b?

ⓓ What advantages might be gained by writing an algebraic fraction in different equivalent forms?

Be prepared to explain your ideas to the rest of the class.

> **On Your Own**

Use what you have learned about equivalent forms of algebraic fractions to complete the following tasks.

a. Write each of the following expressions in equivalent form as a single algebraic fraction. Assume $x \neq 0$ where necessary.

- $\dfrac{7}{9} + \dfrac{11}{x}$
- $\dfrac{3}{4}(5x + 7)$
- $\left(\dfrac{2x^2}{5}\right)\left(\dfrac{10}{7x}\right)$

b. Write each of these expressions in equivalent form as a sum of two or more algebraic fractions, each in simplest possible form:

- $\dfrac{125 + x}{5}$
- $\dfrac{6x^2 + 3x}{3x}$ $(x \neq 0)$
- $\dfrac{27p^4 + 9p^2 + 3}{9p^2}$ $(p \neq 0)$
- $\dfrac{36x + 72x^2}{36x}$ $(x \neq 0)$

MORE

Modeling • Organizing • Reflecting • Extending

Modeling

1. When you have the rule for a function relating height and time of a moving object, you can use tables, graphs, and algebraic reasoning to deduce information about the motion. Explain each step in the following argument that uses given information to create a rule relating height and time for the flight of a softball hit into the air.

a. The ball was hit from near ground level and returned to the ground 4 seconds later. In building a model for the (*time*, *height*) relationship, why does it make sense to start with $h(t) = t(t - 4)$?

b. Why is the rule in Part a equivalent to $h(t) = t^2 - 4t$?

c. To account for the effect of Earth's gravity, we need a factor of -16, so a better model might be $h(t) = -16(t^2 - 4t)$. Why is this revised model equivalent to $h(t) = -16t^2 + 64t$?

d. Why does the model in Part c imply that the initial velocity of the ball must have been 64 feet per second? Why does it also suggest that the ball reached a maximum height of 64 feet?

2. When a pizza restaurant leased a small truck for home deliveries, the lease cost \$4,000 for a year. Operation of the truck, including maintenance, averaged about \$0.36 per mile of operation. Thus, annual cost for the delivery truck depended on the number of miles it was driven.

a. Write a function rule giving total operating costs as a function of the number of miles m that the truck was driven.

b. Write a function rule giving cost per mile as a function of the number of miles m the truck was driven. Then write that rule in a different but equivalent form.

c. Which of the two forms in Part b do you believe is more informative, and which is more convenient for calculation?

d. Sketch a graph of the per-mile cost function for as many as 20,000 miles per year, and explain what the shape of that graph says about how cost per mile changes as the number of miles increases. Explain also how that pattern could be predicted by inspecting either of the rule forms themselves.

3. Suppose that in designing packaging for one of its products, the Miracle-Gro® fertilizer company wants a package to be made from 1,000 cm² of cardboard. The company also wants the box to have a square base as indicated by the sketch on the right.

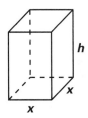

a. Write an equation showing the relation between the surface area 1,000, the height h, and the base edge lengths x of the proposed container.

b. Write another equation showing height h as a function of the base edge length x.

c. Show how the expression for h in Part b can be written in several other equivalent forms.

d. Which of the expressions for h in Parts b and c seems to best describe the relation between x and h?

e. Use one of your expressions for height as a function of fixed area and base edge length to produce a graph that shows the way height changes as edge length changes. Explain how you can predict the pattern of that graph by analyzing the symbolic expressions for h.

4. In Investigation 2 of this lesson, you examined an area model for representing and factoring perfect square polynomials. The expression $x^3 + 15x^2 + 75x + 125$ can be represented by a volume model as shown at the right. This polynomial is an example of a *perfect cube polynomial*.

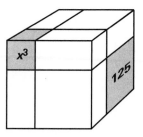

a. Explain why the volume of this cube can be represented by
$$x^3 + 15x^2 + 75x + 125.$$

b. Write a factored-form expression giving the volume of this cube.

c. Give an example of another perfect cube polynomial. Draw a sketch illustrating how you know it is a perfect cube.

Organizing

1. Write the following expressions in equivalent forms that meet the specified conditions.

a. Write these in standard polynomial form:

- $(x + 3)(x + 5)$
- $(2m - 4)(m + 8)$
- $(r - 7)(r + 7)$
- $(x + 12)^2$
- $(t - 8)^2$
- $(w + 5)(w - 3)$
- $(x - 4)(x - 1)$
- $(2v + 3)(4 - v)$
- $(3x + 2)(x^2 + 4x - 5)$

b. Write these in factored form:

- $x^2 - 121$
- $p^2 - 121p$
- $x^2 + 9x + 18$
- $r^2 + 6r + 9$
- $x^2 - 9x + 18$

2. Solve the following equations using symbolic reasoning alone.

   a. $x^2 - 121 = 0$

   b. $x^2 + 9x + 18 = 0$

   c. $(x + 3)(x + 5) = 0$

   d. $x^2 - 9x + 18 = 0$

   e. $x^2 - 121x = 0$

3. From your study of fractions, you should recall that $\frac{0}{4} = 0$ and $\frac{4}{0}$ is undefined.

   a. The connection between multiplication and division guarantees that for any nonzero numbers a and b, $\frac{a}{b} = c$ is equivalent to $a = bc$. Show that if this relation is to hold for any values of a and b, then $\frac{0}{4}$ must equal 0 and $\frac{4}{0}$ must be undefined. (**Hint:** If $0 = 4c$, what must be true of c? If $4 = 0c$, what must be true of c?)

   b. Use the above idea to determine values of x for which the following function rules are equal to 0 and for which they are undefined. When a function rule is undefined for some values of the input variable, those input values must be excluded from the domain of the function.

   - $f(x) = \frac{8}{x}$
   - $f(x) = \frac{x + 2}{3x}$
   - $f(x) = \frac{x - 7}{x + 8}$
   - $f(x) = \frac{x}{(x - 3)(2x + 1)}$

4. Write polynomial or fractional function rules with the following properties.

   a. $f(13) = 0$ and $f(10) = 0$.

   b. $f(1) = 0$ and $f(-2)$ is undefined.

   c. $f(0) = 0$ and $f(12) = 0$.

   d. $f(x)$ is a quadratic function and $f(x) = 0$ only when $x = -3$.

   e. $f(15) = 0$ and $f(-15) = 0$.

5. Using symbolic reasoning alone, what information can you determine about the graph of $f(x)$ in the following cases?

   a. $f(x) = (x - 7)(x + 3)$

   b. $f(x) = 7 + \frac{3}{x}$

   c. $f(x) = \frac{x - 5}{x + 2}$

   d. $f(x) = x^2 - 81$

Reflecting

1. What does it mean to say a quadratic expression is factorable? How could you convince a classmate that a particular quadratic expression is not factorable?

2. Suppose a function has a symbolic rule in the form $f(x) = (x - a)(x + b)$.

   a. How can you tell immediately the values of x for which $f(x) = 0$?

   b. What property of zero and multiplication is used in your answer to Part a?

   c. How do you find the corresponding zero if one of the factors of $f(x)$ is a linear expression like $(cx + d)$?

3. Compare the calculations involved in evaluating fractional expressions of these two types: $\frac{r + s}{t}$ and $m + \frac{n}{k}$.

   a. If you use a calculator to evaluate such expressions when specific values of the variables are given, what sequences of keystrokes would you use?

   b. Which form is easier to use for finding values of the variables that make the fractions 0? For finding values for which the fractions are undefined?

   c. What general operations are required to write fractions of the first type in the form of the second type and vice versa?

4. By now you've learned how to test equivalence of algebraic function rules by comparing calculator tables and graphs and by analyzing the symbolic expressions themselves.

   a. How do you decide which method (tables, graphs, or symbol manipulation) to use in a given situation?

   b. What can be learned from each method that is not clear from the others?

5. Study the algebraic reasoning used in the *Peanuts* cartoon below.

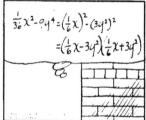

PEANUTS reprinted by permission of United Feature Syndicate, Inc.

   a. Is the building's factorization correct? If not, identify the error in its reasoning.

   b. What do you think was the key idea that enabled the building to get started on this problem? If possible, give an example of another higher-degree polynomial to which this idea could be applied.

Extending

1. Consider all quadratics of the type $(x + h)^2$, where x is the input variable and h is a fixed number.

   a. Expand that expression into an equivalent expression in standard polynomial form.

   b. Compare the following quadratic polynomials to the pattern in Part a to identify those that can be written easily as squares of linear binomials in the form $(x + h)^2$.

   - $x^2 + 10x + 25$
   - $x^2 + 6x + 16$
   - $x^2 - 10x + 25$
   - $x^2 + 12x + 36$
   - $x^2 - 7x + 49$

2. Consider quadratics of the type $(mx + h)^2$, where x is the input variable and m and h are fixed numbers.

   a. Expand the expression $(mx + h)^2$ into an equivalent expression in standard polynomial form.

   b. Compare the following quadratic polynomials to the pattern in Part a to identify those that can be written as squares of linear binomials in the form $(mx + h)^2$.

   - $9x^2 + 12x + 4$
   - $4x^2 - 4x + 1$
   - $49x^2 + 42x + 9$

3. What sorts of tables and graphs do you expect for the following general types of function rules? Test your ideas with a number of specific examples, and then summarize and explain your findings.

   a. Products like $y = (ax)(bx)$

   b. Products like $y = (ax + b)(cx + d)$

   c. Quotients like $y = \dfrac{ax^2}{bx}$

   d. Quotients like $y = \dfrac{ax^2 + bx + c}{dx + e}$

4. When the Hindu mathematician Bhaskara (1114–1185) first recorded a diagram similar to the one below, no explanation other than the word "behold" was offered. If you view the diagram through the combined "lenses" of geometry and algebra, what do you see?

BEHOLD!

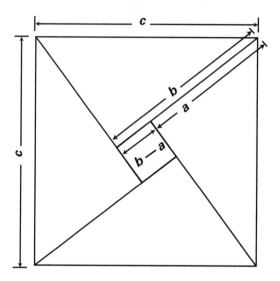

5. Justify each step in the following rewriting of a given quadratic $ax^2 + bx + c$ into a form that involves the square of a binomial and a constant term.

$$ax^2 + bx + c = (ax^2 + bx) + c \qquad (1)$$

$$= a\left(x^2 + \frac{b}{a}x\right) + c \qquad (2)$$

$$= a\left(x^2 + \frac{b}{a}x + \frac{b^2}{4a^2}\right) + \left(c - \frac{b^2}{4a}\right) \qquad (3)$$

$$= a\left(x + \frac{b}{2a}\right)^2 + \left(c - \frac{b^2}{4a}\right) \qquad (4)$$

$$= a\left(x + \frac{b}{2a}\right)^2 + \left(\frac{4ac - b^2}{4a}\right) \qquad (5)$$

Lesson 4 ▶ Reasoning to Solve Equations and Inequalities

In earlier work in this unit, you modeled situations with several variables and equations. For example, suppose you were given business plans for a concert showing how operating cost and ticket sale income were expected to relate to ticket price x.

Cost: $C(x) = 22{,}500 - 100x$

Income: $I(x) = 2{,}500x - 50x^2$

A graph of those two functions looks like this:

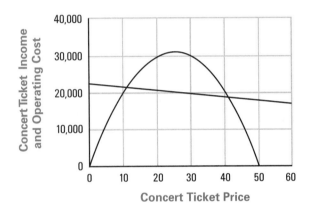

Think About This Situation

Questions important to planning the concert can be answered by solving equations and inequalities involving the cost and income functions.

ⓐ What would you learn from solutions of the following?

- $I(x) = C(x)$
- $I(x) > C(x)$
- $I(x) < C(x)$

ⓑ How would you solve the equation and inequalities in Part a using the following tools?

- Technology
- Reasoning about the symbolic function rules (without the help of calculator tables or graphs)

INVESTIGATION 1 ▸ Reasoning about Linear Equations and Inequalities

Situations involving comparison of business plans often involve linear functions, leading to questions requiring the solution of linear equations and inequalities. For example, a pizza company considering lease options for a delivery truck might have choices like those shown below. In each case, the lease cost (in dollars) is a function of lease time (in weeks).

   Plan A: $A(t) = 2,500 + 75t$

   Plan B: $B(t) = 1,000 + 90t$

1. What do the numbers 2,500 and 1,000 tell about the conditions of each lease? What do the numbers 75 and 90 tell?

2. At the start, Plan A is more expensive than Plan B. To see when the lease costs might be equal, you could solve the equation $2,500 + 75t = 1,000 + 90t$. One way to solve that equation is to reason like this:

$$2,500 + 75t = 1,000 + 90t$$
$$1,500 + 75t = 90t$$
$$1,500 = 15t$$
$$100 = t$$

   a. Justify each step in the solution process.

   b. How can you check that $t = 100$ is the solution? What does $t = 100$ tell about the truck-lease plans?

   c. How could you arrive at the same result with a different sequence of steps?

3. Now, consider the inequality $2,500 + 75t < 1,000 + 90t$.

   a. What will a solution to this inequality tell about the truck-leasing situation?

   b. Why does each step in the following reasoning make sense?

$$2,500 + 75t < 1,000 + 90t$$
$$2,500 < 1,000 + 15t$$
$$1,500 < 15t$$
$$100 < t$$

   c. What does the solution $100 < t$ tell about the truck-leasing situation?

   d. How can you check the solution?

   e. Use similar reasoning to solve the inequality $2,500 + 75t > 1,000 + 90t$, and explain what the solution tells about the truck-leasing situation.

In solving the equations and inequalities that compare two truck-lease plans, it is helpful to keep in mind what the parts of each expression mean. Now try to use similar reasoning patterns to solve equations and inequalities without such clues.

4. Solve each of the following equations by symbolic reasoning alone. Record each step in your reasoning. Check your solutions.

   a. $2x + 15 = 45 + x$

   b. $10 - 4x = 3x - 4$

   c. $7x - 11 = 10$

   d. $-6x - 15 = 4x + 10$

   e. $25 = 10 - 5x$

5. Solve each of the following inequalities by symbolic reasoning alone. Record each step in your reasoning. Check your answers.

   a. $3x + 10 < 14$ **b.** $13 + 5x > 23$

   c. $8x + 12 < 46$ **d.** $80 + 6x > 200$

6. Here are three solutions of inequalities that lead to incorrect results. In each case, show with function tables or graphs that the proposed solutions are not correct. Then find and correct the error in the reasoning process.

   a. Solve: $5x + 20 < 3x$

               $20 < -2x$

            $-10 < x$

   b. Solve: $11x - 19 < 15x + 17$

               $11x < 15x + 36$

             $-4x < 36$

               $x < -9$

   c. Solve: $10 + 9x < 3x - 8$

           $18 + 9x < 3x$

             $18 < -6x$

            $-3 < x$

7. Solve each of the following inequalities by symbolic reasoning alone. Show each step in your reasoning. Check your answers.

   a. $3x + 10 < 5x + 4$

   b. $23 - 5x > 7x - 13$

   c. $8x + 12 < 46 - 9x$

   d. $80 + 6x > 21x - 15$

Two equations or inequalities are called **equivalent** if they have identical solutions. One strategy for solving linear equations and inequalities is to start with the given equation or inequality and construct a sequence of simpler forms, each equivalent to its predecessor, until you get an equation or inequality so simple that the solution is obvious. The challenge is to find ways of writing equivalent equations and inequalities that do become progressively simpler.

8. Which of the following pairs of equations and inequalities are equivalent? Explain your reasoning in each case.

   a. $3x + 2 = 5$ and $3x = 3$

   b. $7x - 8 = 12 + 3x$ and $4x = 20$

   c. $\frac{1}{3}x + 9 = 6$ and $x + 9 = 18$

   d. $10x + 15 = 35$ and $2x + 3 = 7$

   e. $10x + 15 = 35$ and $10x = 20$

   f. $3x + 2 < 5$ and $3x < 3$

   g. $7x - 8 > 12 + 3x$ and $4x > 20$

   h. $10x + 15 < 35$ and $2x + 3 < 7$

   i. $10x + 15 > 35$ and $10x > 20$

9. Look back over the pairs of equations and inequalities in Activity 8 and your answers to the equivalence question. What operations on equations and inequalities seem likely to produce simpler equivalent forms?

Checkpoint

Many situations call for comparing two linear functions like the following:

$$f(x) = a + bx \qquad g(x) = c + dx$$

a What overall strategy and specific reasoning steps would you use to solve an equation of the form $a + bx = c + dx$? Explain how you could check the solution.

b What overall strategy and specific reasoning steps would you use to solve an inequality of the form $a + bx < c + dx$? How could you check the answer?

c How do the graphs of expressions like $y = a + bx$ and $y = c + dx$ illustrate solutions to the equations and inequalities described in Parts a and b? How would those solutions appear in tables of values for the two functions?

Be prepared to explain your strategies and reasoning to the entire class.

On Your Own

Two cellular telephone service plans offer monthly costs (in dollars) that are functions of time used (in minutes) with the following rules:

$$B(t) = 35 + 0.30t$$

$$C(t) = 25 + 0.50t$$

Write and solve (without use of technology) equations and inequalities that help in answering these questions:

a. Under what conditions will Plan B cost less than Plan C?

b. Under what conditions will Plan B cost the same as Plan C?

c. Under what conditions will Plan C cost less than Plan B?

In each case, show how you can use a calculator to check your solutions.

INVESTIGATION 2 Reasoning about Quadratic Equations and Inequalities

Two key questions are often associated with quadratic function models of the form $f(x) = ax^2 + bx + c$:

- What is the maximum (minimum) value and where does it occur?
- For what values of the input variable x will $f(x) = 0$?

In the case of the concert-planning model described at the start of this lesson, the quadratic income function was $I(x) = 2,500x - 50x^2$. The two key questions can be stated in this way:

- What ticket price will lead to maximum projected income from ticket sales?
- What ticket prices will produce no projected ticket income at all?

You can answer both questions by scanning a table or graph of $(x, I(x))$ values. But you can also get the answers easily by using algebraic reasoning.

1. Justify each step in the following analysis of the concert-income situation.

   a. Solving the equation $2,500x - 50x^2 = 0$ will help.

   b. The equation in Part a is equivalent to $50x(50 - x) = 0$.

   c. $50x(50 - x) = 0$ when $x = 0$ or when $x = 50$.

   d. The maximum income will occur when $x = 25$.

   e. That income is $31,250.

2. Unfortunately, many quadratic equations are not easy to solve using the type of factoring that worked so well in Activity 1. For example, consider the problem of finding projected break-even prices for the planned concert. Those are the prices for which income from ticket sales will equal expenses for operating costs. Since the cost equation for this situation was $C(x) = 22,500 - 100x$, this problem requires solving the equation $2,500x - 50x^2 = 22,500 - 100x$.

   a. You can start by writing an equivalent equation with a quadratic expression equal to 0:

$$-50x^2 + 2,600x - 22,500 = 0$$

   Why is this equation equivalent to the original?

   b. Factor the left side of this equation to get $-50(x^2 - 52x + 450) = 0$. Why is this factored form equivalent to the equation in Part a?

The form of the equation given in Part b does not look easy to continue to solve by factoring!

There is another way you can solve quadratic equations, even when factoring seems impossible. You can use the **quadratic formula**. If $ax^2 + bx + c = 0$ (and $a \neq 0$), then the **roots** of the equation are

$$x = -\frac{b}{2a} \pm \frac{\sqrt{b^2 - 4ac}}{2a}$$

or, writing these separately,

$$x = -\frac{b}{2a} + \frac{\sqrt{b^2 - 4ac}}{2a} \quad \text{and} \quad x = -\frac{b}{2a} - \frac{\sqrt{b^2 - 4ac}}{2a}$$

(You'll explore a derivation of this formula in Lesson 5.)

3. Solve the break-even equation $-50x^2 + 2,600x - 22,500 = 0$ using the quadratic formula.

   a. Give the values for a, b, and c.

   b. Evaluate $-\frac{b}{2a}$.

   c. Evaluate $\frac{\sqrt{b^2 - 4ac}}{2a}$.

   d. Now calculate $x = -\frac{b}{2a} + \frac{\sqrt{b^2 - 4ac}}{2a}$ and $x = -\frac{b}{2a} - \frac{\sqrt{b^2 - 4ac}}{2a}$.

   e. Describe at least three different ways to check your calculated roots in Part d. Check the roots in the original equation using one of those methods.

   f. Use the quadratic formula to solve the equation $x^2 - 52x + 450 = 0$. Compare the result to the answer in Part d and explain similarities or differences.

4. Some computer software and some calculators have a "solve" feature that allows you to solve equations directly, if one side of the equation is equal to 0. The procedure for using these solving capabilities varies. You may need to consult your manual to learn how to use the feature.

```
EQUATION SOLVER
eqn : 0 = –50x²+2600
x – 22500
```

Use the solve feature on your calculator or computer software to check your solutions to Parts d and f of Activity 3.

5. Now consider the quadratic equation $x^2 - 6x + 5 = 0$. A graph of the function $f(x) = x^2 - 6x + 5$ is shown below.

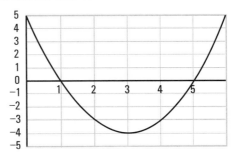

a. Give the values for a, b, and c that should be used to solve $x^2 - 6x + 5 = 0$ with the quadratic formula.

b. Evaluate $-\dfrac{b}{2a}$.

c. Evaluate $\dfrac{\sqrt{b^2 - 4ac}}{2a}$.

d. Now calculate $x = -\dfrac{b}{2a} + \dfrac{\sqrt{b^2 - 4ac}}{2a}$ and $x = -\dfrac{b}{2a} - \dfrac{\sqrt{b^2 - 4ac}}{2a}$.

e. Compare the quadratic formula calculations to the graph of $f(x) = x^2 - 6x + 5$. What information is provided by the expression $-\dfrac{b}{2a}$? By the expression $\dfrac{\sqrt{b^2 - 4ac}}{2a}$?

6. Use the quadratic formula to solve each of the following quadratic equations. Then try to solve the same equations by factoring. In each case, check your work by using the solve feature on your calculator or computer software or by substituting your proposed roots for x into the equation.

a. $-2x^2 - 3x + 7 = 0$

b. $5x^2 - x - 4 = 0$

c. $3x^2 - 2x + 1 = 0$

d. $-x^2 + 2x - 3 = 0$

e. $4x^2 + 12x + 9 = 0$

7. Now look back at your work in Activity 6 and search for connections between the quadratic formula calculations and the graphs of the corresponding function rules.

- Explain the special significance of the equation $x = -\dfrac{b}{2a}$ for a quadratic function with rule in the form $f(x) = ax^2 + bx + c$.
- What information is provided by the expression $\dfrac{\sqrt{b^2 - 4ac}}{2a}$?

Test your ideas in each of the following cases by graphing the function and the vertical line $x = -\dfrac{b}{2a}$. (If you choose to use your calculator rather than sketching your graph, consult your manual as needed.)

a. $f(x) = 2x^2 + 4x - 9$

b. $f(x) = 3x^2 - 2x - 5$

c. $f(x) = x^2 + 6x - 10$

d. $f(x) = -x^2 + 2x - 9$

8. Think about the ways in which the graph of $f(x) = ax^2 + bx + c$ could intersect the x-axis. How many possible roots could the equation $ax^2 + bx + c = 0$ have?

a. Use the quadratic formula to solve each equation and identify the step that first shows the number of roots you can expect.

- $x^2 + 8x + 12 = 0$
- $x^2 + 8x + 16 = 0$
- $x^2 + 8x + 20 = 0$

b. Sketch graphs of the quadratic functions corresponding to the three equations above, and explain how those graphs show the number of roots in each case.

9. Suppose that $f(x)$, $g(x)$, $j(x)$, and $h(x)$ are quadratic functions with the zeroes indicated below. Find values of x for which each of these functions would have maximum or minimum values. Then write possible rules for the functions in factored form.

a. $f(6) = 0$ and $f(-2) = 0$

b. $g(-7) = 0$ and $g(3) = 0$

c. $j(-2) = 0$ and $j(-5) = 0$

d. $h(2) = 0$ and $h(4.5) = 0$

10. Explain how the quadratic formula can help you determine the minimum value of the function $f(x) = 4x^2 - 7x - 10$.

11. The quadratic formula and other equation-solving methods can be used to solve quadratic inequalities as well. Examine the graph of the function $f(x) = 2x^2 - 5x - 12$ at the right. It has zeroes at $x = -1.5$ and $x = 4$.

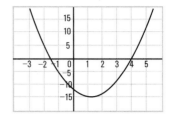

a. Explain how the number line graph below shows the solution of the quadratic inequality $2x^2 - 5x - 12 < 0$.

b. How does the number line graph in Part a relate to the graph of the function $f(x) = 2x^2 - 5x - 12$?

c. Make a number line graph showing the solution of the quadratic inequality $2x^2 - 5x - 12 > 0$.

d. How would you modify the number line graph in Part c to show the solution of the inequality $2x^2 - 5x - 12 \geq 0$?

12. Using Activity 11 as an example, if needed, solve the following quadratic inequalities.

a. $x^2 - x - 6 < 0$ b. $x^2 - x - 6 > 0$

c. $-x^2 + 5x + 6 > 0$ d. $-2x^2 - 3x + 5 < 0$

e. $x^2 - 8x + 16 \leq 0$ f. $x^2 - 8x + 16 > 0$

Checkpoint

Quadratic functions, with graphs that are parabolas, can be written with symbolic rules in the form $f(x) = ax^2 + bx + c$. You have learned to solve the related quadratic equations $ax^2 + bx + c = 0$ using the quadratic formula.

a Explain the steps that you would take to determine the zeroes and the minimum value of the function $f(x) = 3x^2 - 2x - 8$.

b What are the advantages and disadvantages of solving quadratic equations by factoring? By using the quadratic formula? By using the solve feature of your calculator or computer software?

c How can you use the quadratic formula or the solve feature to find a factored form of a quadratic function rule?

d How does use of the quadratic formula show whether a given equation will have 2, 1, or 0 roots? How will this information appear in a graph?

Be prepared to share your methods and thinking with the class.

▶ On Your Own

Use what you have learned about the quadratic formula to complete the following tasks.

a. Find the zeroes and the lines of symmetry for the graphs of the following functions.

- $f(x) = x^2 - 4x + 1$
- $g(x) = x^2 + 6x - 11$
- $h(x) = x^2 - 24$

b. For each of the following functions, find the minimum or maximum value of the function.

- $f(x) = x^2 - 3x + 9$
- $g(x) = -x^2 + 8x + 2$
- $h(x) = x^2 - 49$

c. Graph solutions for these quadratic inequalities:

- $x^2 - 3x - 4 > 0$
- $x^2 + x - 6 < 0$
- $-x^2 - 2x + 3 > 0$

MORE
Modeling • Organizing • Reflecting • Extending

Modeling

1. Owners of the Polar City Bears baseball team have two sources of operating profit: admission tickets and concession sales. Both depend on the number of fans who attend a game.

Experience suggests the following function rules for predicting profit from the number of people attending a game.

Profit from ticket sales: $T(x) = 7.50x - 5,000$

Profit from concession sales: $C(x) = 3.00x - 750$

a. How do you think the numbers 7.50, 3.00, 5,000, and 750 in the profit functions relate to the operation of the baseball team and its concession stands?

Write and solve (without calculator tables or graphs) equations and inequalities to help you answer the following questions. Record all steps in your reasoning.

b. For what number of tickets sold will the concession operation break even?

c. For what number of tickets sold will the team operation break even, without considering concessions?

d. For what number of tickets sold will concession profit be greater than ticket sale profit?

e. For what number of tickets sold will concession profit be less than ticket sale profit?

f. For what number of tickets sold will concession profit be equal to ticket sale profit?

2. The architect of a planned domed athletic stadium proposed the general shape shown in the following sketch. The peak of the roof was to be a parabolic curve with equation $f(x) = -0.0016x^2 + 75$, where x is distance in yards from the center of the building and $f(x)$ is the height of the dome in yards.

 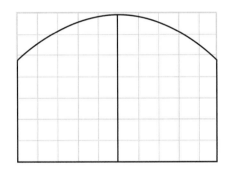

a. What is the maximum height of the dome?

b. If the total length of the building is 250 yards, what is the minimum height of the dome?

c. Solve the inequality $-0.0016x^2 + 75 \geq 60$ and explain what it tells about the dome design.

3. For staff members at the Grand Canyon Outfitters store in the Columbia Mall, pay depends in part on the dollar value of their sales. If they work a normal 40-hour week and sell x dollars of merchandise, they will earn $80 + 0.05x$ dollars. At the competing store, Rocky Mountain Trails, staff members earn pay on a different scale. For a similar 40-hour week with x dollars of sales, they will earn $120 + 0.03x$ dollars.

a. What do the numbers 80, 0.05, 120, and 0.03 in the two rules tell about how pay is calculated?

Write and solve (without calculator tables or graphs) equations and inequalities to help you answer the following questions. Record all steps in your reasoning.

b. Under what conditions will pay at Grand Canyon Outfitters be equal to pay at Rocky Mountain Trails?

c. Under what conditions will pay at Grand Canyon Outfitters be greater than pay at Rocky Mountain Trails?

d. Under what conditions will pay at Grand Canyon Outfitters be less than pay at Rocky Mountain Trails?

e. What dollar value of sales will be required at Grand Canyon Outfitters for a sales staff person to earn more than $100?

f. If a sales staff person at Rocky Mountain Trails was paid $180 in one week, what was the dollar value of the merchandise that the person sold?

4. During the summer, James sells decorative wood-cuttings at two different locations. Since the two locations are very different, in the past he has had to consider two different weekly revenue functions, one for the store in the city and another for the store in the country. If x is the price (in dollars) for a cutting, the two revenue functions are:

City store: $R_1(x) = (150 - 4x)x$

Country store: $R_2(x) = (90 - 2x)x$

a. What price will give the maximum weekly revenue for the city store?

b. What price will give the maximum weekly revenue for the country store?

c. James wants to charge the same price at both stores. What price will maximize the combined revenue?

Organizing

1. Solve each of the following linear equations or inequalities without using calculator tables or graphs. In each case, show and justify each step of your solution process. Then show how your answer can be checked.

   a. $5x + 4 = 3x - 112$

   b. $4x + 20 < 9 - 3x$

   c. $-9x + 12.5 = 13.4x - 22.4$

   d. $4x - 9 < 13 + 6x$

   e. $18x + 7 > 107 - 7x$

2. Solve each of the following quadratic equations without using calculator tables or graphs. In each case, show and justify each step of your solution process. Then show how your answer can be checked using a graph of the related function.

   a. $x^2 + 3x + 1 = 0$

   b. $2x^2 + 7x + 9 = 0$

   c. $x^2 - 10x + 25 = 0$

   d. $2x^2 + 15x + 18 = 0$

   e. $3x^2 - 7x - 6 = 0$

3. Consider linear equations of the form $ax + b = cx + d$. Give specific examples of such equations (and sketches of graphs for the functions involved) illustrating the cases in which the equation will have one solution, no solutions, and infinitely many solutions.

4. Consider quadratic equations of the form $ax^2 + bx + c = 0$. Give specific examples (other than those in previous problems you've solved) and sketches of graphs for the functions involved illustrating cases in which the equation will have exactly two roots, exactly one root, and no roots. In each case, show how use of the quadratic formula will lead to the conclusion illustrated in the function graphs.

5. Refer to Modeling Task 4 on page 236.

   a. What is the average of the two prices that will maximize the weekly revenue when the stores are considered separately?

   b. How does this compare to the price that will maximize revenue when the same price is charged at both stores? Explain why this is the case.

Reflecting

1. What do you see as the advantages and disadvantages of using calculator-based methods (tables, graphs, a solve feature) versus reasoning with symbolic forms in solving the following?

   a. Linear equations

   b. Linear inequalities

   c. Quadratic equations

   d. Quadratic inequalities

2. Think about how you solved linear and quadratic equations by reasoning with the symbolic forms themselves.

   a. Describe the main ideas in solving a linear equation or inequality by formal reasoning for a student who hasn't learned that skill yet.

   b. Describe the main ideas in solving a quadratic equation by factoring for a student who has not learned that skill yet.

   c. Describe the main ideas in solving a quadratic equation by using the quadratic formula for a student who has not learned that skill yet.

3. Describe a type of problem that you have encountered in your science classes that requires algebraic thinking similar to the thinking you have done in this unit.

4. Quadratic functions have been used to model aspects of such structures as the St. Louis Gateway Arch, shown at the right. The height (in feet) of the St. Louis Arch, as a function of the distance (in feet) from one base, can be approximated by $h(x) = 4.2x - 0.007x^2$. (The curve is actually more complicated, but this quadratic model  comes reasonably close.) Explain how you can use symbolic reasoning to figure out the width of the arch at the base and the maximum height of the arch.

5. Given a quadratic function $f(x) = ax^2 + bx + c$, how can you tell by examining the symbolic rule and thinking about its graph whether the function has a maximum or minimum value? Whether it has 0, 1, or 2 zeroes?

Extending

1. Parabolas, the graphs of quadratic functions, come in many different specific shapes.

   a. Find a rule for a quadratic function that has zeroes at $x = -1$ and $x = 5$. Find the maximum or minimum value of your function and the value of x at which that maximum or minimum value occurs.

   b. Use your results from Part a to find rules for two other quadratic functions $g(x)$ and $h(x)$ with the following properties:

   ■ $g(-1) = 0$, $g(5) = 0$, and $g(x)$ has a minimum value of -18.

   ■ $h(-1) = 0$, $h(5) = 0$, and $h(x)$ has a maximum value of 27.

   c. How many different quadratic functions will have their zeroes at $x = -1$ and $x = 5$? Prepare an argument supporting your answer.

2. Explain how to solve a quadratic inequality, without use of a calculator table or graph, by working through the specific example $2x^2 - 7x - 15 < 0$. Show all of your reasoning steps.

3. Consider the profit function $P(x) = -0.004x^2 + 61.1x - 125{,}000$, which gives the profit for a rock band concert as a function of the number of tickets sold. Write and solve an inequality representing the question, "How many tickets must be sold to get a profit of at least \$80,000?" Explain how the quadratic formula can be used to find that solution and how the solution can be found using calculator tables and graphs of a suitable function.

4. Solve each quadratic equation below without use of technology. Then check your results.

   a. $2x^2 - 7x - 15 = 10 - 4x$

   b. $2x^2 - 7x - 15 = -x^2 + 5x + 10$

5. Explore a variety of specific cases to find answers to the following questions.

   a. In general, how many solutions could occur in an equation of the form $ax^2 + bx + c = dx + e$? How would those possibilities be shown by a function graph?

   b. In general, how many solutions could occur in an equation of the form $ax^2 + bx + c = dx^2 + ex + f$? How would those possibilities be shown by a function graph?

Lesson 5

Proof through Algebraic Reasoning

Algebraic reasoning—that is, rewriting symbolic expressions, equations, and inequalities in equivalent forms—can be very helpful in convincing yourself and others that observed patterns are *always true*. Algebraic reasoning also helps in understanding the patterns themselves. For example, study the following number "trick" that an Alaskan teacher often uses to amaze her students. She directs each student in the class to think of a number between 0 and 10 and perform the indicated calculations.

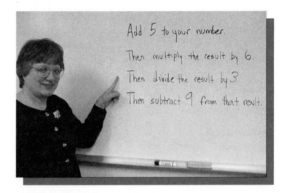

Add 5 to your number.
Then multiply the result by 6.
Then divide the result by 3.
Then subtract 9 from that result.

At this point, she asks various students to tell her their final results, and she quickly identifies the numbers that each started with. For example, when a student reported his final result as 19, she immediately guessed his original number to be 9; when another reported 13, the teacher correctly guessed that she had started with 6.

Think About This Situation

The students were suspicious that their teacher had simply memorized all the possible results from the indicated calculations, so they asked her to stretch the rules to allow starting numbers from 0 to 20 and then from 0 to 50. She still guessed their starting numbers correctly every time.

a What do you think the starting number is when the final calculation results in a 9? When it results in a 17?

b Can you think of a way to use algebraic reasoning to uncover and prove the teacher's number-guessing strategy?

INVESTIGATION 1 Proving It Always Works

You can use algebraic reasoning to prove that some patterns will always hold, to reveal some patterns that start well but break down when all cases are considered, and to develop some useful general rules of your own.

1. Think again about the number-guessing trick on the previous page.

   a. Using the letter n to represent the starting number, write a single expression that shows how all calculations combine to produce the result reported to the teacher.

   b. Write an expression that is equivalent to the one you wrote for Part a but in simplest form possible.

   c. See if you can figure out the easy mental arithmetic the teacher uses to deduce starting numbers from the final results that are reported to her.

   d. Modify the third direction of the number trick to read: Then divide the result by 2. What strategy would the teacher use to guess the starting number for this revised trick?

   e. Revise the original number trick so that no matter what number you start with, the result at the end of the trick is always the starting number.

2. Here's another mathematics teacher's amazing number trick.

   a. See if you can figure out how and why it works by testing some specific start numbers and then writing the operations in algebraic form.

   Step 1:   Think of a number between 50 and 100.

   Step 2:   Add 76 to the number.

   Step 3:   Cross out the digit in the hundreds place and add that number to the remaining two-digit number.

   Step 4:   Subtract the result in Step 3 from the original number.

   The teacher then pulls a sealed envelope from her desk and gives it to a student to open. Inside is a slip of paper with the result of Step 4 already on it.

   b. Now see if you can vary the trick to make one of your own. Test your trick with students in another group.

3. Sometimes number patterns lead to conjectures that aren't true. For example, one student looked at the following pattern of squares and cubes for whole numbers:

x^2	0	1	4	9	16	25	36	49	64	81
x^3	0	1	8	27	64	125	216	343	512	729

   The student concluded that $x^3 \geq x^2$ for all nonnegative numbers.

a. Why is the inequality $x^3 \geq x^2$ equivalent to $x^3 - x^2 \geq 0$?

b. Why is the inequality $x^3 - x^2 \geq 0$ equivalent to $x^2(x - 1) \geq 0$?

c. For what values of x is the inequality $x^2(x - 1) \geq 0$ true?

4. In linear programming problems and applications of algebra to geometry, you used linear equations written in the form $ax + by = c$. The values of a, b, and c were determined by problem conditions.

   a. Identify the slope and coordinates of the x- and y-intercepts of each line below.

   - $3x + 2y = 5$
   - $-2x + 5y = 10$
   - $x - 4y = 9$

   b. Based on your results from Part a, formulate general rules for calculating the slope and intercepts of any line with an equation given in the form $px + qy = r$, where $q \neq 0$.

   c. Use algebraic reasoning with equivalent expressions and equations to prove that your rules in Part b will always work.

5. Some of you may have completed Extending Task 5, page 224, in Lesson 3. In that task, you were asked to justify that the quadratic expression $ax^2 + bx + c$ is equivalent to $a\left(x + \dfrac{b}{2a}\right)^2 + \dfrac{4ac - b^2}{4a}$.

   Use that fact and algebraic reasoning to justify each remaining step in the following derivation of the quadratic formula.

   $ax^2 + bx + c = 0$ is equivalent to $a\left(x + \dfrac{b}{2a}\right)^2 + \left(\dfrac{4ac - b^2}{4a}\right) = 0$,

   which is equivalent to $a\left(x + \dfrac{b}{2a}\right)^2 = \left(\dfrac{b^2 - 4ac}{4a}\right)$,

   which is equivalent to $\left(x + \dfrac{b}{2a}\right)^2 = \dfrac{b^2 - 4ac}{4a^2}$,

   which is equivalent to $x + \dfrac{b}{2a} = \pm\sqrt{\dfrac{b^2 - 4ac}{4a^2}}$ provided $b^2 - 4ac \geq 0$,

   which is equivalent to $x = -\dfrac{b}{2a} \pm \sqrt{\dfrac{b^2 - 4ac}{4a^2}}$,

   which is equivalent to $x = -\dfrac{b}{2a} \pm \dfrac{\sqrt{b^2 - 4ac}}{2a}$.

In Investigation 1, you used algebraic reasoning to analyze number tricks, patterns of squares and cubes, slopes and intercepts of linear equations, and the quadratic formula.

a What do you get from arguments with symbolic reasoning that you can't get from checking specific examples?

b How can checking specific numerical and graphical examples help you in making general arguments?

c If you were asked to list some of the algebraic properties and reasoning strategies that were used in Activities 1 through 5, what properties and strategies would you mention?

Be prepared to share your thinking and identified properties and strategies with the entire class.

On Your Own

Use algebraic reasoning to complete the following tasks involving expressions, equations, and inequalities.

a. Prove that whatever the starting number, the following instructions always will bring you back to that number plus 1:

Think of a number.

Double that number and add 7.

Multiply the result by 5 and subtract 25.

Divide the result by 10.

b. Find a formula that gives the solution of $ax + b = cx + d$ for x in terms of a, b, c, and d. Show why the formula works and how it reveals cases in which the equation is not satisfied by *any* value of x.

c. Use an argument like the one you developed in Activity 3 to prove that $x^2 \geq x$ except when $0 < x < 1$.

INVESTIGATION 2 ▶ Algebraic Reasoning in Geometry and Statistics

So far, you have used reasoning strategies for writing expressions, equations, and inequalities in equivalent symbolic forms primarily for studying questions about quantitative variables related by functions. But those same strategies are often helpful in proving relationships in geometry, trigonometry, and statistics as well.

For example, in earlier work you've seen that when a geometric shape is modeled in a coordinate plane with number pairs for points and equations for lines, many questions can be answered using simple calculations. If you have a question about a general parallelogram, you can represent the figure in a coordinate plane like this:

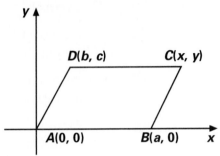

1. Use algebraic reasoning and what you know about slopes of lines and distances to complete the following tasks involving the quadrilateral *ABCD*, above.

   a. Prove that if quadrilateral *ABCD* is to be a parallelogram, then

   ■ $y = c$ and

   ■ $x = a + b$

   b. Prove that opposite sides of parallelogram *ABCD* are the same length.

   c. Find expressions for the midpoints of the two diagonals $\overline{AC}$ and $\overline{DB}$, and show that they are identical. What general property of parallelograms have you proved?

One of the most famous and useful theorems in geometry is the Pythagorean Theorem. In Course 1, you discovered this theorem by constructing squares on the sides of various right triangles, calculating their areas, and looking for a pattern relating the areas. You found that in any right triangle with legs *a* and *b* and hypotenuse *c*, $c^2 = a^2 + b^2$. You now can establish this theorem in general using a combination of algebraic and geometric reasoning.

2. Consider the relation between the large square below and the regions into which it has been divided: a smaller square and four right triangles.

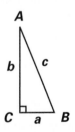

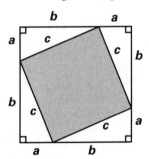

   a. How can you be sure that the shaded region is a square?

b. Express the area of the large square in two different ways, one using only *a* and *b* and the other using all three lengths *a*, *b*, and *c*.

c. Equate the two expressions from Part b and show how algebraic reasoning can lead from that equation to the Pythagorean Theorem as a conclusion.

There are three important relationships in trigonometry that are closely connected to the Pythagorean Theorem. In the "Multiple-Variable Models" unit, you examined a derivation of the Law of Sines, relating sides and angles of any triangle. The Law of Sines guarantees that if *ABC* is a triangle with angles *A*, *B*, and *C* and opposite sides *a*, *b*, and *c*, then

$$\frac{\sin A}{a} = \frac{\sin B}{b} = \frac{\sin C}{c}$$

or equivalently

$$\frac{a}{\sin A} = \frac{b}{\sin B} = \frac{c}{\sin C}.$$

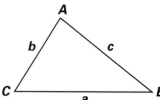

Another important relationship is the Law of Cosines, which was stated and used without proof or derivation in the same unit. It guarantees that in any triangle *ABC* as described above,

$$c^2 = a^2 + b^2 - 2ab \cos C.$$

With the algebraic reasoning principles that you've studied in this unit, it's now possible to prove this important relationship.

3. To prove the Law of Cosines, consider the diagram at the right, where *h* is the altitude of △*ABC* from vertex *A*, dividing side *CB* into segments of lengths *x* and *a* − *x* .

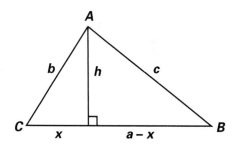

    a. Use the Pythagorean Theorem to express h^2 in two ways, first in terms of b^2 and x^2 and then in terms of c^2 and $(a - x)^2$.

    b. Use the two expressions for h^2 from Part a to write an equation expressing c^2 in terms of $(a - x)^2$, b^2, and x^2. Then expand $(a - x)^2$ and simplify the resulting expression for c^2 as much as possible.

    c. Express *x* in terms of *b* and cos *C*, and substitute that expression for *x* in the relation you got in Part b. Your result should be the Law of Cosines!

Note: You should be suspicious of the way the proof is guided by particular relations in the diagram. Your proof is valid only if ∠*C* is acute or right. There is another possible picture, with an obtuse angle at *C*. You can finish the proof by examining that case in Extending Task 2 on page 251.

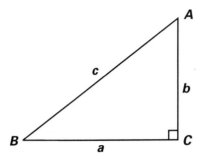

4. Now consider the third very important trigonometric relation with close connections to the Pythagorean Theorem. You can use your skill in algebraic reasoning to prove that for any angle B in a right triangle, $(\sin B)^2 + (\cos B)^2 = 1$. Consider the situation pictured in the diagram at the left.

   a. Express $\sin B$ and $\cos B$ in terms of the sides of the given right triangle.

   b. Express the Pythagorean relation among a^2, b^2, and c^2.

   c. Find a way to combine the relationships of Parts a and b to get the equation $(\sin B)^2 + (\cos B)^2 = 1$.

   d. Investigate whether this relation holds for angles whose measures are greater than or equal to 90°. Make a conjecture.

In previous courses, you have investigated the effects of data transformations on measures of center and variability. You can use variables and a combination of algebraic and statistical reasoning to prove these properties.

5. Suppose a data set consists of five values: x_1, x_2, x_3, x_4, x_5.

   a. Write an algebraic expression for the mean, $\bar{x}$, of this set.

   b. Now multiply each data value by a constant c and write an expression for the mean $\bar{x}_T$ of this transformed set.

   c. Use algebraic properties to prove that $\bar{x}_T = c\bar{x}$.

   d. Explain how similar reasoning could be used to show $\bar{x}_T = c\bar{x}$, if there were n data values.

   e. Prove that if a constant c is added to each of the original five data values, then the mean $\bar{x}_T$ of the transformed set is given by $\bar{x}_T = \bar{x} + c$.

Checkpoint

The activities of Investigation 2 have demonstrated ways that algebraic reasoning can be used to prove important general properties of geometric figures, trigonometric relations, and descriptive statistics.

a What general strategies and specific techniques for working with algebraic expressions did you find useful in the various activities?

b How would you describe in words what is proven by the arguments in each of Activities 2 through 4?

c How would you describe in words what is proven by the arguments in Activity 5?

d How is a *proof* different from reasoning that gives several examples of an interesting pattern?

Be prepared to explain your strategies and descriptions to the entire class.

Use algebraic reasoning to answer the following general questions and to provide proofs about relations in geometry and statistics.

a. When a rectangle is modeled with coordinate methods, the situation can be pictured like this:

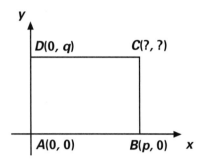

- What must the coordinates of point C be?
- Use the above result to prove that the diagonals of any rectangle are equal in length.

b. The range of a numerical data set is the difference between the largest and smallest values. How, if at all, will the range change in the following cases? Prove your answer in each case.

- Each data value is increased by adding the same fixed amount c.
- Each data value is multiplied by the same positive constant c.

MORE
Modeling • Organizing • Reflecting • Extending

Modeling

1. Shown below are calculator programs for solving any equations of the following types.

Type I: $ax + b = c$
Type II: $ax^2 + b = c$

```
PROGRAM: I
: Input "A = ",A
: Input "B = ",B
: Input "C = ",C
: (C–B)/A→X
: Disp "THE SOLUTION IS ",
  X
```

```
PROGRAM: II
: Input "A = ",A
: Input "B = ",B
: Input "C = ",C
: √((C–B)/A)→X
: Disp "THE SOLUTIONS
  ARE ",X
: Disp –X
```

a. Use algebraic reasoning to prove that the formula used in line 4 of the first program is correct.

b. For what input values of *a*, *b*, and *c* will the equation $ax + b = c$ have a solution?

c. Use algebraic reasoning to prove that the formula used in line 4 of the second program is correct. Why are both values of *x* and –*x* displayed?

d. For what input values of *a*, *b*, and *c* will the equation $ax^2 + b = c$ have solutions?

2. In any square, there is a relation between the lengths of the sides *s* and the diagonals *d*. Use the Pythagorean Theorem and algebraic reasoning to derive an expression showing how *d* is a function of *s*.

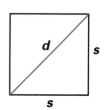

3. A circle is the set of all points in a plane that are a given distance from a given point in the plane (called the center).

a. Shown below on the left is a circle with radius 3 and center at the origin.

- Prove that the point with coordinates $(2, \sqrt{5})$ is on the circle.

- State the coordinates of seven other points on the circle.

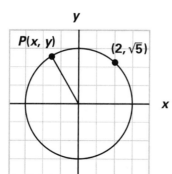 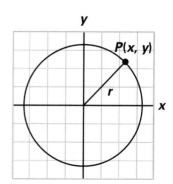

b. Prove that the equation of the circle on the left above is $x^2 + y^2 = 9$.

c. Is the relation $x^2 + y^2 = 9$ a function? Why or why not?

d. Prove that the equation of any circle with center at the origin and radius *r* is $x^2 + y^2 = r^2$.

e. Use algebraic reasoning to find a way to graph $x^2 + y^2 = 9$ using a graphing calculator or computer software.

4. Another measure of the center of a set of data is the **midrange**, the number that is halfway between the largest and smallest data values. (The midrange, like the mean, may or may not be a member of the data set.) Suppose a data set consists of n values $x_1, x_2, ..., x_n$ ordered from smallest to largest.

a. Write a formula for the midrange MR.

b. How, if at all, will the midrange change if a constant c is added to each member of the data set? Prove your answer.

c. How, if at all, will the midrange change if each member of the data set is multiplied by a positive constant c? Prove your answer.

d. Recall that unlike the mean, the median is resistant to outliers. Is the midrange resistant to outliers? Explain your reasoning.

Organizing

1. If you use a calculator to graph $y = x^2$ and $y = x^4$, it may look as if $x^2 \leq x^4$ for all values of x. Use the zoom feature on a graphing calculator and inspection of tables for each relation to test that conjecture. Then use algebraic reasoning to prove your conclusion.

2. In constructing a proof with algebraic reasoning, what principles are available to help you with the following tasks?

a. Show that two expressions are equivalent to each other.

b. Show that two equations or inequalities are equivalent to each other.

3. Inspect the quadratic formula and explain how you can use it to discover whether a quadratic equation has

a. only one root.

b. no roots.

4. Use algebraic reasoning to prove each of the following rules for working with polynomial expressions.

a. For all a, b, c, and d: $(ax + b) + (cx + d) = (a + c)x + (b + d)$ for all x.

b. For all a and b: $(x + a)(x + b) = x^2 + (a + b)x + ab$ for all x.

c. For all a: $(x + a)^2 = x^2 + 2ax + a^2$ for all x.

Reflecting

1. In what ways should an algebraic proof increase a person's confidence in some pattern involving numbers, geometric shapes, trigonometric relations, or statistics?

2. How do the goals and methods of proof in mathematics compare to those that you'd expect in fields like science, politics, or law?

3. Suppose the following vertex-edge graph represents six businesses that are protected by the Allied Security Service and the typical time (in minutes) it takes for a night inspector to travel from place to place.

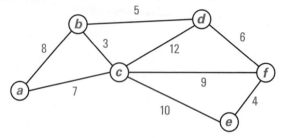

a. How would you find the most efficient route for the nightly check of each of the businesses?

b. How would you prove that a particular route is the most efficient?

c. How does the proof in Part b differ from proof strategies using reasoning with symbolic algebra?

4. Here is a visual "proof" that $(x + p)(x + q) = x^2 + (p + q)x + pq$, for any p and q.

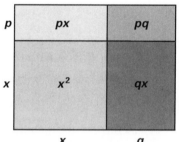

$$(x + p)(x + q) = x^2 + px + qx + pq$$
$$= x^2 + (p + q)x + pq$$

How does this compare to an algebraic proof based on the distributive property? Which do you find more convincing? Which is easier to remember?

Extending

1. The following number trick has puzzled both students and researchers in number theory. Think of a positive integer and then follow these instructions:

Step 1: Write the number.

Step 2: If the number is 1, stop.

Step 3: If the number is even, divide it by 2 and then return to Step 1; follow through the sequence of steps with this new number.

Step 4: If the number is odd, multiply it by 3, add 1, and then return to Step 1 and follow the sequence of steps with the new number.

a. Test this trick with several numbers, and then make a conjecture about the output of the sequence of steps.

b. Could a computer or calculator program be used to prove your conjecture? If so, how? If not, why not?

c. Your conjecture should be true for any positive integer that is a power of 2. Prove that it is.

d. For what other sets of positive integers can you prove your conjecture?

2. The diagram at the right shows a triangle in which the angle at vertex C is obtuse and an altitude from A lies outside the triangle. Revise the proof given in Investigation 2, Activity 3 (page 245) to establish the Law of Cosines in this case.

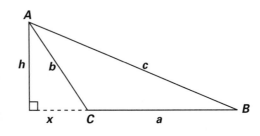

3. In the "Multiple-Variable Models" unit, you used a diagram like the one below to examine a derivation of the Law of Sines.

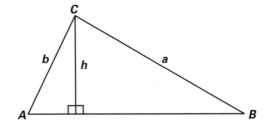

$$\frac{\sin A}{a} = \frac{\sin B}{b}$$

a. The key to the derivation was to write two expressions for h, one in terms of $\sin A$ and b and the other in terms of $\sin B$ and a. See if you can reconstruct the derivation on your own. If you have difficulty, see page 29.

b. Modify the argument in Part a to cover the case in which the altitude lies outside $\triangle ABC$ as in the diagram below.

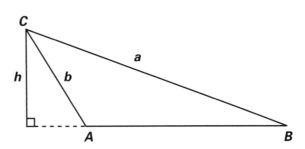

4. In Modeling Task 3, page 248, you developed a coordinate model for a circle with radius r and center at the origin. Similar reasoning can be used to develop an equation for any circle given its center and radius.

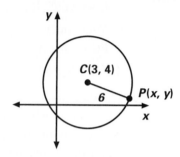

a. Shown above is a circle with center $C(3, 4)$ and radius 6. Write an equation for this circle.

b. Write your equation from Part a in expanded form: $x^2 + y^2 + ax + by = c$.

c. Prove that the equation of a circle with center $C(h, k)$ and radius r is $(x - h)^2 + (y - k)^2 = r^2$.

d. In a calculus text, the following equation was given as an equation of a circle:

$$x^2 + y^2 + 6x - 4y = 12$$

Rebecca believed she could reason as follows to determine the center and radius of the circle and then easily sketch it.

$x^2 + y^2 + 6x - 4y = 12$ is equivalent to $(x^2 + 6x) + (y^2 - 4y) = 12$,

which is equivalent to $(x^2 + 6x + 9) + (y^2 - 4y + 4) = 12 + 9 + 4$,

which is equivalent to $(x + 3)^2 + (y - 2)^2 = 25$.

Explain Rebecca's strategy and how it is related to your earlier work with recognizing the form of perfect square quadratics. Sketch the circle in a coordinate plane.

e. Use algebraic reasoning to identify the center and radius of each circle below, and then sketch the circle in a coordinate plane.

- $x^2 + y^2 + 12x - 2y = -21$
- $x^2 + y^2 + 8y = 9$

Lesson 6 · Looking Back

In this unit, you have studied functions and used symbolic notation to express and reason about relations among variables modeled by those functions. You've discovered a variety of principles and strategies for manipulating symbolic expressions into equivalent forms and applied them to reveal important properties of relationships, to solve equations and inequalities, and to prove the generality of patterns in algebra, geometry, trigonometry, and statistics. The tasks in this section will help you review these important topics.

1. The Blackstone Plaza shopping mall has a total of 100,000 square feet of floor space for stores to rent. The mall rents in units of 1,000 square feet, and monthly income and operating costs (in dollars) depend on the number of floor space units x that are rented. The models below approximate the indicated quantities when the mall has 40% to 85% of its space occupied.

Sources of Income: Basic rent payments $r(x) = -30x^2 + 5,000x$

                            Monthly surcharge for improvements $s(x) = 300x$

Operating Costs: Maintenance and security $m(x) = 200x$

                            Property taxes, utilities for common
                               areas, and promotion $t(x) = 40,000$

   a. Write algebraic rules for two functions $I(x)$ and $C(x)$ showing how monthly *income* and operating *costs* of the mall depend on the amount of floor space rented.

   b. Evaluate $r(50)$, $s(50)$, $m(50)$, $t(50)$, $I(50)$, and $C(50)$, and explain what each tells about the Blackstone Plaza.

c. Explore tables and graphs of the income and cost functions, and then describe both the practical and the theoretical domains and ranges for those functions.

d. Write two algebraic rules for the function $P(x)$ showing how Blackstone Plaza's monthly operating *profit* depends on floor space rented. Give one rule in standard polynomial form and the other in an informative equivalent form. Explain how algebraic properties guarantee equivalence of the two rules.

e. Evaluate $P(40)$ and explain what the result tells about profits for the mall.

f. Explain how you can test the equivalence of the two profit rules in Part d with function tables and graphs.

g. Explore tables and graphs of $P(x)$, and then describe both practical and theoretical domains and ranges for the profit function.

2. Write and solve, by symbolic reasoning methods of this unit, equations and inequalities so that you can answer the following questions about Blackstone Plaza business prospects.

a. If the mall reports operating costs of $56,000, how much floor space must have been rented to stores?

b. How many units of store floor space must be rented for the mall to produce an income of $210,000?

c. At what floor space rental levels will mall operating costs exceed $51,000?

d. At what rental levels will mall income equal operating costs?

3. In studying the Blackstone Plaza profit situation, you will find that $P(x) = 0$ at $x \approx 8$ and $x \approx 162$. How does this information help you locate the rental level that will produce maximum profit for the mall? Can the mall profit be maximum when some space is still unrented?

4. To compare the profitability of Blackstone Plaza to similar properties, the owners believed it would make sense to calculate their profit per 1,000 square feet of store floor space.

a. What is the profit per 1,000 square feet of floor space when $x = 40$, $x = 60$, and $x = 80$?

b. Write several equivalent algebraic expressions for a function $A(x)$ showing how profit per square foot of rented floor space changes as x increases. Include one that you believe involves the simplest calculations and another that best shows the contribution of each income and cost component. Be prepared to explain how you know the various expressions are equivalent.

5. The owners of Blackstone Plaza decided that by constructing an office building attached to their mall, they could increase traffic in the stores, making the mall more desirable for stores and thus increasing their own profit. They collected various kinds of information about construction and operating costs and the relation between rent charged and amount of space that would be rented. They determined that the relation between monthly rent charged r (in dollars per square foot) and monthly profit $P(r)$ (in thousands of dollars) from the new building would be approximated well by the following rule:

$$P(r) = -8r^2 + 48r - 40$$

a. What values of r (the rent per square foot per month) seem reasonable to consider as the practical domain of this function and what values seem unreasonable? (**Hint:** Look at advertisements for apartment and house rentals in a local newspaper, and think about the relation between the area of a house or apartment and typical monthly rent for such space. Then remember that commercial space is generally a bit more expensive.)

b. Sketch a graph of the function over what seems to be a practical domain, and explain what the shape of that graph tells about the relation between rent charged and profit prospects for the new building.

Solve each of the following quadratic equations and inequalities, using factoring or the quadratic formula, and explain what each answer tells about the relation between monthly rent charges and profit for the planned building.

c. $-8r^2 + 48r - 40 = 0$ d. $-8r^2 + 48r - 40 > 0$

e. $-8r^2 + 48r - 40 = 15$ f. $-8r^2 + 48r - 40 > 15$

g. $-8r^2 + 48r - 40 < 10$

6. Use algebraic properties to write each of the following expressions for polynomial function rules in equivalent standard form.

a. $f(x) = 5x^2 - 4x^3 + 12 - 9x$ b. $g(x) = 7x(11 - 4x) + 3x - 9$

c. $h(x) = (x + 4)(2x - 3) + 7$ d. $j(x) = 4(x + 3)^2 - 7(x - 8)$

7. Think about the relationships between symbolic and graphical representations of quadratic functions.

a. What is the relationship between the factors of a quadratic expression and the zeroes of the function defined by that expression?

b. What is the relationship between the zeroes of a quadratic function and the line of symmetry of its graph?

8. Given $f(x) = 2x^2 + x + 2$ and $g(x) = 3x - 1$, write standard polynomial rules for each of the following combinations of those functions. Be prepared to use algebraic properties to justify each step in your reasoning.

a. $f(x) + g(x)$ b. $f(x) - g(x)$

c. $f(x) \times g(x)$ d. $5[f(x)] - 3[g(x)]$

9. Solve these equations and inequalities by reasoning with the symbolic expressions alone. Then draw graphs illustrating each solution.

   a. $2(x - 3) + 5(x + 2) = 0$ b. $5x - 7 < 15 + 3x$

   c. $0 \leq 2x^2 + 3x + 1$ d. $x^2 + 5x + 6 = 1 - x$

10. Describe four different methods for solving the equation $x^2 + 2x - 15 = 0$. Use one of the methods to solve the equation and show how that solution can be checked without use of a calculator.

11. For each of the following quadratic functions, decide whether it has 0, 1, or 2 zeroes. Then explain how the graph of the function illustrates the number of solutions.

   a. $g(x) = 2x^2 + 5x + 3$ b. $h(x) = -x^2 - 7x - 1$

   c. $j(x) = 6x^2 - 2x + 1$ d. $p(x) = x^2 + 2x - 1$

12. Explain the relationship between the graph of $f(x) = ax^2 + bx + c$, $x = \frac{-b}{2a}$, and the value $\frac{\sqrt{b^2 - 4ac}}{2a}$.

13. Write each of the following algebraic expressions in standard polynomial form. Be prepared to explain the properties of algebraic operations that justify each answer.

   a. $(x + 7)(x - 7)$ b. $(x + 7)^2$

   c. $(x - 3)(x + 8)$ d. $(2x + 5)(x - 4)$

14. Write each of the following polynomials as a product of linear factors.

   a. $x^2 + 7x + 12$ b. $x^2 + 6x + 9$

   c. $x^2 - 25$ d. $x^2 - 7x - 8$

   e. $3x^2 - 7x + 2$

15. The quadratic formula gives the roots of $ax^2 + bx + c = 0$ where $a \neq 0$. Using algebraic reasoning with the formula also reveals interesting relationships between the roots.

   a. Prove that the sum of the roots of $ax^2 + bx + c = 0$ is $-\frac{b}{a}$.

   b. Prove that the product of the roots of $ax^2 + bx + c = 0$ is $\frac{c}{a}$.

   c. Suppose the quadratic equation $ax^2 + bx + c = 0$ were rewritten in the equivalent form $x^2 + mx + n = 0$. Write expressions for m and n in terms of a, b, and c. What does Part a above show about m, the coefficient of x? What does Part b show about n, the constant term?

Checkpoint

In this unit, you have studied functions and algebraic reasoning. As you answer the following questions, think about the significance of what you have learned.

ⓐ What are some of the advantages of using function notation "$f(x) = ...$" rather than the equation form "$y = ...$" to express a relationship between variables?

ⓑ What strategies are useful in determining the theoretical and practical domains for functions that are used as models of problem situations?

ⓒ What are the advantages and disadvantages of using simplest standard forms of polynomial expressions?

ⓓ What algebraic properties are used in simplifying polynomial expressions like $5(x^2 + 4x) - x(3 + 4x) + 7(x + 9)$, and how can you check that two given expressions are actually equivalent?

ⓔ What properties of numbers and operations guide combination and separation of fractional algebraic expressions like $\frac{4x}{3} + \frac{7}{x}$ and $\frac{6x^2 + 8x}{2x}$ (where $x \neq 0$)?

ⓕ What general strategies are involved in the use of symbolic reasoning to solve linear equations and inequalities? To solve quadratic equations and inequalities?

ⓖ How can algebraic reasoning provide proof that patterns you find will hold, even in cases you've not checked?

Be prepared to share your descriptions and thinking with the entire class.

▶On Your Own

Write, in outline form, a summary of the important mathematical concepts and methods developed in this unit. Organize your summary so that it can be used as a quick reference in future units and courses.

Shapes and
Geometric Reasoning

Lesson 1

Reasoned Arguments

Careful reasoning, whether it is concerned with mathematics, science, history, or daily affairs, is important if you want to have faith in the conclusions reached. Often, reasoning about daily affairs, such as in politics, government, business, or the legal system, is flawed because meanings of basic terms, as well as assumptions and relations involving the terms, are in dispute. For example, when President Bush announced his 2002 budget, he stated that the Department of Education was getting $44.5 billion in appropriations, an 11.5% increase over the 2001 funding level. The Democrats disagreed and claimed that it was only a 4.2% increase. The discrepancy was the result of either including or excluding the advance appropriation that had been granted to the Department of Education during 2001, and adjusting or not adjusting for inflation.

There are many claims made in daily affairs that you should carefully analyze to be sure that what you are being told follows logically from information and facts that you know are correct. Consider the following two advertisements.

I wished a thousand times for a brighter smile. One tube of Dentacleen gave it to me. The guys with the great smiles always had dates. With Dentacleen my smiles are bright too.

A brain harassed by a pen that runs dry loses its brilliance, power, and expression. Hence, our pens have 102% more ink capacity.

Think About This Situation

The toothpaste and ballpoint pen ads are each intended to persuade you to purchase a particular product. Analyze each of the claims. For each example, answer the following:

a What facts are to be assumed by the reader? Do these assumptions seem reasonable?

b What conclusion would you make? Explain your reasoning.

c What similar claims have you recently seen in the media?

In this unit, you will expand your ability to make reasoned arguments or **proofs** in the context of geometric situations. As in algebraic reasoning, the goal is to reach conclusions by applying correct logical principles to combinations of previously proven or assumed facts and relations.

INVESTIGATION 1 Analyzing Arguments

In mathematics, in other academic fields, and in daily affairs, it is important to be able to analyze and understand arguments provided by other people. As you may have noted in your discussion of the "Think About This Situation" on the previous page, assumptions have an important influence on such arguments. In the next two activities, you are asked to identify and think about assumptions that are being made.

1. Examine the claim below, from a newspaper advertisement for The Men's Wearhouse.

We sell men's clothing for less than our competitors do, because our store is not in the high rent district.

Decide whether each of the following statements was taken for granted (assumed) in the above advertisement. If the statement was assumed, indicate whether you think it is probably true or probably false. Explain your thinking.

a. The competitors charge more than The Men's Wearhouse for men's clothing.

b. It is necessary for a store to charge more for clothing as rent increases.

c. Rent is the only factor that influences the price of clothing.

d. The Men's Wearhouse charges less for every piece of men's clothing.

e. All of The Men's Wearhouse competitors are in the high rent district.

f. A store that accepts only cash (no credit cards) can charge less for clothing.

g. A high volume of sales at The Men's Wearhouse permits it to sell clothing for less than its competitors.

h. The Men's Wearhouse always sells its clothing at the lowest possible prices.

i. The quality of clothing at The Men's Wearhouse is similar to the quality of clothing at competing stores.

2. At the beginning of a new school year, Rosa and her college roommate Wendy bought 180 square feet of carpeting for their dorm room. Later in the semester, while on a shopping excursion, they found a wallpaper border pattern that they loved. They decided to purchase enough paper to run a strip around their dorm room. Rosa suggested buying 56 feet from the 60-yard roll. Wendy thought they would need 58 feet of the border strip.

 a. What assumptions might each have made that led them to their conclusions about the amount of paper to buy?

 b. If Rosa and Wendy had a third roommate, is it possible that independently she might have suggested yet a third length of paper for the room? Explain her possible assumptions.

 c. In your group, discuss what length of wallpaper border strip you might have purchased. What assumptions would you make? Explain your rationale.

Now consider the role that assumptions play in mathematical arguments.

3. You have probably noticed that when you add two odd integers, the sum always seems to be an even integer. In Maria and Toby's mathematics class, it is commonplace for observations of patterns like this to lead to conjectures and then to attempted proofs. Maria and Toby's conjecture was the following:

 If a and b are odd integers, then a + b (the sum) is an even integer.

Both students tried to prove the conjecture independently. Maria's proof went as follows:

  If a and b are odd integers, then a and b can be written $a = 2m + 1$ and $b = 2n + 1$, where m and n are other integers.

  If $a = 2m + 1$ and $b = 2n + 1$, then $a + b = 2m + 1 + 2n + 1$.

  If $a + b = 2m + 1 + 2n + 1$, then $a + b = 2m + 2n + 2$.

  If $a + b = 2m + 2n + 2$, then $a + b = 2(m + n + 1)$.

  If $a + b = 2(m + n + 1)$, then $a + b$ is an even integer.

Toby took some square counters and reasoned, "I can use these to prove the sum of any two odd numbers is even. For example, if I take the numbers 5 and 11 and organize the counters as shown, you can see the pattern."

5   **+**   **11**

☐ ☐ ☐   ▢ ▢ ▢ ▢ ▢

☐ ☐   ▢ ▢ ▢ ▢ ▢ ▢

"You can see that when you put the sets together (add the numbers), the two extra blocks will form a pair and the answer is always even."

16

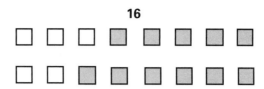

   a. Look at Maria's first statement. What does she assume? What additional assumptions, facts, or algebraic properties did she use within her argument?

   b. Next look at Toby's argument. What did he assume?

   c. Does Maria's argument prove the conjecture? Describe the features of her argument that support your position.

   d. Does Toby's argument prove the conjecture? Describe the features of his argument that support your position.

   e. How can Toby's model of odd numbers help you understand Maria's proof?

4. Below is a restatement of Modeling Task 3 Part b from Lesson 2 of the "Symbol Sense and Algebraic Reasoning" unit (page 203).

Given: b_1 and b_2 are the lengths of the bases of the trapezoid shown, with height h.

Prove: The area of the trapezoid is $A = \frac{1}{2}h(b_2 - b_1) + b_1h$.

Study each of the three sample student arguments that follow.

Barbara's argument:

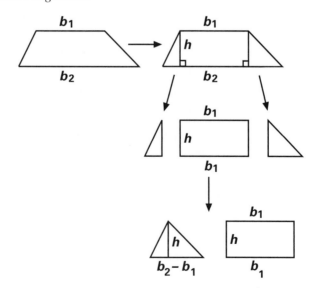

So the area of the trapezoid is $\frac{1}{2}h(b_2 - b_1) + b_1h$.

Hsui's argument: The area of a trapezoid with bases b_1 and b_2 and altitude h is $\frac{1}{2}h(b_2 - b_1) + b_1h$ because the trapezoid can be cut up into a b_1-by-h rectangle with area b_1h and two triangles with altitude h, which together make a triangle with area $\frac{1}{2}h(b_2 - b_1)$.

Jorge's argument: The area of the trapezoid is $\frac{1}{2}h(b_2 - b_1) + b_1h$ because you can cut up the shape and find the areas of the individual pieces.

Each of these student arguments was offered as a justification of the area formula for a trapezoid: $A = \frac{1}{2}h(b_2 - b_1) + b_1h$.

  a. Look back at Barbara's, Hsui's, and Jorge's arguments. What assumptions did each make at the beginning of his or her argument? What assumptions and facts did each student use within his or her argument?

  b. As a group, decide which of these arguments do a good job of justifying the formula and which do not.

  c. Describe the features of an argument that your group thought was good. What could you *add* to that argument to improve it?

  d. Choose an argument your group thought was not good. Describe why your group decided it was not good.

  e. Of the good arguments, which one do you prefer? Explain your preference.

5. A standard formula for calculating the area A of a trapezoid is $A = \frac{1}{2}h(b_2 + b_1)$. Kenya thought that she could use algebraic reasoning to show that the formula in Activity 4 is equivalent to the standard formula for the area of a trapezoid. Study Kenya's proof shown below.

$$\frac{1}{2}h(b_2 - b_1) + b_1h = \frac{1}{2}hb_2 - \frac{1}{2}hb_1 + b_1h \qquad (1)$$

$$= \frac{1}{2}hb_2 + \frac{1}{2}hb_1 \qquad (2)$$

$$= \frac{1}{2}h(b_2 + b_1) \qquad (3)$$

  a. What mathematical facts and relationships did Kenya assume were true at the beginning of her argument?

  b. What mathematical facts and properties support each step in her argument?

  c. Compare the set of assumptions, facts, and properties used by Kenya to those used in the student arguments in Activity 4.

6. Now look back at the student attempts to prove the mathematical statements in Activities 3 through 5.

  a. Examine these arguments, both good and not so good, and then identify and describe the features of an argument that make it a *valid argument*.

  b. Examine these arguments, both good and not so good, and then describe the different forms in which the arguments were presented. Are there examples that could be described as pictorial, flow diagram, chain of if-then statements, or paragraph form? Characterize each example you find.

  c. Investigate and then make a conjecture about the sum of any two even integers. What would you do to prove your conjecture?

In this investigation, you examined arguments in terms of their assumptions, their validity, and the form in which they were presented.

a How do the assumptions you make affect the proof of a conjecture?

b Identify what you consider to be the most important characteristics of a valid argument.

c You have seen that different people present their proofs in different forms (for example, in paragraph form, in if-then statement chains, or pictorially). Which forms are easiest to understand? To check for validity? To think of and produce?

Be prepared to share your group's thinking with the rest of the class.

On Your Own

Fresh Makeup

Give your skin a treat with Fresh Makeup, the clean, fresh, look that lets your skin breathe. That keeps your skin glowing. That lets you face the world like a queen.

After reading the above advertisement, Karen showed it to her mother, saying, "Mom, look. This ad says I can drop out of school and have an easy life. All I need to do is use Fresh Makeup." You can imagine her mother's response!

Here is the argument Karen constructed.

If I use Fresh Makeup, then my skin can breathe.

If my skin breathes, then it will glow.

If my skin glows, then I'll face life like I'm a queen.

If I can face life like a queen, then I'll have an easy life.

a. What assumptions does this argument make?

b. Is this a valid argument? Describe the characteristics of the argument that led you to conclude that it was or was not valid.

c. Describe the form of Karen's proof.

INVESTIGATION 2 ▶ Reasoning *to* and *from* If-Then Statements

Maria's argument in Activity 3 of the previous investigation (page 262) involved reasoning with a chain of if-then statements. That kind of reasoning is based on a fundamental principle of logic:

> *If you have a known fact*   (an if-then statement that is always true)
>
> *and you also know*   the "if" part is true in a particular case,
>
> *you can conclude*   the "then" part is true in that case.

For example, consider how this principle supports the reasoning in the last statement of Maria's proof.

Known fact: If $p = 2n$, where n is an integer, then p is an even integer.

Given: $a + b = 2(m + n + 1)$, where m and n are integers.

Conclusion: $a + b$ is an even integer.

1. In your group, decide what can be concluded from each of the following sets of statements.

   a. *Known fact:* If $f(x) = ax^2 + bx + c$ is a quadratic function with $a < 0$, then $f(x)$ has a maximum value.

   Given: $g(x) = -8x^2 + 5x - 2$

   Conclusion: ?

   b. *Known fact:* If A and B are two independent events, then the probability $P(A \text{ and } B) = P(A) \cdot P(B)$.

   Given: Josh and Jeanette are playing a game in which they each draw a card from separate standard decks of playing cards. They are curious about the probability that both will draw a red card.

   Conclusion: ?

   c. *Known fact:* If a connected vertex-edge graph has vertices all of even degree, then the graph has an Euler circuit.

   Given: The degrees of the vertices of a connected graph G are 2, 4, 2, 4, 2, 4, 2, 4, 2, 4.

   Conclusion: ?

   d. *Known fact:* If a data set with mean $\bar{x}$ and mean absolute deviation (MAD) d is transformed by adding a constant c to each value, then the mean of the transformed data set is $\bar{x} + c$ and the MAD is d.

   Given: The Oak Park hockey team has a mean height of 5 feet 9 inches and a MAD of $2\frac{1}{2}$ inches. Ice skates add approximately $1\frac{3}{4}$ inches to the height of a skater.

   Conclusion: ?

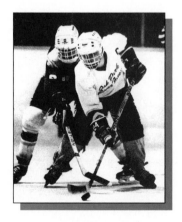

e. *Known fact:* Under a size transformation with center at the origin and magnitude k, the area of the image of a figure is $k^2 \cdot$ area of the pre-image.

Given: Hexagon $P'Q'R'S'T'U'$ is the image under a size transformation with center at the origin and magnitude 3 of hexagon $PQRSTU$ whose area is 32 cm^2.

Conclusion: ?

2. If-then statements and reasoning patterns can be represented symbolically. For example, the reasoning pattern you used in Activity 1 can be represented as follows:

	Words	Symbolic form
Known fact:	"If p then q" is always true,	$p \Rightarrow q$
Given:	**and** p is true in a particular case,	p
Conclusion:	**thus** q is true in that case.	q

The clause corresponding to p (following "if") is called the **hypothesis**. The clause corresponding to q (following "then") is called the **conclusion**.

a. In Activity 1 Part a, identify the if-then statement, the hypothesis, and the conclusion.

b. For the known fact in Part e of Activity 1, identify p, q, and $p \Rightarrow q$.

c. Write, in if-then form, the statement "All sophomores at Calvin High School take physical education." What is the hypothesis? The conclusion?

■ If Tommy is a sophomore at Calvin, what can you conclude?

■ If Rosa is taking a physical education class at Calvin, what can you conclude? Explain your reasoning.

The "known facts" you used in Activity 1 were relationships you probably discovered and, as a class, agreed upon in previous mathematics courses. Your discoveries were probably based on studying cases or experimenting, collecting data, and searching for patterns.

3. In your group, discuss some possible case explorations or experiments that might have suggested the statements given as known facts in Activity 1.

4. Reasoning from patterns based on analysis of specific cases is called **inductive reasoning**. You use this kind of reasoning often in mathematics and in everyday life.

a. Suppose during the last month you visited four friends, each of whom has a cat. In each case, you noticed that your eyes began to itch and water after a while. What might you conclude? How is this an example of inductive reasoning?

b. Record, from each group member, at least one example of how he or she has used inductive reasoning outside of mathematics class.

Now consider some examples of inductive reasoning in mathematics.

5. Recall that the *degree* of a vertex in a vertex-edge graph without loops is the number of edges meeting at the vertex. Use inductive reasoning and Parts a through c below to develop a conjecture about the *sum* of the degrees of the vertices of a vertex-edge graph with no loops.

   a. For each of the graphs shown, determine the number of edges, the degree of each vertex, and the sum of the degrees of the vertices. Organize your results in a table. Leave room to extend your table.

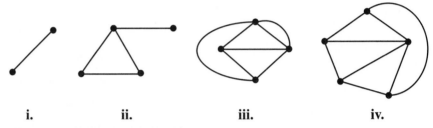

   i.   **ii.**   **iii.**   **iv.**

   b. Draw four additional vertex-edge graphs. Find the number of edges and the sum of the degrees of the vertices for each graph. Record your findings in your table.

   c. If you have a vertex-edge graph with 10 edges, what do you think is the sum of the degrees of the vertices? Check your prediction with a drawing.

   d. Write a conjecture relating the number of edges E and the sum of the degrees of the vertices S.

   e. State your conjecture in if-then form.

   f. Are you absolutely positive that your conjecture is true for all possible vertex-edge graphs? Explain.

In Activity 5, you developed a conjecture by looking for patterns in specific cases. In the next activity, you will examine two conjectures already formulated. The first conjecture involves prime numbers.

6. Recall that a **prime number** is an integer greater than 1 that has exactly two positive factors, 1 and the number itself. The first 10 primes are 2, 3, 5, 7, 11, 13, 17, 19, 23, and 29. Study Benjamin's conjecture below, which proposes a way to produce prime numbers using a quadratic expression:

   If n is a positive integer, then $n^2 - n + 41$ is a prime number.

   a. Test Benjamin's conjecture by examining some specific cases. Choose several positive values for n and see if the formula gives a prime number. Share the work in your group.

   b. Based on your calculations, does the conjecture seem correct? Can you conclude for sure that it is always true? Explain your reasoning.

   c. Now test $n^2 - n + 41$ for $n = 41$. Is the result a prime number? Why or why not?

   d. What would you say to Benjamin about the correctness of his conjecture?

7. Now examine Teri's conjecture about a property of square roots:

If x is a positive real number, then $\sqrt{x} \leq x$.

Write a response to Teri about the correctness of her conjecture.

Checkpoint

Inductive reasoning is used to generalize observed patterns. Such generalizations are frequently expressed in if-then form.

ⓐ Describe how you can identify the hypothesis and conclusion in an if-then statement.

ⓑ Describe some activities that a person might do when reasoning inductively.

ⓒ Why is it not possible to prove a statement using inductive reasoning?

ⓓ How can you show that a conjecture is *not* true?

Be prepared to share your group's ideas with the entire class.

▶ On Your Own

Make a conjecture about what happens when you choose any four consecutive positive integers, add the middle two, and then subtract the smallest of the four from that sum. Describe the procedure you used to generate your conjecture.

32, 33, 34, 35

Sherlock Holmes, Master of Deduction

Inductive reasoning may lead to an if-then statement that is plausible. However, the statement may or may not always be true. Another type of reasoning, **deductive reasoning**, involves reasoning *from* facts, definitions, and accepted properties *to* new statements using principles of logic. Under correct deductive reasoning, the conclusions reached are certain, not just plausible.

8. Compare the conjectures members of your group made in the above "On Your Own" task.

   a. Choose one conjecture that all of you believe is probably always true. Write the conjecture in if-then form.

   b. If *n* represents the smallest of four consecutive integers, how would you represent the other three numbers?

   c. Using your representations in Part b, prove your conjecture in Part a.

The algebraic reasoning you used in Activity 8 and in the previous unit to prove general statements about number patterns and relationships in geometry, trigonometry, and statistics is a form of deductive reasoning. In the next activity, you will examine how deductive reasoning is used to establish a relationship in discrete mathematics.

9. In Activity 5, your group may have arrived at the following conjecture:

If G is a vertex-edge graph with E edges, none of which are loops, then the sum of the degrees of the vertices S is equal to 2E.

Here is an argument that is claimed to be a proof of this conjecture. Study it carefully.

If G is a vertex-edge graph with E edges, none of which are loops, then each of the E edges joins two vertices.

If each of the E edges joins two vertices, then each of the E edges contributes 2 to the sum of the degrees of the vertices S.

If each of the E edges contributes 2 to the sum of the degrees of the vertices S, then $S = 2E$.

Therefore, if G is a vertex-edge graph with E edges, none of which are loops, then the sum of the degrees of the vertices S is $2E$.

a. Does this argument convince you that the conjecture is correct? Why or why not?

b. Is the argument based on information that is known to be correct? Look critically at each of the first three if-then statements. Are they correct? Explain why or why not.

c. What do the first two statements in the proof have in common? How are the common parts used differently? Is the same true for the second and third statements?

d. How is the final if-then statement derived from the first three if-then statements in the proof?

e. Rewrite this proof in a different form that you find easy to understand and to write.

10. In Investigation 1, you examined conjectures about the sum of two odd integers.

a. Now, suppose a is an odd integer and b is an even integer. What can you conclude about their sum?

b. Write your conjecture as an if-then statement.

c. Write a deductive argument that you could use to convince the most skeptical person that your conjecture is, in fact, correct.

d. What known mathematical facts did you use in your argument?

e. Share and compare your argument with others in class. How do they differ in form and in assumptions?

11. Tonja made the following conjecture about odd integers:

If a and b are consecutive odd integers, then their sum is divisible by 4.

a. Give three examples of pairs of consecutive odd integers. Why are they "consecutive"?

b. Test Tonja's conjecture for the pairs of integers in Part a.

c. Give either a counterexample or a deductive proof of Tonja's conjecture.

Checkpoint

Consider this conjecture:

The product of a positive even integer and a positive odd integer is even.

ⓐ How could you arrive at this conjecture by using inductive reasoning?

ⓑ Write this conjecture in if-then form.

ⓒ How could you use deductive reasoning to prove this conjecture?

Be prepared to explain your group's responses to the entire class.

Inductive reasoning and deductive reasoning are important and often complementary aspects of mathematical thinking. Inductive reasoning often leads to conjectures of new relationships or properties. These conjectures may or may not always be true. Deductive reasoning provides a way to establish, using principles of logic, that a conjecture is always true.

▶On Your Own

Examine the following if-then statements about properties of numbers.

  i. If a, b, and c are consecutive positive integers, then $a + b + c$ is divisible by 3.

  ii. If a, b, and c are consecutive positive integers, then $a + b + c$ is divisible by 6.

  iii. If x is a real number, then $-x < x$.

  iv. If x is a nonzero real number, then $x > \frac{1}{x}$.

a. Use inductive reasoning to help you decide which statements might be correct and which are incorrect.

b. For each statement that is incorrect, give a counterexample.

c. Write a proof that could convince a skeptic that the correct statements are true.

MORE

Modeling • Organizing • Reflecting • Extending

Modeling

1. The United States Supreme Court has ruled that each state has power over all schools in the state and it is the responsibility of the state to require the following:

   ■ "That all children of proper age attend some school."

   ■ "That teachers shall be of good moral character and patriotic disposition."

   a. What words and phrases need to be defined clearly in order that a state may discharge its duty?

   b. Write a defining statement for "school" and "teacher."

   c. Do your definitions in Part b permit a parent to educate a child at home? Explain.

   d. What is meant by "good moral character"? How could a state certify that a teacher has good moral character?

2. In the early 1980s, a constitutional amendment requiring a balanced budget for the federal government was proposed. In the late 1990s, the question of such an amendment was still being discussed. Part of the discussion included when the amendment could take effect. One writer reasoned that since the 18th Amendment was ratified in 13 months, the 19th in 15 months, the 20th in 11 months, and the 21st in 9.5 months, once a balanced-budget amendment has been submitted to the people, the ratification time will be about a year.

   a. What conjecture is the writer making? Write it in if-then form.

   b. What argument is given to support the conjecture?

   c. Does the argument establish the conjecture? Explain.

3. Underlying the beliefs of an individual are numerous assumptions. Anyone who accepts a conclusion regarding an issue at the same time accepts certain assumptions on which that conclusion might depend, even though the particular assumptions are not explicit. (Note, however, that two people might base the same conclusion on entirely different assumptions.) The facts and assumptions on which logical arguments are built must be correct for the argument to be valid, so it's important to consider them carefully.

Choose one of the following topics. Clearly state your position regarding the topic. (The descriptions given do not present every possible position; if you have a different opinion, express it!) Then try to state all of the facts and assumptions on which your position depends.

a. *Balanced Federal Budget* Some people believe that spending should be cut or taxes should be raised (or both) so that federal income and spending each year are equal. Some people believe that deficit spending is acceptable.

b. *School Uniforms* Many public schools have considered requiring a particular uniform that all students must wear. Some people believe this allows students to ignore differences in economic status. Some people believe this suppresses individual expression.

c. *School Awards* Some high school students think that there should be a set of fixed criteria for honors and awards and that once these criteria are attained, the honor or award should be granted. Some students think that a set of fixed criteria is not flexible enough to meet various situations or circumstances.

d. *College Affirmative Action* Some people believe that affirmative action programs for college admissions should be maintained so some individuals who belong to certain groups will have a better opportunity to attend college. Some people believe that college admissions should be granted on a standard of merit and accomplishment that is fixed for all people.

4. Bishiva claims that the product of any two positive odd integers is also an odd integer.

    a. Test Bishiva's claim for five different pairs of odd integers. What seems to be true?

    b. Provide an argument that Bishiva is correct or produce a counterexample to establish that he is not correct.

Organizing

1. Most statements in mathematics are written in if-then form or can be expressed in that form. Think about the mathematics you have studied this year and in previous courses. Write one correct if-then statement related to each of the topics listed below.

    a. Vertex-edge graphs   **b.** Linear equations

    c. Parallelograms   **d.** A data distribution

    e. Exponential functions   **f.** Translations

    g. Correlation coefficients   **h.** Similar shapes

    i. Matrices   **j.** Trigonometric functions

2. Activity 2 of Investigation 2 (page 267) illustrated a symbolic model for reasoning with an if-then statement. You can also think of if-then statements geometrically using **Venn diagrams**.

a. Examine these if-then statements and the corresponding Venn diagrams.

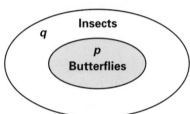

$p \Rightarrow q$
If a creature is a butterfly,
then it is an insect.

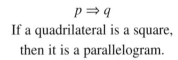

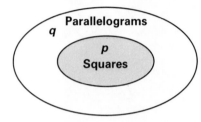

$p \Rightarrow q$
If a quadrilateral is a square,
then it is a parallelogram.

- If you know that a monarch is a butterfly, what can you conclude?
- If you know that quadrilateral *WXYZ* is a square, what can you conclude?

b. Refer to Investigation 2, Activity 2 Part c (page 267). Represent your if-then statement geometrically with a Venn diagram. How can you use the Venn diagram in reasoning about Tommy's situation in that activity?

c. A common error in deductive reasoning is to assume that because an if-then statement $p \Rightarrow q$ is always true, the *converse* statement $q \Rightarrow p$ is also always true.

- Write the converse of each statement in Part a.
- How do the Venn diagrams in Part a show that the converse of a statement is not always true? How is this analysis related to your reasoning about the case of Rosa in Activity 2 Part c of Investigation 2 (page 267)?

3. Among the algebraic properties you used in the "Symbol Sense and Algebraic Reasoning" unit were the commutative and associative properties for addition.

a. Write these properties in if-then form.

b. When Karl finds himself in a situation in which he needs to add three numbers such as 27 + 19 + 43, he thinks "27 plus 43 is 70, plus 19 equals 89." He says he uses the "Switch Property for Addition":

If a, b, and c are real numbers, then (a + b) + c = (a + c) + b.

Show how you can use the commutative and associative properties and a chain of if-then reasoning to prove Karl's Switch Property.

4. *Number theory* is a branch of mathematics that has flourished since ancient times and continues to be an important field of mathematical activity, particularly in the applied area of *coding* (encrypting messages so only the intended recipients can read them). One of the first definitions appearing in the theory of numbers is a definition for *factor* or *divisor*. An integer *b* is a factor (divisor) of an integer *a* provided there is an integer *c* such that $a = bc$.

a. One of the first theorems in number theory is the following:

> *If a, b, and c are integers where a is a factor of b and a is a factor of c, then a is a factor of b + c.*

Test this theorem for some specific cases to develop an understanding for what it is saying. Then write a deductive argument showing that the theorem is always true.

b. Form a new if-then statement as follows: Use the hypothesis of the theorem in Part a and replace the conclusion with "*a* is a factor of *bm* + *cn* for all integers *m* and *n*."

- Do you think this new if-then statement is always true? Explain your reasoning.

- If you think the statement is true, write a proof of it. If not, give a counterexample.

Reflecting

1. If you think about it, inductive reasoning is a common form of reasoning in the world around you. Give an example of how inductive reasoning might be used by the following people:

a. An automobile driver

b. A golfer

c. A medical researcher

2. Explain how inductive and deductive reasoning differ. In doing mathematics, how does one form of reasoning support the other?

3. Identify two or three occupations or professions in which you think deductive reasoning is used extensively. Explain how you think such reasoning is used.

4. Examine the following cartoon. Is the child's argument a valid argument? What would you say to the child if you were his parent?

THE BORN LOSER reprinted by permission of Newspaper Enterprise Association, Inc.

5. The reasoning pattern illustrated in Activity 2 of Investigation 2 (page 267) is sometimes called "affirming the hypothesis," "the law of detachment," or "*modus ponens*." Why do you think these labels are used for that reasoning pattern? Which label makes most sense to you?

Extending

1. Consider the following if-then statement:

   If two lines are parallel to a third line, then they are parallel to each other.

This statement is of the form $p \Rightarrow q$, where p is the clause "two lines are parallel to a third line" and q is the clause "they are parallel to each other." Use these clauses in completing Parts a through e.

   a. Write in words the statement $q \Rightarrow p$.

   b. If the *negation* of a simple statement r is "not r," write the negations of the given statements p and q.

   c. Write in words the statement not $q \Rightarrow$ not p.

   d. Write in words the statement not $p \Rightarrow$ not q.

e. It can be proven that $p \Rightarrow q$ is a correct statement. Are the "related" statements in Parts a, c, and d correct or incorrect? For each incorrect statement, draw a sketch showing a counterexample.

f. Look up in a dictionary the words *converse*, *contrapositive*, and *inverse*. How do these terms apply to Parts a through e?

2. Many people, such as auto technicians, make a living out of repairing things. Often repairs can be done at home if you have the right tools and can reason deductively. The first step in making a repair is identifying the problem. Examine the troubleshooting chart below for diagnosing problems that often occur with small engines, such as the one on a lawn mower.

a. What are the first things you should check if the engine runs but the mower does not?

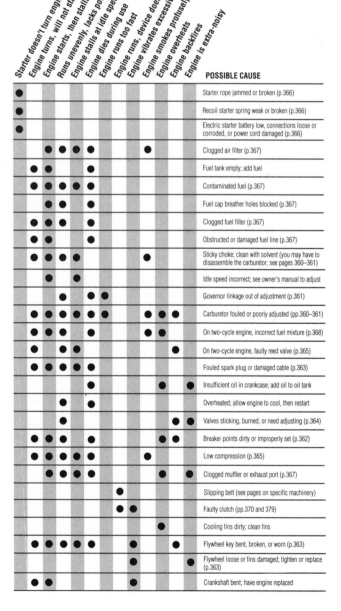

Four-cycle engine with horizontal crankshaft

Fuel tank · Piston · Air filter · Spark plug · Valve · Cylinder · Connecting rod · Crankshaft · Carburetor · Muffler · Camshaft drive gear

PROBLEM

Starter doesn't turn engine	Engine turns, will not start	Engine starts, then stalls	Runs unevenly, lacks power	Engine stalls at idle speed	Engine dies during use	Engine runs too fast	Engine runs, device doesn't	Engine vibrates excessively	Engine smokes profusely	Engine overheats	Engine backfires	Engine is extra-noisy	POSSIBLE CAUSE
●													Starter rope jammed or broken (p.366)
●													Recoil starter spring weak or broken (p.366)
●													Electric starter battery low, connections loose or corroded, or power cord damaged (p.366)
		●	●	●	●				●				Clogged air filter (p.367)
	●	●		●									Fuel tank empty; add fuel
	●	●	●	●									Contaminated fuel (p.367)
	●	●	●	●									Fuel cap breather holes blocked (p.367)
	●	●		●									Clogged fuel filter (p.367)
	●	●		●									Obstructed or damaged fuel line (p.367)
	●	●	●	●					●				Sticky choke; clean with solvent (you may have to disassemble the carburetor; see pages 360–361)
		●		●									Idle speed incorrect; see owner's manual to adjust
			●		●	●							Governor linkage out of adjustment (p.361)
	●	●	●	●	●				●	●	●		Carburetor fouled or poorly adjusted (pp.360–361)
	●	●	●		●				●	●			On two-cycle engine, incorrect fuel mixture (p.368)
	●		●		●							●	On two-cycle engine, faulty reed valve (p.365)
	●	●	●	●	●								Fouled spark plug or damaged cable (p.363)
					●					●		●	Insufficient oil in crankcase; add oil to oil tank
			●		●								Overheated; allow engine to cool, then restart
			●							●		●	Valves sticking, burned, or need adjusting (p.364)
	●	●	●							●	●		Breaker points dirty or improperly set (p.362)
	●	●	●	●	●		●						Low compression (p.365)
		●	●	●	●					●		●	Clogged muffler or exhaust port (p.367)
							●						Slipping belt (see pages on specific machinery)
							●	●					Faulty clutch (pp.370 and 379)
										●			Cooling fins dirty; clean fins
	●	●	●	●	●			●			●		Flywheel key bent, broken, or worn (p.363)
								●				●	Flywheel loose or fins damaged; tighten or replace (p.363)
	●	●						●					Crankshaft bent; have engine replaced

b. What should you check if the engine starts and then stalls?

c. Some of the "possible causes" listed in the Troubleshooting chart often suggest a next course of action. Explain how if-then reasoning is used in these cases.

3. Suppose p and q represent two statements. Describe under what conditions for p and q you think each of the following *compound statements* is true.

a. p and q

b. p or q

c. p if and only if q

d. not (p and q)

e. not (p or q)

4. Recall that the basic if-then reasoning pattern can be represented symbolically as shown at the right. In the symbolic form, everything above the horizontal line is accepted as correct or true. What is written below the line is supposed to follow logically from the accepted information. Shown below are several other possible reasoning patterns. Which patterns show valid reasoning, and which show invalid reasoning? Justify your conclusions.

$$\begin{array}{l} p \Rightarrow q \\ \underline{p \qquad} \\ q \end{array}$$

a.
$$\begin{array}{l} p \Rightarrow q \\ \underline{q \Rightarrow r} \\ p \Rightarrow r \end{array}$$

b.
$$\begin{array}{l} p \Rightarrow q \\ \underline{q \qquad} \\ p \end{array}$$

c.
$$\begin{array}{l} p \Rightarrow q \\ \underline{\text{not } q} \\ \text{not } p \end{array}$$

d.
$$\begin{array}{l} p \Rightarrow q \\ \underline{\text{not } p} \\ \text{not } q \end{array}$$

e.
$$\begin{array}{l} p \Rightarrow \text{not } q \\ \underline{p \qquad\quad} \\ \text{not } q \end{array}$$

f.
$$\begin{array}{l} p \Rightarrow q \\ q \Rightarrow r \\ \underline{r \Rightarrow s} \\ p \Rightarrow s \\ \underline{p \qquad} \\ s \end{array}$$

g.
$$\begin{array}{l} p \Rightarrow q \\ \underline{p \qquad} \\ q \\ \underline{q \Rightarrow r} \\ r \\ \underline{r \Rightarrow s} \\ s \end{array}$$

INVESTIGATION 3 Reasoning about Intersecting Lines and Angles

Skill in reasoning, like skill in sculpting, playing a musical instrument, or playing a sport, comes from practicing that skill and reflecting on the process. In the previous unit, you reasoned in algebraic settings. Using certain assumptions about the operations on and relations among real numbers, you were able to rewrite symbolic expressions in equivalent simpler forms. In this investigation, and in the remainder of the unit, you will sharpen your reasoning skills in geometric settings. As you progress through the unit, pay particular attention to the assumptions you make to support your reasoning, as well as to the validity of the reasoning.

The photo at the right illustrates two of the simplest and most common shapes in a plane: lines and angles. When two lines intersect at a single point, several angles are formed. By varying the size of the base angle, the truck bed can be raised or lowered. Consider how changing the size of this base angle seems to affect the sizes of the angles formed by the two lines. In Activity 1, you will use a geometric model of this situation to gather evidence that may further support your thinking.

1. In the diagram below, lines k and n intersect at point A, forming the numbered angles shown.

    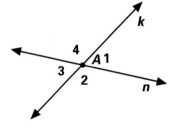

    a. If $m\angle 1 = 72°$, what can you say about $m\angle 2$? About $m\angle 3$? About $m\angle 4$?

    b. If $m\angle 2 = 130°$, what can you say about $m\angle 1$? About $m\angle 3$? About $m\angle 4$?

    c. In general, what relationships among the angles do you think are true? Make a list of them.

    d. Will the general relationships you listed for Part c hold for any pair of intersecting lines? Test your conjectures using specific examples.

    e. Pairs of angles like $\angle 1$ and $\angle 4$ are called **linear pairs** of angles. Name other pairs of angles in the diagram that form a linear pair.

    f. Pairs of angles like $\angle 2$ and $\angle 4$ are called **vertical angles.** Name another pair of vertical angles.

    g. Write an if-then statement about vertical angles that you think is *always* correct. You may want to begin as follows: If two lines intersect, then … .

    h. Compare your conjecture to those of other groups.

In the remainder of this lesson, you will continue to use inductive reasoning to discover possible relations among lines and angles, but you will also attempt to use deductive reasoning to prove your conjectures are always true. To reason deductively, you must first have some known facts to reason from. For the remainder of this unit, you are to assume as a known fact the following property of linear pairs of angles.

Linear Pair Property

If two angles are a linear pair, then the sum of their measures is 180°.

2. Study the following attempt by one group of students to prove the conjecture they made in Part g of Activity 1. Based on the labeling of the diagram below, they set out to prove the following:

   If lines n and k intersect at point A, then $m\angle 1 = m\angle 3$.

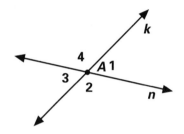

They reasoned as follows:

   (1)   If lines n and k intersect at A, then $m\angle 1 + m\angle 2 = 180°$.

   (2)   If lines n and k intersect at A, then $m\angle 2 + m\angle 3 = 180°$.

   (3)   If $m\angle 1 + m\angle 2 = 180°$ and $m\angle 2 + m\angle 3 = 180°$, then $m\angle 1 + m\angle 2 = m\angle 2 + m\angle 3$.

   (4)   If $m\angle 1 + m\angle 2 = m\angle 2 + m\angle 3$, then $m\angle 1 = m\angle 3$.

   a. Explain why each of the statements above is or is not correct.

   b. Now, in your group, write an argument to show the following: If lines n and k intersect at point A, then $m\angle 2 = m\angle 4$.

   c. What features of a valid argument are illustrated by the given proof and by the one you constructed?

In mathematics, a statement that has been proved using deductive reasoning with accepted facts and relations is called a **theorem**. The statement proved in Activity 2 is sometimes referred to as the **Vertical Angles Theorem**. (Not all theorems are given names.) After a theorem has been proved, it may be used to prove other conjectures. As the unit progresses, you will want to know which theorems have been proved. Thus, you should prepare a geometry toolkit by listing assumptions, such as the Linear Pair Property, and proven theorems. Add each new theorem to your toolkit as it is proved.

3. Referring to the labeled diagram at the right, determine the angle measures in the following situations.

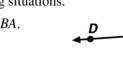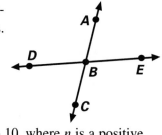

   a. Suppose m∠CBE = 102°. Find m∠DBA. Find m∠ABE.

   b. Suppose m∠CBE + m∠ABD = 144°. Find m∠DBC.

   c. Suppose m∠CBE = 2n + 5 and m∠DBC = 3n + 10, where n is a positive integer. Find the measures of ∠CBE and ∠DBC.

4. In the diagram at the right, the three lines intersect at point B. Line AD is perpendicular to line EC (written $\overleftrightarrow{AD} \perp \overleftrightarrow{EC}$).

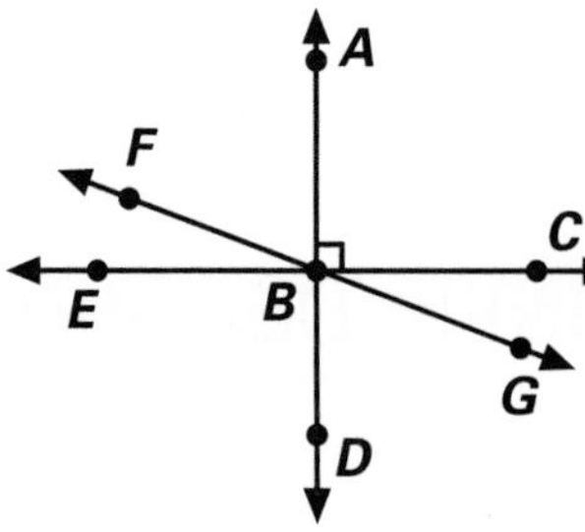

   a. If *any* three lines intersect at B, what is true about each pair of these lines?

   b. What is m∠DBC?

   c. Suppose m∠FBE = 27°. Find m∠FBA and m∠FBD. Find m∠EBG.

   d. Suppose m∠FBA = 51°. Find m∠ABG and m∠FBE.

   e. How would your answers to Part c change if m∠FBE = p, 0° < p < 90°?

Checkpoint

In the diagram at the right, suppose the lines intersect so that m∠DBA = m∠CBD.

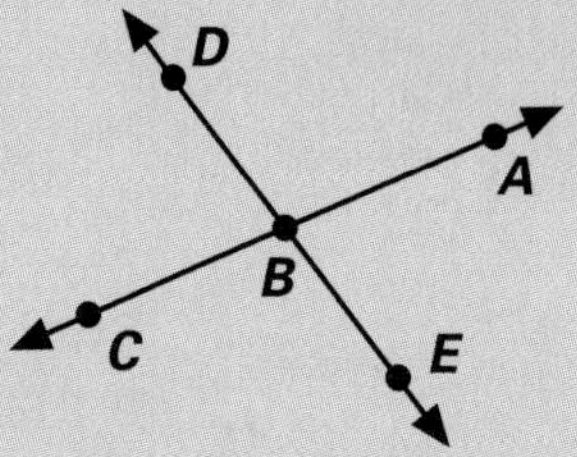

ⓐ What can you conclude about these two angles? Prepare an argument to prove your conjecture.

ⓑ What can you conclude about the other angles in the diagram? Prepare a proof of your conclusion.

ⓒ What mathematical facts did you use to help prove your statements in Parts a and b? Were these facts assumed statements or theorems?

ⓓ Describe the relationship between $\overleftrightarrow{AC}$ and $\overleftrightarrow{DE}$.

Be prepared to share your conjectures and explain your proofs.

In geometry, some pairs of angles have special names. In Investigation 3, you worked with vertical angles, linear pairs, and supplementary angles. **Vertical angles** share only a vertex. (They are across from each other.) The angles in a **linear pair** share a vertex and one side (they are *adjacent* to each other), *and* their noncommon sides form a straight angle. **Supplementary angles** are two angles that have measures that add to 180°. They need not be a linear pair.

On Your Own

In the diagram at the right, segments AD and BE (denoted $\overline{AD}$ and $\overline{BE}$) intersect at point C and m$\angle ECD$ = m$\angle CDE$. Write a proof or give a counterexample for each of the following conjectures.

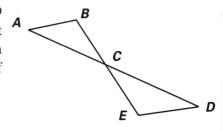

a. If the given conditions hold, then m$\angle ACB$ = m$\angle CDE$.

b. If the given conditions hold, then m$\angle CAB$ = m$\angle CDE$.

INVESTIGATION 4 Parallel Lines, Transversals, and Angles

When a line intersects another line, four angles are formed; some of the pairs have equal measures, and some pairs are supplementary angles. When a line intersects *two* lines, many more relationships are possible. Perhaps the most interesting case is when the two lines are parallel, as with the various pairs of support beams on the sides of the John Hancock Building in Chicago, shown at the right.

Lines in a plane that do not intersect are called **parallel lines**. In the diagram below, line m is parallel to line n (written $m \parallel n$). Line p, which intersects the two lines, is called a **transversal**. Find some examples of transversals in the photo of the John Hancock Building.

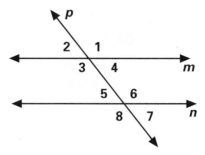

1. In the diagram above, the angles at each point of intersection are numbered so that they can be easily identified.

a. What pairs of angles, if any, appear to be equal in measure? List them.

b. What angle pairs appear to be supplementary angles? List them.

282   UNIT 4 · SHAPES AND GEOMETRIC REASONING

c. Draw another pair of parallel lines and a transversal. Number the angles as in the figure on the previous page. Do the same pairs of angles appear equal in measure? Supplementary?

Angles that are in the same relative position with respect to each parallel line and the transversal are called **corresponding angles**. In the diagram on the previous page, angles 1 and 6 are corresponding angles; similarly, angles 3 and 8 are corresponding.

2. Examine the diagram you drew for Part c of Activity 1.

   a. Name two pairs of corresponding angles, other than angles 1 and 6 or angles 3 and 8. Were the corresponding angles among the pairs of angles that you thought had equal measure? Were they supplementary angles?

   b. Suppose m∠1 = 123°. Find the measures of as many angles as you can.

3. Now consider the labeled diagram below. In this diagram, m ‖ n and p is the transversal intersecting m and n.

   a. Descriptive names are also given to pairs of angles other than the corresponding angles, when the angles are formed by a transversal and two parallel lines. For each name and angle pair given, describe how such angles can be identified in a diagram, and give one more example of such a pair.

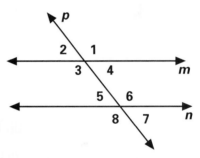

   - **Interior angles on the same side of the transversal:** ∠4 and ∠6
   - **Exterior angles on the same side of the transversal:** ∠2 and ∠8
   - **Alternate interior angles:** ∠3 and ∠6
   - **Alternate exterior angles:** ∠8 and ∠1

   b. Using your work in Activities 1 and 2, identify a relationship that seems to exist for each kind of angle pair named in Part a. Write your observations in if-then form, beginning as follows: If two parallel lines are intersected by a transversal, then … .

4. For this activity, *assume* the following as a known fact:

   If two parallel lines are cut by a transversal, then corresponding angles have equal measure.

   a. Using this assumption, construct arguments to prove that each of your conjectures in Part b of Activity 3 is correct. Share the workload among your group members.

   b. Discuss each argument within your group. Correct any errors in reasoning. Make sure each member can prove each statement.

Checkpoint

In the diagram at the right below, *p* and *m* are parallel lines.

a Give the name for each pair of angles below.

- ∠2 and ∠8
- ∠4 and ∠5
- ∠1 and ∠3
- ∠3 and ∠5
- ∠6 and ∠2

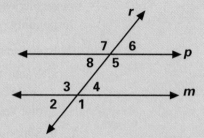

b Using the relation in Activity 4 about corresponding angles, explain how the measures of each pair of angles in Part a are related.

Be prepared to share and compare your group's list of angle names and relations with those of other groups.

▶On Your Own

In the diagram below, $\overleftrightarrow{AD}$ and $\overleftrightarrow{EH}$ are parallel. Name the second angle in the pair identified, and use the relation about corresponding angles in Activity 4 to show how the measures of the angles in the pair are related.

a. ∠*ABC*, corresponding angles

b. ∠*ABC*, alternate exterior angles

c. ∠*ABC*, exterior angles on the same side of the transversal

d. ∠*DBF*, alternate interior angles

e. ∠*DBF*, interior angles on the same side of the transversal

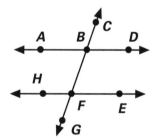

Now refer back to the assumption in Activity 4. With that assumption, you can conclude that if two parallel lines are cut by a transversal, then certain relations among the angles will always be true. The following related question is also important:

What relations among the angles formed when two lines are cut by a third line allow you to conclude that the lines are parallel?

5. Conduct the following experiment:

   a. Draw a line *XY* on your paper. Choose two different points on the line and label them *A* and *B* as shown here. Draw a line *BC* through *B* so that m∠*YBC* = 38°. Draw a line *AD* through *A* so that m∠*YAD* = 38° and *D* and *C* are on the same side of $\overleftrightarrow{XY}$. Examine $\overleftrightarrow{BC}$ and $\overleftrightarrow{AD}$. What appears to be true about these two lines?

   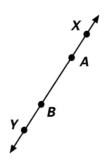

   b. Repeat the experiment in Part a, but this time use m∠*YBC* = m∠*YAD* = 111°. What do you observe about $\overleftrightarrow{BC}$ and $\overleftrightarrow{AD}$ this time?

   c. Write a conjecture in if-then form that generalizes the observations you made in the experiments.

In order to reason deductively about parallel lines and figures formed by parallel lines, you need to begin with some information about when two lines are parallel. The conjecture you made in Activity 5 should be basically the same as the statement below:

   If two lines are cut by a transversal so that corresponding angles have equal measure, then the lines are parallel.

   This is the **converse** of the assumption made in Activity 4. There you assumed that if two parallel lines are cut by a transversal, then corresponding angles have equal measure. The converse is formed by interchanging the hypothesis with the conclusion. The converse of a true if-then statement is not necessarily true. In symbols, the converse of "If *p*, then *q*" is "If *q*, then *p*." The truth of "If *p*, then *q*" does not assure the truth of "If *q*, then *p*."

   For the remainder of this unit, you can assume that both the statement in Activity 4 and its converse are true. These statements are combined in the *Parallel Lines Property*.

> **Parallel Lines Property**
>
> In a plane, two lines cut by a transversal are parallel if and only if corresponding angles have the same measure.

6. It is reasonable to ask if there are other relations between two angles formed by a line intersecting two other lines that would allow you to conclude that the two lines are parallel.

   a. Consider the relations between the pairs of angles named in Part a of Activity 3 (page 283). If the angles in the pair have equal measure (or are supplementary), does that ensure that the lines are parallel? Working as a group, make a list of those relations that appear to guarantee that the lines are parallel.

   b. Write each of your conjectures in Part a in if-then form.

c. Each group member should choose a different if-then statement and then try to prove it.

d. Share and discuss the reasoning in your proof with the rest of your group. Correct any reasoning errors found.

e. As a group, choose one of your statements and its proof to share and discuss with the entire class.

Checkpoint

The Parallel Lines Property implies more than the relation between parallel lines and corresponding angles.

a What other conditions on angles will be true when two parallel lines are cut by a transversal?

b What other conditions on angles formed by two lines and a transversal will ensure that the lines are parallel?

Be prepared to share and compare your group's list of conditions with those of other groups.

On Your Own

Using the angles and lines identified in the diagram below, decide whether each of the following conditions ensures that $q \parallel r$. Explain your reasoning in each case.

a. $m\angle 2 = m\angle 7$

b. $m\angle 8 = m\angle 4$

c. $m\angle 4 + m\angle 5 = 180°$

d. $m\angle 1 = m\angle 3$

e. $m\angle 3 = m\angle 5$

f. $m\angle 3 + m\angle 4 = 180°$

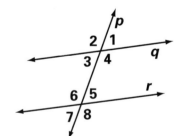

7. In the diagram shown at the right, *GUSH* is a quadrilateral with diagonal *GS*; $m\angle 1 + m\angle 2 = 90°$; $m\angle 2 + m\angle 3 = 90°$. Is it correct to conclude that $\overleftrightarrow{GU}$ and $\overleftrightarrow{SH}$ are parallel? If so, prove it. If not, give a counterexample.

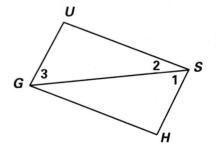

8. In previous courses, you have used the fact that the sum of the measures of the angles of a triangle is 180°.

a. Test the plausibility of this fact by conducting the following experiment. Have each group member cut out a paper model of a different-shaped triangle. Label the angles with 1, 2, and 3. Tear off the angles and place them next to each other at a point. What kind of angle appears to have been formed?

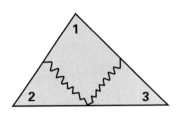

b. The diagram at the right shows △*ABC* and line *k* drawn parallel to line *AC* through point *B*.

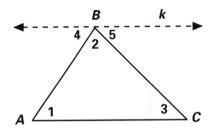

- If you draw a line *l* through point *B* and parallel to $\overleftrightarrow{AC}$, how must it be related to line *k*?

- Write a deductive argument to show that m∠1 + m∠2 + m∠3 = 180°.

Checkpoint

In this investigation, you reasoned both inductively and deductively about angles formed by parallel lines and a transversal.

ⓐ What statements did you accept to be true without proof?

ⓑ What theorems and their converses were you able to prove about parallel lines and the angles they form with a transversal?

ⓒ What is the main idea behind your proof of the theorem that the sum of the measures of the angles of a triangle is 180°?

Be prepared to share and compare your responses with those of others.

▶ **On Your Own**

In the diagram at the right, $\overleftrightarrow{AD}$ and $\overleftrightarrow{HE}$ are cut by transversal $\overleftrightarrow{GC}$. Angles 1 and 2 are supplementary. Can you conclude $\overleftrightarrow{AD} \parallel \overleftrightarrow{HE}$? If so, prove it; if not, find a counterexample.

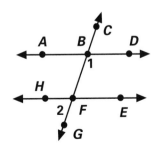

MORE

Modeling • Organizing • Reflecting • Extending

Modeling

1. The photo at the right shows a carpenter's bevel, which is used to draw parallel lines.

   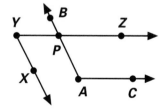

   a. Where is the transversal?

   b. How are angles 1 and 3 related? How do you know?

   c. Is $\overleftrightarrow{AB} \parallel \overleftrightarrow{CD}$? How do you know?

   d. How are angles 2 and 3 related? How do you know?

2. Draw an angle *BAC*, like the one at the right, on your paper. Now draw another angle *XYZ* so that the sides *BA* and *XY* are parallel and the sides *CA* and *ZY* are parallel.

   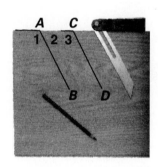

   a. Draw several different angles for *XYZ*, some with the sides pointing in the same directions as those of ∠*BAC* and some with the sides pointing in the opposite directions. What relation, if any, exists between ∠*BAC* and ∠*XYZ*?

   b. In the diagram at the right, the sides of the two angles point in the same directions. How are ∠*XYZ* and ∠*BAC* related? Write a proof of your claim.

   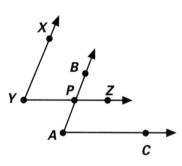

   c. In this diagram, side *YX* points in the direction opposite to side *AB*, while the other sides point in the same direction. How are ∠*XYZ* and ∠*BAC* related? Prove your claim.

   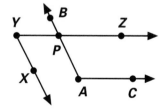

   d. Write one if-then statement summarizing the results in Parts a through c. It could begin like this:

   If the sides of two angles are parallel in pairs, then ... .

3. A plumb line (weight hanging by a string) is attached to a wall near the ceiling, as shown at the right.

   a. What angle does the string make with the wall baseboard?

   b. How could the plumb line be used to straighten a picture in a rectangular frame? What mathematics justifies your response?

   c. How could the plumb line be used to place shelving on the wall so the shelves were parallel to the floor? Explain.

4. The sparkle of a diamond results from light being reflected from facet to facet of the jewel and then directly to the eye of the observer. When a light ray strikes a smooth surface, such as a facet of a jewel, the angle at which the ray strikes the surface is congruent to the angle at which the ray leaves the surface. A diamond can be cut in such a way that a light ray entering the top will be parallel to the same ray as it exits the top.

   Examine the cross sections of the two diamonds shown below. The diamond at the left has been cut too deeply. The entering and exiting light rays are not parallel. The diamond on the right appears to be cut correctly.

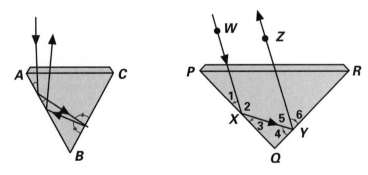

   a. Use deductive reasoning to determine the measure of $\angle Q$ at the base of the diamond to ensure that the entering and exiting light rays will be parallel.

   b. Explain how you could use inductive reasoning to conjecture what the measure of $\angle Q$ should be to ensure that the entering and exiting light rays will be parallel.

   c. What are the advantages of deductive reasoning in this case?

   d. As you have seen before, when modeling a situation, it often helps to make simplifying assumptions. Consult with a science teacher about reflection and refraction of light and the modeling of the diamond cut. What simplifying assumptions were made in this situation?

Organizing

1. In Activity 8 of Investigation 4, page 287, you proved that the sum of the measures of the angles of a triangle is 180°. Decide whether each of the following statements is correct. If correct, prove the statement. Otherwise, give a counterexample. (Note that an **acute angle** is an angle whose measure is less than 90°.)

   a. If the measures of two angles of one triangle are equal to the measures of two angles of another triangle, then the measures of the third angles are equal.

   b. The sum of the measures of the acute angles of a right triangle is 90°.

   c. If two angles of a triangle are acute, then the third angle is not acute.

   d. If a triangle is equiangular (all angles have the same measure), then each angle has measure 60°.

2. In the diagram at the right, lines *l* and *m* are parallel, and lines *m* and *n* are parallel. Line *p* intersects each of these lines.

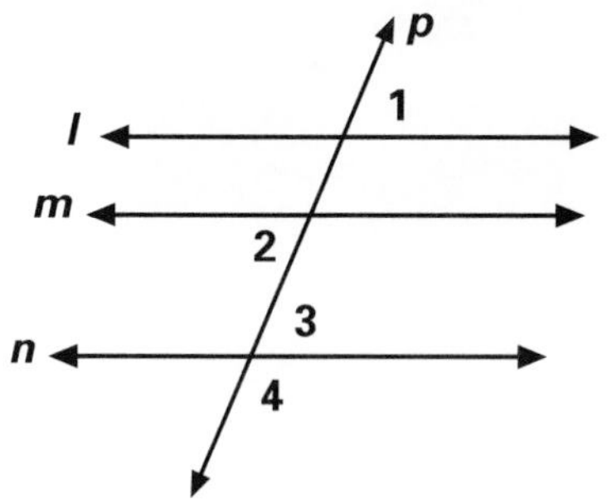

   a. Are angles 1 and 2 equal in measure or supplementary? Explain.

   b. How are the measures of angles 1 and 4 related? Explain your reasoning.

   c. Using your deductions in Parts a and b, prove that lines *l* and *n* are parallel.

   d. Write an if-then statement that summarizes what you have proved.

3. In the diagram below, lines *l*, *m*, and *n* are parallel and contain the points shown.

   a. Write an equation for each line.

   b. On a copy of this diagram, draw lines perpendicular to each line through its *y*-intercept.

   c. How are the lines you drew in Part b related to each other?

   d. Prove your conclusion in Part c using ideas from Investigation 4.

   e. Prove your conclusion in Part c using the equations of the lines and algebraic reasoning.

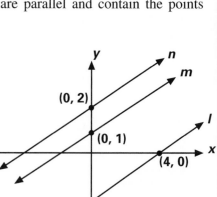

4. Refer to the diagrams below.

    a. Lines *l* and *m* are parallel. m∠1 = 26 + 5*x* and m∠2 = 34 + *x*. Find the values of *x*, m∠1, and m∠2.

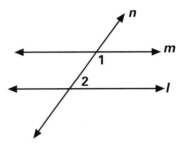

    b. Triangle *ABC* is a right triangle. m∠A = 5*x* + 3 and m∠B = 2*x* + 3. Find the value of *x*, m∠A, and m∠B.

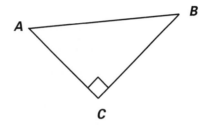

5. The figure *CATS* is a trapezoid with $\overline{AT} \parallel \overline{CS}$.

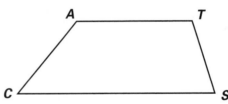

    a. What can you conclude about ∠C and ∠A? About ∠T and ∠S?

    b. Write an if-then statement summarizing one of your observations in Part a and prove it is correct.

    c. Suppose m∠C = m∠S. What can you conclude about ∠A and ∠T? Write a proof.

6. A recurring topic in your study of mathematics has been fitting models to data patterns. If a scatterplot reveals a linear pattern, you have produced linear models in two ways: estimating the model by eye and finding the least squares regression line. As you saw in Course 2, the calculations to determine the slope and *y*-intercept of the least squares regression line involve every point. If the data set has outliers, this line may be influenced a great deal. In contrast, the **median-median line** is highly resistant to the effects of outliers. The *median-fit* procedure outlined on the next page uses ideas from both statistics and geometry.

a. Examine the following data from a study of the amount of exposure in nine Oregon counties to radioactive waste from a nuclear reactor in Hanford, Washington, and the rate of deaths due to cancer in these counties.

Radioactive Waste Exposure

County	Index of Exposure	Cancer Deaths (per 100,000 residents)
Sherman	1.3	114
Wasco	1.6	138
Umatilla	2.5	147
Morrow	2.6	130
Gilliam	3.4	130
Hood River	3.8	162
Columbia	6.4	178
Clatsop	8.3	210
Portland	11.6	208

Source: *Journal of Environmental Health*, National Environmental Health Association, May–June 1965.

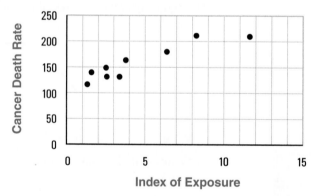

On a copy of this scatterplot, find the median-median line as follows:

- Draw two vertical lines to divide the scatterplot into three sets of equal size, if possible. (If this is not possible, the outer sets should contain the same number of points.)

- Next, find the median point for each set; that is, find the point whose x-coordinate is the median of the x values of all points in that set and whose y-coordinate is the median of the y values. Plot these points and mark each. You will locate three points, one for each set.

- Place a clear ruler on the median points of the two outer sets. This determines the general direction of the linear model. To account for the median point of the middle set, move the ruler one-third the distance to that point. Be sure to keep the ruler parallel to its original position. Draw the line. This is the median-median line.

b. What property of parallel lines is used in drawing the median-median line? Is only one such median-median line possible?

c. Calculate the median-median (med-med) line using your calculator, if it has such an option. Is it nearly the same as the line you drew? If not, why do you think it is different?

d. How do you think the least squares regression line for these data will be related to the median-median line? Check your conjecture.

e. Examine the data in the table below.

x	1	2	3	4	5	6	7	8	9
y	1	2	3	4	5	30	7	8	9

- Predict the equation of the median-median line.
- Predict how the least squares line will be influenced by the point (6, 30).
- Check your predictions.

Reflecting

1. In this lesson, you were introduced to proving mathematical statements in geometric settings. What did you find to be most difficult about constructing a proof? What is it that makes this so difficult? How are you trying to overcome the difficulty?

2. Parallel lines were defined to be lines in a plane that do not intersect. Is it possible for two lines in three-dimensional space neither to be parallel nor to intersect? Illustrate your reasoning.

3. In Investigation 4, you saw that if you *assume* the Parallel Lines Property, then it is possible to prove other conditions on angles that result when parallel lines are cut by a transversal. It is also possible to prove other conditions on angles that ensure two lines are parallel.

a. Rewrite the Parallel Lines Property as two if-then statements.

b. Replace each occurrence of the phrase "corresponding angles" with "alternate interior angles" in your statements in Part a.

c. Suppose next year's math class *assumes* your statements in Part b as its Parallel Lines Property.

- Could the class then *prove* the statements in Part a? Explain your reasoning.
- Could the class prove the relationships between parallelism of lines and angles on the same side of the transversal? Explain.

d. What, if anything, can you conclude about geometric reasoning from your work in Parts a through c?

4. In the book *Through the Looking Glass, and What Alice Found There,* Humpty-Dumpty asserts, "When I use a word, it means just what I choose it to mean—neither more nor less." However, as you know in everyday life, words often have several different meanings. To reason logically, the meanings of key words must be strictly defined as they will be used in the arguments. Formulating descriptions or definitions of terms is an important part of doing mathematical research.

  a. In the diagram below, point *B* is *between* points *A* and *C*. Devise a way to describe what this means. Could numbers help you in some way?

  b. In the diagram below, ray *PB* (denoted $\overrightarrow{PB}$) is between rays *PA* and *PC*. Devise a way to describe what this means. Could you use numbers in some way?

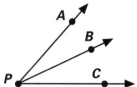

5. In the diagram below, lines *m* and *n* intersect at point *A* in such a way that m∠1 = *x*°. Analyze the argument following the diagram.

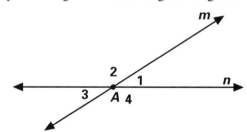

  Since m∠1 = *x*° and m∠1 + m∠2 = 180°, m∠2 = 180° − *x*°.

  Since m∠2 = 180° − *x*° and m∠3 + m∠2 = 180°, m∠3 = 180° − (180° − *x*°).

  Since m∠3 = 180° − (180° − *x*°), then m∠3 = *x*°.

  a. Is this a valid proof? On what mathematical relationships is it based?

  b. Should this proof be classified as geometric reasoning, algebraic reasoning, or something else? Explain your rationale.

  c. State the theorem proved here.

Extending

1. An **exterior angle** of a triangle is formed when one side is extended. The sides of the angle are the extension and a side of the triangle.

   a. Draw △ABC on your paper. Extend sides BC and AC to show the two exterior angles at vertex C. How are these angles related?

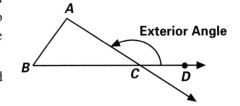

   b. How is exterior angle ACD related to ∠ACB?

   c. How is exterior angle ACD related to ∠B and ∠A?

   d. Now consider the diagram at the right showing exterior angles 1, 2, and 3 of △ABC. What is the sum of their measures?

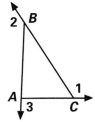

   e. State and prove a conjecture about the sum of the measures of the exterior angles of any triangle, one exterior angle at each vertex.

2. Exterior angles of any polygon can be formed as was done for the triangles in Extending Task 1.

   a. Draw a pentagon. Without using a protractor, do the following:

   ■ Find the sum of the measures of its angles.

   ■ Find the sum of the measures of its exterior angles, one angle at each vertex.

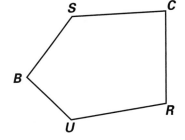

   b. In your previous coursework, you may have discovered that the sum of the measures of the interior angles of a convex *n*-gon is $(n - 2)180°$. Explain why this formula makes sense.

   c. Experiment or use deductive reasoning to find a formula for the sum of the measures of the exterior angles of a convex *n*-gon, one angle at each vertex.

3. Draw a line *l* and locate two points on it. At each point, draw a line perpendicular to line *l*.

   a. Make a conjecture about the relation between the two lines perpendicular to line *l*. Write it in if-then form.

   b. Prove your conjecture or produce a counterexample.

4. Use a compass or computer drawing software to draw a circle with center C and radius 2 inches. Choose a length, n, between 0.5 and 3.5 inches.

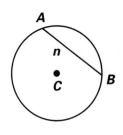

   a. Draw four different chords of length n in your circle. (A **chord** is a segment with its endpoints on a circle. See chord AB at the right.)

   b. Carefully, draw and measure the angle formed by joining the endpoints of your chords to the center C. (Such angles are called **central angles** because the vertex is the center of the circle.)

   c. What do you observe about the angle measures found in Part b? Do you think this will be true for each central angle formed by a chord of length n?

   d. What happens to the central angle as the length n increases? As the length n decreases?

5. Use a compass or computer drawing software to draw a circle with center C. Then draw a chord AB in the circle.

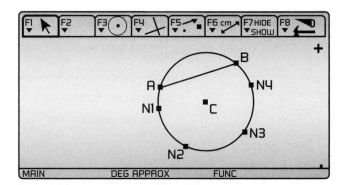

   a. Choose four points, N_i ($i = 1, 2, 3, 4$) on the circle and on the same side of the line containing chord AB. Carefully draw and measure the angles, $\angle AN_iB$. (These angles are called *inscribed angles*.)

   b. What do you observe about the measures of these angles?

   c. Is there any relationship between the measure of an inscribed angle, $\angle AN_iB$, and the central angle, $\angle ACB$? If so, describe it.

   d. Suppose the four points, N_i, were all on the other side of the line containing chord AB. How are the angles, $\angle AN_iB$, related to each other? To the angles you drew in Part a?

Lesson 2

Reasoning about Similar and Congruent Triangles

A triangle is the only rigid polygon. Since it is rigid, it is fundamental to the design of many structures, both large and small. Some bridges and large construction cranes, as well as the supports for roofs, use triangles to maintain rigidity. When a roof sags, it is often the result of a breakdown in the material of the supporting triangles.

Architects and draftspeople often need to make scale drawings of triangles and shapes based on triangles that are *similar* to the real things that they are designing. Manufacturers of the components of shapes based on triangles need to know the measurements that must be made to ensure that triangular components are *congruent*. Even so, there will be small variations in the parts, and these variations must be monitored by quality control procedures.

Think About This Situation

A draftsperson and a manufacturer examine the same triangular structure.

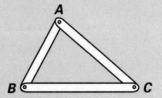

ⓐ Suppose the draftsperson wants to make a scale drawing for later use in designing a similar structure. What is the minimum amount of information about the triangle needed to make such a drawing?

ⓑ Suppose the manufacturer wants to construct a congruent copy of the structure. What is the minimum amount of information about the triangle needed to replicate it?

INVESTIGATION 1 ▶ When Are Two Triangles Similar?

If two plane shapes are **similar**, such as the two pentagons shown below, then corresponding angles have the same measure and the lengths of corresponding sides are constant multiples of each other. The constant multiplier is called the *scale factor*.

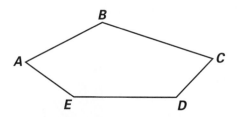

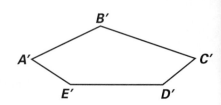

In the diagram above, $ABCDE \sim A'B'C'D'E'$. The symbol $\sim$ means "is similar to." It follows that $m\angle A = m\angle A'$, $m\angle B = m\angle B'$, and so on. If the scale factor is k, you can also conclude that $B'C' = k \cdot BC$, $A'E' = k \cdot AE$, $DC = \frac{1}{k} \cdot D'C'$, and so on.

1. Suppose $\triangle ABC \sim \triangle PQR$ and the scale factor relating $\triangle ABC$ to $\triangle PQR$ is 5. In your group, write as many mathematical statements as you can about pairs of corresponding angles and about pairs of corresponding sides.

Knowing that two triangles are similar allows you to conclude that the three pairs of corresponding angles are congruent and the three pairs of corresponding sides are related by the same scale factor. Conversely, if you know that the three pairs of corresponding angles are congruent and the three pairs of corresponding sides are related by the same scale factor, you can conclude that the triangles are similar. In this investigation, you will explore whether fewer than all six conditions will ensure that two triangles are similar. In conducting this investigation, you will use the Law of Sines and the Law of Cosines. The Law of Sines was derived in Unit 1, "Multiple-Variable Models." The Law of Cosines was proved in Unit 3, "Symbol Sense and Algebraic Reasoning." These two laws are reproduced below.

Law of Sines

In any triangle ABC, if a, b, and c are the lengths of the sides opposite $\angle A$, $\angle B$, and $\angle C$ respectively, then:

$$\frac{a}{\sin A} = \frac{b}{\sin B} = \frac{c}{\sin C}$$

Law of Cosines

In any triangle ABC, if a, b, and c are the lengths of the sides opposite $\angle A$, $\angle B$, and $\angle C$ respectively, then:

$$a^2 = b^2 + c^2 - 2bc \cos A$$
$$b^2 = a^2 + c^2 - 2ac \cos B$$
$$c^2 = a^2 + b^2 - 2ab \cos C$$

2. Begin by reexamining the Law of Cosines to see what it tells you about the characteristics of a particular triangle *ABC*.

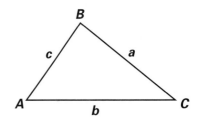

a. The first form of the Law of Cosines says $a^2 = b^2 + c^2 - 2bc \cos A$. How many variables are in this equation? What are they? What do they represent?

b. If you know only that *b* is 5, can you determine the value of *a*? Explain.

■ Can you determine m∠*A*? Explain.

■ Can *c* be determined? Why or why not?

c. If you know the values of *a* and *c*, can you determine either *b* or m∠*A*? Both *b* and m∠*A*? Explain your reasoning.

d. If you know the values of *a*, *b*, and m∠*A*, can you determine the value of *c*? Explain. If you know values for *a*, *b*, and *c*, can you find m∠*A*? Why or why not?

e. Suppose you know *b*, *c*, and m∠*A*. Write an equation (*a* = ...) that expresses the relation between *a* and these variables.

f. What equation can you solve to find cos *B*? To find cos *C*?

3. Suppose in △*ABC*, m∠*A*, *b*, and *c* are given as follows: m∠*A* = 43°, *b* = 15 cm, and *c* = 11 cm.

a. In finding values for *a*, m∠*B*, and m∠*C*, which measure would you find first? Why? Find the value of that measure.

b. Which measure would you find second? Why? Determine the remaining two values.

c. Is it possible to find more than one value for *a*, m∠*B*, or m∠*C*? Explain your reasoning.

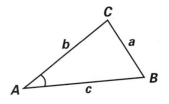

d. In general, if you know m∠*A*, *b*, and *c*, can values for *a*, m∠*B*, and m∠*C* be found? Could any of *a*, m∠*B*, or m∠*C* have two or more values when m∠*A*, *b*, and *c* are given? Explain.

e. Summarize your work in Parts a through d in an if-then statement that begins as follows:

In a triangle, if the lengths of two sides and the measure of the angle included between those sides are known, then ... .

4. Examine △*ABC* and △*XYZ* shown below. In both cases, you have information given about two sides and an included angle. (In △*XYZ*, *k* is a constant.)

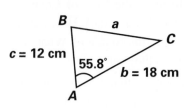

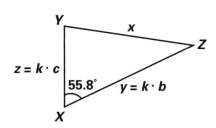

a. In △*ABC*, m∠*A* = 55.8°, *b* = 18 cm, and *c* = 12 cm. Are *a*, m∠*B*, and m∠*C* *uniquely determined*? That is, is there exactly one value possible for each? Find *a*.

b. In △*XYZ*, m∠*X* = m∠*A* = 55.8°, *z* = *k* · *c* = 12*k* cm, and *y* = *k* · *b* = 18*k* cm, where *k* is a constant. Explain why *x*, m∠*Y*, and m∠*Z* are uniquely determined.

c. Use the Law of Cosines to find *x*. Are *x* and *a* related in the same way as *y* and *b* or as *z* and *c*? Explain your reasoning.

d. Find m∠*B* and m∠*Y*. How are they related?

e. Find m∠*C* and m∠*Z*. How are they related?

f. Considering all the information in Parts a through e, what can you conclude about △*ABC* and △*XYZ*?

g. Suppose you know that in △*ABC* and △*XYZ*, m∠*C* = m∠*Z*, *x* = *ka*, and *y* = *kb*. Could you prove that △*ABC* ~ △*XYZ*? If so, explain how. If not, explain why not.

h. Summarize your work in Parts a through g by completing the following statement:

If an angle of one triangle has the same measure as an angle of a second triangle, and if the lengths of the corresponding sides including these angles are related by a scale factor k, then … .

Compare your statement to those of other groups. Resolve any differences.

Your conclusion in Part h of Activity 4 gives at least a partial answer to the question of finding minimal conditions that will ensure two triangles are similar. In the next several activities, you will explore other sets of minimal conditions.

5. Refer to △*ABC* shown at the right.

a. Suppose *a* = 10 cm, *b* = 18 cm, and *c* = 12 cm. Is it possible to calculate the measures of angles *A*, *B*, and *C*? If so, do so. If not, explain why not.

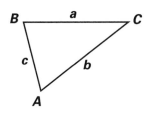

b. In general, suppose for any △*ABC* you know *a*, *b*, and *c*. Can the measures of the three angles be determined? If so, can you find more than one possible measure for each of the angles? Explain your reasoning.

6. Suppose now you know that in △*ABC* and △*XYZ*, *x* = *ka*, *y* = *kb*, and *z* = *kc*.

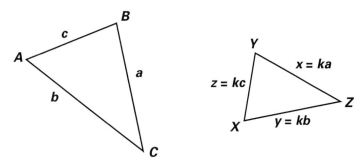

To prove △*ABC* ~ △*XYZ*, you need to deduce that corresponding angles have the same measure. Sharing the workload among your group, write deductive arguments for each of the following equalities.

a. m∠*A* = m∠*X*

b. m∠*B* = m∠*Y*

c. m∠*C* = m∠*Z*

7. The generalization you stated and proved in Activity 4 is called the **Side-Angle-Side Similarity Theorem**, or just SAS Similarity Theorem, for short.

a. How can you use the name of the theorem to help you remember your generalization?

b. The results of your work in Activity 6 establish a **Side-Side-Side Similarity Theorem**. Write this SSS Similarity Theorem in if-then form.

So far, you have used only the Law of Cosines to deduce conditions that ensure pairs of triangles are similar. In the next two activities, you will use the Law of Sines to explore other conditions that might ensure similarity of two triangles.

8. Begin by reexamining the first part of the Law of Sines for △*ABC*: $\frac{a}{\sin A} = \frac{b}{\sin B}$.

a. How many variables are there in this equation? What does each represent?

b. Solve the equation above for *a*. For *b*. For $\sin A$. For $\sin B$.

c. If *b* = 5, m∠*A* = 40°, and m∠*B* = 58°, what other measures can you deduce? Find the measures.

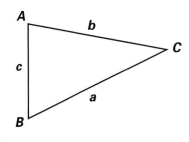

d. What information do you need to know in order to determine *a*? To determine *b*? To determine $\sin A$? To determine m∠*B*?

e. If you know m∠*A*, m∠*B*, and *a*, can you determine m∠*C*, *b*, and *c*? Explain how. Are their values unique? Why or why not?

f. Summarize your work in Parts a through e by completing the following statement:

> *In a triangle, if the measures of two angles and the length of a side opposite one of them are known, then ... .*

9. In Activities 4 and 6, you needed to know three corresponding measures of the pair of triangles involved to determine that the triangles were similar. In this activity, you will examine a situation in which only two corresponding measures of two triangles are known.

a. Suppose you are given $\triangle ABC$ and $\triangle XYZ$ in which $m\angle X = m\angle A$ and $m\angle Y = m\angle B$. Do you think these triangles are similar? Why or why not?

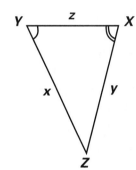 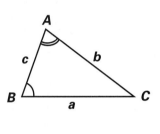

b. Examine the proposed proof by one group of students, shown below and on the next page. Discuss each part of their argument within your group; then answer the questions following the proof.

Proof:
We first looked at the ratio of the lengths of a pair of corresponding sides.
Let $k = \frac{x}{a}$. Then $x = ka$.

For $\triangle ABC$, we know that $\frac{a}{\sin A} = \frac{b}{\sin B}$.
So, $b = \frac{a \sin B}{\sin A}$.

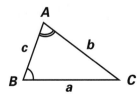

Similarly for $\triangle XYZ$, $\frac{x}{\sin X} = \frac{y}{\sin Y}$. So, $y = \frac{x \sin Y}{\sin X}$.

It follows that $y = \frac{ka \sin Y}{\sin X}$.

Since $m\angle Y = m\angle B$ and $m\angle X = m\angle A$, $y = ka \frac{\sin B}{\sin A}$.

Since $b = \frac{a \sin B}{\sin A}$, it follows that $y = kb$.

Since $m\angle X = m\angle A$ and $m\angle Y = m\angle B$, then $m\angle Z = m\angle C$.

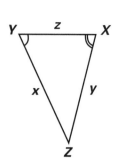

We've shown $x = ka$, $y = kb$, and $m\angle Z = m\angle C$, so $\triangle ABC \sim \triangle XYZ$ by the SAS Similarity Theorem.

- Are there any errors? If so, can you correct them?

- Why can the students conclude that $y = \frac{ka \sin Y}{\sin X}$?

- Why can they conclude that $y = \frac{ka \sin B}{\sin A}$?

- Why can they conclude that $m\angle Z = m\angle C$?

- Does their argument convince you that the triangles are similar?

- Why can the SAS Similarity Theorem be used in the last step of the argument?

- Could the group of students have reasoned differently at the end? How?

c. Write an if-then statement of the theorem proved in this activity. What name would you give the theorem?

Checkpoint

In this investigation, you explored conditions for similarity of two triangles.

a Based on your work in this investigation, identify three sets of conditions on the sides and angles of a pair of triangles that ensure that the two triangles are similar.

b For each set of conditions, identify the key assumptions and theorems used in deducing the result.

c Explain how you can determine the scale factor for two triangles known to be similar.

Be prepared to share your conclusions and analyses of methods of proof with the entire class.

The three triangle similarity conditions—SAS, SSS, and AA—developed and used in this investigation are the only minimal conditions that, when satisfied, allow you to conclude that a pair of triangles are similar.

On Your Own

For each Part a through e, suppose a pair of triangular braces have the given characteristics. For the parts in which △*ABC* ~ △*PQR*, explain how you know that the triangles are similar and give the scale factor. For cases in which △*ABC* is not similar to △*PQR*, give a reason for your conclusion.

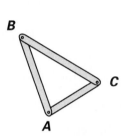
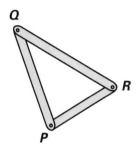

a. m∠*A* = 57°, m∠*B* = 38°, m∠*P* = 57°, m∠*R* = 95°

b. *AB* = 8, *BC* = 12, m∠*B* = 35°, *PQ* = 20, *QR* = 30, m∠*Q* = 35°

c. *AB* = *BC*, m∠*B* = m∠*Q*, *PQ* = *QR*

d. *AC* = 4, *BC* = 16, *BA* = 18, *PR* = 10, *QR* = 40, *PQ* = 48

e. *AB* = 12, m∠*A* = 63°, m∠*C* = 83°, m∠*P* = 63°, m∠*Q* = 34°, *PQ* = 12

f. Create your own set of side lengths for △*ABC* and △*PQR* that satisfy SSS with a scale factor of 3.

INVESTIGATION 2 ▶ When Are Two Triangles Congruent?

Shown at the right is another view of the John Hancock Building in Chicago. In Investigation 4 of Lesson 1, page 282, you observed patterns and relationships involving parallel lines and transversals on the sides of the building. If you look closer, you will also note interesting patterns of *similar* and *congruent* triangles.

1. In your group, examine the patterns of triangles on the exterior of the Hancock Center.

a. Identify a pair of similar triangles in the photo and explain why you know they are similar.

b. Identify a pair of triangles that you think are congruent. Explain why you think they are congruent.

In the previous investigation, you determined three sets of conditions that could be used to ensure that two triangular structures are similar. Mass production of interchangeable parts is based on the congruence of the parts, within very small tolerances. You will begin your study of congruence by considering the minimal conditions that ensure two triangles are congruent.

2. When two triangles are **congruent**, corresponding angles have the same measure and corresponding sides have the same length. Angles with the same measure are called *congruent angles*. Segments with the same length are called *congruent segments*.

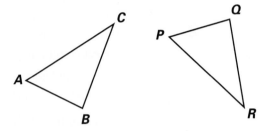

a. Suppose △ABC and △PQR shown above are congruent; this is denoted △ABC ≅ △PQR. The symbol ≅ means "is congruent to." The orders *A-B-C* and *P-Q-R* indicate a particular correspondence between the vertices: *A* corresponds to *P*, *B* corresponds to *Q*, and *C* corresponds to *R*. Write six statements of congruence relating the angles and sides of these triangles.

b. If m∠A = 73° and PQ = 7 cm, what other measures do you know?

c. Consider the following two if-then statements, which are converses of each other.

   If two triangles are congruent, then they are similar.

   If two triangles are similar, then they are congruent.

   Prove that one of these statements is correct and the other is not.

d. What additional information about scale factors could you add to the false statement so that it, too, would be correct?

The results of Parts c and d of Activity 2 suggest the following definition of **congruent triangles**:

Two triangles are congruent if and only if they are similar with a scale factor of 1.

This definition of congruence implies that congruence is just a special kind of similarity.

3. Now investigate how you might modify the conditions that ensure similarity so that they could also be used to ensure congruence of two triangles.

   a. What does the SSS Similarity Theorem say?

     ■ How can you modify the hypothesis of the theorem so that the conclusion involves congruence of triangles?

     ■ Write a statement of an SSS Congruence Theorem.

   b. What does the SAS Similarity Theorem say?

     ■ Explain how the theorem can be modified so that the triangles are congruent.

     ■ Write a statement of an SAS Congruence Theorem.

   c. The third similarity theorem is the AA Similarity Theorem. How does this theorem differ from the SSS and SAS Similarity Theorems?

     ■ What needs to be added to the AA Similarity Theorem to make it into a correct statement about conditions that ensure congruence of the triangles? There are two possible different additions, each of which gives a correct congruence theorem. Find them both.

     ■ Write complete statements of each of these new congruence theorems. Give them appropriate short names.

4. In Activity 8 of Investigation 1 (page 301), you used the Law of Sines to show that when the measures of two angles and the length of a side opposite one of them are known, the remaining angle measure and side lengths are uniquely determined. Investigate whether the measures of the angles of a triangle are uniquely determined when you know the lengths of two sides and the measure of an angle opposite one of them.

   a. First examine a special case.
     Let $m\angle A = 40°$ and $AB = 6$ cm. Draw $\angle A$ and segment AB as shown.

   b. Now find point(s) C on the ray AD so that $BC = 4.5$ cm. Draw segment(s) BC.

   c. What can you conclude about the triangle(s) drawn?

   d. Use the Law of Sines to find $\sin C$.

   e. Is there a unique $\angle C$ whose sine has the value calculated in Part d? Why does this occur when sines are calculated?

5. Do you think it is possible to derive a SSA Congruence Theorem or a SSA Similarity Theorem? Explain your reasoning.

6. Examine each of the following pairs of triangles and the markings showing congruence of corresponding angles and sides. In each case, decide whether the information given by the markings ensures that the triangles are congruent. If the triangles are congruent, cite an appropriate theorem to support your conclusion.

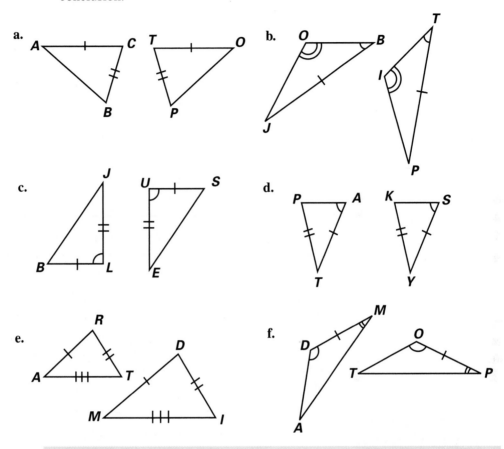

On Your Own

Following are possible sets of conditions on the angles and sides of △*DEF* and △*XYZ*. Decide whether the given conditions ensure congruence, similarity, or neither, and justify each decision by citing an appropriate theorem.

a. *DE* = *XY*, *EF* = 8 cm, *YZ* = 8 cm, ∠*E* ≅ ∠*Y*

b. ∠*D* ≅ ∠*X*, m∠*Z* = 40°, m∠*F* = 40°, *DE* = 10 cm, *XY* = 10 cm

c. m∠*D* = 73°, m∠*E* = 47°, m∠*X* = 47°, m∠*Z* = 60°, *EF* = *YZ*

d. ∠*D* ≅ ∠*X*, $\overline{DE}$ ≅ $\overline{XY}$, $\overline{EF}$ ≅ $\overline{YZ}$

e. *DE* = 10 cm = *XY*, $\overline{EF}$ ≅ $\overline{YZ}$, $\overline{DF}$ ≅ $\overline{XZ}$

f. m∠*D* = 83°, m∠*Z* = 83°, m∠*F* = 57°, m∠*Y* = 40°

g. $\overline{DE}$ ≅ $\overline{EF}$, $\overline{XY}$ ≅ $\overline{YZ}$, $\overline{DF}$ ≅ $\overline{XZ}$

You now know minimal sets of information about a triangle that would permit you to make a similar or congruent copy of it. Sometimes you may be working in a situation or provided with a shape that is comprised of triangles, as in Activities 7, 8, and 9 below. Typically, you know some information about the situation or the shape and need to determine whether you have enough information to conclude that the triangles involved are congruent or similar. In such situations, it usually helps to first mark corresponding parts of the triangles to show congruences, as illustrated in Activity 6. The same marking indicates the same size or a congruence.

7. The diagram at the right illustrates how a carpenter's square is often used to bisect an angle. The square is positioned as shown so that *PQ* = *RQ* and *PS* = *SR*.

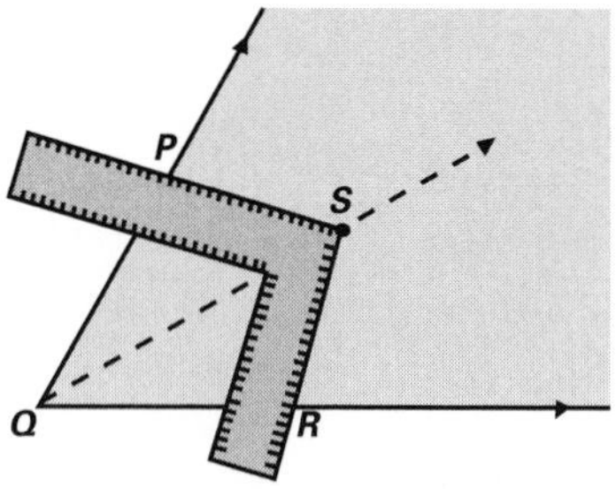

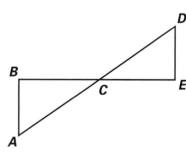

   a. Explain why this information is sufficient to conclude that △*PQS* ≅ △*RQS*.

   b. Why does $\overrightarrow{QS}$ bisect ∠*PQR*?

8. For each part below, draw and mark a copy of the diagram to aid you in your reasoning.

   a. Conditions: $\overline{BC}$ ≅ $\overline{CE}$ and $\overline{AC}$ ≅ $\overline{CD}$
   Prove: △*ABC* ≅ △*DEC*

   b. Conditions: ∠*B* ≅ ∠*E* and $\overline{BC}$ ≅ $\overline{CE}$
   Prove: △*ABC* ≅ △*DEC*

   c. Conditions: $\overleftrightarrow{BA}$ ∥ $\overleftrightarrow{DE}$ and *C* is the midpoint of $\overline{AD}$
   Prove: △*ABC* ≅ △*DEC*

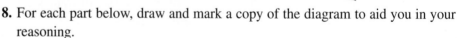

9. For each part below, draw and mark a diagram to aid you in preparing a proof.

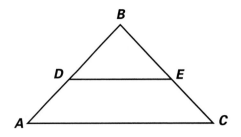

  a. Conditions: $AB = 2DB$ and $BC = 2EB$
    Prove: $\triangle DBE \sim \triangle ABC$

  b. Conditions: $\overleftrightarrow{DE} \parallel \overleftrightarrow{AC}$
    Prove: $\triangle ABC \sim \triangle DBE$

  c. Conditions: $\angle BED \cong \angle C$
    Prove: $\triangle ABC \sim \triangle DBE$

Checkpoint

Think about some of the strategies you use and the decisions you make when reasoning about the congruence or similarity of two triangles.

a What information do you need in order to conclude that two triangles are congruent?

b How are the conditions ensuring congruence of two triangles different from the conditions ensuring similarity?

c How does marking a diagram to show congruent parts help you decide congruence or similarity of triangles?

Be prepared to explain your ideas to the entire class.

The four triangle congruence conditions developed and used in this investigation — SAS, SSS, ASA, and AAS—are the only minimal conditions that, when satisfied, imply that a pair of triangles are congruent.

On Your Own

For each set of information given below, draw and mark a copy of the diagram. Then decide if $\triangle ABC \cong \triangle DEF$ or $\triangle ABC \sim \triangle DEF$. Explain your reasoning.

  a. $\angle B \cong \angle E$, $\angle A \cong \angle EDF$, and $\overline{AC} \cong \overline{FD}$

  b. $\overleftrightarrow{AB} \parallel \overleftrightarrow{DE}$ and $\overleftrightarrow{BC} \parallel \overleftrightarrow{EF}$

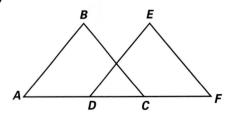

  c. $\overline{AD} \cong \overline{FC}$, $\overline{BC} \parallel \overline{EF}$, and $\angle B \cong \angle E$

  d. $\overline{BC} \cong \overline{ED}$, $\overline{AB} \cong \overline{FE}$, and $\angle A \cong \angle F$

  e. $\overline{AD} \cong \overline{FC}$, $\overline{BC} \cong \overline{EF}$, and $\overline{AB} \cong \overline{DE}$

MORE

Modeling

1. Examine each pair of triangles. Determine, using the information given, whether the triangles are congruent, the triangles are similar, or the information is inconclusive. Explain your reasoning.

a.

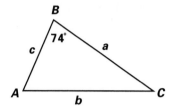

b.

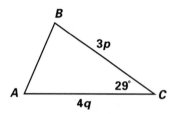

c.

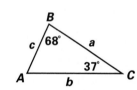 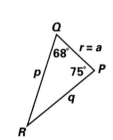

d.

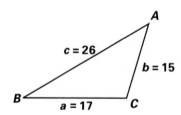 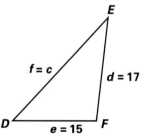

e.

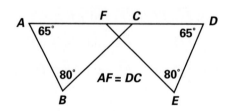

2. Prove, if it is possible, that $\triangle ABC \cong \triangle EDC$ or $\triangle ABC \sim \triangle EDC$ under each of the following conditions. If it is not possible, explain why not.

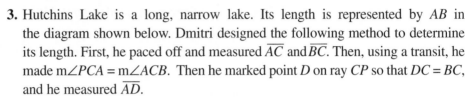

   a. C is the midpoint of $\overline{BD}$ and $m\angle B = m\angle D$.

   b. C is the midpoint of both $\overline{AE}$ and $\overline{BD}$.

   c. $\angle A \cong \angle E$ and $\angle B \cong \angle D$.

   d. $\overleftrightarrow{AB} \parallel \overleftrightarrow{DE}$ and $AB = 2 \cdot DE$.

3. Hutchins Lake is a long, narrow lake. Its length is represented by AB in the diagram shown below. Dmitri designed the following method to determine its length. First, he paced off and measured $\overline{AC}$ and $\overline{BC}$. Then, using a transit, he made $m\angle PCA = m\angle ACB$. Then he marked point D on ray CP so that $DC = BC$, and he measured $\overline{AD}$.

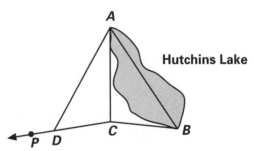

Hutchins Lake

   a. Prove, if you can, that $\triangle ABC \cong \triangle ADC$.

   b. Dmitri claimed $AB = AD$. Is he correct? Justify your answer.

   c. Andrea claimed she could find the length AB of the lake without sighting $\triangle ADC$. Suppose $AC = 5$ km, $BC = 2$ km, and $m\angle ACB = 100°$. What is the length of Hutchins Lake?

4. A flashlight is directed perpendicularly at a vertical wall 24 cm away. A cardboard triangle with sides of lengths 3, 4, and 5 cm is positioned directly between the light and the wall, parallel to the wall.

   a. Suppose the shadow of the 4-cm side is 10 cm. Find the lengths of the shadows of the other two sides.

   b. Suppose the shadow of the 5-cm side is 7.5 cm. Find the lengths of the other two sides of the shadow.

   c. How far from the light source should you place the cardboard triangle so that the 4-cm side has a 12-cm shadow?

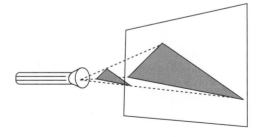

Organizing

1. Prove, if possible, that $\triangle TOS \cong \triangle TOP$ under each set of conditions below.

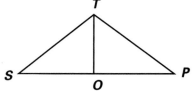

   a. $\overline{ST} \cong \overline{TP}$ and $\angle STO \cong \angle PTO$.

   b. $\overline{TO}$ is the perpendicular bisector of $\overline{SP}$.

   c. $\overline{TO} \perp \overline{SP}$ and $m\angle S = m\angle P$.

   d. $ST = TP$ and O is the midpoint of $\overline{SP}$.

2. Refer to the diagram of quadrilateral $ABCD$.

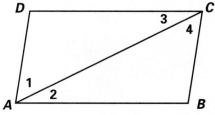

   a. Suppose that $m\angle 2 = m\angle 3$ and $m\angle B = m\angle D$. Can you conclude $AB = CD$? Write a justification.

   b. Suppose you know $AB = CD$ and $m\angle 2 = m\angle 3$. Can you conclude $\overleftrightarrow{AD} \parallel \overleftrightarrow{BC}$. Write a justification.

   c. Can you conclude $\overline{AD}$ is perpendicular to $\overline{DC}$ if you know $AD = CB$ and $m\angle 1 = m\angle 4$? Justify your position.

   d. Can you conclude $AB = CD$ if you know $m\angle 1 = m\angle 4$, $\overline{AD} \perp \overline{CD}$, and $\overline{AB} \perp \overline{BC}$? Justify your position.

3. Right triangles are special triangles in that one of the angles is known to measure $90°$. Investigate which of the following conditions ensure the congruence of a pair of *right* triangles. Write a proof of each condition that you believe is correct. Provide a counterexample for each incorrect statement.

   a. If the legs in one right triangle are congruent to the corresponding legs in another right triangle, then the triangles are congruent.

   b. If a leg and an acute angle in one right triangle are congruent to a corresponding leg and acute angle in another right triangle, then the triangles are congruent.

   c. If the hypotenuse and an acute angle in one right triangle are congruent to the corresponding hypotenuse and acute angle in another right triangle, then the triangles are congruent.

   d. If an acute angle in one right triangle is congruent to the corresponding acute angle in another right triangle, then the triangles are congruent.

4. The arguments or proofs you have been writing in this unit are sometimes called *synthetic proofs*. Your proofs involved reasoning from a combination of assumed or established statements which were independent of a coordinate system. In this task, you will write and compare two different proofs of the following theorem:

   If a line segment joins the midpoints of two sides of a triangle, then it is parallel to the third side.

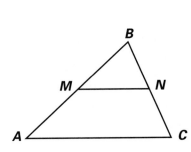
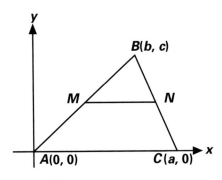

a. Make and mark a copy of the diagram on the left above. Write a synthetic proof that $\overleftrightarrow{MN} \parallel \overleftrightarrow{AC}$.

b. Use the labeled diagram on the right above to help you write a proof, using coordinates, that $\overleftrightarrow{MN} \parallel \overleftrightarrow{AC}$.

c. Compare your two proofs.

 ■ Which proof was easier for you to construct? Why?

 ■ Which proof would be easier for you to explain to someone else? Why?

d. Write another conclusion that you think follows from the hypothesis that $\overline{MN}$ joins the midpoints of two sides of a triangle. Write a proof of your conjecture. Did you use synthetic or coordinate methods?

Reflecting

1. Given two angles, there is a variety of conditions that would allow you to conclude without measuring that the angles are congruent. For example, if you know the angles are vertical angles, then you know they are congruent. What other conditions will allow you to conclude two angles are congruent? List as many as you can.

2. Think about the information conveyed by the abbreviations of the names of the various triangle similarity and congruence theorems.

   a. SAS is often thought of as "two sides and the included angle." In what sense is the angle included?

   b. ASA is often thought of as "two angles and the included side." In what sense is the side included?

3. Throughout this unit, you have been using several kinds of mathematical statements: definitions, conjectures, properties, and theorems. What are the differences among these kinds of statements?

4. Knowing that two pairs of corresponding angles in two triangles are congruent ensures that the triangles are similar, but it does *not* ensure that they are congruent. Why?

5. In your previous mathematics courses, you investigated representations, properties, and applications of three sets of geometric transformations: rigid transformations, size transformations, and similarity transformations.

a. Draw a Venn diagram (see page 274) illustrating the relationship between these three sets of transformations.

b. Explain how these transformations are related to the ideas of similarity and congruence.

Extending

1. The Law of Cosines can be derived using the distance formula, but you need to use trigonometric expressions for the coordinates of the vertex of the triangle that is not on the *x*-axis. Examine the coordinate representation of $\triangle ABC$ below.

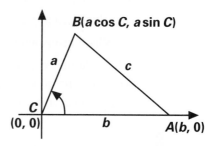

a. Explain why the coordinates of point *B* are $(a \cos C, a \sin C)$.

b. Find c^2 using the distance formula and the coordinates of points *A* and *B*.

c. Simplify your expression in Part b to give the Law of Cosines for c^2. You will need to use a proven result from Investigation 2 of Lesson 5 in the "Symbol Sense and Algebraic Reasoning" unit (pages 243 to 246).

2. *Dissection* of shapes into several congruent shapes is a source for commercial games and an interesting class of geometric problems. The triangle below is dissected into four congruent shapes, each similar to the large triangle.

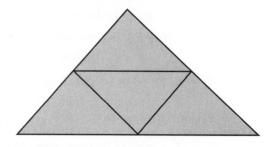

Dissect each of the following shapes into four shapes similar to the given shape but congruent to each other.

a.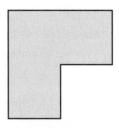

b.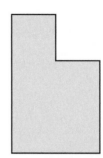

c.

d.

e.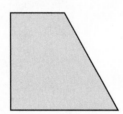

f.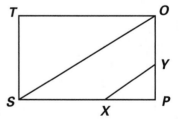

3. Two right triangles can be proved to be congruent when the hypotenuse and leg of one are congruent respectively to the hypotenuse and leg of another. Construct a convincing argument that this is correct.

4. In the diagram here, quadrilateral *STOP* is a rectangle and $\overline{SO}$ is a diagonal.

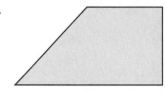

a. Assuming $\overleftrightarrow{XY} \parallel \overleftrightarrow{SO}$, prove that $\triangle XYP \sim \triangle SOP$.

b. Assuming $\overleftrightarrow{XY} \parallel \overleftrightarrow{SO}$, prove that $\triangle XYP \sim \triangle OST$.

c. Assuming $\overleftrightarrow{XY} \parallel \overleftrightarrow{SO}$, and *Y* is the midpoint of $\overline{OP}$, prove the following:

■ *X* is the midpoint of $\overline{SP}$.

■ $SO = 2 \cdot XY$.

INVESTIGATION 3 Reasoning with Congruence and Similarity Conditions

Reproduced below is a lithograph by M. C. Escher called *Ascending and Descending*. The stairway is a vivid reminder that you cannot always believe your eyes.

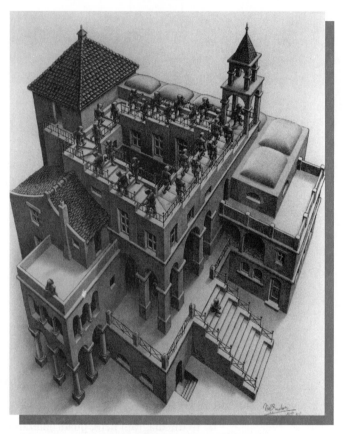

1. Provide an argument why what appears to be true about the stairway cannot possibly be true in the real world.

Even simple figures such as the ones at the right can be deceiving to the eye. Which segment connecting the V shapes is longer? Direct measurement is one way to settle a claim about segment lengths or angle measures. If the segments or angles are parts of triangles, the four triangle congruence theorems (SSS, SAS, ASA, and AAS) and the three triangle similarity theorems (SSS, SAS, and AA) are important and often-used tools to settle geometric claims and conjectures. If you can prove it, your eyes are not deceiving you. If you cannot prove it, look for a counterexample.

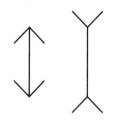

2. Consider this conjecture:

A diagonal of a rectangle forms two congruent triangles.

  a. Draw and label a diagram that illustrates the conjecture. Does it seem to be correct?

  b. Write the conjecture in if-then form, in terms of your labeled diagram.

  c. List some characteristics of rectangles. Could any of these be used to help you prove the conjecture?

  d. Which congruent triangle theorem might you use in your proof? Explain your choice.

  e. Individually, write a proof of this conjecture. Compare your proof to those of others in your group.

  f. Replace the word "rectangle" in the conjecture with "parallelogram." Is this new conjecture correct? Explain your reasoning.

Often, information about a specific figure is given, and a conjecture (what you or someone else saw) is proposed. Your task is to confirm the conjecture with a proof or show it is wrong with a counterexample.

3. Suppose you are given the following information about the figure shown at the right.

$$\overline{ST} \cong \overline{SP} \text{ and } \overline{TO} \cong \overline{PO}$$

Can you conclude that $\triangle STO \cong \triangle SPO$? Write a proof or give a counterexample.

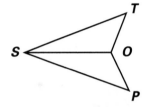

4. In the diagram below, $\overline{BD}$ is perpendicular to $\overline{AE}$ and C is the midpoint of both $\overline{BD}$ and $\overline{AE}$.

  a. Prove that $\triangle ABC \cong \triangle EDC$.

  b. Use the given information and your proof that $\triangle ABC \cong \triangle EDC$ to explain why you can also conclude each of the following:

  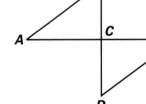

   ▪ $\overline{AB} \cong \overline{DE}$

   ▪ $\angle ABC \cong \angle EDC$

   ▪ $\overleftrightarrow{AB} \parallel \overleftrightarrow{DE}$

  c. Can you also conclude that $\overline{BD} \cong \overline{AE}$? Why or why not?

5. For the four lines shown, $\overleftrightarrow{AB} \parallel \overleftrightarrow{DE}$ and C is the midpoint of $\overline{BD}$.

  a. Prove that $\triangle ABC \cong \triangle EDC$.

  b. Using your work in Part a, explain why you also can conclude that C is the midpoint of $\overline{AE}$.

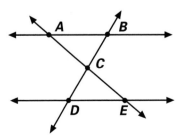

In the last two activities, you were asked to deduce further conclusions after you had proved two triangles congruent. The conclusions were based on the congruence of the triangles: once triangles are known to be congruent, then all the corresponding angles and sides are also known to be congruent. This is summarized by saying "corresponding parts of congruent triangles are congruent."

Similarity, as well as congruence, is often suggested visually. Again, "looking similar" is not good enough, particularly for an architect or an engineer. They must "know" two shapes are similar. So again, reasoning about the geometry is used to ensure the correctness of the visual impression.

6. Examine the diagram at the right. Does △ABC appear to be similar to △EDC? For each condition below, determine if that condition will *guarantee* △ABC ~ △EDC. Justify your conclusion.

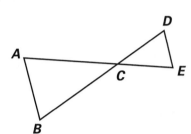

   a. $\overleftrightarrow{AB} \parallel \overleftrightarrow{DE}$

   b. $BC = 2DC$ and $AB = 2ED$

   c. $\frac{AB}{ED} = \frac{BC}{CD} = \frac{AC}{CE}$

7. Refer to the diagram below for this activity.

   a. Prove that if $\overleftrightarrow{DE} \parallel \overleftrightarrow{BC}$, then $\frac{AC}{AE} = \frac{AB}{AD}$.

   b. Prove that if △ABC ~ △ADE, then $\overleftrightarrow{ED} \parallel \overleftrightarrow{CB}$.

   c. Write another if-then statement about this diagram that you could prove.

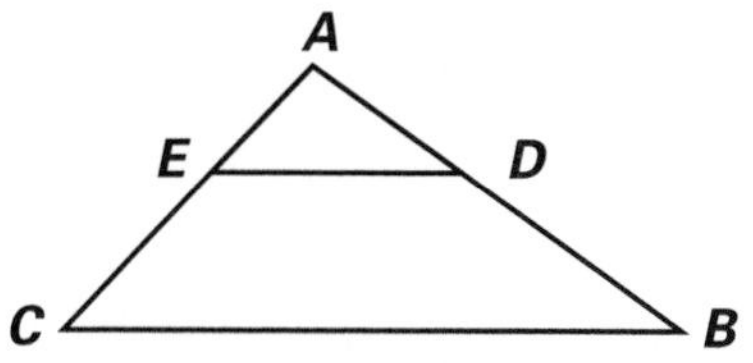

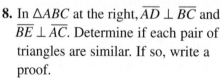

8. In △ABC at the right, $\overline{AD} \perp \overline{BC}$ and $\overline{BE} \perp \overline{AC}$. Determine if each pair of triangles are similar. If so, write a proof.

   a. △ADC ~ △BEC

   b. △ADB ~ △BEA

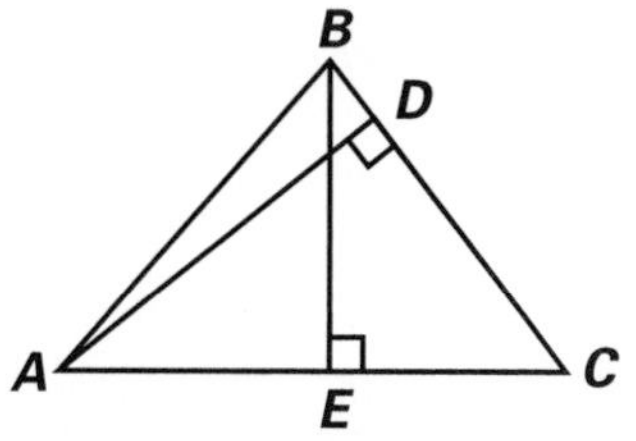

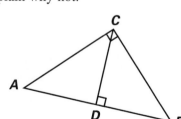

9. In the diagram below, △ABC is a right triangle and $\overline{CD}$ is an altitude to the hypotenuse. Use deductive reasoning to determine which conclusions are valid. If a conclusion is not valid, explain why not.

   a. △ADC ~ △ACB

   b. △CDB ~ △ACB

   c. △ADC ~ △CDB

   d. $CD^2 = AD \cdot BD$

   e. $CA^2 = BA \cdot DA$

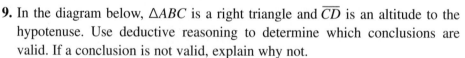

In the diagram below, S and T are the midpoints of $\overline{PQ}$ and $\overline{QR}$ respectively, and $ST = TU$.

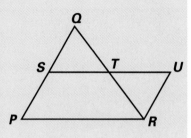

a Describe a strategy you would use to prove that $SQ = UR$.

b Describe a strategy you would use to prove $ST = \frac{1}{2} \cdot PR$.

c What type of quadrilateral does $PSUR$ appear to be? Describe a strategy you would use to prove your conjecture.

Be prepared to share your thinking with the class.

On Your Own

In the diagram below, $m\angle 1 = m\angle 2$ and $\overline{PB} \perp \overline{AC}$.

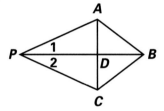

a. Which of the following conclusions can you deduce?

- $\triangle PAD \sim \triangle PCD$
- $\triangle PAD \cong \triangle PCD$
- $PA = PC$
- $\triangle PAB \cong \triangle PCB$

b. Choose one conclusion you can deduce and write an argument proving it.

MORE
Modeling • Organizing • Reflecting • Extending

Modeling

1. Drafters and people involved in industrial design use a variety of tools in their work. Depending on the nature of the task, these tools vary from sophisticated CAD (computer-assisted design) software to *compasses* (instruments for drawing circles and arcs) and *straightedges* (devices for drawing lines that have no marks for measuring).

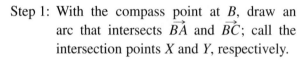

a. Draw an acute angle, ∠ABC. Using a compass, a straightedge, and the algorithm below, construct the bisector of ∠ABC. A **bisector of an angle** is a ray that begins at the vertex of the angle and divides the angle into two angles of equal measure.

Angle Bisector Algorithm: To bisect ∠ABC, do the following.

Step 1: With the compass point at B, draw an arc that intersects $\overrightarrow{BA}$ and $\overrightarrow{BC}$; call the intersection points X and Y, respectively.

Step 2: With the compass point at point X (and then at point Y) and using a radius greater than $\frac{1}{2}XY$, draw two arcs that intersect in the interior of ∠ABC. Label the point of intersection D.

Step 3: Draw the ray BD. Ray BD bisects ∠ABC.

b. Prove that this algorithm produces the bisector of an angle. That is, prove that $\overrightarrow{BD}$ bisects ∠ABC.

c. Can this algorithm be used to construct the bisector of an obtuse angle? Explain your reasoning.

2. In this task, you will examine an algorithm for duplicating an angle using a straightedge and a compass or using a computer-based drawing program.

a. Carefully draw an angle, ∠ABC. Then use the following algorithm to construct an angle congruent to ∠ABC.

Angle Construction Algorithm: To construct an angle PQR congruent to the given angle, ∠ABC, do the following.

Step 1: Use a straightedge to draw $\overrightarrow{QR}$.

Step 2: With B as the center, construct an arc that intersects sides $\overrightarrow{BA}$ and $\overrightarrow{BC}$ of ∠ABC; label the intersections points D and E respectively.

Step 3: With point Q as the center and radius BD, construct an arc which intersects $\overrightarrow{QR}$; label the intersection point S.

Step 4: With center point S and radius DE, construct an arc which intersects the arc in Step 3. Label the intersection point P.

Step 5: Draw $\overrightarrow{QP}$. Then ∠PQR ≅ ∠ABC.

b. Prove that the two angles in Step 5 are congruent.

c. Carefully draw a triangle, △XYZ. Design and test an algorithm for using a compass and a straightedge to construct △ABC so that △ABC ≅ △XYZ. Prove that your algorithm will always work.

3. In the diagram at the right, $AE = k \cdot AC$ and $AD = k \cdot AB$.

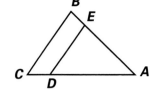

a. Can you prove that $m\angle AED = m\angle ACB$? If so, do it.

b. Can you prove that $\overleftrightarrow{BC} \parallel \overleftrightarrow{ED}$? If so, do it.

c. Can you prove that $\frac{AE}{AC} = \frac{ED}{CB}$? If so, do it.

4. In the diagram below, $\triangle ABC \sim \triangle XYZ$ with scale factor k. So $XY = k \cdot AB$. In each part below, you are given additional information.

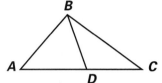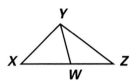

a. In addition, $\overrightarrow{BD}$ bisects $\angle ABC$, and $\overrightarrow{YW}$ bisects $\angle XYZ$. Prove that $YW = k \cdot BD$.

b. In addition, point D is the midpoint of $\overline{AC}$, and W is the midpoint of $\overline{XZ}$. Prove that $YW = k \cdot BD$.

c. In addition, $\overline{BD} \perp \overline{AC}$ and $\overline{YW} \perp \overline{XZ}$. Prove that $YW = k \cdot BD$.

5. In the diagram shown here, $\overline{TO} \cong \overline{SP}$, $\overleftrightarrow{TO} \parallel \overleftrightarrow{SP}$, and $\overleftrightarrow{TH} \parallel \overleftrightarrow{PA}$.

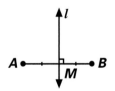

a. Prove that $\overline{TH} \cong \overline{PA}$.

b. Prove that $\triangle STH \cong \triangle OPA$.

Organizing

1. A **perpendicular bisector of a segment** is a line (or segment or ray) that is perpendicular to the segment at its midpoint.

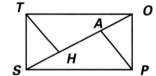

a. Refer back to the Angle Bisector Algorithm in Modeling Task 1, page 320. How could you modify that algorithm to develop a *Perpendicular Bisector Algorithm* for a segment *AB*?

b. Draw a segment *AB*. Use your algorithm and a compass and straightedge to construct the perpendicular bisector of the segment. Prove that your algorithm produces the perpendicular bisector of $\overline{AB}$.

2. Refer back to your proof of the Angle Construction Algorithm, which you developed in Part b of Modeling Task 2 (page 320).

a. On which of the congruence theorems (SAS, ASA, AAS, or SSS) did your proof depend?

b. Develop triangle construction algorithms that are based on two of the other congruence theorems. Test your algorithms and explain why they will always work.

3. Suppose $\triangle ABC \sim \triangle XYZ$ with scale factor k such that $XY = k \cdot AB$.

   a. Is it correct to say $\frac{XY}{AB} = \frac{YZ}{BC} = \frac{XZ}{AC}$? If so, what is the common ratio? Explain your reasoning.

   b. Find the value of $\frac{XY}{AB} + \frac{YZ}{BC}$. Find the value of $\frac{XY + YZ}{AB + BC}$.

   c. If $\frac{XY}{AB} = \frac{YZ}{BC}$, do the equations below necessarily follow? For each, explain why or why not.

     ■ $\frac{XY + AB}{AB} = \frac{YZ + BC}{BC}$

     ■ $\frac{XY - AB}{AB} = \frac{YZ - BC}{BC}$

4. Recall that a proportion is a statement that two ratios are equal, such as $\frac{a}{b} = \frac{c}{d}$.

   a. Suppose $\triangle ABC \sim \triangle XYZ$ and the scale factor is k. Why is it correct to say the corresponding sides are proportional?

   b. Restate the SAS and SSS Similarity Theorems using the language of proportions.

   c. Solve this proportion for t: $\frac{t + 3}{5} = \frac{t}{4}$.

5. Prove or disprove each of the following statements.

   a. If $\overline{AB}$ and $\overline{CD}$ are congruent chords in a circle with center O, then the central angles, $\angle AOB$ and $\angle COD$, are congruent.

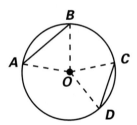

   b. If a line through the center of a circle is perpendicular to a chord AB, then it bisects the chord.

Reflecting

1. In this unit, you have used the term "corresponding angles" in the context of parallel lines cut by a transversal and in the contexts of similarity and congruence of triangles. Draw sketches illustrating the different meanings of "corresponding angles."

2. Is similarity or congruence harder for you to detect visually? Is similarity or congruence of shapes more difficult for you to prove? Explain your thinking.

3. What determines the shape of a polygon, its angles or its sides? Explain your reasoning.

4. A quick test that engravers and photographers use to determine whether two shapes are similar is illustrated in the diagram below.

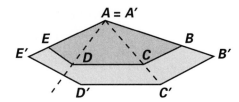

One shape is placed on top of the other so that the vertices of a pair of corresponding angles are at the same point and corresponding sides coincide. If each line from the vertex of an angle of one polygon contains the corresponding vertex of the other, then the shapes are similar. Explain why this is, or is not, a valid test.

5. A very useful geometric fact is that *any* point on the perpendicular bisector of a segment is equidistant from the endpoints of the segment (see Organizing Task 1, page 321).

   a. Explain why this fact is true.

   b. Write this fact in if-then form.

   c. Write the converse of the statement in Part b. Is the converse a correct statement in this case? Why or why not?

Extending

1. After the Pythagorean Theorem, the Triangle Inequality Theorem is perhaps one of the geometry theorems most widely used in mathematics. The theorem captures a very simple idea: The shortest distance between two points is a straight line.

Triangle Inequality Theorem

The sum of the lengths of two sides of a triangle is greater than the length of the third side.

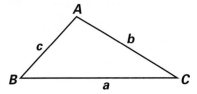

Use the Law of Cosines and the fact that $\cos A \geq -1$ to prove that in $\triangle ABC$, $b + c > a$.

2. Use the following diagram for Parts a and b.

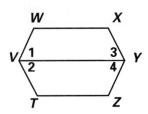

a. Given: $\angle 1 \cong \angle 2$, $\overline{VW} \cong \overline{VT}$, $\overline{WX} \cong \overline{TZ}$, and $\overline{XY} \cong \overline{YZ}$

Prove: $\angle W \cong \angle T$ (*Hint:* You need triangles; draw some segments to form them.)

b. Given: $\overline{WV} \cong \overline{VT}$, $\angle 1 \cong \angle 2$, $\angle 3 \cong \angle 4$, and $\overline{XY} \cong \overline{YZ}$

Prove: $\overline{WX} \cong \overline{TZ}$

3. Recall that an isosceles triangle is a triangle with at least two sides congruent. Suppose triangle *PQR* is an isosceles triangle in which $\overline{QR} \cong \overline{PR}$.

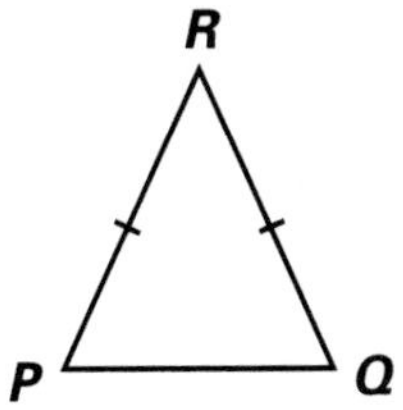

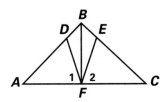

a. Using the idea of line symmetry, what can you conclude about $\angle P$ and $\angle Q$?

b. Prove your conjecture in Part a by first drawing the bisector of $\angle R$ on a copy of the diagram.

c. Prove your conjecture in Part a by first drawing a segment connecting point *R* and the midpoint of $\overline{PQ}$ on a copy of the diagram.

d. Write a coordinate proof of your conjecture in Part a by first placing $\triangle PQR$ on a coordinate system with $P(0, 0)$, $Q(2a, 0)$, and $R(a, b)$.

4. In the diagram at the right, $\overline{BF}$ is the perpendicular bisector of $\overline{AC}$ (see Organizing Task 1, page 321) and $\angle 1 \cong \angle 2$. Prove that $\overline{DB} \cong \overline{BE}$.

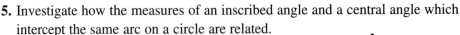

5. Investigate how the measures of an inscribed angle and a central angle which intercept the same arc on a circle are related.

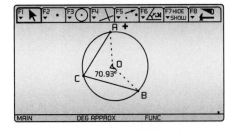

a. Suppose $\angle ACB$ is inscribed in a circle with center *O* and *O* is on $\overline{CB}$. Determine the relation between the measures of $\angle ACB$ and $\angle AOB$.

b. Suppose $\angle ACB$ is inscribed in a circle with center *O* and *O* is not on $\overline{CB}$. Determine the relation between the measures of $\angle ACB$ and $\angle AOB$.

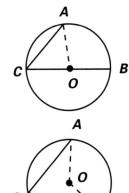

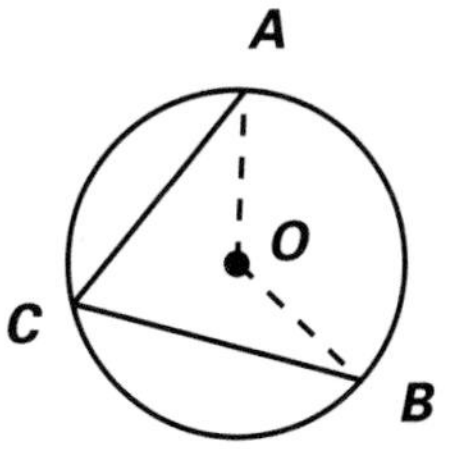

c. The degree measure of *minor arc AB* (written $\overparen{AB}$) is the measure of its central angle, $\angle AOB$. What is the relation between the measures of an inscribed angle and its intercepted arc?

Parallelograms: Necessary and Sufficient Conditions

Lesson 3

At the beginning of this unit, you had a small set of geometric tools to use to prove the correctness of conjectures. These included the Pythagorean Theorem, the Law of Sines, and the Law of Cosines, which were proved in previous units. Now you have a large inventory at your disposal. You have properties of parallel lines and several relations among pairs of angles when two parallel lines are cut by a transversal. You have properties of similar triangles and ways to prove them similar. And you have properties of congruent triangles and methods to conclude when two triangles are congruent. These are some of the most important properties and relations in Euclidean geometry.

Properties and relations involving parallelism of lines, congruence of triangles, and similarity of triangles can help you establish properties of other polygons. In this lesson, you will explore conditions that will ensure that a quadrilateral is a parallelogram.

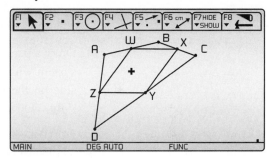

Think About This Situation

Using a geometry drawing program (as illustrated above) or paper and pencil, draw a quadrilateral and name it *ABCD*. Find the midpoints of the sides and connect them in order to obtain quadrilateral *WXYZ*.

a What special kind of quadrilateral does *WXYZ* appear to be?

b Investigate this situation for special quadrilaterals such as squares, rectangles, parallelograms, trapezoids, and kites. In each case, what seems to be true about the resulting quadrilateral?

c What theorem is suggested by your observation in Parts a and b?

d What do you think the next step should be?

INVESTIGATION 1 ▶ Reasoning about Parallelograms

In previous courses, you have investigated applications of parallelograms and their properties. Such applications range from the design of pop-up greeting cards to the design of windshield wipers and outdoor swings. You probably have a good idea of what a parallelogram is, but in order to have a starting point for reasoning about parallelograms, everyone must agree on the same definition.

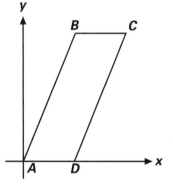

> *A quadrilateral is a **parallelogram** if and only if both pairs of opposite sides are parallel.*

Recall that the "if and only if" in this definition allows you to use either part of the definition as given information to conclude the other part. In the following activities, you will investigate how the definition allows you to place a parallelogram on a coordinate system and specify its vertices.

1. Draw a parallelogram *ABCD* on a coordinate system with one vertex at the origin and one side on the positive *x*-axis, as shown at the right.

   a. What are the coordinates of point *A*? Record these on your diagram.

   b. Consider vertex *D*. If $AD = c$ units, what is the *x*-coordinate of point *D*? What is the *y*-coordinate of point *D*? Record these on your diagram.

   c. Now consider vertex *B*. If $AB = p$ units, is *p* the *x*-coordinate of point *B*? Is the *y*-coordinate *p*? Explain.

   d. Call the coordinates of point *B* (*a*, *b*) and record them on your diagram. How are sides $\overline{BC}$ and $\overline{AD}$ related? What is the *y*-coordinate of point *C*? Explain your reasoning.

   e. How can you use the fact that side *AB* and side *DC* are parallel to help determine the *x*-coordinate of point *C*? Record the coordinates of point *C* on your diagram.

   f. Compare your coordinate labeling of parallelogram *ABCD* to those of other groups. Resolve any differences.

2. For each of the parallelograms shown, determine the coordinates of point *C*.

a.

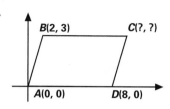

b.

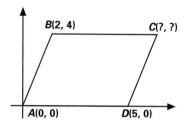

c.

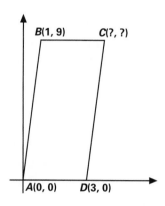

d.

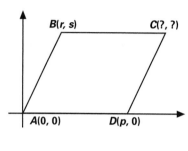

As you saw in Unit 3, "Symbol Sense and Algebraic Reasoning," placing shapes on a coordinate system and assigning general coordinates to their vertices provides an algebraic tool for reasoning about the shapes.

3. Examine the following two arguments that $\overline{AB} \cong \overline{CD}$ in parallelogram *ABCD*.

Kara

Hans

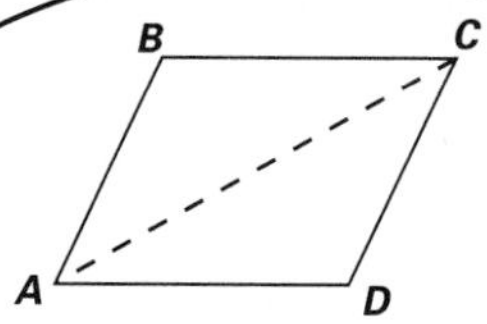

First draw $\overline{AC}$ in parallelogram *ABCD*.
Since $\overline{AB} \parallel \overline{CD}$, m∠*BAC* = m∠*DCA*
because they are alternate interior angles.
Since $\overline{BC} \parallel \overline{AD}$, m∠*BCA* = m∠*DAC*.
$\overline{AC}$ is a corresponding side of △*ABC* and △*CDA*.
So △*ABC* ≅ △*CDA* by *ASA*.
It follows by corresponding parts that $\overline{AB} \cong \overline{CD}$.

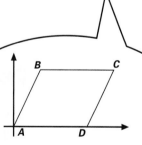

First place *ABCD* on a coordinate system with point *A*
at the origin and point *D* on the *x*-axis.
The vertices have coordinates $A(0, 0)$, $B(a, b)$, $C(a + c, b)$,
and $D(c, 0)$.
Using the distance formula:

$$AB = \sqrt{(a-0)^2 + (b-0)^2} = \sqrt{a^2 + b^2}$$

$$CD = \sqrt{(a+c-c)^2 + (b-0)^2} = \sqrt{a^2 + b^2}$$

Thus, $AB = CD$ or $\overline{AB} \cong \overline{CD}$.

a. Is Hans' argument valid? What previously proved information did he use?

b. Is Kara's argument valid? What information did she use to make her argument?

c. Could Hans conclude other facts about parallelograms once he deduced $\triangle ABC \cong \triangle CDA$? What other facts?

d. Could Kara also conclude other facts about parallelograms once she used the distance formula to get $AB = CD$? What other facts?

e. Whose proof is easiest to follow and why? Which of these methods of proof would you have used and why?

Hans' proof is called a **synthetic proof** because it applies to a figure with no coordinates. Kara's argument is called an **analytic** or **coordinate proof** since it uses coordinates. Sometimes one argument form is easier and sheds more light on other possible deductions than the other.

4. Listed below are conjectures about properties of every parallelogram. Examine each to see if your group thinks it is correct. If you think it is correct, construct a proof. If you think it is incorrect, give a counterexample. Share the work among your group members. Then discuss each other's proofs.

If a quadrilateral is a parallelogram, then the following is true:

a. Opposite angles are congruent.

b. Opposite sides are congruent.

c. Adjacent angles are supplementary.

d. All angles are congruent.

e. Each diagonal divides the shape into two congruent triangles.

f. The diagonals bisect each other.

g. The diagonals are congruent.

h. The diagonals are perpendicular.

Checkpoint

In addition to its recognizable shape, a parallelogram has many geometric properties that can be proved.

a Make a list summarizing the properties about the sides, angles, and diagonals of a parallelogram that you were able to prove.

b How do synthetic and analytic arguments differ?

Be prepared to share your list and explanation with the entire class.

On Your Own

A **rectangle** may be defined as a parallelogram with a right angle.

Since a rectangle is a parallelogram, everything about parallelograms is also true about rectangles. Using inductive reasoning, make a conjecture about a property of all rectangles that is not also true for all parallelograms. Develop a proof for your conjecture.

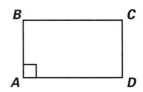

You now have a list of theorems that give properties of parallelograms. These are useful whenever you know that a quadrilateral is a parallelogram. If a quadrilateral is *not* known to be a parallelogram, then you cannot conclude that any of those properties hold. In the remainder of this investigation, you will explore conditions that ensure that a quadrilateral is a parallelogram. You already know one condition from the definition of a parallelogram. Namely, if a quadrilateral has two pairs of opposite sides parallel, then the quadrilateral is a parallelogram.

5. Examine this conjecture that Shiomo made after drawing and analyzing a few quadrilaterals.

   If a quadrilateral has two pairs of opposite sides congruent, then the quadrilateral is a parallelogram.

   a. Experiment with drawings to see if this conjecture makes sense.

   b. Construct a proof or a counterexample of Shiomo's conjecture.

6. Here are additional conditions that may or may not ensure that a quadrilateral is a parallelogram. Investigate each conjecture by drawing shapes satisfying the conditions and checking to see if the quadrilateral is a parallelogram. Share the workload among members of your group. Compile a group list of conditions that seem to guarantee that a quadrilateral is a parallelogram.

   a. If a quadrilateral has two pairs of opposite angles congruent, then it is a parallelogram.

   b. If a quadrilateral has one pair of opposite angles and a pair of opposite sides congruent, then it is a parallelogram.

   c. If a quadrilateral has diagonals that bisect each other, it is a parallelogram.

   d. If a quadrilateral has one pair of opposite sides parallel and the other pair of opposite sides congruent, then it is a parallelogram.

   e. If a quadrilateral has two distinct pairs of adjacent sides congruent, then it is a parallelogram.

   f. If a quadrilateral has one pair of opposite sides congruent and parallel, then it is a parallelogram.

7. For each condition you listed in Activity 6, construct a proof that your conjecture is correct. Share the workload and then discuss the proofs within your group.

Checkpoint

Make a list of several conditions on a quadrilateral that guarantee it to be a parallelogram.

Be prepared to demonstrate to the class a proof of each condition in your list.

On Your Own

The figure *STOP* is a quadrilateral. For each set of conditions, explain why the conditions do or do not ensure that *STOP* is a parallelogram.

a. $\angle S \cong \angle O$ and $\angle T \cong \angle P$

b. $\overline{ST} \parallel \overline{OP}$ and $\overline{TO} \cong \overline{SP}$

c. $\overline{ST} \cong \overline{OP}$ and $\overline{TO} \cong \overline{SP}$

d. $\angle S \cong \angle O$ and $\overline{ST} \cong \overline{OP}$

e. $\overline{ST} \cong \overline{TO}$ and $\overline{OP} \cong \overline{PS}$

f. M is the midpoint of $\overline{SO}$ and of $\overline{TP}$

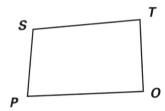

INVESTIGATION 2 Special Kinds of Parallelograms

One special parallelogram, with a pair of congruent adjacent sides, is a rhombus. Since every parallelogram has its *opposite* sides congruent, it follows that a rhombus has four congruent sides. (Why?) The rhombus shown at the left below can be used to make a pair of tiles called a *dart* and a *kite*. In the first course of *Contemporary Mathematics in Context*, you may have discovered that a rhombus will form a tiling of the plane that has translation symmetry. What is interesting about these particular figures, discovered by Roger Penrose, a professor at the University of Oxford, is that copies of these two shapes can be used to form a tiling, a portion of which is shown at the right below, which does *not* have translation symmetry.

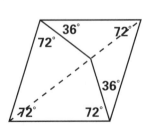

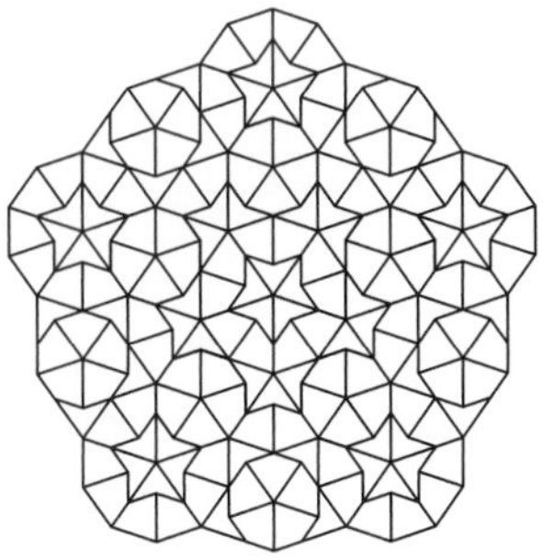

Penrose Tiles quilt made by
Elaine Krajenke Ellison

Penrose's discovery is based on a particular rhombus. In the next two activities, you will explore additional properties of any rhombus.

1. Sketch several different rhombuses with and without their diagonals.

   a. What are some properties of a rhombus that are consequences of the fact that a rhombus is a parallelogram?

   b. Now visually inspect your sketches. Make a group list of other characteristics observed in the sketches that might be correct for all rhombuses.

   c. Write each of your conjectures in if-then form.

   d. Construct proofs for your conjectures. Share the work and then discuss the proofs within your group.

2. Given below are various conditions on a parallelogram. Determine if each condition is sufficient to conclude that the parallelogram is a rhombus. For each condition that seems to ensure that the parallelogram is a rhombus, write the corresponding if-then statement and a proof.

   a. The diagonals bisect each other.

   b. The diagonals are perpendicular.

   c. The diagonals bisect the angles.

   d. A pair of adjacent angles are congruent.

Now refer back to the "Think About This Situation" at the beginning of this lesson, page 325. You and your classmates may have conjectured that the shape formed by connecting the midpoints of consecutive sides of a quadrilateral is a parallelogram. In the remainder of this investigation, you will examine this situation further.

3. Consider first the case of connecting midpoints of two sides of a triangle.

   a. Draw several triangles and locate the midpoints of two sides for each one. Connect the midpoints in each. What appears to be true about the segment determined by the midpoints?

   b. In △*ABC*, *M* is the midpoint of $\overline{AB}$ and *N* is the midpoint of $\overline{AC}$. How does △*AMN* appear to be related to △*ABC*? Prove that your observation is correct.

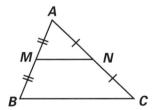

   c. Given your deduction in Part b, prove that $\overleftrightarrow{MN} \parallel \overleftrightarrow{BC}$.

   d. What can you conclude about the relative lengths of $\overleftrightarrow{MN}$ and $\overleftrightarrow{BC}$? Why?

The theorem you proved in Activity 3 Parts c and d is often called the **Midpoint Connector Theorem for Triangles**.

4. The midpoint connector theorem which you conjectured for quadrilaterals may be stated as follows:

   If the midpoints of consecutive sides of any quadrilateral are connected, the resulting quadrilateral is a parallelogram.

   a. Draw a diagram representing the **Midpoint Connector Theorem for Quadrilaterals**.

   b. Write a proof of this theorem.

Checkpoint

As quadrilaterals become more specialized, they exhibit properties in addition to the properties for more general cases.

ⓐ List two properties of every rhombus that are not properties of every parallelogram.

ⓑ How does your work in this lesson with the Midpoint Connector Theorem for Quadrilaterals illustrate how inductive reasoning and deductive reasoning support each other?

ⓒ A rectangle is a special kind of quadrilateral. If the midpoints of consecutive sides of any rectangle are connected, is a special kind of parallelogram formed? Write an argument justifying your conclusion.

Be prepared to share your responses and reasoning with the entire class.

▶ On Your Own

Consider the following information about quadrilateral *ABCD*.

- $\overline{AC} \perp \overline{BD}$
- $\overline{AC}$ bisects $\angle A$ and $\angle C$

a. Make several sketches of quadrilaterals satisfying these conditions.

b. Do the sketches suggest *ABCD* is a parallelogram? A rhombus?

c. State one conjecture about *ABCD* that you think is always true.

d. Prove your conjecture.

Modeling • Organizing • Reflecting • Extending

Modeling

1. When a building construction crew lays the foundation for a house or garage, they often need to be certain that the foundation is rectangular.

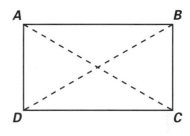

a. They first measure the sides of quadrilateral *ABCD* and find that *AB = DC* and *AD = BC*. What can they conclude? Why?

b. Next, they measure the diagonals and find that *AC = BD*. Prove why they then can conclude that *ABCD* is a rectangle.

c. Once the test in Part a has been completed, there are other ways to ensure that the foundation is rectangular. One method that does not involve measuring such long distances is as follows:

■ Mark a point *P* on $\overline{AB}$ so that *AP* = 3 feet.

■ Mark a point *Q* on $\overline{AD}$ so that *AQ* = 4 feet.

■ Measure $\overline{PQ}$. If *PQ* = 5 feet, then the foundation is rectangular.

Explain why this method works.

d. A carpenter's square is often used to make a quick test for a right angle. Once the test in Part a has been completed, how many corners would need to be tested with a carpenter's square to ensure that the foundation is rectangular?

e. If you had a carpenter's square, could you avoid the test in Part a? Explain your reasoning.

2. The diagram at the right illustrates a quadrilateral with $DA = CB$ and $DC = AB$. Points D and C are fixed in place.

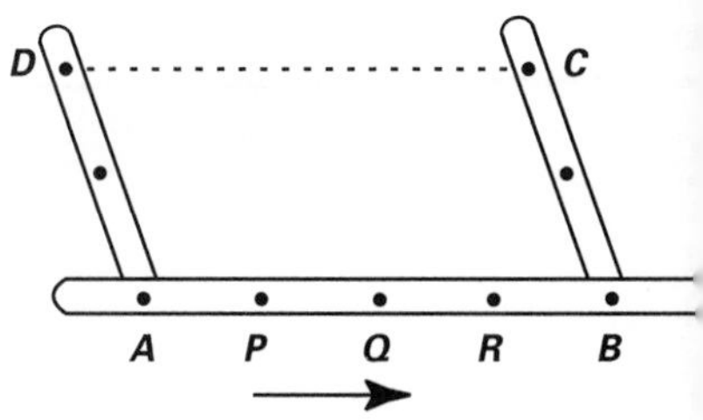

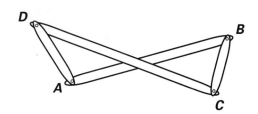

   a. Make a similar linkage using plastic or cardboard strips and paper fasteners.

   b. What shape is $ABCD$? Explain.

   c. If $\overline{AD}$ is turned about point D, what path does point A follow? Explain.

   d. If $\overline{AD}$ is turned about point D, what paths do points P, Q, and R follow? Explain.

   e. What happens to $\overline{DB}$ and $\overline{AC}$ as $\overline{DA}$ turns about point D?

3. $ABCD$ is a parallelogram linkage with $\overline{AB}$ fixed and $\overline{DC}$ crossing $\overline{AB}$.

   a. Construct a model of this linkage using plastic or cardboard strips and paper fasteners.

   b. If point D is turned clockwise about point A, what type of path does point C follow?

   c. If $AB = DC = 6$ cm and $AD = 2$ cm, how will varying the length of $\overline{BC}$ affect the motion of point C?

4. For the diagram below, $\triangle ORQ \cong \triangle TSQ$ and O is the midpoint of $\overline{PR}$. Prove each of the following conclusions.

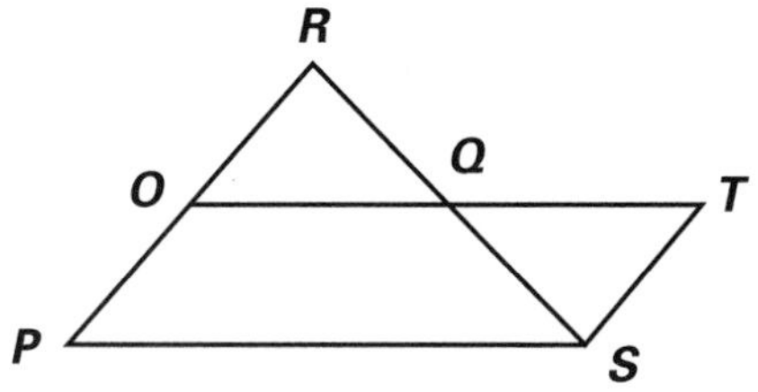

   a. Q is the midpoint of $\overline{RS}$.

   b. $POTS$ is a parallelogram.

   c. $\triangle TSQ \sim \triangle PRS$

   d. $PS = 2 \cdot OQ$

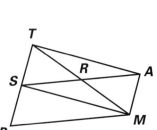

5. In the diagram below, $STAM$ is a rectangle and $SAMP$ is a parallelogram. Prove, if you can, that $\triangle TMP$ is an isosceles triangle. If the triangle is not isosceles, explain how you know.

Organizing

1. A rectangle may be defined in several ways. Here are two ways:

   ■ A quadrilateral is a *rectangle* if and only if it is a parallelogram and it has one right angle.

   ■ A quadrilateral is a *rectangle* if and only if it is a parallelogram and it has one pair of congruent adjacent angles.

   For each statement below, use one definition or the other to prove that the statement is correct or find a counterexample.

   a. If a quadrilateral is a rectangle, then it has four right angles.

   b. If a quadrilateral is a rectangle, then it has congruent diagonals.

   c. If a quadrilateral is a rectangle, then its diagonals are perpendicular.

   d. If a quadrilateral is a rectangle, then it has diagonals that bisect each other.

   e. If the diagonals of a parallelogram are congruent, then the parallelogram is a rectangle.

2. A **square** is a parallelogram with one right angle and one pair of adjacent sides congruent. Use this definition of a square to prove the statements in Parts a through d.

   a. If a quadrilateral is a square, then it is a rectangle.

   b. If a quadrilateral is a square, then it is a rhombus.

   c. If a quadrilateral is a square, then the diagonals are perpendicular to and bisect each other.

   d. If a quadrilateral is a square, then the diagonals bisect the angles of the square.

3. Quadrilaterals come in a variety of specialized shapes. There are trapezoids, kites, parallelograms, rhombuses, rectangles, and squares, as well as everyday quadrilaterals with no special additional characteristics.

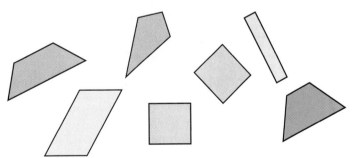

   a. Suppose you know that a characteristic X is true for parallelograms. For which other quadrilaterals must characteristic X also be true? Explain your reasoning.

   b. Suppose a characteristic Y is true for all kites. Which other quadrilaterals must also have characteristic Y? Explain your reasoning.

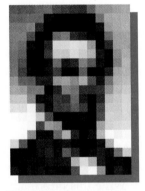

This pattern of squares was created in an experiment to determine the amount of detail needed for a picture to be recognizable.

c. Complete a copy of the *quadrilateral tree* shown at the right by writing the names of the quadrilaterals in the ovals. If the oval for a shape is connected to one or more ovals *above* it, then that shape must also be an example of the shape or shapes in the ovals to which it is connected.

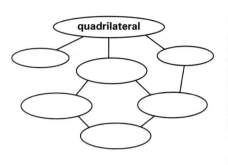

d. How can you use the quadrilateral tree to help decide on responses to questions like those in Parts a and b on the previous page?

4. Definitions are stated in "if and only if" form: *p if and only if q*. This is done because *p if and only if q* means

■ *p* if *q* ($q \Rightarrow p$) and

■ *p* only if *q* ($p \Rightarrow q$).

Thus, you can conclude *p* when you know *q*, and you can conclude *q* when you know *p*.

a. Consider the definition of a parallelogram: *A quadrilateral is a parallelogram if and only if both pairs of opposite sides are parallel.* In which direction is the definition being used when you conclude that the opposite sides of a parallelogram are parallel? In which direction is it being used when you conclude that a quadrilateral is a parallelogram because its opposite sides are parallel?

b. In Investigation 1, page 326, you proved (i) that the opposite sides of a parallelogram are congruent and (ii) that if the opposite sides of a quadrilateral are congruent, then the figure is a parallelogram. Write this information in a single "if and only if" statement.

c. Review the statements of other theorems about parallelograms and rhombuses you proved in Investigations 1 and 2. Combine those that can be combined into single "if and only if" statements.

d. If you were asked to prove "*r* if and only if *s*," what two things would you need to do?

5. Parallelograms are related to translations. Each side of a parallelogram is the translation image of its opposite side. What is the magnitude of such translations? How can the direction be represented?

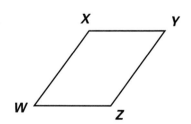

Reflecting

1. Your work in this lesson with the Midpoint Connector Theorem for Quadrilaterals can be thought of as a mathematical journey. It began with experimentation, which led to a conjecture, and ended with a proof.

   a. Write a paragraph outlining what you believe to be the main features of this journey.

   b. What aspects of this journey were most interesting to you? Why?

   c. Give another instance of a similar mathematical journey you made in this unit.

2. The Midpoint Connector Theorem for Quadrilaterals is an amazing result. It was first proved by a French mathematician, Pierre Varignon (1654–1722). A more recent unexpected result was discovered when applying the following "point connector" algorithm.

   Step 1: Carefully draw a large $\triangle ABC$. Choose a point X between points B and C.

   Step 2: Through point X, draw a segment parallel to $\overline{AB}$. Label the point of intersection with $\overline{AC}$ as point Y.

   Step 3: Through point Y, draw a segment parallel to $\overline{BC}$. Label the intersection with $\overline{AB}$ as point Z.

   Step 4: Through point Z, draw a segment parallel to $\overline{AC}$. Label the point of intersection with $\overline{BC}$ as point X'.

   Step 5: Repeat steps 2 through 4 starting with the point X'. Label the new points Y', Z', and X'' respectively.

   a. What appears to be true about X and X'''?

   b. Is there a point X on $\overline{BC}$ so that after applying this algorithm, $X = X'$?

3. Which mathematical activity do you think is more important: discovering properties of a shape, such as those of a parallelogram, or using certain properties to conclude that a shape must be a particular type of shape, such as a parallelogram? Explain your position.

4. One of the most commonly asked questions by students learning to write mathematical proofs is "How do you know where to begin?" Based on your experiences in this unit and in previous ones, how would you respond to this question?

Extending

1. Suppose you had two parallelograms *ABCD* and *STOP*. What would be the least amount of information about the two needed for you to prove each statement below?

   a. *STOP* ~ *ABCD*

   b. *STOP* ≅ *ABCD*

2. Look back at Part b of the "Think About This Situation" on page 325.

   a. What conjecture did (or can you) make about the quadrilateral formed by connecting, in order, the midpoints of the sides of the following special quadrilaterals:

   square
   rectangle
   parallelogram (other than a square or rectangle)
   trapezoid
   kite

   b. Select two of your conjectures and for each, write

   ■ a synthetic proof,

   ■ a coordinate proof.

3. An **equilic quadrilateral** is a quadrilateral with a pair of congruent opposite sides that, when extended, meet to form a 60° angle. The other two sides are called *bases*.

   a. Draw an equilic quadrilateral.

   b. Quadrilateral *ABCD* is equilic with bases $\overline{AB}$ and $\overline{CD}$ and $\overline{AD} \cong \overline{BC}$.

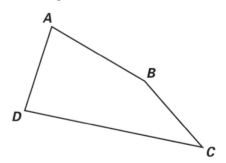

   ■ Could base $\overline{AB}$ be parallel to base $\overline{CD}$? Explain your reasoning.

   ■ Could $\overline{AB} \cong \overline{CD}$? Explain.

   ■ Find m∠*D* + m∠*C*.

   ■ Find m∠*A* + m∠*B*.

c. Suppose you have an equilic quadrilateral *ABCD* with $\overline{AD} \cong \overline{BC}$ and diagonals $\overline{AC}$ and $\overline{BD}$; points *J*, *K*, *L*, and *M* are midpoints of sides $\overline{AB}$ and $\overline{CD}$ and diagonals $\overline{AC}$ and $\overline{BD}$ respectively. How are the four points *J*, *K*, *L*, and *M* related? Prove you are correct.

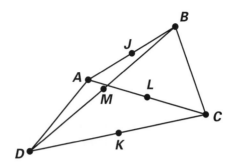

d. Draw an equilic quadrilateral *ABCD* with $\overline{AD} \cong \overline{BC}$ and *AB* < *CD*. Draw an equilateral triangle on base $\overline{AB}$ that shares no points with the interior of quadrilateral *ABCD*. Label the third vertex *P*. How are points *P*, *C*, and *D* related? Prove your conjecture.

4. Carefully draw an example of each quadrilateral listed below. Then carefully draw or construct the bisectors of each angle and call the four points of intersection of pairs of bisectors *W*, *X*, *Y*, and *Z*. Consider quadrilateral *WXYZ* in each case. If *WXYZ* is identifiable as a special kind of quadrilateral, name it. Prove you are correct.

a. Parallelogram

b. Kite

c. Rectangle

d. Isosceles trapezoid

e. Trapezoid

f. General quadrilateral

Looking Back

In this unit, you were involved in an extended journey in geometric thinking. Beginning with some accepted mathematical ideas, you were able to deduce many additional relations. You started by proving relations among angles formed by two intersecting lines or by two parallel lines cut by a transversal. You then used the Law of Cosines and the Law of Sines to deduce the similarity and congruence conditions for triangles. Finally, you used the latter tools to investigate and prove properties of parallelograms and related quadrilaterals.

The journey was long but important. It illustrated well the way new mathematics is developed: A person or group of people thinks there is a possible new relation in a setting, explores it with examples, makes a conjecture, and then tries to confirm the conjecture deductively based on accepted mathematical knowledge. In the activities that follow, you will have the opportunity to review this process and the major theorems and to apply them in new settings.

1. Suppose you are given a theorem in the form "if *s*, then *t*," where *s* and *t* are mathematical statements.

   a. Explain the significance of the mathematical information given in statement *s*.

   b. Suppose you know the statement "if *s*, then *t*" is correct.

   ■ If you also know the conditions in *s* are satisfied in a particular situation, what can you conclude about the conditions in *t* for that situation? Give an example that illustrates this kind of reasoning in geometry. Give an example that illustrates this kind of reasoning in algebra.

   ■ What can you conclude about the statement *t* if you know nothing about the truth of the statement *s*?

2. You are given *l* ∥ *m*, *m* ∥ *n*, and a transversal *t* as shown. Prove each statement below under these conditions.

   a. *l* ∥ *n*

   b. ∠1 ≅ ∠3

   c. ∠2 and ∠3 are supplementary

   d. ∠2 ≅ ∠6

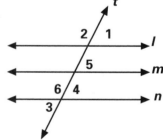

3. When a billiard ball with no spin and medium speed is banked off the cushion of a table, the angles at which it strikes and leaves the cushion are congruent.

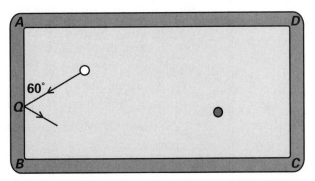

a. On a copy of the billiards table, sketch the path of the ball as it rebounds from $\overline{AB}$, from $\overline{BC}$, from $\overline{CD}$, from $\overline{AD}$, and from $\overline{AB}$ again. (This assumes that the ball has enough speed to travel the whole path, of course!) Label the points where the ball strikes the cushions R, S, T, and U respectively.

b. At what angle does the ball leave $\overline{AB}$ the second time? Explain your reasoning.

c. What appears to be true about $\overline{QR}$ and $\overline{ST}$? Write a proof of your conjecture.

d. At what point on the cushion $\overline{BC}$ would you aim if you wish to bank the white ball off that side and strike the orange ball? (Hint: Consider the reflection image of the orange ball across $\overleftrightarrow{BC}$.)

■ On a copy of the billiards table, draw the path of the white ball.

■ Prove that if the ball has no spin and sufficient speed, it will follow the drawn path and strike the orange ball.

4. For the diagram below, $\overline{PS} \cong \overline{QR}$, $\overline{PT} \cong \overline{QT}$, and $\overline{ST} \cong \overline{RT}$.

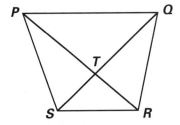

a. Identify and name eight triangles in the diagram.

b. Which pairs of the eight triangles seem to be congruent? Name each pair.

c. Based on the given information, prove or disprove that each identified pair of triangles are congruent.

d. Are the remaining pairs of triangles similar? If so, provide an argument.

e. What can you conclude about $\overline{PQ}$ and $\overline{SR}$ when you know the given information? Write a proof for your conjecture.

5. Civil engineers, urban planners, and design engineers are frequently confronted with "traffic center" problems. In mathematical terms, these problems often involve locating a point that is equidistant from three or more given points or for which the sum of its distances from the given points is as small as possible. In cases involving three given points that are vertices of a triangle, the problems can be solved by using geometric theorems which you are now able to prove. In the first two parts of this task, you are to write and analyze a synthetic proof and an analytic proof of the following theorem:

> *The midpoint of the hypotenuse of a right triangle is equidistant from its vertices.*

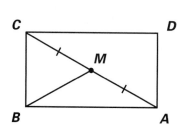
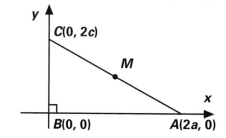

a. In the diagram on the left, $\triangle ABC$ is composed of two adjacent sides and a diagonal of rectangle $ABCD$. Using that diagram, write a synthetic proof that if M is the midpoint of $\overline{AC}$, then $MA = MB = MC$.

b. Using the diagram above on the right, write an analytic proof that if M is the midpoint of $\overline{AC}$, then $MA = MB = MC$.

c. For the proof in Part b, why do you think the coordinates of points A and C were assigned $(2a, 0)$ and $(0, 2c)$ rather than simply $(a, 0)$ and $(0, c)$ respectively?

d. While deductive reasoning is always used in proving theorems, this form of reasoning can also be used to discover new theorems. Look back at Reflecting Task 5 on page 323. How can you use the fact given in that task to determine where to locate a point D so that it is equidistant from the vertices of a general triangle ABC?

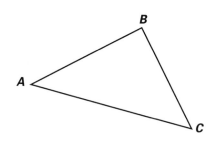

6. In the diagram below, $\overleftrightarrow{DF} \parallel \overleftrightarrow{AB}$, $\overleftrightarrow{ED} \parallel \overleftrightarrow{AC}$, $BD = 6$, $DC = 4$, $FC = 6$, and $AE = 3$.

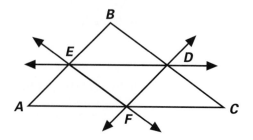

a. Prove $\triangle ABC \sim \triangle FDC$.

b. Find AF.

c. Find EB.

d. Is $\overleftrightarrow{EF} \parallel \overleftrightarrow{BC}$? Explain.

e. Is $\triangle ABC \sim \triangle DFE$? Why or why not?

f. Identify each quadrilateral in the diagram that is a parallelogram. Give a justification for each claim.

7. Below, $ABCD$ is a parallelogram and M is the midpoint of $\overline{AB}$. $\overline{DM}$ and $\overline{CB}$ are extended to meet at point N.

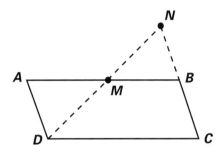

a. Prove $\triangle AMD \cong \triangle BMN$.

b. Compare the areas of $\triangle DNC$ and parallelogram $ABCD$.

8. In this unit, you were able to deduce many new geometric relations. You began with the Pythagorean Theorem, the Law of Cosines, and the Law of Sines, which you proved in previous units, and you assumed the Linear Pairs Property and Parallel Lines Property to be true.

   Some of the theorems you proved are represented below as vertices of a concept map.

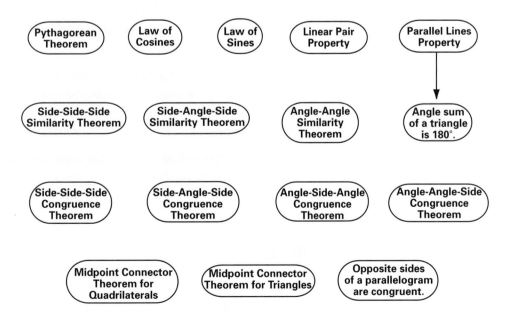

a. On a copy of the concept map on the previous page, draw a directed edge *from* a vertex labeled A *to* a vertex labeled B if Statement A was used to prove Theorem B.

b. Use your completed concept map to identify which of these properties and theorems contributed to the Midpoint Connector Theorem for Quadrilaterals. Include statements that contributed directly, by being used in the proof, or indirectly, by being used to prove a theorem on which the proof depended.

c. Add a new vertex representing some other theorem you proved in this unit. Draw directed edges from other vertices whose statements were somehow needed in the proof of this theorem. (You may want to use a different color.)

Checkpoint

In this unit, you have extended your understanding of geometric shapes and sharpened your skills in mathematical reasoning.

ⓐ When trying to prove an if-then statement, with what facts would you begin? What would you try to deduce?

ⓑ Identify at least two relations between angles formed by two lines and a transversal that ensure the lines are parallel. Draw and label a sketch to illustrate the relations.

ⓒ What conditions on two triangles ensure that the triangles are congruent? Are similar?

ⓓ How are the ideas of congruence and similarity related?

ⓔ Identify at least four conditions that permit you to conclude that a pair of angles are congruent.

ⓕ Identify at least two conditions on a quadrilateral that guarantee that it is a parallelogram.

ⓖ In the first Checkpoint of this unit, page 265, you were asked to identify what you considered to be the most important characteristics of a valid argument. Now that you have completed the unit, answer the question again and compare your thinking then and now.

Be prepared to share your descriptions, conclusions, and reasoning with the entire class.

On Your Own

Write, in outline form, a summary of the important mathematical concepts and methods developed in this unit. Organize your summary so that it can be used as a quick reference in future units and courses.

Index of Mathematical Topics

Symbols

μ, *363*
σ, *364*
Σ, *525*
θ, *555*

A

Absolute value function
    horizontal shifts, *463*
    horizontal stretching and
        compression, *466–468*
    rules and tables, *442–443,*
        445, 463
    vertical stretching and
        shrinking, *449–452*
    vertical translation,
        442–443
Addition
    associative property of,
        194, 274
    commutative property of,
        194, 274
Addition Rule for mutually
    exclusive events, *404–*
    415
Affirming the hypothesis, 276
Algebra, 25–45, 170–186
Algebraic equations, rewriting
    in equivalent forms, 15
Algebraic expressions
    common mistakes when
        writing, 195
    not equivalent, using
        graph to show, 204
Algebraic operations, 187–224
Algebraic properties, 194
Algebraic reasoning, 240–252
    to find center and radius
        of a circle, 252
    in geometry, 243–247
    to minimize distance, *559*
    in statistics, 243–247
Amplitude, *429*
Analytic proof, 328
Angle Bisector Algorithm, 320
Angle Construction Algorithm,
    320
Angles, 282–287
    adjacent, 281
    alternate exterior, 283
    alternate interior, 283
    bisecting, 308, 320
    central, measure of, 296
    central versus inscribed,
        324
    congruent, 305
    corresponding, 283
    exterior, on same side of
        transversal, 283
    included, 313
    inscribed, measures of, 296
    inscribed versus central,
        324

    interior, on same side of
        transversal, 283
    linear pair of, 279, 281
    Linear Pair Property, 280
    reasoning about, 279–282
    supplementary, 281
    vertical, 279, 281
Area, maximizing, *555–556*
Arguments
    good, 264
    reasoned, 260–296
    synthetic proofs, 312
    valid, 264
Arithmetic growth, *506*
    and linear models, *507*
    recursive formula versus
        function formula,
        506–507
Arithmetic sequence, *506, 515*
    equations, *507*
    function formula, *507*
    interpreting formulas, *508*
    recursive formula, *506*
    sum of terms, *512*
Arrow's Theorem, 102–105
    fairness conditions,
        103–104
Associative property
    of addition, 194, 274
    determining if new opera-
        tions have, 207
    of multiplication, 194
Assumptions, identifying,
    261–265
Asymptotes
    horizontal, *433*
    and inverse functions, *440*
    vertical, *433*
Average, properties of
    operation, 205
Average run length, *412*

B

Bias in surveys, sources of,
    121–124
    information collection,
        122–123
    nonresponse, 123
    sample selection, 122
    wording of survey, 122
Binomials, geometric illustra-
    tion proof for multiply-
    ing two, 250
Borda count vote-analysis
    method, 98

C

Cause-and-effect relationship,
    564
Ceiling function, 185
Census, 117
    when to take, 117

Chaos, *533, 541*
Chord, 296, 322
Circle
    and algebraic reasoning,
        252
    average area, 132
    average radius, 132
    equation of, 248
    equation of, center not at
        origin, 252, *475*
    survey, 125–126
    theorem about, 322
Closed-form formula for a
    sequence, *525*
Coefficients in standard qua-
    dratic form related to
    factored form, 211
Combinations, 110
Combined recursive formulas,
    510
    function formula, *523, 542*
    and linear function itera-
        tion, *546–547*
    and recursive formulas
        for arithmetic and geo-
        metric sequences, *510*
Combined variation, 10, *427*
Common difference, *508*
Commutative property
    of addition, 194, 274
    determining if new
        operations have, 207
    of multiplication, 194
Compasses, 319
Complete graphs, *516–518*
Compound statement, 278
Conclusion, 267
Condorcet vote-analysis
    method, 97–98
Confidence intervals, 153–164
    box plot charts to find,
        155
    likely populations,
        154–159
    margin of error, 156
    90%, 156
    properties of, 157
    and sample size, 159
Congruent triangles, 297–324
    consequences of, 305
    definition, 305
    theorems, 306, 309
Consistent fairness condition,
    103
Constraints, 64
    inequalities, 69
Contrapositive, 277
Converse, 277, 285
    and Venn diagram, 274
Coordinate proof, 328
Correction term, 35
Correlation coefficient, *563–564*
    effect of outliers, *564*
    formulas for, *379*
    and standardized scores,
        379
Cosine ratio, 27

Cosines, Law of, 32–36, 298
    coordinate proof of, 314
    to find angle measures, 34
    to find length, 34
    proof of, 245, 251
    versus Pythagorean
        Theorem, 35
    when to use, 35
Counterexamples, use of,
    268
Cubic functions
    patterns in graphs of, *426*
    rules, *446*
    table patterns, *446*
    vertical translation, *446*

D

Dart, 330
Decisive fairness condition, 103
Deductive reasoning, 269, 271
    to establish a relation-
        ship, 270
    versus inductive, 275
Detachment, law of, 276
Diagram, marking, 308
Difference equations. *See
    Recursive formulas.*
Digraph of pairwise-compari-
    son method, 110–111
Direct variation relationships,
    426
    and sequential change,
        503–504
Discrete dynamical systems,
    491
Dissection of shapes, 314
Distance, minimum, *558–561*
    ways to find, *559*
Distributive property
    diagrams illustrating,
        206
    multiplication of linear
        factors using, 210
    of multiplication over
        addition, 194
    of multiplication over
        subtraction, 194
Division, 215–218
Divisor, 275
Domain, 177, *438*
    practical, 177
    theoretical, 177

E

Equality, properties of, 15, 37,
    62
    to solve equations, 37
    to solve proportions, 39

Linear functions, *432*
  graphs, *424*
  interpreting patterns in
    tables and graphs, 175
  and long-term behavior
    of function iteration,
    535–536
  rate of change, *424*
  reflection across the
    x-axis, *466*
  symbolic expressions,
    424
  tables of values, *424*
  vertical translation, *445*
Linear inequalities, 78–79
  calculator-based methods
    versus symbolic reason-
    ing to solve, 238
  graphs of, 78
  solving systems of, by
    graphing, 79
Linear models
  and arithmetic growth,
    507
  discrete view, *505–529*
  interpreting, 53
  and patterns in table of
    values and shape of
    graph, 50
Linear Pair Property, 280
Linear pairs, 279
Linear programming, 63–85
  finding best feasible
    points, 74–77
  linear equations and
    inequalities, 78–79
  using an algebraic
    model, 68–73
Lines, intersecting
  reasoning about, 279–282
  theorems about, 295
Lines in 3-dimensional space,
  293
Linked equations, 46–62
Linked variables, 2–24
  patterns in indirect and
    inverse variation situa-
    tions, 3–5
  patterns in values of
    direct/inverse combined
    variation, 14–16
  rates and times, combin-
    ing, 11–14
Logistic equations and long-
  term behavior, *532, 541*
Long-term behavior
  additional amount
    added/subtracted, *490*
  and function iteration,
    532
  increase/decrease rate,
    490
  influence on, by initial
    conditions, *489–490*
  initial population, *489*
  and logistic equations,
    532
Lower control limit (LCL), *389*

M

Majority winner vote-analysis
  method, 97
Margin of error, 135, 156,
  160–161

Matrices
  to model sequential
    change, *499–500*
  to solve a system of three
    linear equations, *517*
Matrix addition, properties of,
  205
Maximums and transformations,
  458
Mean
  effect of adding constant
    to data values, *352–353*
  effect of multiplying data
    values by constant, *352*
Mean absolute deviation
  (MAD), *348*
  effect of adding constant
    to data values, *351*
  effect of multiplying data
    values by constant, *351*
  versus standard deviation,
    350
Mean of population symbol
  (μ), *363*
Mean of sample ($\bar{x}$), *363*
Median-fit procedure, 291
Median-median line, 291
  using calculator to find,
    293
Midline of the graph, *438*
Midpoint Connector Theorems,
  332
Midpoint formula, 19
Midrange, properties of, 249
Minimums and transformations,
  458
Minor arc, 324
Modified box plot, 137
Modified runoff vote-analysis
  method, 106
Modus ponens, 276
Multiple variable equations,
  solving, 13
Multiple-variable models, 1–90
  algebra, 25–45
  geometry, 25–45
  linear programming,
    63–85
  linked equations, 46–62
  linked variables, 2–24
  trigonometry, 25–45
Multiplication Rule for
  independent events,
  404–405
Mutually exclusive events
  Addition Rule,
    404–411
  definition, *409*
  versus independent
    events, *414*

N

Negation of a simple statement, 276
n-gon, formula for sum of
  measures of exterior
  angles, 295
90% box plot, 137
  for different sample sizes,
    144–145
  to find confidence inter-
    vals, 155–156
  finding the width of,
    150
  interval of likely out-
    comes, 142

  patterns in, 142
  and sample size, 146
  using simulation and
    technology to construct,
    140
90% confidence interval, 156
  interpreting, 157
90% confidence level, formula
  to estimate margin of
  error for, 161
Nondictatorship fairness condition, 103
Nonlinear systems of equations, solving, 51, 54
Normal distribution, *362–383*
  characteristics, *363–371*
  equation of a curve, *381*
  overall shape, *367–368*
  and percentile rank,
    369–375
  relation to distribution of
    its standardized values,
    378
  relation to standard
    deviation, *363–371*
  standardizing scores,
    371–375
  using sums to create, *399*
Normally distributed, *363*
NOW-NEXT equations, *438*
  function iteration, *531*
  for sequential change,
    489–491
  subscript notation, *492*
  and transformations,
    460–461
Number theory, 275
Numerical iteration to find
  fixed points, *538*

O

Objective function, 69
Opinion poll, 116
Opposite of a difference, 199
Opposite of a sum, 199
Optimization problems, *552*
Ordered fairness condition,
  103
Outcomes, sample
  likely versus unlikely,
    140–143, 147
  as proportions, 146
  as totals, 146
Outlier, *347*
  effect on mean and stan-
    dard deviation,
    353, 357
Out-of-control processes,
  394–395
Out-of-control signals, *385–393*
  due to mean changing,
    385
  due to standard deviation
    changing, *385*
  false alarms, *402–405*
  tests, *390–392*
Output, 177

P

Pairwise-comparison vote-
  analysis method, 97–98,
  110–111
Parabola, finding vertex of,
  211

Parallel lines, 282–287
  theorems, 283, 285,
    290
Parallel Lines Property, 285
Parallelograms, 325–339
  definition, 326, 336
  properties of, 244
  reasoning about,
    326–330
  rhombus, 330
  theorems, 317, 327–328
Parameters and patterns in
  tables and graphs, *431*
Patterns
  in direct and inverse
    variation situations, 3–5
  in values of direct,
    inverse, and combined
    variation, 15
Percentile rank and normal distribution, *369–375*
  interpreting *z*-score to
    find, *374*
  table, *373*
Perimeter, minimizing, *557*
Period, *429*
Periodic change, *428–430*
Periodic functions, 43
  changing amplitude, *450*
  from function rule, *467*
  from graph, *466*
  horizontal shifts, *464*
  reflection across the
    x-axis, *446*
  symbolic rules, *429, 464*
  and vertical translation,
    444
Permutations, 110, *415*
Perpendicular Bisector
  Algorithm, 321
Piecewise-defined function,
  186
Plane, tiling the, *553*
Plot over time, *384, 387*
Plurality winner vote-analysis
  method, 97
  compared to sequential-
    elimination method, 114
Point of inflection, *382*
Point-slope equation of a line,
  19
Points-for-preferences vote-
  analysis method, 98
Polygon
  angle measures of regular,
    554
  area/perimeter of regular,
    553
  formula for sum of mea-
    sures of angles, 295
  rigid, 297
Polynomial
  higher-degree, 212
  perfect cube, factoring,
    220
  quadratic, 212
  standard form, 196
Polynomial functions
  discrete view, *505–529*
  writing rules for given
    zeroes, 210
Population, 117
Power functions, *432*
Preference table, 94
Preferential voting, 93–96
Present value, *502*
Prime number, 268

Index of Contexts

Photo Credits

Photo Credits

Haupt; **215** Jack Demuth; **216** John Dziekan/Chicago Tribune; **219** (top) Jose More/Chicago Tribune, (bottom) Miracle-Gro® is a registered trademark of Scotts Company; **222** PEANUTS reprinted by permission of United Feature Syndicate, Inc.; **225** Gregg Mancuso/Tony Stone Images; **229** Jack Demuth; **234** Brian Stablyk/Tony Stone Images; **235** Bob Langer/Chicago Tribune; **236** Bob Langer/Chicago Tribune; **240** Jim Laser; **250** Chuck Berman/Chicago Tribune; **253** Hardy Wetting/Chicago Tribune; **255** Bill Hedrich; **259** Helaman Ferguson sculptor/Terry Clough photographer; **260** Image © BCOP/© Sanford; **261** Michael Budrys/Chicago Tribune; **262** Tony Berardi/Chicago Tribune; **265** PhotoDisc; **266** Bob Langer/Chicago Tribune; **267** James Crump/Chicago Tribune; **269** Switzerland Tourism; **273** Walter Kale/Chicago Tribune; **274** (top) Department of Agriculture, (bottom) George Thompson/Chicago Tribune; **276** THE BORN LOSER reprinted by permission of Newspaper Enterprise Association, Inc.; **277** (left) Tecumseh Products Company, Grafton WI, (right) Reprinted from NEW FIX IT YOURSELF MANUAL, 1996 The reader's Digest Association, Inc. Used by permission; **279** *Geometry with Applications and Problem Solving,* Addison-Wesley Publishing Company; **282** Chicago Tribune; **288** from SCOTT FORESMAN GEOMETRY by Christian R. Hirsch et al. ©1990 by Scott, Foresman and Company. Reprinted by permissions of Addison Wesley Educational Publishers, Inc.; **289** (left) L. Clarke/CORBIS; (right) from SCOTT FORESMAN GEOMETRY by Christian R. Hirsch et al. ©1990 by Scott, Foresman and Company. Reprinted by permissions of Addison Wesley Educational Publishers, Inc.; **291** Texas Instruments Incorporated, Dallas, TX; **294** *The Annotated Alice* by Lewis Carroll/Illustrator John Tenniel, Clarkson N. Potter, Inc.; **297** Bob Lalnger/Chicago Tribune; **298** J. Messerschmidt/Bruce Coleman, Inc.; **302** David Klobucar/Chicago Tribune; **304** John Mulcahy/Chicago Tribune; **308** Courtesy Megan Klobucar/Chicago Tribune; **316** "Ascending and Descending" by M.C. Escher. ©1998 Cordon Art-Baarn-Holland. All rights reserved. **318** George Thompson/Chicago Tribune; **326** Whisperglide, Hugo MN; **331** Elaine Krajenke Ellison/Orie Shafer photographer; **333** (top) Carl Hugare/Chicago Tribune; (bottom) Hickson Bender; **335** Glencoe file photo; **341** Carl Hugare/Chicago Tribune.